S0-BWD-853

经 典 原 版 书 库

人工智能

智能系统指南

（英文版·第3版）

Artificial Intelligence

A Guide to Intelligent Systems (Third Edition)

（澳） **Michael Negnevitsky** 著
塔斯马尼亚大学

机械工业出版社
China Machine Press

本书版权登记号：图字：01-2011-4256

图书在版编目（CIP）数据

人工智能：智能系统指南（英文版·第3版）/（澳）尼格尼维斯基（Negnevitsky, M.）著．—北京：机械工业出版社，2011.9
（经典原版书库）
书名原文：Artificial Intelligence: A Guide to Intelligent Systems, Third Edition

ISBN 978-7-111-35822-0

I. 人… II. 尼… III. 人工智能–英文 IV. TP18

中国版本图书馆 CIP 数据核字（2011）第 181825 号

机械工业出版社（北京市西城区百万庄大街22号 邮政编码 100037）
责任编辑：迟振春
北京京师印务有限公司印刷
2011 年 9 月第 1 版第 1 次印刷
150mm × 214mm · 15.5 印张
标准书号：ISBN 978-7-111-35822-0
定价：49.00 元

凡购本书，如有缺页、倒页、脱页，由本社发行部调换
客服热线：（010）88378991；88361066
购书热线：（010）68326294；88379649；68995259
投稿热线：（010）88379604
读者信箱：hzjsj@hzbook.com

出版者的话

文艺复兴以降，源远流长的科学精神和逐步形成的学术规范，使西方国家在自然科学的各个领域取得了垄断性的优势；也正是这样的传统，使美国在信息技术发展的六十多年间名家辈出、独领风骚。在商业化的进程中，美国的产业界与教育界越来越紧密地结合，计算机学科中的许多泰山北斗同时身处科研和教学的最前线，由此而产生的经典科学著作，不仅擘划了研究的范畴，还揭示了学术的源变，既遵循学术规范，又自有学者个性，其价值并不会因年月的流逝而减退。

近年，在全球信息化大潮的推动下，我国的计算机产业发展迅猛，对专业人才的需求日益迫切。这对计算机教育界和出版界都既是机遇，也是挑战；而专业教材的建设在教育战略上显得举足轻重。在我国信息技术发展时间较短的现状下，美国等发达国家在其计算机科学发展的几十年间积淀和发展的经典教材仍有许多值得借鉴之处。因此，引进一批国外优秀计算机教材将对我国计算机教育事业的发展起到积极的推动作用，也是与世界接轨、建设真正的世界一流大学的必由之路。

机械工业出版社华章公司较早意识到"出版要为教育服务"。自1998年开始，我们就将工作重点放在了遴选、移译国外优秀教材上。经过多年的不懈努力，我们与Pearson，McGraw-Hill，Elsevier，MIT，John Wiley & Sons，Cengage等世界著名出版公司建立了良好的合作关系，从他们现有的数百种教材中甄选出Andrew S. Tanenbaum，Bjarne Stroustrup，Brain W. Kernighan，Dennis Ritchie，Jim Gray，Afred V. Aho，John E. Hopcroft，Jeffrey D. Ullman，Abraham Silberschatz，William Stallings，Donald E. Knuth，John L. Hennessy，Larry L. Peterson等大师名家的一批经典作品，以"计算机科学丛书"为总称出版，供读者学习、研究及珍藏。大理石纹理的封面，也正体现了这套丛书的品位和格调。

"计算机科学丛书"的出版工作得到了国内外学者的鼎力襄助，国内的专家不仅提供了中肯的选题指导，还不辞劳苦地担任了翻译和审校的工作；而原书的作者也相当关注其作品在中国的传播，有的还专程为其书的中译本作序。迄今，"计算机科学丛书"已经出版了近两百个品种，这些书籍在读者中树立了良好的口碑，并被许多高校采用为正式教材和参考书籍。其影印版"经典原版书库"作为姊妹篇也被越来越多实施双语教学的学校所采用。

权威的作者、经典的教材、一流的译者、严格的审校、精细的编辑，这些因素使我们的图书有了质量的保证。随着计算机科学与技术专业学科建设的不断完善和教材改革的逐渐深化，教育界对国外计算机教材的需求和应用都将步入一个新的阶段，我们的目标是尽善尽美，而反馈的意见正是我们达到这一终极目标的重要帮助。华章公司欢迎老师和读者对我们的工作提出建议或给予指正，我们的联系方法如下：

华章网站：www.hzbook.com
电子邮件：hzjsj@hzbook.com
联系电话：(010) 88379604
联系地址：北京市西城区百万庄南街 1 号
邮政编码：100037

华章教育

华章科技图书出版中心

Preface

Another book on artificial intelligence ... I've already seen so many of them. Why should I bother with this one? What makes this book different from the others?

Each year hundreds of books and doctoral theses extend our knowledge of computer, or artificial, intelligence. Expert systems, artificial neural networks, fuzzy systems and evolutionary computation are major technologies used in intelligent systems. Hundreds of tools support these technologies, and thousands of scientific papers continue to push their boundaries. The content of any chapter in this book can be, and in fact is, the subject of dozens of monographs. However, I wanted to write a book that would explain the basics of intelligent systems, and perhaps even more importantly, eliminate the fear of artificial intelligence.

Most of the literature on artificial intelligence is expressed in the jargon of computer science, and crowded with complex matrix algebra and differential equations. This, of course, gives artificial intelligence an aura of respectability, and until recently kept non-computer scientists at bay. But the situation has changed!

The personal computer has become indispensable in our everyday life. We use it as a typewriter and a calculator, a calendar and a communication system, an interactive database and a decision-support system. And we want more. We want our computers to act intelligently! We see that intelligent systems are rapidly coming out of research laboratories, and we want to use them to our advantage.

What are the principles behind intelligent systems? How are they built? What are intelligent systems useful for? How do we choose the right tool for the job? These questions are answered in this book.

Unlike many books on computer intelligence, this one shows that most ideas behind intelligent systems are wonderfully simple and straightforward. The book is based on lectures given to students who have little knowledge of calculus. And readers do not need to learn a programming language! The material in this book has been extensively tested through several courses taught by the author for the last 15 years. Typical questions and suggestions from my students influenced the way this book was written.

The book is an introduction to the field of computer intelligence. It covers rule-based expert systems, fuzzy expert systems, frame-based expert systems, artificial neural networks, evolutionary computation, hybrid intelligent systems, knowledge engineering and data mining.

In a university setting, this book provides an introductory course for under-graduate students in computer science, computer information systems, and engineering. In the courses I teach, my students develop small rule-based and frame-based expert systems, design fuzzy systems, explore artificial neural networks, solve simple optimisation problems using genetic algorithms and develop hybrid neuro-fuzzy systems. They use expert system shells (XpertRule, Exsys Corvid and Visual Rule Studio), MATLAB Fuzzy Logic Toolbox and MATLAB Neural Network Toolbox. I chose these tools because they can easily demonstrate the theory being presented. However, the book is not tied to any specific tool; the examples given in the book are easy to implement with different tools.

This book is also suitable as a self-study guide for non-computer science professionals. For them, the book provides access to the state of the art in knowledge-based systems and computational intelligence. In fact, this book is aimed at a large professional audience: engineers and scientists, managers and businessmen, doctors and lawyers – everyone who faces challenging problems and cannot solve them by using traditional approaches, everyone who wants to understand the tremendous achievements in computer intelligence. The book will help to develop a practical understanding of what intelligent systems can and cannot do, discover which tools are most relevant for your task and, finally, how to use these tools.

I hope that the reader will share my excitement on the subject of artificial intelligence and soft computing and will find this book useful.

The website can be accessed at: http://www.booksites.net/negnevitsky

Michael Negnevitsky
Hobart, Tasmania, Australia
February 2001

Preface to the third edition

The main objective of the book remains the same as in the first edition – to provide the reader with practical understanding of the field of computer intelligence. It is intended as an introductory text suitable for a one-semester course, and assumes the students have only limited knowledge of calculus and little or no programming experience.

In terms of the coverage, this edition introduces a new chapter on data mining and demonstrates several new applications of intelligent tools for solving complex real-world problems. The major changes are as follows:

- In the new chapter, 'Data mining and knowledge discovery', we introduce data mining as an integral part of knowledge discovery in large databases. We consider the main techniques and tools for turning data into knowledge, including statistical methods, data visualisation tools, Structured Query Language, decision trees and market basket analysis. We also present several case studies on data mining applications.

- In Chapter 9, we add a new case study on clustering with a self-organising neural network.

Finally, we have expanded the book's references and bibliographies, and updated the list of AI tools and vendors in the appendix.

Michael Negnevitsky
Hobart, Tasmania, Australia
September 2010

Overview of the book

The book consists of 10 chapters.

In Chapter 1, we briefly discuss the history of artificial intelligence from the era of great ideas and great expectations in the 1960s to the disillusionment and funding cutbacks in the early 1970s; from the development of the first expert systems such as DENDRAL, MYCIN and PROSPECTOR in the 1970s to the maturity of expert system technology and its massive application in different areas in the 1980s and 1990s; from a simple binary model of neurons proposed in the 1940s to a dramatic resurgence of the field of artificial neural networks in the 1980s; from the introduction of fuzzy set theory and its being ignored by the West in the 1960s to numerous 'fuzzy' consumer products offered by the Japanese in the 1980s and world-wide acceptance of 'soft' computing and computing with words in the 1990s.

In Chapter 2, we present an overview of rule-based expert systems. We briefly discuss what knowledge is, and how experts express their knowledge in the form of production rules. We identify the main players in the expert system development team and show the structure of a rule-based system. We discuss fundamental characteristics of expert systems and note that expert systems can make mistakes. Then we review the forward and backward chaining inference techniques and debate conflict resolution strategies. Finally, the advantages and disadvantages of rule-based expert systems are examined.

In Chapter 3, we present two uncertainty management techniques used in expert systems: Bayesian reasoning and certainty factors. We identify the main sources of uncertain knowledge and briefly review probability theory. We consider the Bayesian method of accumulating evidence and develop a simple expert system based on the Bayesian approach. Then we examine the certainty factors theory (a popular alternative to Bayesian reasoning) and develop an expert system based on evidential reasoning. Finally, we compare Bayesian reasoning and certainty factors, and determine appropriate areas for their applications.

In Chapter 4, we introduce fuzzy logic and discuss the philosophical ideas behind it. We present the concept of fuzzy sets, consider how to represent a fuzzy set in a computer, and examine operations of fuzzy sets. We also define linguistic variables and hedges. Then we present fuzzy rules and explain the main differences between classical and fuzzy rules. We explore two fuzzy inference techniques – Mamdani and Sugeno – and suggest appropriate areas for their application. Finally, we introduce the main steps in developing a fuzzy expert system, and illustrate the theory through the actual process of building and tuning a fuzzy system.

In Chapter 5, we present an overview of frame-based expert systems. We consider the concept of a frame and discuss how to use frames for knowledge representation. We find that inheritance is an essential feature of frame-based systems. We examine the application of methods, demons and rules. Finally, we consider the development of a frame-based expert system through an example.

In Chapter 6, we introduce artificial neural networks and discuss the basic ideas behind machine learning. We present the concept of a perceptron as a simple computing element and consider the perceptron learning rule. We explore multilayer neural networks and discuss how to improve the computational efficiency of the back-propagation learning algorithm. Then we introduce recurrent neural networks, consider the Hopfield network training algorithm and bidirectional associative memory (BAM). Finally, we present self-organising neural networks and explore Hebbian and competitive learning.

In Chapter 7, we present an overview of evolutionary computation. We consider genetic algorithms, evolution strategies and genetic programming. We introduce the main steps in developing a genetic algorithm, discuss why genetic algorithms work, and illustrate the theory through actual applications of genetic algorithms. Then we present a basic concept of evolution strategies and determine the differences between evolution strategies and genetic algorithms. Finally, we consider genetic programming and its application to real problems.

In Chapter 8, we consider hybrid intelligent systems as a combination of different intelligent technologies. First, we introduce a new breed of expert systems, called neural expert systems, which combine neural networks and rule-based expert systems. Then we consider a neuro-fuzzy system that is functionally equivalent to the Mamdani fuzzy inference model, and an adaptive neuro-fuzzy inference system (ANFIS), equivalent to the Sugeno fuzzy inference model. Finally, we discuss evolutionary neural networks and fuzzy evolutionary systems.

In Chapter 9, we consider knowledge engineering. First, we discuss what kind of problems can be addressed with intelligent systems, and introduce six main phases of the knowledge engineering process. Then we examine typical applications of expert systems, fuzzy systems, neural networks and genetic algorithms. We demonstrate how to build intelligent systems for solving diagnosis, selection, prediction, classification, clustering and optimisation problems. Finally, we discuss applications of hybrid neuro-fuzzy systems for decision support and time-series prediction.

In Chapter 10, we present an overview of data mining and consider the main techniques for turning data into knowledge. First, we broadly define data mining, and explain the process of data mining and knowledge discovery in large databases. We introduce statistical methods, including principal component analysis, and discuss their limitations. We then examine an application of Structured Query Language in relational databases, and introduce data warehouse and multidimensional data analysis. Finally, we consider the most popular tools of data mining – decision trees and market basket analysis.

The book also has a glossary and an appendix. The glossary contains definitions for over 300 terms used in expert systems, fuzzy logic, neural networks, evolutionary computation, knowledge engineering and data mining. The appendix provides a list of commercially available AI tools.

The book's website can be accessed at: http://www.booksites.net/negnevitsky

Acknowledgements

I am deeply indebted to many people who, directly or indirectly, are responsible for this book coming into being. I am most grateful to Dr Vitaly Faybisovich for his constructive criticism of my research on soft computing, and most of all for his friendship and support in all my endeavours for the last 30 years.

I am also very grateful to numerous reviewers of my book for their comments and helpful suggestions, and to the Pearson Education editors, particularly Keith Mansfield, Owen Knight, Liz Johnson and Rufus Curnow, who led me through the process of publishing and editing this book.

I also thank my undergraduate and postgraduate students from the University of Tasmania, especially my former Ph.D. students Tan Loc Le, Quang Ha, Steven Carter and Mark Lim, whose desire for new knowledge was both a challenge and an inspiration to me.

I am indebted to Professor Stephen Grossberg from Boston University, USA, Professor Frank Palis from the Otto-von-Guericke-Universität Magdeburg, Germany, Professor Hiroshi Sasaki from Hiroshima University, Japan, Professor Walter Wolf from the Rochester Institute of Technology, USA, and Professor Kaoru Hirota from Tokyo Institute of Technology, Japan, for giving me the opportunity to test the book's material on their students.

I am also truly grateful to Dr Vivienne Mawson and Margaret Eldridge for proof-reading the draft text.

Although the first edition of this book appeared a few years ago, I cannot possibly thank all the people who have already used it and sent me their comments. However, I must acknowledge at least those who made especially helpful suggestions: Martin Beck (University of Plymouth, UK), Mike Brooks (University of Adelaide, Australia), Genard Catalano (Columbia College, USA), Warren du Plessis (University of Pretoria, South Africa), Salah Amin Elewa (American University, Egypt), Michael Fang (Zhejiang University, China), John Fronckowiak (Medaille College, USA), Patrick B. Gibson (University of Windsor, Canada), Lev Goldfarb (University of New Brunswick, Canada), Susan Haller (University of Wisconsin, USA), Evor Hines (University of Warwick, UK), Philip Hingston (Edith Cowan University, Australia), Sam Hui (Stanford University, USA), Yong-Hyuk Kim (Kwangwoon University, Korea), David Lee (University of Hertfordshire, UK), Andrew Nunekpeku (University of Ghana), Vasile Palade (Oxford University, UK), Leon Reznik (Rochester Institute of Technology, USA), Simon Shiu (Hong Kong Polytechnic University), Boris Stilman (University of

Colorado, USA), Thomas Uthmann (Johannes Gutenberg-Universität Mainz, Germany), Anne Venables (Victoria University, Australia), Brigitte Verdonk (University of Antwerp, Belgium), Ken Vollmar (Southwest Missouri State University, USA), Kok Wai Wong (Nanyang Technological University, Singapore) and Georgios N. Yannakakis (IT-University of Copenhagen, Denmark).

Contents

Preface   v
Preface to the third edition   vii
Overview of the book   viii
Acknowledgements   xi

1 Introduction to knowledge-based intelligent systems   1

1.1 Intelligent machines, or what machines can do   1
1.2 The history of artificial intelligence, or from the 'Dark Ages'
to knowledge-based systems   4
1.3 Summary   17
Questions for review   21
References   22

2 Rule-based expert systems   25

2.1 Introduction, or what is knowledge?   25
2.2 Rules as a knowledge representation technique   26
2.3 The main players in the expert system development team   28
2.4 Structure of a rule-based expert system   30
2.5 Fundamental characteristics of an expert system   33
2.6 Forward chaining and backward chaining inference
techniques   35
2.7 MEDIA ADVISOR: a demonstration rule-based expert system   41
2.8 Conflict resolution   47
2.9 Advantages and disadvantages of rule-based expert systems   50
2.10 Summary   51
Questions for review   53
References   54

3 Uncertainty management in rule-based expert systems   55

3.1 Introduction, or what is uncertainty?   55
3.2 Basic probability theory   57
3.3 Bayesian reasoning   61
3.4 FORECAST: Bayesian accumulation of evidence   65
3.5 Bias of the Bayesian method   72

3.6	Certainty factors theory and evidential reasoning	74
3.7	FORECAST: an application of certainty factors	80
3.8	Comparison of Bayesian reasoning and certainty factors	82
3.9	Summary	83
	Questions for review	85
	References	85

4   Fuzzy expert systems   **87**

4.1	Introduction, or what is fuzzy thinking?	87
4.2	Fuzzy sets	89
4.3	Linguistic variables and hedges	94
4.4	Operations of fuzzy sets	97
4.5	Fuzzy rules	103
4.6	Fuzzy inference	106
4.7	Building a fuzzy expert system	113
4.8	Summary	125
	Questions for review	126
	References	127
	Bibliography	127

5   Frame-based expert systems   **131**

5.1	Introduction, or what is a frame?	131
5.2	Frames as a knowledge representation technique	133
5.3	Inheritance in frame-based systems	138
5.4	Methods and demons	142
5.5	Interaction of frames and rules	146
5.6	Buy Smart: a frame-based expert system	149
5.7	Summary	161
	Questions for review	163
	References	163
	Bibliography	164

6   Artificial neural networks   **165**

6.1	Introduction, or how the brain works	165
6.2	The neuron as a simple computing element	168
6.3	The perceptron	170
6.4	Multilayer neural networks	175
6.5	Accelerated learning in multilayer neural networks	185
6.6	The Hopfield network	188
6.7	Bidirectional associative memory	196
6.8	Self-organising neural networks	200
6.9	Summary	212
	Questions for review	215
	References	216

7   Evolutionary computation   **219**

7.1	Introduction, or can evolution be intelligent?	219
7.2	Simulation of natural evolution	219
7.3	Genetic algorithms	222

7.4 Why genetic algorithms work   232
7.5 Case study: maintenance scheduling with genetic
algorithms   235
7.6 Evolution strategies   242
7.7 Genetic programming   245
7.8 Summary   254
Questions for review   255
References   256
Bibliography   257

8 Hybrid intelligent systems   **259**

8.1 Introduction, or how to combine German mechanics with
Italian love   259
8.2 Neural expert systems   261
8.3 Neuro-fuzzy systems   268
8.4 ANFIS: Adaptive Neuro-Fuzzy Inference System   277
8.5 Evolutionary neural networks   285
8.6 Fuzzy evolutionary systems   290
8.7 Summary   296
Questions for review   297
References   298

9 Knowledge engineering   **301**

9.1 Introduction, or what is knowledge engineering?   301
9.2 Will an expert system work for my problem?   308
9.3 Will a fuzzy expert system work for my problem?   317
9.4 Will a neural network work for my problem?   323
9.5 Will genetic algorithms work for my problem?   343
9.6 Will a hybrid intelligent system work for my problem?   348
9.7 Summary   357
Questions for review   359
References   362

10 Data mining and knowledge discovery   **365**

10.1 Introduction, or what is data mining?   365
10.2 Statistical methods and data visualisation   369
10.3 Principal component analysis   374
10.4 Relational databases and database queries   386
10.5 The data warehouse and multidimensional data analysis   391
10.6 Decision trees   401
10.7 Association rules and market basket analysis   410
10.8 Summary   418
Questions for review   420
References   421

Glossary   **425**
Appendix: AI tools and vendors   **451**
Index   **471**

Introduction to knowledge-based intelligent systems

1

In which we consider what it means to be intelligent and whether machines could be such a thing.

1.1 Intelligent machines, or what machines can do

Philosophers have been trying for over 2000 years to understand and resolve two big questions of the universe: how does a human mind work, and can non-humans have minds? However, these questions are still unanswered.

Some philosophers have picked up the computational approach originated by computer scientists and accepted the idea that machines can do everything that humans can do. Others have openly opposed this idea, claiming that such highly sophisticated behaviour as love, creative discovery and moral choice will always be beyond the scope of any machine.

The nature of philosophy allows for disagreements to remain unresolved. In fact, engineers and scientists have already built machines that we can call 'intelligent'. So what does the word 'intelligence' mean? Let us look at a dictionary definition.

1 Someone's **intelligence** is their ability to understand and learn things.
2 **Intelligence** is the ability to think and understand instead of doing things by instinct or automatically.

(Essential English Dictionary, Collins, London, 2008)

Thus, according to the first definition, intelligence is the quality possessed by humans. But the second definition suggests a completely different approach and gives some flexibility; it does not specify whether it is some**one** or some**thing** that has the ability to think and understand. Now we should discover what thinking means. Let us consult our dictionary again.

Thinking is the activity of using your brain to consider a problem or to create an idea.

(Essential English Dictionary, Collins, London, 2008)

So, in order to think, someone or something has to have a brain or, in other words, an organ that enables someone or something to learn and understand things, to solve problems and to make decisions. So we can define intelligence as 'the ability to learn and understand, to solve problems and to make decisions'.

The very question that asks whether computers can be intelligent, or whether machines can think, came to us from the 'Dark Ages' of artificial intelligence (from the late 1940s). The goal of **artificial intelligence** (AI) as a science is to make machines do things that would require intelligence if done by humans (Boden, 1977). Therefore, the answer to the question 'Can machines think?' was vitally important to the discipline. However, the answer is not a simple 'Yes' or 'No', but rather a vague or **fuzzy** one. Your everyday experience and common sense would have told you that. Some people are smarter in some ways than others. Sometimes we make very intelligent decisions but sometimes we also make very silly mistakes. Some of us deal with complex mathematical and engineering problems but are moronic in philosophy and history. Some people are good at making money, while others are better at spending it. As humans, we all have the ability to learn and understand, to solve problems and to make decisions; however, our abilities are not equal and lie in different areas. There-fore, we should expect that if machines can think, some of them might be smarter than others in some ways.

One of the earliest and most significant papers on machine intelligence, 'Computing machinery and intelligence', was written by the British mathema-tician Alan Turing over 50 years ago (Turing, 1950). However, it has stood up well to the test of time, and Turing's approach remains universal.

Alan Turing began his scientific career in the early 1930s by rediscovering the Central Limit Theorem. In 1937 he wrote a paper on computable numbers, in which he proposed the concept of a universal machine. Later, during the Second World War, he was a key player in deciphering Enigma, the German military encoding machine. After the war, Turing designed the 'Automatic Computing Engine'. He also wrote the first program capable of playing a complete chess game; it was later implemented on the Manchester University computer. Turing's theoretical concept of the universal computer and his practical experi-ence in building code-breaking systems equipped him to approach the key fundamental question of artificial intelligence. He asked: Is there thought without experience? Is there mind without communication? Is there language without living? Is there intelligence without life? All these questions, as you can see, are just variations on the fundamental question of artificial intelligence: Can machines think?

Turing did not provide definitions of machines and thinking, he just avoided semantic arguments by inventing a game, the **Turing imitation game**. Instead of asking, 'Can machines think?', Turing said we should ask, 'Can machines pass a behaviour test for intelligence?' He predicted that by the year 2000, a computer could be programmed to have a conversation with a human interrogator for five minutes and would have a 30 per cent chance of deceiving the interrogator that it was a human. Turing defined the intelligent behaviour of a computer as the ability to achieve human-level performance in cognitive tasks. In other words, a

Figure 1.1 Turing imitation game: phase 1

computer passes the test if interrogators cannot distinguish the machine from a human on the basis of the answers to their questions.

The imitation game proposed by Turing originally included two phases. In the first phase, shown in Figure 1.1, the interrogator, a man and a woman are each placed in separate rooms and can communicate only via a neutral medium such as a remote terminal. The interrogator's objective is to work out who is the man and who is the woman by questioning them. The rules of the game are that the man should attempt to deceive the interrogator that **he** is the woman, while the woman has to convince the interrogator that **she** is the woman.

In the second phase of the game, shown in Figure 1.2, the man is replaced by a computer programmed to deceive the interrogator as the man did. It would even be programmed to make mistakes and provide fuzzy answers in the way a human would. If the computer can fool the interrogator as often as the man did, we may say this computer has passed the intelligent behaviour test.

Physical simulation of a human is not important for intelligence. Hence, in the Turing test the interrogator does not see, touch or hear the computer and is therefore not influenced by its appearance or voice. However, the interrogator is allowed to ask any questions, even provocative ones, in order to identify the machine. The interrogator may, for example, ask both the human and the

Figure 1.2 Turing imitation game: phase 2

machine to perform complex mathematical calculations, expecting that the computer will provide a correct solution and will do it faster than the human. Thus, the computer will need to know when to make a mistake and when to delay its answer. The interrogator also may attempt to discover the emotional nature of the human, and, thus, he might ask both subjects to examine a short novel or poem or even painting. Obviously, the computer will be required here to simulate a human's emotional understanding of the work.

The Turing test has two remarkable qualities that make it really universal:

- By maintaining communication between the human and the machine via terminals, the test gives us an objective standard view on intelligence. It avoids debates over the human nature of intelligence and eliminates any bias in favour of humans.

- The test itself is quite independent from the details of the experiment. It can be conducted either as a two-phase game as just described, or even as a single-phase game in which the interrogator needs to choose between the human and the machine from the beginning of the test. The interrogator is also free to ask any question in any field and can concentrate solely on the content of the answers provided.

Turing believed that by the end of the 20th century it would be possible to program a digital computer to play the imitation game. Although modern computers still cannot pass the Turing test, it provides a basis for the verification and validation of knowledge-based systems. A program thought intelligent in some narrow area of expertise is evaluated by comparing its performance with the performance of a human expert.

Our brain stores the equivalent of over 10^{18} bits and can process information at the equivalent of about 10^{15} bits per second. By 2020, the brain will probably be modelled by a chip the size of a sugar cube – and perhaps by then there will be a computer that can play – even win – the Turing imitation game. However, do we really want the machine to perform mathematical calculations as slowly and inaccurately as humans do? From a practical point of view, an intelligent machine should help humans to make decisions, to search for information, to control complex objects, and finally to understand the meaning of words. There is probably no point in trying to achieve the abstract and elusive goal of developing machines with human-like intelligence. To build an intelligent computer system, we have to capture, organise and use human expert knowledge in some narrow area of expertise.

1.2 The history of artificial intelligence, or from the 'Dark Ages' to knowledge-based systems

Artificial intelligence as a science was founded by three generations of researchers. Some of the most important events and contributors from each generation are described next.

1.2.1   The 'Dark Ages', or the birth of artificial intelligence (1943–1956)

The first work recognised in the field of artificial intelligence (AI) was presented by Warren McCulloch and Walter Pitts in 1943. McCulloch had degrees in philosophy and medicine from Columbia University and became the Director of the Basic Research Laboratory in the Department of Psychiatry at the University of Illinois. His research on the central nervous system resulted in the first major contribution to AI: a model of neurons of the brain.

McCulloch and his co-author Walter Pitts, a young mathematician, proposed a model of artificial neural networks in which each neuron was postulated as being in a binary state: that is, in either an **on** or **off** condition (McCulloch and Pitts, 1943). They demonstrated that their neural network model was, in fact, equivalent to the Turing machine, and proved that any computable function could be computed by some network of connected neurons. McCulloch and Pitts also showed that simple network structures could learn.

The neural network model stimulated both theoretical and experimental work to model the brain in the laboratory. However, experiments clearly demonstrated that the binary model of neurons was not correct. In fact, a neuron has highly non-linear characteristics and cannot be considered as a simple two-state device. Nonetheless, McCulloch, the second 'founding father' of AI after Alan Turing, had created the cornerstone of neural computing and artificial neural networks (ANNs). After a decline in the 1970s, the field of ANNs was revived in the late 1980s.

The third founder of AI was John von Neumann, the brilliant Hungarian-born mathematician. In 1930, he joined the Princeton University, lecturing in mathematical physics. He was a colleague and friend of Alan Turing. During the Second World War, von Neumann played a key role in the Manhattan Project that built the nuclear bomb. He also became an adviser for the Electronic Numerical Integrator and Calculator (ENIAC) project at the University of Pennsylvania and helped to design the Electronic Discrete Variable Automatic Computer (EDVAC), a **stored program** machine. He was influenced by McCulloch and Pitts's neural network model. When Marvin Minsky and Dean Edmonds, two graduate students in the Princeton mathematics department, built the first neural network computer in 1951, von Neumann encouraged and supported them.

Another of the first-generation researchers was Claude Shannon. He graduated from Massachusetts Institute of Technology (MIT) and joined Bell Telephone Laboratories in 1941. Shannon shared Alan Turing's ideas on the possibility of machine intelligence. In 1950, he published a paper on chess-playing machines, which pointed out that a typical chess game involved about 10^{120} possible moves (Shannon, 1950). Even if the new von-Neumann-type computer could examine one move per microsecond, it would take 3×10^{106} years to make its first move. Thus Shannon demonstrated the need to use heuristics in the search for the solution.

Princeton University was also home to John McCarthy, another founder of AI. He convinced Marvin Minsky and Claude Shannon to organise a summer workshop at Dartmouth College, where McCarthy worked after graduating from Princeton. In 1956, they brought together researchers interested in the study of machine intelligence, artificial neural nets and automata theory. The workshop was sponsored by IBM. Although there were just 10 researchers, this workshop gave birth to a new science called **artificial intelligence**. For the next 20 years the field of AI would be dominated by the participants at the Dartmouth workshop and their students.

1.2.2   The rise of artificial intelligence, or the era of great expectations (1956–late 1960s)

The early years of AI are characterised by tremendous enthusiasm, great ideas and very limited success. Only a few years before, computers had been introduced to perform routine mathematical calculations, but now AI researchers were demonstrating that computers could do more than that. It was an era of great expectations.

John McCarthy, one of the organisers of the Dartmouth workshop and the inventor of the term 'artificial intelligence', moved from Dartmouth to MIT. He defined the high-level language **LISP** – one of the oldest programming languages (FORTRAN is just two years older), which is still in current use. In 1958, McCarthy presented a paper, 'Programs with common sense', in which he proposed a program called the **Advice Taker** to search for solutions to general problems of the world (McCarthy, 1958). McCarthy demonstrated how his program could generate, for example, a plan to drive to the airport, based on some simple axioms. Most importantly, the program was designed to accept new axioms, or in other words new knowledge, in different areas of expertise without being reprogrammed. Thus the Advice Taker was the first complete knowledge-based system incorporating the central principles of knowledge representation and reasoning.

Another organiser of the Dartmouth workshop, Marvin Minsky, also moved to MIT. However, unlike McCarthy with his focus on formal logic, Minsky developed an anti-logical outlook on knowledge representation and reasoning. His theory of frames (Minsky, 1975) was a major contribution to knowledge engineering.

The early work on neural computing and artificial neural networks started by McCulloch and Pitts was continued. Learning methods were improved and Frank Rosenblatt proved the **Perceptron Convergence Theorem**, demonstrating that his learning algorithm could adjust the connection strengths of a perceptron (Rosenblatt, 1962).

One of the most ambitious projects of the era of great expectations was the General Problem Solver (GPS) (Newell and Simon, 1961; 1972). Allen Newell and Herbert Simon from the Carnegie Mellon University developed a general-purpose program to simulate human problem-solving methods. GPS was probably the first attempt to separate the problem-solving technique from the data. It was based on the technique now referred to as **means–ends analysis**.

Newell and Simon postulated that a problem to be solved could be defined in terms of **states**. The means–ends analysis was used to determine a difference between the current state and the desirable state or the **goal state** of the problem, and to choose and apply **operators** to reach the goal state. If the goal state could not be immediately reached from the current state, a new state closer to the goal would be established and the procedure repeated until the goal state was reached. The set of operators determined the solution plan.

However, GPS failed to solve complicated problems. The program was based on formal logic and therefore could generate an infinite number of possible operators, which is inherently inefficient. The amount of computer time and memory that GPS required to solve real-world problems led to the project being abandoned.

In summary, we can say that in the 1960s, AI researchers attempted to simulate the complex thinking process by inventing **general methods** for solving broad classes of problems. They used the general-purpose search mechanism to find a solution to the problem. Such approaches, now referred to as **weak methods**, applied weak information about the problem domain; this resulted in weak performance of the programs developed.

However, it was also a time when the field of AI attracted great scientists who introduced fundamental new ideas in such areas as knowledge representation, learning algorithms, neural computing and computing with words. These ideas could not be implemented then because of the limited capabilities of computers, but two decades later they have led to the development of real-life practical applications.

It is interesting to note that Lotfi Zadeh, a professor from the University of California at Berkeley, published his famous paper 'Fuzzy sets' also in the 1960s (Zadeh, 1965). This paper is now considered the foundation of the fuzzy set theory. Two decades later, fuzzy researchers have built hundreds of smart machines and intelligent systems.

By 1970, the euphoria about AI was gone, and most government funding for AI projects was cancelled. AI was still a relatively new field, academic in nature, with few practical applications apart from playing games (Samuel, 1959; 1967; Greenblatt *et al.*, 1967). So, to the outsider, the achievements would be seen as toys, as no AI system at that time could manage real-world problems.

1.2.3   Unfulfilled promises, or the impact of reality (late 1960s–early 1970s)

From the mid-1950s, AI researchers were making promises to build all-purpose intelligent machines on a human-scale knowledge base by the 1980s, and to exceed human intelligence by the year 2000. By 1970, however, they realised that such claims were too optimistic. Although a few AI programs could demonstrate some level of machine intelligence in one or two toy problems, almost no AI projects could deal with a wider selection of tasks or more difficult real-world problems.

The main difficulties for AI in the late 1960s were:

- Because AI researchers were developing general methods for broad classes of problems, early programs contained little or even no knowledge about a problem domain. To solve problems, programs applied a search strategy by trying out different combinations of small steps, until the right one was found. This method worked for 'toy' problems, so it seemed reasonable that, if the programs could be 'scaled up' to solve large problems, they would finally succeed. However, this approach was wrong.

  Easy, or **tractable**, problems can be solved in polynomial time: that is, for a problem of size n, the time or number of steps needed to find the solution is a polynomial function of n. On the other hand, hard or intractable problems require times that are exponential functions of the problem size. While a polynomial-time algorithm is considered to be efficient, an exponential-time algorithm is inefficient, because its execution time increases rapidly with the problem size. The theory of NP-completeness (Cook, 1971; Karp, 1972), developed in the early 1970s, showed the existence of a large class of non-deterministic polynomial problems (NP problems) that are NP-complete. A problem is called NP if its solution (if one exists) can be guessed and verified in polynomial time; non-deterministic means that no particular algorithm is followed to make the guess. The hardest problems in this class are NP-complete. Even with faster computers and larger memories, these problems are hard to solve.

- Many of the problems that AI attempted to solve were too broad and too difficult. A typical task for early AI was machine translation. For example, the National Research Council, USA, funded the translation of Russian scientific papers after the launch of the first artificial satellite (Sputnik) in 1957. Initially, the project team tried simply replacing Russian words with English, using an electronic dictionary. However, it was soon found that translation requires a general understanding of the subject to choose the correct words. This task was too difficult. In 1966, all translation projects funded by the US government were cancelled.

- In 1971, the British government also suspended support for AI research. Sir James Lighthill had been commissioned by the Science Research Council of Great Britain to review the current state of AI (Lighthill, 1973). He did not find any major or even significant results from AI research, and therefore saw no need to have a separate science called 'artificial intelligence'.

1.2.4 The technology of expert systems, or the key to success (early 1970s–mid-1980s)

Probably the most important development in the 1970s was the realisation that the problem domain for intelligent machines had to be sufficiently restricted. Previously, AI researchers had believed that clever search algorithms and reasoning techniques could be invented to emulate general, human-like, problem-solving methods. A general-purpose search mechanism could rely on elementary reasoning steps to find complete solutions and could use weak knowledge about the domain. However, when weak methods failed, researchers finally realised that the only way to deliver practical results was to solve typical cases in narrow areas of expertise by making large reasoning steps.]

The DENDRAL program is a typical example of the emerging technology (Buchanan *et al.*, 1969). DENDRAL was developed at Stanford University to analyse chemicals. The project was supported by NASA, because an unmanned spacecraft was to be launched to Mars and a program was required to determine the molecular structure of Martian soil, based on the mass spectral data provided by a mass spectrometer. Edward Feigenbaum (a former student of Herbert Simon), Bruce Buchanan (a computer scientist) and Joshua Lederberg (a Nobel prize winner in genetics) formed a team to solve this challenging problem.

The traditional method of solving such problems relies on a generate-and-test technique: all possible molecular structures consistent with the mass spectrogram are generated first, and then the mass spectrum is determined or predicted for each structure and tested against the actual spectrum. However, this method failed because millions of possible structures could be generated – the problem rapidly became intractable even for decent-sized molecules.

To add to the difficulties of the challenge, there was no scientific algorithm for mapping the mass spectrum into its molecular structure. However, analytical chemists, such as Lederberg, could solve this problem by using their skills, experience and expertise. They could enormously reduce the number of possible structures by looking for well-known patterns of peaks in the spectrum, and thus provide just a few feasible solutions for further examination. Therefore, Feigenbaum's job became to incorporate the expertise of Lederberg into a computer program to make it perform at a human expert level. Such programs were later called **expert systems**. To understand and adopt Lederberg's knowledge and operate with his terminology, Feigenbaum had to learn basic ideas in chemistry and spectral analysis. However, it became apparent that Feigenbaum used not only rules of chemistry but also his own heuristics, or rules-of-thumb, based on his experience, and even guesswork. Soon Feigenbaum identified one of the major difficulties in the project, which he called the 'knowledge acquisition bottleneck' – how to extract knowledge from human experts to apply to computers. To articulate his knowledge, Lederberg even needed to study basics in computing.

Working as a team, Feigenbaum, Buchanan and Lederberg developed DENDRAL, the first successful knowledge-based system. The key to their success was mapping all the relevant theoretical knowledge from its general form to highly specific rules ('cookbook recipes') (Feigenbaum *et al.*, 1971).

The significance of DENDRAL can be summarised as follows:

- DENDRAL marked a major 'paradigm shift' in AI: a shift from general-purpose, knowledge-sparse, weak methods to domain-specific, knowledge-intensive techniques.

- The aim of the project was to develop a computer program to attain the level of performance of an experienced human chemist. Using heuristics in the form of high-quality specific rules – rules-of-thumb – elicited from human experts, the DENDRAL team proved that computers could equal an expert in narrow, defined, problem areas.

- The DENDRAL project originated the fundamental idea of the new methodology of expert systems – **knowledge engineering**, which encompassed techniques of capturing, analysing and expressing in rules an expert's 'know-how'.

DENDRAL proved to be a useful analytical tool for chemists and was marketed commercially in the USA.

The next major project undertaken by Feigenbaum and others at Stanford University was in the area of medical diagnosis. The project, called MYCIN, started in 1972. It later became the Ph.D. thesis of Edward Shortliffe (Shortliffe, 1976). MYCIN was a rule-based expert system for the diagnosis of infectious blood diseases. It also provided a doctor with therapeutic advice in a convenient, user-friendly manner.

MYCIN had a number of characteristics common to early expert systems, including:

- MYCIN could perform at a level equivalent to human experts in the field and considerably better than junior doctors.

- MYCIN's knowledge consisted of about 450 independent rules of IF-THEN form derived from human knowledge in a narrow domain through extensive interviewing of experts.

- The knowledge incorporated in the form of rules was clearly separated from the reasoning mechanism. The system developer could easily manipulate knowledge in the system by inserting or deleting some rules. For example, a domain-independent version of MYCIN called EMYCIN (Empty MYCIN) was later produced at Stanford University (van Melle, 1979; van Melle *et al.*, 1981). It had all the features of the MYCIN system except the knowledge of infectious blood diseases. EMYCIN facilitated the development of a variety of diagnostic applications. System developers just had to add new knowledge in the form of rules to obtain a new application.

MYCIN also introduced a few new features. Rules incorporated in MYCIN reflected the uncertainty associated with knowledge, in this case with medical diagnosis. It tested rule conditions (the IF part) against available data or data requested from the physician. When appropriate, MYCIN inferred the truth of a condition through a calculus of uncertainty called **certainty factors**. Reasoning in the face of uncertainty was the most important part of the system.

Another probabilistic system that generated enormous publicity was PROSPECTOR, an expert system for mineral exploration developed by the Stanford Research Institute (Duda *et al.*, 1979). The project ran from 1974 to

1983. Nine experts contributed their knowledge and expertise. To represent their knowledge, PROSPECTOR used a combined structure that incorporated rules and a semantic network. PROSPECTOR had over a thousand rules to represent extensive domain knowledge. It also had a sophisticated support package including a knowledge acquisition system.

PROSPECTOR operates as follows. The user, an exploration geologist, is asked to input the characteristics of a suspected deposit: the geological setting, structures, kinds of rocks and minerals. Then the program compares these characteristics with models of ore deposits and, if necessary, queries the user to obtain additional information. Finally, PROSPECTOR makes an assessment of the suspected mineral deposit and presents its conclusion. It can also explain the steps it used to reach the conclusion.

In exploration geology, important decisions are usually made in the face of uncertainty, with knowledge that is incomplete or fuzzy. To deal with such knowledge, PROSPECTOR incorporated Bayes' rules of evidence to propagate uncertainties through the system. PROSPECTOR performed at the level of an expert geologist and proved itself in practice. In 1980, it identified a molybdenum deposit near Mount Tolman in Washington State. Subsequent drilling by a mining company confirmed the deposit was worth over $100 million. You couldn't hope for a better justification for using expert systems.

The expert systems mentioned above have now become classics. A growing number of successful applications of expert systems in the late 1970s showed that AI technology could move successfully from the research laboratory to the commercial environment. During this period, however, most expert systems were developed with special AI languages, such as LISP, PROLOG and OPS, based on powerful workstations. The need to have rather expensive hardware and complicated programming languages meant that the challenge of expert system development was left in the hands of a few research groups at Stanford University, MIT, Stanford Research Institute and Carnegie Mellon University. Only in the 1980s, with the arrival of personal computers (PCs) and easy-to-use expert system development tools – shells – could ordinary researchers and engineers in all disciplines take up the opportunity to develop expert systems.

A 1986 survey reported a remarkable number of successful expert system applications in different areas: chemistry, electronics, engineering, geology, management, medicine, process control and military science (Waterman, 1986). Although Waterman found nearly 200 expert systems, most of the applications were in the field of medical diagnosis. Seven years later a similar survey reported over 2500 developed expert systems (Durkin, 1994). The new growing area was business and manufacturing, which accounted for about 60 per cent of the applications. Expert system technology had clearly matured.

Are expert systems really the key to success in any field? In spite of a great number of successful developments and implementations of expert systems in different areas of human knowledge, it would be a mistake to overestimate the capability of this technology. The difficulties are rather complex and lie in both technical and sociological spheres. They include the following:

- Expert systems are restricted to a very narrow domain of expertise. For example, MYCIN, which was developed for the diagnosis of infectious blood diseases, lacks any real knowledge of human physiology. If a patient has more than one disease, we cannot rely on MYCIN. In fact, therapy prescribed for the blood disease might even be harmful because of the other disease.

- Because of the narrow domain, expert systems are not as robust and flexible as a user might want. Furthermore, expert systems can have difficulty recognising domain boundaries. When given a task different from the typical problems, an expert system might attempt to solve it and fail in rather unpredictable ways.

- Expert systems have limited explanation capabilities. They can show the sequence of the rules they applied to reach a solution, but cannot relate accumulated, heuristic knowledge to any deeper understanding of the problem domain.

- Expert systems are also difficult to verify and validate. No general technique has yet been developed for analysing their completeness and consistency. Heuristic rules represent knowledge in abstract form and lack even basic understanding of the domain area. It makes the task of identifying incorrect, incomplete or inconsistent knowledge very difficult.

- Expert systems, especially the first generation, have little or no ability to learn from their experience. Expert systems are built individually and cannot be developed fast. It might take from five to ten person-years to build an expert system to solve a moderately difficult problem (Waterman, 1986). Complex systems such as DENDRAL, MYCIN or PROSPECTOR can take over 30 person-years to build. This large effort, however, would be difficult to justify if improvements to the expert system's performance depended on further attention from its developers.

Despite all these difficulties, expert systems have made the breakthrough and proved their value in a number of important applications.

1.2.5 How to make a machine learn, or the rebirth of neural networks (mid-1980s onwards)

In the mid-1980s, researchers, engineers and experts found that building an expert system required much more than just buying a reasoning system or expert system shell and putting enough rules in it. Disillusion about the applicability of expert system technology even led to people predicting an 'AI winter' with severely squeezed funding for AI projects. AI researchers decided to have a new look at neural networks.

By the late 1960s, most of the basic ideas and concepts necessary for neural computing had already been formulated (Cowan, 1990). However, only in the mid-1980s did the solution emerge. The major reason for the delay was technological: there were no PCs or powerful workstations to model and experiment with artificial neural networks. The other reasons were psychological and financial. For example, in 1969, Minsky and Papert had mathematically demonstrated the fundamental computational limitations of one-layer perceptrons (Minsky and Papert, 1969). They also said there was no reason to expect that more complex multilayer perceptrons would represent much. This certainly would not encourage anyone to work on perceptrons and, as a result, most AI researchers deserted the field of artificial neural networks in the 1970s.

In the 1980s, because of the need for brain-like information processing, as well as the advances in computer technology and progress in neuroscience, the field of neural networks experienced a dramatic resurgence. Major contributions to both theory and design were made on several fronts. Grossberg established a new principle of self-organisation (**adaptive resonance theory**), which provided the basis for a new class of neural networks (Grossberg, 1980). Hopfield introduced neural networks with feedback – **Hopfield networks**, which attracted much attention in the 1980s (Hopfield, 1982). Kohonen published a paper on **self-organised maps** (Kohonen, 1982). Barto, Sutton and Anderson published their work on **reinforcement learning** and its application in control (Barto *et al.*, 1983). But the real breakthrough came in 1986 when the **back-propagation learning algorithm**, first introduced by Bryson and Ho in 1969 (Bryson and Ho, 1969), was reinvented by Rumelhart and McClelland in *Parallel Distributed Processing: Explorations in the Microstructures of Cognition* (Rumelhart and McClelland, 1986). At the same time, back-propagation learning was also discovered by Parker (Parker, 1987) and LeCun (LeCun, 1988), and since then has become the most popular technique for training multilayer perceptrons. In 1988, Broomhead and Lowe found a procedure to design **layered feedforward networks** using radial basis functions, an alternative to multilayer perceptrons (Broomhead and Lowe, 1988).

Artificial neural networks have come a long way from the early models of McCulloch and Pitts to an interdisciplinary subject with roots in neuroscience, psychology, mathematics and engineering, and will continue to develop in both theory and practical applications. However, Hopfield's paper (Hopfield, 1982) and Rumelhart and McClelland's book (Rumelhart and McClelland, 1986) were the most significant and influential works responsible for the rebirth of neural networks in the 1980s.

1.2.6 Evolutionary computation, or learning by doing (early 1970s onwards)

Natural intelligence is a product of evolution. Therefore, by simulating biological evolution, we might expect to discover how living systems are propelled towards high-level intelligence. Nature learns by doing; biological systems are not told how to adapt to a specific environment – they simply compete for survival. The fittest species have a greater chance to reproduce, and thereby to pass their genetic material to the next generation.

The evolutionary approach to AI is based on the computational models of natural selection and genetics. Evolutionary computation works by simulating a population of individuals, evaluating their performance, generating a new population, and repeating this process a number of times.

Evolutionary computation combines three main techniques: genetic algorithms, evolutionary strategies and genetic programming.

The concept of genetic algorithms was introduced by John Holland in the early 1970s (Holland, 1975). He developed an algorithm for manipulating artificial 'chromosomes' (strings of binary digits), using such genetic operations as selection, crossover and mutation. Genetic algorithms are based on a solid theoretical foundation of the Schema Theorem (Holland, 1975; Goldberg, 1989).

In the early 1960s, independently of Holland's genetic algorithms, Ingo Rechenberg and Hans-Paul Schwefel, students of the Technical University of Berlin, proposed a new optimisation method called evolutionary strategies (Rechenberg, 1965). Evolutionary strategies were designed specifically for solving parameter optimisation problems in engineering. Rechenberg and Schwefel suggested using random changes in the parameters, as happens in natural mutation. In fact, an evolutionary strategies approach can be considered as an alternative to the engineer's intuition. Evolutionary strategies use a numerical optimisation procedure, similar to a focused Monte Carlo search.

Both genetic algorithms and evolutionary strategies can solve a wide range of problems. They provide robust and reliable solutions for highly complex, non-linear search and optimisation problems that previously could not be solved at all (Holland, 1995; Schwefel, 1995).

Genetic programming represents an application of the genetic model of learning to programming. Its goal is to evolve not a coded representation of some problem, but rather a computer code that solves the problem. That is, genetic programming generates computer programs as the solution.

The interest in genetic programming was greatly stimulated by John Koza in the 1990s (Koza, 1992; 1994). He used genetic operations to manipulate symbolic code representing LISP programs. Genetic programming offers a solution to the main challenge of computer science – making computers solve problems without being explicitly programmed.

Genetic algorithms, evolutionary strategies and genetic programming represent rapidly growing areas of AI, and have great potential.

1.2.7   The new era of knowledge engineering, or computing with words (late 1980s onwards)

Neural network technology offers more natural interaction with the real world than do systems based on symbolic reasoning. Neural networks can learn, adapt to changes in a problem's environment, establish patterns in situations where rules are not known, and deal with fuzzy or incomplete information. However, they lack explanation facilities and usually act as a black box. The process of training neural networks with current technologies is slow, and frequent retraining can cause serious difficulties.

Although in some special cases, particularly in knowledge-poor situations, ANNs can solve problems better than expert systems, the two technologies are not in competition now. They rather nicely complement each other.

Classic expert systems are especially good for closed-system applications with precise inputs and logical outputs. They use expert knowledge in the form of rules and, if required, can interact with the user to establish a particular fact. A major drawback is that human experts cannot always express their knowledge in terms of rules or explain the line of their reasoning. This can prevent the expert system from accumulating the necessary knowledge, and consequently lead to its failure. To overcome this limitation, neural computing can be used for extracting hidden knowledge in large data sets to obtain rules for expert systems (Zahedi, 1993; Medsker and Leibowitz, 1994). ANNs can also be used for correcting rules in traditional rule-based expert systems (Omlin and Giles, 1996). In other words, where acquired knowledge is incomplete, neural networks can refine the knowledge, and where the knowledge is inconsistent with some given data, neural networks can revise the rules.

Another very important technology dealing with vague, imprecise and uncertain knowledge and data is **fuzzy logic**. Most methods of handling imprecision in classic expert systems are based on the probability concept. MYCIN, for example, introduced certainty factors, while PROSPECTOR incorporated Bayes' rules to propagate uncertainties. However, experts do not usually think in probability values, but in such terms as **often**, **generally**, **sometimes**, **occasionally** and **rarely**. Fuzzy logic is concerned with the use of fuzzy values that capture the meaning of words, human reasoning and decision making. As a method to encode and apply human knowledge in a form that accurately reflects an expert's understanding of difficult, complex problems, fuzzy logic provides the way to break through the computational bottlenecks of traditional expert systems.

At the heart of fuzzy logic lies the concept of a linguistic variable. The values of the linguistic variable are words rather than numbers. Similar to expert systems, fuzzy systems use IF-THEN rules to incorporate human knowledge, but these rules are fuzzy, such as

IF speed is high THEN stopping_distance is long

IF speed is low THEN stopping_distance is short

Fuzzy logic or **fuzzy set theory** was introduced by Professor Lotfi Zadeh, Berkeley's electrical engineering department chairman, in 1965 (Zadeh, 1965). It provided a means of computing with words. However, acceptance of fuzzy set theory by the technical community was slow and difficult. Part of the problem was the provocative name – 'fuzzy' – which seemed too light-hearted to be taken seriously. Eventually, fuzzy theory, ignored in the West, was taken seriously in the East – by the Japanese. It has been used successfully since 1987 in Japanese-designed dishwashers, washing machines, air conditioners, television sets, copiers and even cars.

The introduction of fuzzy products gave rise to tremendous interest in this apparently 'new' technology first proposed over 30 years ago. Hundreds of books and thousands of technical papers have been written on this topic. Some of the classics are: *Fuzzy Sets, Neural Networks and Soft Computing* (Yager and Zadeh, eds, 1994); *The Fuzzy Systems Handbook* (Cox, 1999); *Fuzzy Engineering* (Kosko, 1997); *Expert Systems and Fuzzy Systems* (Negoita, 1985); and also the best-seller science book *Fuzzy Thinking* (Kosko, 1993), which popularised the field of fuzzy logic.

Most fuzzy logic applications have been in the area of control engineering. However, fuzzy control systems use only a small part of fuzzy logic's power of knowledge representation. Benefits derived from the application of fuzzy logic models in knowledge-based and decision-support systems can be summarised as follows (Cox, 1999; Pedrycz and Gomide, 2007; Turban *et al.*, 2010):

- **Improved computational power.** Fuzzy rule-based systems perform faster than conventional expert systems and require fewer rules. A fuzzy expert system merges the rules, making them more powerful. Lotfi Zadeh believes that in a few years most expert systems will use fuzzy logic to solve highly non-linear and computationally difficult problems.

- **Improved cognitive modelling.** Fuzzy systems allow the encoding of knowledge in a form that reflects the way experts think about a complex problem. They usually think in such imprecise terms as **high** and **low**, **fast** and **slow**, **heavy** and **light**, and they also use such terms as **very often** and **almost never**, **usually** and **hardly ever**, **frequently** and **occasionally**. In order to build conventional rules, we need to define the crisp boundaries for these terms, thus breaking down the expertise into fragments. However, this fragmentation leads to the poor performance of conventional expert systems when they deal with highly complex problems. In contrast, fuzzy expert systems model imprecise information, capturing expertise much more closely to the way it is represented in the expert mind, and thus improve cognitive modelling of the problem.

- **The ability to represent multiple experts.** Conventional expert systems are built for a very narrow domain with clearly defined expertise. It makes the system's performance fully dependent on the right choice of experts. Although a common strategy is to find just one expert, when a more complex expert system is being built or when expertise is not well defined, **multiple experts** might be needed. Multiple experts can expand the domain, synthesise expertise and eliminate the need for a world-class expert, who is likely to be both very expensive and hard to access. However, multiple experts seldom reach close agreements; there are often differences in opinions and even conflicts. This is especially true in areas such as business and management where no simple solution exists and conflicting views should be taken into account. Fuzzy expert systems can help to represent the expertise of multiple experts when they have opposing views.

Although fuzzy systems allow expression of expert knowledge in a more natural way, they still depend on the rules extracted from the experts, and thus might be smart or dumb. Some experts can provide very clever fuzzy rules – but some just guess and may even get them wrong. Therefore, all rules must be tested and tuned, which can be a prolonged and tedious process. For example, it took Hitachi engineers several years to test and tune only 54 fuzzy rules to guide the Sendai Subway System.

Using fuzzy logic development tools, we can easily build a simple fuzzy system, but then we may spend days, weeks and even months trying out new rules and tuning our system. How do we make this process faster or, in other words, how do we generate good fuzzy rules automatically?

In recent years, several methods based on neural network technology have been used to search numerical data for fuzzy rules. Adaptive or neural fuzzy systems can find new fuzzy rules, or change and tune existing ones based on the data provided. In other words, data in – rules out, or experience in – common sense out.

So, where is knowledge engineering heading?

Expert, neural and fuzzy systems have now matured and have been applied to a broad range of different problems, mainly in engineering, medicine, finance, business and management. Each technology handles the uncertainty and ambiguity of human knowledge differently, and each technology has found its place in knowledge engineering. They no longer compete; rather they complement each other. A synergy of expert systems with fuzzy logic and neural computing improves adaptability, robustness, fault tolerance and speed of knowledge-based systems. Besides, computing with words makes them more 'human'. It is now common practice to build intelligent systems using existing theories rather than to propose new ones, and to apply these systems to real-world problems rather than to 'toy' problems.

1.3 Summary

We live in the era of the knowledge revolution, when the power of a nation is determined not by the number of soldiers in its army but the knowledge it possesses. Science, medicine, engineering and business propel nations towards a higher quality of life, but they also require highly qualified and skilful people. We are now adopting intelligent machines that can capture the expertise of such knowledgeable people and reason in a manner similar to humans.

The desire for intelligent machines was just an elusive dream until the first computer was developed. The early computers could manipulate large databases effectively by following prescribed algorithms, but could not reason about the information provided. This gave rise to the question of whether computers could ever think. Alan Turing defined the intelligent behaviour of a computer as the ability to achieve human-level performance in a cognitive task. The Turing test provided a basis for the verification and validation of knowledge-based systems.

In 1956, a summer workshop at Dartmouth College brought together 10 researchers interested in the study of machine intelligence, and a new science – artificial intelligence – was born.

Since the early 1950s, AI technology has developed from the curiosity of a few researchers to a valuable tool to support humans making decisions. We have seen historical cycles of AI from the era of great ideas and great expectations in the 1960s to the disillusionment and funding cutbacks in the early 1970s; from the development of the first expert systems such as DENDRAL, MYCIN and PROSPECTOR in the 1970s to the maturity of expert system technology and its massive applications in different areas in the 1980s/ 1990s; from a simple binary model of neurons proposed in the 1940s to a dramatic resurgence of the field of artificial neural networks in the 1980s; from the introduction of fuzzy set theory and its being ignored by the West in the 1960s to numerous 'fuzzy' consumer products offered by the Japanese in the 1980s and world-wide acceptance of 'soft' computing and computing with words in the 1990s.

The development of expert systems created knowledge engineering, the process of building intelligent systems. Today it deals not only with expert systems but also with neural networks and fuzzy logic. Knowledge engineering is still an art rather than engineering, but attempts have already been made to extract rules automatically from numerical data through neural network technology.

Table 1.1 summarises the key events in the history of AI and knowledge engineering from the first work on AI by McCulloch and Pitts in 1943 to the recent trends of combining the strengths of expert systems, fuzzy logic and neural computing in modern knowledge-based systems capable of computing with words.

The most important lessons learned in this chapter are:

- Intelligence is the ability to learn and understand, to solve problems and to make decisions.

- Artificial intelligence is a science that has defined its goal as making machines do things that would require intelligence if done by humans.

- A machine is thought intelligent if it can achieve human-level performance in some cognitive task. To build an intelligent machine, we have to capture, organise and use human expert knowledge in some problem area.

- The realisation that the problem domain for intelligent machines had to be sufficiently restricted marked a major 'paradigm shift' in AI from general-purpose, knowledge-sparse, weak methods to domain-specific, knowledge-intensive methods. This led to the development of expert systems – computer programs capable of performing at a human-expert level in a narrow problem area. Expert systems use human knowledge and expertise in the form of specific rules, and are distinguished by the clean separation of the knowledge and the reasoning mechanism. They can also explain their reasoning procedures.

Table 1.1   A summary of the main events in the history of AI and knowledge engineering

Period	Key events
The birth of artificial intelligence (1943–1956)	McCulloch and Pitts, *A Logical Calculus of the Ideas Immanent in Nervous Activity*, 1943 Turing, *Computing Machinery and Intelligence*, 1950 The Electronic Numerical Integrator and Calculator project (von Neumann) Shannon, *Programming a Computer for Playing Chess*, 1950 The Dartmouth College summer workshop on machine intelligence, artificial neural nets and automata theory, 1956
The rise of artificial intelligence (1956–late 1960s)	*LISP* (McCarthy) The General Problem Solver (GPR) project (Newell and Simon) Newell and Simon, *Human Problem Solving*, 1972 Minsky, *A Framework for Representing Knowledge*, 1975
The disillusionment in artificial intelligence (late 1960s–early 1970s)	Cook, *The Complexity of Theorem Proving Procedures*, 1971 Karp, *Reducibility Among Combinatorial Problems*, 1972 The Lighthill Report, 1971
The discovery of expert systems (early 1970s–mid-1980s)	DENDRAL (Feigenbaum, Buchanan and Lederberg, Stanford University) MYCIN (Feigenbaum and Shortliffe, Stanford University) PROSPECTOR (Stanford Research Institute) *PROLOG* – a Logic Programming Language (Colmerauer, Roussel and Kowalski, France) EMYCIN (Stanford University) Waterman, *A Guide to Expert Systems*, 1986
The rebirth of artificial neural networks (mid-1980s onwards)	Hopfield, *Neural Networks and Physical Systems with Emergent Collective Computational Abilities*, 1982 Kohonen, *Self-Organized Formation of Topologically Correct Feature Maps*, 1982 Rumelhart and McClelland, *Parallel Distributed Processing*, 1986 The First IEEE International Conference on Neural Networks, 1987 Haykin, *Neural Networks*, 1994 Neural Network, MATLAB Application Toolbox (The MathWorks, Inc.)

Table 1.1 (cont.)

Period	Key events
Evolutionary computation (early 1970s onwards)	Rechenberg, *Evolutionsstrategien – Optimierung Technischer Systeme Nach Prinzipien der Biologischen Information*, 1973
	Holland, *Adaptation in Natural and Artificial Systems*, 1975
	Koza, *Genetic Programming: On the Programming of the Computers by Means of Natural Selection*, 1992
	Schwefel, *Evolution and Optimum Seeking*, 1995
	Fogel, *Evolutionary Computation – Towards a New Philosophy of Machine Intelligence*, 1995
Computing with words (late 1980s onwards)	Zadeh, *Fuzzy Sets*, 1965
	Zadeh, *Fuzzy Algorithms*, 1969
	Mamdani, *Application of Fuzzy Logic to Approximate Reasoning Using Linguistic Synthesis*, 1977
	Sugeno, *Fuzzy Theory*, 1983
	Japanese 'fuzzy' consumer products (dishwashers, washing machines, air conditioners, television sets, copiers)
	Sendai Subway System (Hitachi, Japan), 1986
	Negoita, *Expert Systems and Fuzzy Systems*, 1985
	The First IEEE International Conference on Fuzzy Systems, 1992
	Kosko, *Fuzzy Thinking*, 1993
	Yager and Zadeh, *Fuzzy Sets, Neural Networks and Soft Computing*, 1994
	Cox, *The Fuzzy Systems Handbook*, 1994
	Zadeh, *Computing with Words – A Paradigm Shift*, 1996
	Fuzzy Logic, MATLAB Toolbox (The MathWorks, Inc.)
	Neural Networks, MATLAB Toolbox (The MathWorks, Inc.) Berkeley Initiative in Soft Computing (BISC) http://www-bisc.cs.berkeley.edu

- One of the main difficulties in building intelligent machines, or in other words in knowledge engineering, is the 'knowledge acquisition bottleneck' – extracting knowledge from human experts.

- Experts think in imprecise terms, such as **very often** and **almost never**, **usually** and **hardly ever**, **frequently** and **occasionally**, and use linguistic variables, such as **high** and **low**, **fast** and **slow**, **heavy** and **light**. Fuzzy logic or fuzzy set theory provides a means to compute with words. It concentrates on the use of fuzzy values that capture the meaning of words, human reasoning and decision making, and provides a way of breaking through the computational burden of traditional expert systems.

- Expert systems can neither learn nor improve themselves through experience. They are individually created and demand large efforts for their development. It can take from five to ten person-years to build even a moderate expert system. Machine learning can accelerate this process significantly and enhance the quality of knowledge by adding new rules or changing incorrect ones.

- Artificial neural networks, inspired by biological neural networks, learn from historical cases and make it possible to generate rules automatically and thus avoid the tedious and expensive processes of knowledge acquisition, validation and revision.

- Integration of expert systems and ANNs, and fuzzy logic and ANNs improve the adaptability, fault tolerance and speed of knowledge-based systems.

Questions for review

1 Define intelligence. What is the intelligent behaviour of a machine?

2 Describe the Turing test for artificial intelligence and justify its validity from a modern standpoint.

3 Define artificial intelligence as a science. When was artificial intelligence born?

4 What are **weak methods**? Identify the main difficulties that led to the disillusion with AI in the early 1970s.

5 Define expert systems. What is the main difference between weak methods and the expert system technology?

6 List the common characteristics of early expert systems such as DENDRAL, MYCIN and PROSPECTOR.

7 What are the limitations of expert systems?

8 What are the differences between expert systems and artificial neural networks?

9 Why was the field of ANNs reborn in the 1980s?

10 What are the premises on which fuzzy logic is based? When was fuzzy set theory introduced?

11 What are the main advantages of applying fuzzy logic in knowledge-based systems?

12 What are the benefits of integrating expert systems, fuzzy logic and neural computing?

References

Barto, A.G., Sutton, R.S. and Anderson C.W. (1983). Neurolike adaptive elements that can solve difficult learning control problems, *IEEE Transactions on Systems, Man and Cybernetics*, SMC-13, 834–846.

Boden, M.A. (1977). *Artificial Intelligence and Natural Man*. Basic Books, New York.

Broomhead, D.S. and Lowe, D. (1988). Multivariable functional interpolation and adaptive networks, *Complex Systems*, 2, 321–355.

Bryson, A.E. and Ho, Y.-C. (1969). *Applied Optimal Control*. Blaisdell, New York.

Buchanan, B.G., Sutherland, G.L. and Feigenbaum, E.A. (1969). Heuristic DENDRAL: a program for generating explanatory hypotheses in organic chemistry, *Machine Intelligence 4*, B. Meltzer, D. Michie and M. Swann, eds, Edinburgh University Press, Edinburgh, Scotland, pp. 209–254.

Cook, S.A. (1971). The complexity of theorem proving procedures, *Proceedings of the Third Annual ACM Symposium on Theory of Computing*, New York, pp. 151–158.

Cowan, J.D. (1990). Neural networks: the early days, *Advances in Neural Information Processing Systems 2*, D.S. Tourefzky, ed., Morgan Kaufman, San Mateo, CA, pp. 828–842.

Cox, E. (1999). *The Fuzzy Systems Handbook: A Practitioner's Guide to Building, Using, and Maintaining Fuzzy Systems*, 2nd edn. Academic Press, San Diego, CA.

Duda, R., Gaschnig, J. and Hart, P. (1979). Model design in the PROSPECTOR consultant system for mineral exploration, *Expert Systems in the Microelectronic Age*, D. Michie, ed., Edinburgh University Press, Edinburgh, Scotland, pp. 153–167.

Durkin, J. (1994). *Expert Systems: Design and Development*. Prentice Hall, Englewood Cliffs, NJ.

Feigenbaum, E.A., Buchanan, B.G. and Lederberg, J. (1971). On generality and problem solving: a case study using the DENDRAL program, *Machine Intelligence 6*, B. Meltzer and D. Michie, eds, Edinburgh University Press, Edinburgh, Scotland, pp. 165–190.

Fogel, D.B. (1995). *Evolutionary Computation – Towards a New Philosophy of Machine Intelligence*. IEEE Press, Piscataway, NJ.

Goldberg, D.E. (1989). *Genetic Algorithms in Search, Optimisation and Machine Learning*. Addison-Wesley, Reading, MA.

Greenblatt, R.D., Eastlake, D.E. and Crocker, S.D. (1967). The Greenblatt Chess Program, *Proceedings of the Fall Joint Computer Conference*, pp. 801–810.

Grossberg, S. (1980). How does a brain build a cognitive code? *Psychological Review*, 87, 1–51.

Holland, J.H. (1975). *Adaptation in Natural and Artificial Systems*. University of Michigan Press, Ann Arbor.

Holland, J.H. (1995). *Hidden Order: How Adaptation Builds Complexity*. Perseus Books, New York.

Hopfield, J.J. (1982). Neural networks and physical systems with emergent collective computational abilities, *Proceedings of the National Academy of Sciences of the USA*, 79, 2554–2558.

Karp, R.M. (1972). Reducibility among combinatorial problems, *Complexity of Computer Computations*, R.E. Miller and J.W. Thatcher, eds, Plenum, New York, pp. 85–103.

Kohonen, T. (1982). Self-organized formation of topologically correct feature maps, *Biological Cybernetics*, 43, 59–69.

Kosko, B. (1993). *Fuzzy Thinking: The New Science of Fuzzy Logic*. Hyperion, New York.

Kosko, B. (1997). *Fuzzy Engineering*. Prentice Hall, Upper Saddle River, NJ.

Koza, J.R. (1992). *Genetic Programming: On the Programming of the Computers by Means of Natural Selection*. MIT Press, Cambridge, MA.

Koza, J.R. (1994). *Genetic Programming II: Automatic Discovery of Reusable Programs*. MIT Press, Cambridge, MA.

LeCun, Y. (1988). A theoretical framework for back-propagation, *Proceedings of the 1988 Connectionist Models Summer School*, D. Touretzky, G. Hilton and T. Sejnowski, eds, Morgan Kaufmann, San Mateo, CA, pp. 21–28.

Lighthill, J. (1973). Artificial intelligence: a general survey, *Artificial Intelligence: A Paper Symposium*. J. Lighthill, N.S. Sutherland, R.M. Needham, H.C. Longuest-Higgins and D. Michie, eds, Science Research Council of Great Britain, London.

McCarthy, J. (1958). Programs with common sense, *Proceedings of the Symposium on Mechanisation of Thought Processes*, vol. 1, London, pp. 77–84.

McCulloch, W.S. and Pitts, W. (1943). A logical calculus of the ideas immanent in nervous activity, *Bulletin of Mathematical Biophysics*, 5, 115–137.

Medsker, L. and Leibowitz, J. (1994). *Design and Development of Expert Systems and Neural Computing*. Macmillan, New York.

Minsky, M.L. (1975). A framework for representing knowledge, *The Psychology of Computer Vision*, P. Winston, ed., McGraw-Hill, New York, pp. 211–277.

Minsky, M.L. and Papert, S.A. (1969). *Perceptrons*. MIT Press, Cambridge, MA.

Negoita, C.V. (1985). *Expert Systems and Fuzzy Systems*. Benjamin/Cummings, Menlo Park, CA.

Newell, A. and Simon, H.A. (1961). GPS, a program that simulates human thought, *Lernende Automatten*, H. Billing, ed., R. Oldenbourg, Munich, pp. 109–124.

Newell, A. and Simon, H.A. (1972). *Human Problem Solving*. Prentice Hall, Englewood Cliffs, NJ.

Omlin, C.W. and Giles, C.L. (1996). Rule revision with recurrent neural networks, *IEEE Transactions on Knowledge and Data Engineering*, 8(1), 183–188.

Parker, D.B. (1987). Optimal algorithms for adaptive networks: second order back propagation, second order direct propagation, and second order Hebbian learning, *Proceedings of the IEEE 1st International Conference on Neural Networks*, San Diego, CA, vol. 2, pp. 593–600.

Pedrycz, W. and Gomide, F. (2007). *Fuzzy Systems Engineering: Toward Human-Centric Computing*. John Wiley, Hoboken, NJ.

Rechenberg, I. (1965). *Cybernetic Solution Path of an Experimental Problem*. Ministry of Aviation, Royal Aircraft Establishment, Library Translation No. 1122, August.

Rechenberg, I. (1973). *Evolutionsstrategien – Optimierung Technischer Systeme Nach Prinzipien der Biologischen Information*. Friedrich Frommann Verlag (Günther Holzboog K.G.), Stuttgart–Bad Cannstatt.

Rosenblatt, F. (1962). *Principles of Neurodynamics*. Spartan, Chicago.

Rumelhart, D.E. and McClelland, J.L., eds (1986). *Parallel Distributed Processing: Explorations in the Microstructures of Cognition*, 2 vols. MIT Press, Cambridge, MA.

Samuel, A.L. (1959). Some studies in machine learning using the game of checkers, *IBM Journal of Research and Development*, 3(3), 210–229.

Samuel, A.L. (1967). Some studies in machine learning using the game of checkers II – recent progress, *IBM Journal of Research and Development*, 11(6), 601–617.

Schwefel, H.-P. (1995). *Evolution and Optimum Seeking*. John Wiley, New York.

Shannon, C.E. (1950). Programming a computer for playing chess, *Philosophical Magazine*, 41(4), 256–275.

Shortliffe, E.H. (1976). *MYCIN: Computer-Based Medical Consultations*. Elsevier Press, New York.

Turban, E., Sharda, R. and Delen, D. (2010). *Decision Support and Business Intelligent Systems*, 9th edn. Prentice Hall, Englewood Cliffs, NJ.

Turing, A.M. (1950). Computing machinery and intelligence, *Mind*, 59, 433–460.

van Melle, W. (1979). A domain independent production-rule system for consultation programs, *Proceedings of the IJCAI 6*, pp. 923–925.

van Melle, W., Shortliffe, E.H. and Buchanan B.G. (1981). EMYCIN: a domain-independent system that aids in constructing knowledge-based consultation programs, *Machine Intelligence, Infotech State of the Art Report 9*, no. 3.

Waterman, D.A. (1986). *A Guide to Expert Systems*. Addison-Wesley, Reading, MA.

Yager, R.R. and Zadeh, L.A., eds (1994). *Fuzzy Sets, Neural Networks and Soft Computing*. Van Nostrand Reinhold, New York.

Zadeh, L. (1965). Fuzzy sets, *Information and Control*, 8(3), 338–353.

Zahedi, F. (1993). *Intelligent Systems for Business: Expert Systems with Neural Networks*. Wadsworth, Belmont, CA.

Rule-based expert systems   2

In which we introduce the most popular choice for building knowledge-based systems: rule-based expert systems.

2.1 Introduction, or what is knowledge?

In the 1970s, it was finally accepted that to make a machine solve an intellectual problem one had to know the solution. In other words, one has to have knowledge, 'know-how', in some specific domain.

What is knowledge?
Knowledge is a theoretical or practical understanding of a subject or a domain. Knowledge is also the sum of what is currently known, and apparently knowledge is power. Those who possess knowledge are called experts. They are the most powerful and important people in their organisations. Any successful company has at least a few first-class experts and it cannot remain in business without them.

Who is generally acknowledged as an expert?
Anyone can be considered a domain expert if he or she has deep knowledge (of both facts and rules) and strong practical experience in a particular domain. The area of the domain may be limited. For example, experts in electrical machines may have only general knowledge about transformers, while experts in life insurance marketing might have limited understanding of a real-estate insurance policy. In general, an expert is a skilful person who can do things other people cannot.

How do experts think?
The human mental process is internal, and it is too complex to be represented as an algorithm. However, most experts are capable of expressing their knowledge in the form of rules for problem solving. Consider a simple example. Imagine you meet an alien! He wants to cross a road. Can you help him? You are an expert in crossing roads – you've been on this job for several years. Thus you are able to teach the alien. How would you do this?

You explain to the alien that he can cross the road safely when the traffic light is green, and he must stop when the traffic light is red. These are the basic rules. Your knowledge can be formulated as the following simple statements:

```
IF     the 'traffic light' is green
THEN   the action is go

IF     the 'traffic light' is red
THEN   the action is stop
```

These statements represented in the IF-THEN form are called **production rules** or just **rules**. The term 'rule' in AI, which is the most commonly used type of knowledge representation, can be defined as an IF-THEN structure that relates given information or facts in the IF part to some action in the THEN part. A rule provides some description of how to solve a problem. Rules are relatively easy to create and understand.

2.2 Rules as a knowledge representation technique

Any rule consists of two parts: the IF part, called the **antecedent** (**premise** or **condition**), and the THEN part, called the **consequent** (**conclusion** or **action**).
The basic syntax of a rule is

```
IF     <antecedent>
THEN   <consequent>
```

In general, a rule can have multiple antecedents joined by the keywords AND (conjunction), OR (disjunction) or a combination of both. However, it is a good habit to avoid mixing conjunctions and disjunctions in the same rule.

```
IF     <antecedent 1>
AND    <antecedent 2>
       .
       .
       .
AND    <antecedent n>
THEN   <consequent>

IF     <antecedent 1>
OR     <antecedent 2>
       .
       .
       .
OR     <antecedent n>
THEN   <consequent>
```

The consequent of a rule can also have multiple clauses:

IF   <antecedent>
THEN   <consequent 1>
       <consequent 2>

       .

       .

       .

       <consequent *m*>

The antecedent of a rule incorporates two parts: an **object** (**linguistic object**) and its **value**. In our road crossing example, the linguistic object 'traffic light' can take either the value *green* or the value *red*. The object and its value are linked by an **operator**. The operator identifies the object and assigns the value. Operators such as *is, are, is not, are not* are used to assign a symbolic value to a linguistic object. But expert systems can also use mathematical operators to define an object as numerical and assign it to the numerical value. For example,

IF   'age of the customer' < 18
AND   'cash withdrawal' > 1000
THEN   'signature of the parent' is required

Similar to a rule antecedent, a consequent combines an object and a value connected by an operator. The operator assigns the value to the linguistic object. In the road crossing example, if the value of *traffic light* is *green*, the first rule sets the linguistic *object* action to the value *go*. Numerical objects and even simple arithmetical expression can also be used in a rule consequent.

IF   'taxable income' > 16283
THEN   'Medicare levy' = 'taxable income' $* 1.5 / 100$

Rules can represent relations, recommendations, directives, strategies and heuristics (Durkin, 1994).

Relation
IF   the 'fuel tank' is empty
THEN   the car is dead

Recommendation
IF   the season is autumn
AND   the sky is cloudy
AND   the forecast is drizzle
THEN   the advice is 'take an umbrella'

Directive
IF   the car is dead
AND   the 'fuel tank' is empty
THEN   the action is 'refuel the car'

Strategy

```
IF      the car is dead
THEN    the action is 'check the fuel tank';
        step1 is complete

IF      step1 is complete
AND     the 'fuel tank' is full
THEN    the action is 'check the battery';
        step2 is complete
```

Heuristic

```
IF      the spill is liquid
AND     the 'spill pH' < 6
AND     the 'spill smell' is vinegar
THEN    the 'spill material' is 'acetic acid'
```

2.3   The main players in the expert system development team

As soon as knowledge is provided by a human expert, we can input it into a computer. We expect the computer to act as an intelligent assistant in some specific domain of expertise or to solve a problem that would otherwise have to be solved by an expert. We also would like the computer to be able to integrate new knowledge and to show its knowledge in a form that is easy to read and understand, and to deal with simple sentences in a natural language rather than an artificial programming language. Finally, we want our computer to explain how it reaches a particular conclusion. In other words, we have to build an **expert system**, a computer program capable of performing at the level of a human expert in a narrow problem area.

The most popular expert systems are rule-based systems. A great number have been built and successfully applied in such areas as business and engineering, medicine and geology, power systems and mining. A large number of companies produce and market software for rule-based expert system development – expert system shells for personal computers.

Expert system shells are becoming particularly popular for developing rule-based systems. Their main advantage is that the system builder can now concentrate on the knowledge itself rather than on learning a programming language.

What is an expert system shell?

An expert system shell can be considered as an expert system with the knowledge removed. Therefore, all the user has to do is to add the knowledge in the form of rules and provide relevant data to solve a problem.

Let us now look at who is needed to develop an expert system and what skills are needed.

In general, there are five members of the expert system development team: the domain expert, the knowledge engineer, the programmer, the project

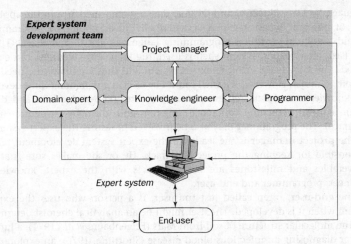

Figure 2.1 The main players of the expert system development team

manager and the end-user. The success of their expert system entirely depends on how well the members work together. The basic relations in the development team are summarised in Figure 2.1.

The **domain expert** is a knowledgeable and skilled person capable of solving problems in a specific area or **domain**. This person has the greatest expertise in a given domain. This expertise is to be captured in the expert system. Therefore, the expert must be able to communicate his or her knowledge, be willing to participate in the expert system development and commit a substantial amount of time to the project. The domain expert is the most important player in the expert system development team.

The **knowledge engineer** is someone who is capable of designing, building and testing an expert system. This person is responsible for selecting an appropriate task for the expert system. He or she interviews the domain expert to find out how a particular problem is solved. Through interaction with the expert, the knowledge engineer establishes what reasoning methods the expert uses to handle facts and rules and decides how to represent them in the expert system. The knowledge engineer then chooses some development software or an expert system shell, or looks at programming languages for encoding the knowledge (and sometimes encodes it him- or herself). And finally, the knowl- edge engineer is responsible for testing, revising and integrating the expert system into the workplace. Thus, the knowledge engineer is committed to the project from the initial design stage to the final delivery of the expert system, and even after the project is completed, he or she may also be involved in maintaining the system.

The **programmer** is the person responsible for the actual programming, describing the domain knowledge in terms that a computer can understand. The programmer needs to have skills in symbolic programming in such AI languages as LISP, PROLOG and OPS5 and also some experience in the application of different types of expert system shells. In addition, the programmer should know conventional programming languages like C, Pascal, FORTRAN and Basic. If an expert system shell is used, the knowledge engineer can easily encode the knowledge into the expert system and thus eliminate the need for the programmer. However, if a shell cannot be used, a programmer must develop the knowledge and data representation structures (knowledge base and database), control structure (inference engine) and dialogue structure (user interface). The programmer may also be involved in testing the expert system.

The **project manager** is the leader of the expert system development team, responsible for keeping the project on track. He or she makes sure that all deliverables and milestones are met, interacts with the expert, knowledge engineer, programmer and end-user.

The **end-user**, often called just the **user**, is a person who uses the expert system when it is developed. The user might be an analytical chemist determining the molecular structure of soil from Mars (Feigenbaum *et al.*, 1971), a junior doctor diagnosing an infectious blood disease (Shortliffe, 1976), an exploration geologist trying to discover a new mineral deposit (Duda *et al.*, 1979), or a power system operator needing advice in an emergency (Negnevitsky, 2008). Each of these users of expert systems has different needs, which the system must meet: the system's final acceptance will depend on the user's satisfaction. The user must not only be confident in the expert system performance but also feel comfortable using it. Therefore, the design of the user interface of the expert system is also vital for the project's success; the end-user's contribution here can be crucial.

The development of an expert system can be started when all five players have joined the team. However, many expert systems are now developed on personal computers using expert system shells. This can eliminate the need for the programmer and also might reduce the role of the knowledge engineer. For small expert systems, the project manager, knowledge engineer, programmer and even the expert could be the same person. But all team players are required when large expert systems are developed.

2.4 Structure of a rule-based expert system

In the early 1970s, Newell and Simon from Carnegie Mellon University proposed a production system model, the foundation of the modern rule-based expert systems (Newell and Simon, 1972). The production model is based on the idea that humans solve problems by applying their knowledge (expressed as production rules) to a given problem represented by problem-specific information. The production rules are stored in the long-term memory and the problem-specific information or facts in the short-term memory. The production system model and the basic structure of a rule-based expert system are shown in Figure 2.2.

A rule-based expert system has five components: the knowledge base, the database, the inference engine, the explanation facilities and the user interface.

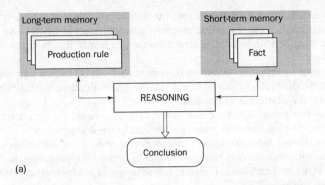

(a)

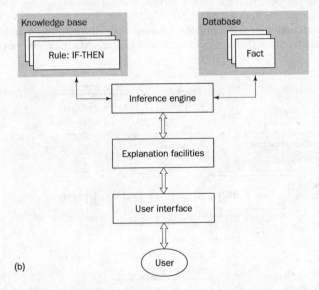

(b)

Figure 2.2 Production system and basic structure of a rule-based expert system: (a) production system model; (b) basic structure of a rule-based expert system

The **knowledge base** contains the domain knowledge useful for problem solving. In a rule-based expert system, the knowledge is represented as a set of rules. Each rule specifies a relation, recommendation, directive, strategy or heuristic and has the IF (condition) THEN (action) structure. When the condition part of a rule is satisfied, the rule is said to **fire** and the action part is executed.

The **database** includes a set of facts used to match against the IF (condition) parts of rules stored in the knowledge base.

The **inference engine** carries out the reasoning whereby the expert system reaches a solution. It links the rules given in the knowledge base with the facts provided in the database.

The **explanation facilities** enable the user to ask the expert system **how** a particular conclusion is reached and **why** a specific fact is needed. An expert system must be able to explain its reasoning and justify its advice, analysis or conclusion.

The **user interface** is the means of communication between a user seeking a solution to the problem and an expert system. The communication should be as meaningful and friendly as possible.

These five components are essential for any rule-based expert system. They constitute its core, but there may be a few additional components.

The **external interface** allows an expert system to work with external data files and programs written in conventional programming languages such as C, Pascal, FORTRAN and Basic. The complete structure of a rule-based expert system is shown in Figure 2.3.

The **developer interface** usually includes knowledge base editors, debugging aids and input/output facilities.

All expert system shells provide a simple **text editor** to input and modify rules, and to check their correct format and spelling. Many expert systems also

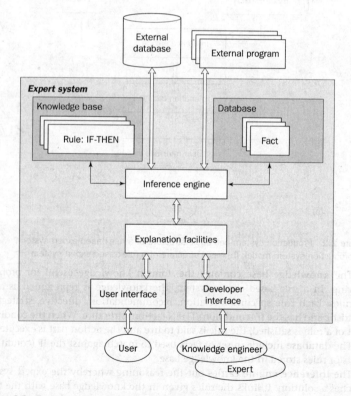

Figure 2.3   Complete structure of a rule-based expert system

include **book-keeping facilities** to monitor the changes made by the knowledge engineer or expert. If a rule is changed, the editor will automatically store the change date and the name of the person who made this change for later reference. This is very important when a number of knowledge engineers and experts have access to the knowledge base and can modify it.

Debugging aids usually consist of **tracing facilities** and **break packages**. Tracing provides a list of all rules fired during the program's execution, and a break package makes it possible to tell the expert system in advance where to stop so that the knowledge engineer or the expert can examine the current values in the database.

Most expert systems also accommodate input/output facilities such as **run-time knowledge acquisition**. This enables the running expert system to ask for needed information whenever this information is not available in the database. When the requested information is input by the knowledge engineer or the expert, the program resumes.

In general, the developer interface, and knowledge acquisition facilities in particular, are designed to enable a domain expert to input his or her knowledge directly in the expert system and thus to minimise the intervention of a knowledge engineer.

2.5 Fundamental characteristics of an expert system

An expert system is built to perform at a human expert level in a **narrow, specialised domain**. Thus, the most important characteristic of an expert system is its high-quality performance. No matter how fast the system can solve a problem, the user will not be satisfied if the result is wrong. On the other hand, the speed of reaching a solution is very important. Even the most accurate decision or diagnosis may not be useful if it is too late to apply, for instance, in an emergency, when a patient dies or a nuclear power plant explodes. Experts use their practical experience and understanding of the problem to find short-cuts to a solution. Experts use rules-of-thumb or **heuristics**. Like their human counterparts, expert systems should apply heuristics to guide the reasoning and thus reduce the search area for a solution.

A unique feature of an expert system is its **explanation capability**. This enables the expert system to review its own reasoning and explain its decisions. An explanation in expert systems in effect traces the rules fired during a problem-solving session. This is, of course, a simplification; however, a real or 'human' explanation is not yet possible because it requires basic understanding of the domain. Although a sequence of rules fired cannot be used to justify a conclusion, we can attach appropriate fundamental principles of the domain expressed as text to each rule, or at least each high-level rule, stored in the knowledge base. This is probably as far as the explanation capability can be taken. However, the ability to explain a line of reasoning may not be essential for some expert systems. For example, a scientific system built for experts may not be required to provide extensive explanations, because the conclusion it reaches can be self-explanatory to other experts; a simple rule-tracing might be quite appropriate. On the other hand, expert systems used in decision making usually demand complete and thoughtful explanations, as the cost of a wrong decision may be very high.

Expert systems employ **symbolic reasoning** when solving a problem. Symbols are used to represent different types of knowledge such as facts, concepts and rules. Unlike conventional programs written for numerical data processing, expert systems are built for knowledge processing and can easily deal with qualitative data.

Conventional programs process data using algorithms or, in other words, a series of well-defined step-by-step operations. An algorithm always performs the same operations in the same order, and it always provides an exact solution. Conventional programs do not make mistakes – but programmers sometimes do. Unlike conventional programs, expert systems do not follow a prescribed sequence of steps. They permit inexact reasoning and can deal with incomplete, uncertain and fuzzy data.

Can expert systems make mistakes?

Even a brilliant expert is only a human and thus can make mistakes. This suggests that an expert system built to perform at a human expert level also should be allowed to make mistakes. But we still trust experts, although we do recognise that their judgements are sometimes wrong. Likewise, at least in most cases, we can rely on solutions provided by expert systems, but mistakes are possible and we should be aware of this.

Does it mean that conventional programs have an advantage over expert systems?

In theory, conventional programs always provide the same 'correct' solutions. However, we must remember that conventional programs can tackle problems if, and only if, the data is complete and exact. When the data is incomplete or includes some errors, a conventional program will provide either no solution at all or an incorrect one. In contrast, expert systems recognise that the available information may be incomplete or fuzzy, but they can work in such situations and still arrive at some reasonable conclusion.

Another important feature that distinguishes expert systems from conventional programs is that **knowledge is separated from its processing** (the knowledge base and the inference engine are split up). A conventional program is a mixture of knowledge and the control structure to process this knowledge. This mixing leads to difficulties in understanding and reviewing the program code, as any change to the code affects both the knowledge and its processing. In expert systems, knowledge is clearly separated from the processing mechanism. This makes expert systems much easier to build and maintain. When an expert system shell is used, a knowledge engineer or an expert simply enters rules in the knowledge base. Each new rule adds some new knowledge and makes the expert system smarter. The system can then be easily modified by changing or subtracting rules.

Table 2.1 Comparison of expert systems with conventional systems and human experts

Human experts	Expert systems	Conventional programs
Use knowledge in the form of rules-of-thumb or heuristics to solve problems in a narrow domain.	Process knowledge expressed in the form of rules and use symbolic reasoning to solve problems in a **narrow domain**.	Process data and use algorithms, a series of well-defined operations, to solve general numerical problems.
In a human brain, knowledge exists in a compiled form.	Provide a **clear separation of knowledge from its processing**.	Do not separate knowledge from the control structure to process this knowledge.
Capable of explaining a line of reasoning and providing the details.	**Trace the rules fired** during a problem-solving session and **explain how** a particular conclusion was reached and **why** specific data was needed.	Do not explain how a particular result was obtained and why input data was needed.
Use inexact reasoning and can deal with incomplete, uncertain and fuzzy information.	Permit **inexact reasoning** and can deal with incomplete, uncertain and fuzzy data.	Work only on problems where data is complete and exact.
Can make mistakes when information is incomplete or fuzzy.	**Can make mistakes** when data is incomplete or fuzzy.	Provide no solution at all, or a wrong one, when data is incomplete or fuzzy.
Enhance the quality of problem solving via years of learning and practical training. This process is slow, inefficient and expensive.	Enhance the quality of problem solving by adding new rules or adjusting old ones in the knowledge base. When new knowledge is acquired, **changes are easy** to accomplish.	Enhance the quality of problem solving by changing the program code, which affects both the knowledge and its processing, making changes difficult.

The characteristics of expert systems discussed above make them different from conventional systems and human experts. A comparison is shown in Table 2.1.

2.6 Forward chaining and backward chaining inference techniques

In a rule-based expert system, the domain knowledge is represented by a set of IF-THEN production rules and data is represented by a set of facts about the current situation. The inference engine compares each rule stored in the

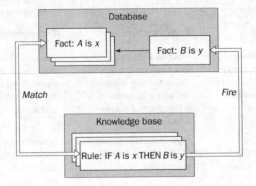

Figure 2.4 The inference engine cycles via a match–fire procedure

knowledge base with facts contained in the database. When the IF (condition) part of the rule matches a fact, the rule is **fired** and its THEN (action) part is executed. The fired rule may change the set of facts by adding a new fact, as shown in Figure 2.4. Letters in the database and the knowledge base are used to represent situations or concepts.

The matching of the rule IF parts to the facts produces **inference chains**. The inference chain indicates how an expert system applies the rules to reach a conclusion. To illustrate chaining inference techniques, consider a simple example.

Suppose the database initially includes facts A, B, C, D and E, and the knowledge base contains only three rules:

Rule 1: IF Y is true
         AND D is true
         THEN Z is true

Rule 2: IF X is true
         AND B is true
         AND E is true
         THEN Y is true

Rule 3: IF A is true
         THEN X is true

The inference chain shown in Figure 2.5 indicates how the expert system applies the rules to infer fact Z. First Rule 3 is fired to deduce new fact X from given fact A. Then Rule 2 is executed to infer fact Y from initially known facts B and E, and already known fact X. And finally, Rule 1 applies initially known fact D and just-obtained fact Y to arrive at conclusion Z.

An expert system can display its inference chain to explain how a particular conclusion was reached; this is an essential part of its explanation facilities.

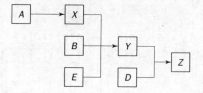

Figure 2.5 An example of an inference chain

The inference engine must decide when the rules have to be fired. There are two principal ways in which rules are executed. One is called **forward chaining** and the other **backward chaining** (Waterman and Hayes-Roth, 1978).6pt>

2.6.1 Forward chaining

The example discussed above uses forward chaining. Now consider this technique in more detail. Let us first rewrite our rules in the following form:

Rule 1: $Y \& D \to Z$

Rule 2: $X \& B \& E \to Y$

Rule 3: $A \to X$

Arrows here indicate the IF and THEN parts of the rules. Let us also add two more rules:

Rule 4: $C \to L$

Rule 5: $L \& M \to N$

Figure 2.6 shows how forward chaining works for this simple set of rules.

Forward chaining is the **data-driven** reasoning. The reasoning starts from the known data and proceeds forward with that data. Each time only the topmost rule is executed. When fired, the rule adds a new fact in the database. Any rule can be executed only once. The match–fire cycle stops when no further rules can be fired.

In the first cycle, only two rules, Rule 3: $A \to X$ and Rule 4: $C \to L$, match facts in the database. Rule 3: $A \to X$ is fired first as the topmost one. The IF part of this rule matches fact A in the database, its THEN part is executed and new fact X is added to the database. Then Rule 4: $C \to L$ is fired and fact L is also placed in the database.

In the second cycle, Rule 2: $X \& B \& E \to Y$ is fired because facts B, E and X are already in the database, and as a consequence fact Y is inferred and put in the database. This in turn causes Rule 1: $Y \& D \to Z$ to execute, placing fact Z in the database (cycle 3). Now the match–fire cycles stop because the IF part of Rule 5: $L \& M \to N$ does not match **all** facts in the database and thus Rule 5 cannot be fired.

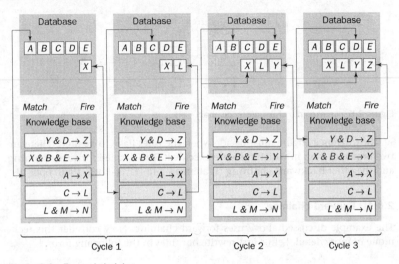

Figure 2.6 Forward chaining

Forward chaining is a technique for gathering information and then inferring from it whatever can be inferred. However, in forward chaining, many rules may be executed that have nothing to do with the established goal. Suppose, in our example, the goal was to determine fact Z. We had only five rules in the knowledge base and four of them were fired. But Rule 4: $C \rightarrow L$, which is unrelated to fact Z, was also fired among others. A real rule-based expert system can have hundreds of rules, many of which might be fired to derive new facts that are valid, but unfortunately unrelated to the goal. Therefore, if our goal is to infer only one particular fact, the forward chaining inference technique would not be efficient.

In such a situation, backward chaining is more appropriate.

2.6.2 Backward chaining

Backward chaining is the **goal-driven** reasoning. In backward chaining, an expert system has the goal (a hypothetical solution) and the inference engine attempts to find the evidence to prove it. First, the knowledge base is searched to find rules that might have the desired solution. Such rules must have the goal in their THEN (action) parts. If such a rule is found and its IF (condition) part matches data in the database, then the rule is fired and the goal is proved. However, this is rarely the case. Thus the inference engine puts aside the rule it is working with (the rule is said to **stack**) and sets up a new goal, a sub-goal, to prove the IF part of this rule. Then the knowledge base is searched again for rules that can prove the sub-goal. The inference engine repeats the process of stacking the rules until no rules are found in the knowledge base to prove the current sub-goal.

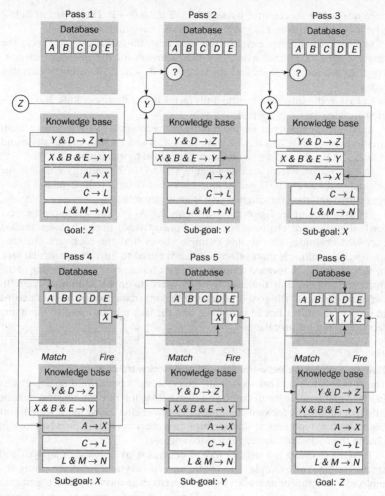

Figure 2.7 Backward chaining

Figure 2.7 shows how backward chaining works, using the rules for the forward chaining example.

In Pass 1, the inference engine attempts to infer fact Z. It searches the knowledge base to find the rule that has the goal, in our case fact Z, in its THEN part. The inference engine finds and stacks Rule 1: $Y \& D \rightarrow Z$. The IF part of Rule 1 includes facts Y and D, and thus these facts must be established.

In Pass 2, the inference engine sets up the sub-goal, fact Y, and tries to determine it. First it checks the database, but fact Y is not there. Then the knowledge base is searched again for the rule with fact Y in its THEN part. The inference engine locates and stacks Rule 2: $X \& B \& E \rightarrow Y$. The IF part of Rule 2 consists of facts X, B and E, and these facts also have to be established.

In Pass 3, the inference engine sets up a new sub-goal, fact X. It checks the database for fact X, and, when that fails, searches for the rule that infers X. The inference engine finds and stacks Rule 3: $A \rightarrow X$. Now it must determine fact A.

In Pass 4, the inference engine finds fact A in the database, Rule 3: $A \rightarrow X$ is fired and new fact X is inferred.

In Pass 5, the inference engine returns to the sub-goal fact Y and once again tries to execute Rule 2: $X \& B \& E \rightarrow Y$. Facts X, B and E are in the database and thus Rule 2 is fired and a new fact, fact Y, is added to the database.

In Pass 6, the system returns to Rule 1: $Y \& D \rightarrow Z$ trying to establish the original goal, fact Z. The IF part of Rule 1 matches all facts in the database, Rule 1 is executed and thus the original goal is finally established.

Let us now compare Figure 2.6 with Figure 2.7. As you can see, four rules were fired when forward chaining was used, but just three rules when we applied backward chaining. This simple example shows that the backward chaining inference technique is more effective when we need to infer one particular fact, in our case fact Z. In forward chaining, the data is known at the beginning of the inference process, and the user is never asked to input additional facts. In backward chaining, the goal is set up and the only data used is the data needed to support the direct line of reasoning, and the user may be asked to input any fact that is not in the database.

How do we choose between forward and backward chaining?

The answer is to study how a domain expert solves a problem. If an expert first needs to gather some information and then tries to infer from it whatever can be inferred, choose the forward chaining inference engine. However, if your expert begins with a hypothetical solution and then attempts to find facts to prove it, choose the backward chaining inference engine.

Forward chaining is a natural way to design expert systems for analysis and interpretation. For example, DENDRAL, an expert system for determining the molecular structure of unknown soil based on its mass spectral data (Feigenbaum et al., 1971), uses forward chaining. Most backward chaining expert systems are used for diagnostic purposes. For instance, MYCIN, a medical expert system for diagnosing infectious blood diseases (Shortliffe, 1976), uses backward chaining.

Can we combine forward and backward chaining?

Many expert system shells use a combination of forward and backward chaining inference techniques, so the knowledge engineer does not have to choose between them. However, the basic inference mechanism is usually backward chaining. Only when a new fact is established is forward chaining employed to maximise the use of the new data.

2.7 MEDIA ADVISOR: a demonstration rule-based expert system

To illustrate some of the ideas discussed above, we next consider a simple rule-based expert system. The Leonardo expert system shell was selected as a tool to build a decision-support system called MEDIA ADVISOR. The system provides advice on selecting a medium for delivering a training program based on the trainee's job. For example, if a trainee is a mechanical technician responsible for maintaining hydraulic systems, an appropriate medium might be a workshop, where the trainee could learn how basic hydraulic components operate, how to troubleshoot hydraulics problems and how to make simple repairs to hydraulic systems. On the other hand, if a trainee is a clerk assessing insurance applications, a training program might include lectures on specific problems of the task, as well as tutorials where the trainee could evaluate real applications. For complex tasks, where trainees are likely to make mistakes, a training program should also include feedback on the trainee's performance.

Knowledge base

/* MEDIA ADVISOR: a demonstration rule-based expert system

Rule: 1
if   the environment is papers
or   the environment is manuals
or   the environment is documents
or   the environment is textbooks
then the stimulus_situation is verbal

Rule: 2
if   the environment is pictures
or   the environment is illustrations
or   the environment is photographs
or   the environment is diagrams
then the stimulus_situation is visual

Rule: 3
if   the environment is machines
or   the environment is buildings
or   the environment is tools
then the stimulus_situation is 'physical object'

Rule: 4
if   the environment is numbers
or   the environment is formulas
or   the environment is 'computer programs'
then the stimulus_situation is symbolic

Rule: 5
if   the job is lecturing
or   the job is advising
or   the job is counselling
then   the stimulus_response is oral

Rule: 6
if   the job is building
or   the job is repairing
or   the job is troubleshooting
then   the stimulus_response is 'hands-on'

Rule: 7
if   the job is writing
or   the job is typing
or   the job is drawing
then   the stimulus_response is documented

Rule: 8
if   the job is evaluating
or   the job is reasoning
or   the job is investigating
then   the stimulus_response is analytical

Rule: 9
if   the stimulus_situation is 'physical object'
and   the stimulus_response is 'hands-on'
and   feedback is required
then   medium is workshop

Rule: 10
if   the stimulus_situation is symbolic
and   the stimulus_response is analytical
and   feedback is required
then   medium is 'lecture – tutorial'

Rule: 11
if   the stimulus_situation is visual
and   the stimulus_response is documented
and   feedback is not required
then   medium is videocassette

Rule: 12
if   the stimulus_situation is visual
and   the stimulus_response is oral
and   feedback is required
then   medium is 'lecture – tutorial'

Rule: 13
if   the stimulus_situation is verbal
and   the stimulus_response is analytical
and   feedback is required
then   medium is 'lecture – tutorial'

Rule: 14
if   the stimulus_situation is verbal
and   the stimulus_response is oral
and   feedback is required
then   medium is 'role-play exercises'

/* The SEEK directive sets up the goal of the rule set

seek medium

Objects

MEDIA ADVISOR uses six linguistic objects: *environment, stimulus_situation, job, stimulus_response, feedback* and *medium*. Each object can take one of the allowed values (e.g. object *environment* can take the value of *papers, manuals, documents, textbooks, pictures, illustrations, photographs, diagrams, machines, buildings, tools, numbers, formulas, computer programs*). An object and its value constitute a fact (for instance, the *environment* is *machines*, and the *job* is *repairing*). All facts are placed in the database.

Object	Allowed values	Object	Allowed values
environment	papers	job	lecturing
	manuals		advising
	documents		counselling
	textbooks		building
	pictures		repairing
	illustrations		troubleshooting
	photographs		writing
	diagrams		typing
	machines		drawing
	buildings		evaluating
	tools		reasoning
	numbers		investigating
	formulas		
	computer programs	stimulus_response	oral
			hands-on
			documented
			analytical
stimulus_situation	verbal		
	visual		
	physical object	feedback	required
	symbolic		not required

Options

The final goal of the rule-based expert system is to produce a solution to the problem based on input data. In MEDIA ADVISOR, the solution is a medium selected from the list of four options:

    medium is workshop
    medium is 'lecture – tutorial'
    medium is videocassette
    medium is 'role-play exercises'

Dialogue

In the dialogue shown below, the expert system asks the user to input the data needed to solve the problem (the environment, the job and feedback). Based on the answers supplied by the user (answers are indicated by arrows), the expert system applies rules from its knowledge base to infer that the *stimulus_situation* is *physical object*, and the *stimulus_response* is *hands-on*. Rule 9 then selects one of the allowed values of *medium*.

What sort of environment is a trainee dealing with on the job?
⇒ **machines**

Rule: 3
if   the environment is machines
or   the environment is buildings
or   the environment is tools
then   the stimulus_situation is 'physical object'

In what way is a trainee expected to act or respond on the job?
⇒ **repairing**

Rule: 6
if   the job is building
or   the job is repairing
or   the job is troubleshooting
then   the stimulus_response is 'hands-on'

Is feedback on the trainee's progress required during training?
⇒ **required**

Rule: 9
if   the stimulus_situation is 'physical object'
and   the stimulus_response is 'hands-on'
and   feedback is required
then   medium is workshop

medium is workshop

Inference techniques

The standard inference technique in Leonardo is backward chaining with opportunistic forward chaining, which is the most efficient way to deal with the available information. However, Leonardo also enables the user to turn off either backward or forward chaining, and thus allows us to study each inference technique separately.

Forward chaining is data-driven reasoning, so we need first to provide some data. Assume that

> the environment is **machines**
> > **'environment'** instantiated by user input to **'machines'**

> the job is **repairing**
> > **'job'** instantiated by user input to **'repairing'**

> feedback is **required**
> > **'feedback'** instantiated by user input to **'required'**

The following process will then happen:

Rule: 3 fires	**'stimulus_situation'** instantiated by Rule: 3 to **'physical object'**
Rule: 6 fires	**'stimulus_response'** instantiated by Rule: 6 to **'hands-on'**
Rule: 9 fires	**'medium'** instantiated by Rule: 9 to **'workshop'**
No rules fire	stop

Backward chaining is goal-driven reasoning, so we need first to establish a hypothetical solution (the goal). Let us, for example, set up the following goal:

> **'medium'** is **'workshop'**

Pass 1	
Trying Rule: 9	Need to find object **'stimulus_situation'**
Rule: 9 stacked	Object **'stimulus_situation'** sought as **'physical object'**
Pass 2	
Trying Rule: 3	Need to find object **'environment'**
Rule: 3 stacked	Object **'environment'** sought as **'machines'**
ask environment	
⇒**machines**	**'environment'** instantiated by user input to **'machines'**
Trying Rule: 3	**'stimulus_situation'** instantiated by Rule: 3 to **'physical object'**
Pass 3	
Trying Rule: 9	Need to find object **'stimulus_response'**
Rule: 9 stacked	Object **'stimulus_response'** sought as **'hands-on'**

Pass 4

Trying Rule: 6	Need to find object **'job'**
Rule: 6 stacked	Object **'job'** sought as **'building'**

ask job

⇒ **repairing**   **'job'** instantiated by user input to **'repairing'**

Trying Rule: 6   **'stimulus_response'** instantiated by Rule: 6 to **'hands-on'**

Pass 5

Trying Rule: 9	Need to find object **'feedback'**
Rule: 9 stacked	Object **'feedback'** sought as **'required'**

ask feedback

⇒ **required**   **'feedback'** instantiated by user input to **'required'**

Trying Rule: 9   **'medium'** instantiated by Rule: 9 to **'workshop'**

medium is workshop

It is useful to have a tree diagram that maps a consultation session with an expert system. A diagram for MEDIA ADVISOR is shown in Figure 2.8. The root node is the goal; when the system is started, the inference engine seeks to determine the goal's value.

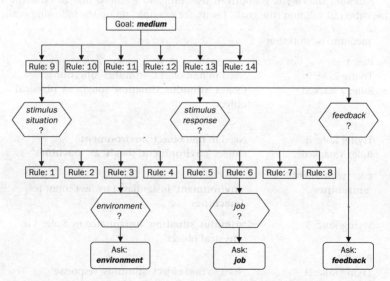

Figure 2.8 Tree diagram for the rule-based expert system MEDIA ADVISOR

Does MEDIA ADVISOR handle all possible situations?

When we start to use our expert system more often, we might find that the provided options do not cover all possible situations. For instance, the following dialogue might occur:

What sort of environment is a trainee dealing with on the job?
⇒**illustrations**

In what way is a trainee expected to act or respond on the job?
⇒**drawing**

Is feedback on the trainee's progress required during training?
⇒**required**

I am unable to draw any conclusions on the basis of the data.

Thus, MEDIA ADVISOR in its present state cannot handle this particular situation. Fortunately, the expert system can easily be expanded to accommodate more rules until it finally does what the user wants it to do.

2.8 Conflict resolution

Earlier in this chapter, we considered two simple rules for crossing a road. Let us now add a third rule. We will get the following set of rules:

Rule 1:
IF   the 'traffic light' is green
THEN   the action is go

Rule 2:
IF   the 'traffic light' is red
THEN   the action is stop

Rule 3:
IF   the 'traffic light' is red
THEN   the action is go

What will happen?

The inference engine compares IF (condition) parts of the rules with data available in the database, and when conditions are satisfied the rules are set to fire. The firing of one rule may affect the activation of other rules, and therefore the inference engine must allow only one rule to fire at a time. In our road crossing example, we have two rules, Rule 2 and Rule 3, with the same IF part. Thus both of them can be set to fire when the condition part is satisfied. These rules represent a conflict set. The inference engine must determine which rule to fire from such a set. A method for choosing a rule to fire when more than one rule can be fired in a given cycle is called **conflict resolution**.

If the traffic light is red, which rule should be executed?
In forward chaining, **both** rules would be fired. Rule 2 is fired first as the top-most one, and as a result its THEN part is executed and linguistic object *action* obtains value *stop*. However, Rule 3 is also fired because the condition part of this rule matches the fact *'traffic light' is red*, which is still in the database. As a consequence, object *action* takes new value *go*. This simple example shows that the rule order is vital when the forward chaining inference technique is used.

How can we resolve a conflict?
The obvious strategy for resolving conflicts is to establish a goal and stop the rule execution when the goal is reached. In our problem, for example, the goal is to establish a value for linguistic object *action*. When the expert system determines a value for *action*, it has reached the goal and stops. Thus if the *traffic light* is *red*, Rule 2 is executed, object *action* attains value *stop* and the expert system stops. In the given example, the expert system makes a right decision; however, if we arranged the rules in the reverse order, the conclusion would be wrong. It means that the rule order in the knowledge base is still very important.

Are there any other conflict resolution methods?
Several methods are in use (Shirai and Tsuji, 1985; Brachman and Levesque, 2004; Giarratano and Riley, 2004):

- Fire the rule with the highest priority. In simple applications, the priority can be established by placing the rules in an appropriate order in the knowledge base. Usually this strategy works well for expert systems with around 100 rules. However, in some applications, the data should be processed in order of importance. For example, in a medical consultation system (Durkin, 1994), the following priorities are introduced:

  Goal 1. Prescription is? Prescription

  RULE 1 Meningitis Prescription1
  (Priority 100)
  IF   Infection is Meningitis
  AND   The Patient is a Child
  THEN Prescription is Number_1
  AND   Drug Recommendation is Ampicillin
  AND   Drug Recommendation is Gentamicin
  AND   Display Meningitis Prescription1

  RULE 2 Meningitis Prescription2
  (Priority 90)
  IF   Infection is Meningitis
  AND   The Patient is an Adult
  THEN Prescription is Number_2
  AND   Drug Recommendation is Penicillin
  AND   Display Meningitis Prescription2

- Fire the most specific rule. This method is also known as the **longest matching strategy**. It is based on the assumption that a specific rule processes more information than a general one. For example,

    Rule 1:
    IF   the season is autumn
    AND   the sky is cloudy
    AND   the forecast is rain
    THEN   the advice is 'stay home'

    Rule 2:
    IF   the season is autumn
    THEN   the advice is 'take an umbrella'

If the *season* is *autumn*, the *sky* is *cloudy* and the *forecast* is *rain*, then Rule 1 would be fired because its antecedent, the matching part, is more specific than that of Rule 2. But if it is known only that the *season* is *autumn*, then Rule 2 would be executed.

- Fire the rule that uses the **data most recently entered** in the database. This method relies on time tags attached to each fact in the database. In the conflict set, the expert system first fires the rule whose antecedent uses the data most recently added to the database. For example,

    Rule 1:
    IF   the forecast is rain   [08:16 PM 11/25/96]
    THEN   the advice is 'take an umbrella'

    Rule 2:
    IF   the weather is wet   [10:18 AM 11/26/96]
    THEN   the advice is 'stay home'

Assume that the IF parts of both rules match facts in the database. In this case, Rule 2 would be fired since the fact *weather* is *wet* was entered after the fact *forecast* is *rain*. This technique is especially useful for real-time expert system applications when information in the database is constantly updated.

The conflict resolution methods considered above are simple and easily implemented. In most cases, these methods provide satisfactory solutions. However, as a program grows larger and more complex, it becomes increasingly difficult for the knowledge engineer to manage and oversee rules in the knowledge base. The expert system itself must take at least some of the burden and understand its own behaviour.

To improve the performance of an expert system, we should supply the system with some knowledge about the knowledge it possesses or, in other words, **metaknowledge**.

Metaknowledge can be simply defined as **knowledge about knowledge**. Metaknowledge is knowledge about the use and control of domain knowledge in an expert system (Waterman, 1986). In rule-based expert systems, metaknowledge is represented by metarules. A metarule determines a strategy for the use of task-specific rules in the expert system.

What is the origin of metaknowledge?

The knowledge engineer transfers the knowledge of the domain expert to the expert system, learns how problem-specific rules are used, and gradually creates in his or her own mind a new body of knowledge, knowledge about the overall behaviour of the expert system. This new knowledge, or metaknowledge, is largely domain independent. For example,

> Metarule 1:
> Rules supplied by experts have higher priorities than rules supplied by novices.

> Metarule 2:
> Rules governing the rescue of human lives have higher priorities than rules concerned with clearing overloads on power system equipment.

Can an expert system understand and use metarules?

Some expert systems provide a separate inference engine for metarules. However, most expert systems cannot distinguish between rules and metarules. Thus metarules should be given the highest priority in the existing knowledge base. When fired, a metarule 'injects' some important information into the database that can change the priorities of some other rules.

2.9   Advantages and disadvantages of rule-based expert systems

Rule-based expert systems are generally accepted as the best option for building knowledge-based systems.

Which features make rule-based expert systems particularly attractive for knowledge engineers?

Among these features are:

- **Natural knowledge representation**. An expert usually explains the problem-solving procedure with such expressions as this: 'In such-and-such situation, I do so-and-so.' These expressions can be represented quite naturally as IF-THEN production rules.

- **Uniform structure**. Production rules have the uniform IF-THEN structure. Each rule is an independent piece of knowledge. The very syntax of production rules enables them to be self-documented.

- **Separation of knowledge from its processing**. The structure of a rule-based expert system provides an effective separation of the knowledge base from the inference engine. This makes it possible to develop different applications using the same expert system shell. It also allows a graceful and easy expansion of the expert system. To make the system smarter, a knowledge engineer simply adds some rules to the knowledge base without intervening in the control structure.

- **Dealing with incomplete and uncertain knowledge**. Most rule-based expert systems are capable of representing and reasoning with incomplete and uncertain knowledge. For example, the rule

IF	season is autumn	
AND	sky is 'cloudy'	
AND	wind is low	
THEN	forecast is clear	{cf 0.1};
	forecast is drizzle	{cf 1.0};
	forecast is rain	{cf 0.9}

  could be used to express the uncertainty of the following statement, 'If the season is autumn and it looks like drizzle, then it will probably be another wet day today.'

  The rule represents the uncertainty by numbers called **certainty factors** {cf 0.1}. The expert system uses certainty factors to establish the degree of confidence or level of belief that the rule's conclusion is true. This topic will be considered in detail in Chapter 3.

All these features of the rule-based expert systems make them highly desirable for knowledge representation in real-world problems.

Are rule-based expert systems problem-free?

There are three main shortcomings:

- **Opaque relations between rules**. Although the individual production rules tend to be relatively simple and self-documented, their logical interactions within the large set of rules may be opaque. Rule-based systems make it difficult to observe how individual rules serve the overall strategy. This problem is related to the lack of hierarchical knowledge representation in the rule-based expert systems.
- **Ineffective search strategy**. The inference engine applies an exhaustive search through all the production rules during each cycle. Expert systems with a large set of rules (over 100 rules) can be slow, and thus large rule-based systems can be unsuitable for real-time applications.
- **Inability to learn**. In general, rule-based expert systems do not have an ability to learn from the experience. Unlike a human expert, who knows when to 'break the rules', an expert system cannot automatically modify its knowledge base, or adjust existing rules or add new ones. The knowledge engineer is still responsible for revising and maintaining the system.

2.10 Summary

In this chapter, we presented an overview of rule-based expert systems. We briefly discussed what knowledge is, and how experts express their knowledge in the form of production rules. We identified the main players in an expert system development team and presented the structure of a rule-based system. We discussed the fundamental characteristics of expert systems and noted that expert systems can make mistakes. We then reviewed the forward and backward chaining inference techniques, and discussed conflict resolution strategies. Finally, we examined the advantages and disadvantages of rule-based expert systems.

The most important lessons learned in this chapter are:

- Knowledge is a theoretical or practical understanding of a subject. Knowledge is the sum of what is currently known.

- An expert is a person who has deep knowledge in the form of facts and rules and strong practical experience in a particular domain. An expert can do things other people cannot.

- The experts can usually express their knowledge in the form of production rules.

- Production rules are represented as IF (antecedent) THEN (consequent) statements. A production rule is the most popular type of knowledge representation. Rules can express relations, recommendations, directives, strategies and heuristics.

- A computer program capable of performing at a human-expert level in a narrow problem domain area is called an expert system. The most popular expert systems are rule-based expert systems.

- In developing rule-based expert systems, shells are becoming particularly common. An expert system shell is a skeleton expert system with the knowledge removed. To build a new expert system application, all the user has to do is to add the knowledge in the form of rules and provide relevant data. Expert system shells offer a dramatic reduction in the development time of expert systems.

- The expert system development team should include the domain expert, the knowledge engineer, the programmer, the project manager and the end-user. The knowledge engineer designs, builds and tests an expert system. He or she captures the knowledge from the domain expert, establishes reasoning methods and chooses the development software. For small expert systems based on expert system shells, the project manager, knowledge engineer, programmer and even the expert could be the same person.

- A rule-based expert system has five basic components: the knowledge base, the database, the inference engine, the explanation facilities and the user interface. The knowledge base contains the domain knowledge represented as a set of rules. The database includes a set of facts used to match against the IF parts of rules. The inference engine links the rules with the facts and carries out the reasoning whereby the expert system reaches a solution. The explanation facilities enable the user to query the expert system about **how** a particular conclusion is reached and **why** a specific fact is needed. The user interface is the means of communication between a user and an expert system.

- Expert systems separate knowledge from its processing by splitting up the knowledge base and the inference engine. This makes the task of building and maintaining an expert system much easier. When an expert system shell is used, a knowledge engineer or an expert simply enter rules in the knowledge base. Each new rule adds some new knowledge and makes the expert system smarter.

- Expert systems provide a limited explanation capability by tracing the rules fired during a problem-solving session.

- Unlike conventional programs, expert systems can deal with incomplete and uncertain data and permit inexact reasoning. However, like their human counterparts, expert systems can make mistakes when information is incomplete or fuzzy.

- There are two principal methods to direct search and reasoning: forward chaining and backward chaining inference techniques. Forward chaining is data-driven reasoning: it starts from the known data and proceeds forward until no further rules can be fired. Backward chaining is goal-driven reasoning: an expert system has a hypothetical solution (the goal), and the inference engine attempts to find the evidence to prove it.

- If more than one rule can be fired in a given cycle, the inference engine must decide which rule to fire. A method for deciding is called conflict resolution.

- Rule-based expert systems have the advantages of natural knowledge representation, uniform structure, separation of knowledge from its processing, and coping with incomplete and uncertain knowledge.

- Rule-based expert systems also have disadvantages, especially opaque relations between rules, ineffective search strategy, and inability to learn.

Questions for review

1 What is knowledge? Explain why experts usually have detailed knowledge of a limited area of a specific domain. What do we mean by heuristic?

2 What is a production rule? Give an example and define two basic parts of the production rule.

3 List and describe the five major players in the expert system development team. What is the role of the knowledge engineer?

4 What is an expert system shell? Explain why the use of an expert system shell can dramatically reduce the development time of an expert system.

5 What is a production system model? List and define the five basic components of an expert system.

6 What are the fundamental characteristics of an expert system? What are the differences between expert systems and conventional programs?

7 Can an expert system make mistakes? Why?

8 Describe the forward chaining inference process. Give an example.

9 Describe the backward chaining inference process. Give an example.

10 List problems for which the forward chaining inference technique is appropriate. Why is backward chaining used for diagnostic problems?

11 What is a conflict set of rules? How can we resolve a conflict? List and describe the basic conflict resolution methods.

12 List advantages of rule-based expert systems. What are their disadvantages?

References

Brachman, R.J. and Levesque, H.J. (2004). *Knowledge Representation and Reasoning.* Elsevier, San Francisco.

Duda, R., Gaschnig, J. and Hart, P. (1979). Model design in the PROSPECTOR consultant system for mineral exploration, *Expert Systems in the Microelectronic Age*, D. Michie, ed., Edinburgh University Press, Edinburgh, Scotland, pp. 153–167.

Durkin, J. (1994). *Expert Systems: Design and Development.* Prentice Hall, Englewood Cliffs, NJ.

Feigenbaum, E.A., Buchanan, B.G. and Lederberg, J. (1971). On generality and problem solving: a case study using the DENDRAL program, *Machine Intelligence 6*, B. Meltzer and D. Michie, eds, Edinburgh University Press, Edinburgh, Scotland, pp. 165–190.

Giarratano, J. and Riley, G. (2004). *Expert Systems: Principles and Programming*, 4th edn. Thomson/PWS Publishing Company, Boston, MA.

Negnevitsky, M. (2008). Computational intelligence approach to crisis management in power systems, *International Journal of Automation and Control*, 2(2/3), 247–273.

Newell, A. and Simon, H.A. (1972). *Human Problem Solving.* Prentice Hall, Englewood Cliffs, NJ.

Shirai, Y. and Tsuji, J. (1985). *Artificial Intelligence: Concepts, Technologies and Applications.* John Wiley, New York.

Shortliffe, E.H. (1976). *MYCIN: Computer-Based Medical Consultations.* Elsevier Press, New York.

Waterman, D.A. (1986). *A Guide to Expert Systems.* Addison-Wesley, Reading, MA.

Waterman, D.A. and Hayes-Roth, F. (1978). An overview of pattern-directed inference systems, *Pattern-Directed Inference Systems*, D.A. Waterman and F. Hayes-Roth, eds, Academic Press, New York.

Uncertainty management in rule-based expert systems

3

In which we present the main uncertainty management paradigms, Bayesian reasoning and certainty factors, discuss their relative merits and consider examples to illustrate the theory.

3.1 Introduction, or what is uncertainty?

One of the common characteristics of the information available to human experts is its imperfection. Information can be incomplete, inconsistent, uncertain, or all three. In other words, information is often unsuitable for solving a problem. However, an expert can cope with these defects and can usually make correct judgements and right decisions. Expert systems also have to be able to handle uncertainty and draw valid conclusions.

What is uncertainty in expert systems?
Uncertainty can be defined as the lack of the exact knowledge that would enable us to reach a perfectly reliable conclusion (Stephanou and Sage, 1987). Classical logic permits only exact reasoning. It assumes that perfect knowledge always exists and the law of the excluded middle can always be applied:

> IF A is true
> THEN A is not false

and

> IF B is false
> THEN B is not true

Unfortunately most real-world problems where expert systems could be used do not provide us with such clear-cut knowledge. The available information often contains inexact, incomplete or even unmeasurable data.

What are the sources of uncertain knowledge in expert systems?
In general, we can identify four main sources: weak implications, imprecise language, unknown data, and the difficulty of combining the views of different

experts (Bonissone and Tong, 1985). Let us consider these sources in more detail.

- **Weak implications**. Rule-based expert systems often suffer from weak implications and vague associations. Domain experts and knowledge engineers have the painful, and rather hopeless, task of establishing concrete correlations between IF (condition) and THEN (action) parts of the rules. Therefore, expert systems need to have the ability to handle vague associations, for example by accepting the degree of correlations as numerical certainty factors.

- **Imprecise language**. Our natural language is inherently ambiguous and imprecise. We describe facts with such terms as **often** and **sometimes**, **frequently** and **hardly ever**. As a result, it can be difficult to express knowledge in the precise IF-THEN form of production rules. However, if the meaning of the facts is quantified, it can be used in expert systems. In 1944, Ray Simpson asked 355 high school and college students to place 20 terms like **often** on a scale between 1 and 100 (Simpson, 1944). In 1968, Milton Hakel repeated this experiment (Hakel, 1968). Their results are presented in Table 3.1.

  Quantifying the meaning of the terms enables an expert system to establish an appropriate matching of the IF (condition) part of the rules with facts available in the database.

- **Unknown data**. When the data is incomplete or missing, the only solution is to accept the value 'unknown' and proceed to an approximate reasoning with this value.

- **Combining the views of different experts**. Large expert systems usually combine the knowledge and expertise of a number of experts. For example, nine experts participated in the development of PROSPECTOR, an expert system for mineral exploration (Duda *et al.*, 1979). Unfortunately, experts seldom reach exactly the same conclusions. Usually, experts have contradictory opinions and produce conflicting rules. To resolve the conflict, the knowledge engineer has to attach a weight to each expert and then calculate the composite conclusion. However, even a domain expert generally does not have the same uniform level of expertise throughout a domain. In addition, no systematic method exists to obtain weights.

In summary, an expert system should be able to manage uncertainties because any real-world domain contains inexact knowledge and needs to cope with incomplete, inconsistent or even missing data. A number of numeric and non-numeric methods have been developed to deal with uncertainty in rule-based expert systems (Bhatnagar and Kanal, 1986). In this chapter, we consider the most popular uncertainty management paradigms: Bayesian reasoning and certainty factors. However, we first look at the basic principles of classical probability theory.

Table 3.1 Quantification of ambiguous and imprecise terms on a time–frequency scale

Ray Simpson (1944)		Milton Hakel (1968)	
Term	**Mean value**	**Term**	**Mean value**
Always	99	Always	100
Very often	88	Very often	87
Usually	85	Usually	79
Often	78	Often	74
Generally	78	Rather often	74
Frequently	73	Frequently	72
Rather often	65	Generally	72
About as often as not	50	About as often as not	50
Now and then	20	Now and then	34
Sometimes	20	Sometimes	29
Occasionally	20	Occasionally	28
Once in a while	15	Once in a while	22
Not often	13	Not often	16
Usually not	10	Usually not	16
Seldom	10	Seldom	9
Hardly ever	7	Hardly ever	8
Very seldom	6	Very seldom	7
Rarely	5	Rarely	5
Almost never	3	Almost never	2
Never	0	Never	0

3.2 Basic probability theory

The basic concept of probability plays a significant role in our everyday life. We try to determine the probability of rain and the prospects of our promotion, the odds that the Australian cricket team will win the next test match, and the likelihood of winning a million dollars in Tattslotto.

The concept of probability has a long history that goes back thousands of years when words like 'probably', 'likely', 'maybe', 'perhaps' and 'possibly' were introduced into spoken languages (Good, 1959). However, the mathematical theory of probability was formulated only in the 17th century.

How can we define probability?

The probability of an event is the proportion of cases in which the event occurs (Good, 1959). Probability can also be defined as a scientific measure of chance. Detailed analysis of modern probability theory can be found in such well-known textbooks as Feller (1966; 1968) and Fine (1973). In this chapter, we examine only the basic ideas used in representing uncertainties in expert systems.

Probability can be expressed mathematically as a numerical index with a range between zero (an absolute impossibility) to unity (an absolute certainty). Most events have a probability index strictly between 0 and 1, which means that each event has **at least** two possible outcomes: favourable outcome or success, and unfavourable outcome or failure.

The probability of success and failure can be determined as follows:

$$P(\text{success}) = \frac{\text{the number of successes}}{\text{the number of possible outcomes}} \qquad (3.1)$$

$$P(\text{failure}) = \frac{\text{the number of failures}}{\text{the number of possible outcomes}} \qquad (3.2)$$

Therefore, if s is the number of times success can occur, and f is the number of times failure can occur, then

$$P(\text{success}) = p = \frac{s}{s+f} \qquad (3.3)$$

$$P(\text{failure}) = q = \frac{f}{s+f} \qquad (3.4)$$

and

$$p + q = 1 \qquad (3.5)$$

Let us consider classical examples with a coin and a dice. If we throw a coin, the probability of getting a head will be equal to the probability of getting a tail. In a single throw, $s = f = 1$, and therefore the probability of getting a head (or a tail) is 0.5.

Consider now a dice and determine the probability of getting a 6 from a single throw. If we assume a 6 as the only success, then $s = 1$ and $f = 5$, since there is just one way of getting a 6, and there are five ways of not getting a 6 in a single throw. Therefore, the probability of getting a 6 is

$$p = \frac{1}{1+5} = 0.1666$$

and the probability of not getting a 6 is

$$q = \frac{5}{1+5} = 0.8333$$

So far, we have been concerned with events that are independent and mutually exclusive (i.e. events that cannot happen simultaneously). In the dice experiment, the two events of obtaining a 6 and, for example, a 1 are mutually exclusive because we cannot obtain a 6 **and** a 1 simultaneously in a single throw. However, events that are not independent may affect the likelihood of one or the other occurring. Consider, for instance, the probability of getting a 6 in a single throw, knowing this time that a 1 has not come up. There are still five ways of not getting a 6, but one of them can be eliminated as we know that a 1 has not been obtained. Thus,

$$p = \frac{1}{1 + (5 - 1)}$$

Let A be an event in the world and B be another event. Suppose that events A and B are not mutually exclusive, but occur conditionally on the occurrence of the other. The probability that event A will occur if event B occurs is called the **conditional probability**. Conditional probability is denoted mathematically as $p(A|B)$ in which the vertical bar represents GIVEN and the complete probability expression is interpreted as 'Conditional probability of event A occurring given that event B has occurred'.

$$p(A|B) = \frac{\text{the number of times } A \text{ and } B \text{ can occur}}{\text{the number of times } B \text{ can occur}} \tag{3.6}$$

The number of times A and B can occur, or the probability that both A and B will occur, is called the **joint probability** of A and B. It is represented mathematically as $p(A \cap B)$. The number of ways B can occur is the probability of B, $p(B)$, and thus

$$p(A|B) = \frac{p(A \cap B)}{p(B)} \tag{3.7}$$

Similarly, the conditional probability of event B occurring given that event A has occurred equals

$$p(B|A) = \frac{p(B \cap A)}{p(A)} \tag{3.8}$$

Hence,

$$p(B \cap A) = p(B|A) \times p(A) \tag{3.9}$$

The joint probability is commutative, thus

$$p(A \cap B) = p(B \cap A)$$

Therefore,

$$p(A \cap B) = p(B|A) \times p(A) \tag{3.10}$$

Substituting Eq. (3.10) into Eq. (3.7) yields the following equation:

$$p(A|B) = \frac{p(B|A) \times p(A)}{p(B)} \tag{3.11}$$

where:

$p(A|B)$ is the conditional probability that event A occurs given that event B has occurred;

$p(B|A)$ is the conditional probability of event B occurring given that event A has occurred;

$p(A)$ is the probability of event A occurring;

$p(B)$ is the probability of event B occurring.

Equation (3.11) is known as the **Bayesian rule**, which is named after Thomas Bayes, an 18th-century British mathematician who introduced this rule.

The concept of conditional probability introduced so far considered that event A was dependent upon event B. This principle can be extended to event A being dependent on a number of mutually exclusive events $B_1, B_2, \ldots, B_n$. The following set of equations can then be derived from Eq. (3.7):

$$p(A \cap B_1) = p(A|B_1) \times p(B_1)$$
$$p(A \cap B_2) = p(A|B_2) \times p(B_2)$$
$$\vdots$$
$$p(A \cap B_n) = p(A|B_n) \times p(B_n)$$

or when combined:

$$\sum_{i=1}^{n} p(A \cap B_i) = \sum_{i=1}^{n} p(A|B_i) \times p(B_i) \tag{3.12}$$

If Eq. (3.12) is summed over an exhaustive list of events for B_i as illustrated in Figure 3.1, we obtain

$$\sum_{i=1}^{n} p(A \cap B_i) = p(A) \tag{3.13}$$

It reduces Eq. (3.12) to the following conditional probability equation:

$$p(A) = \sum_{i=1}^{n} p(A|B_i) \times p(B_i) \tag{3.14}$$

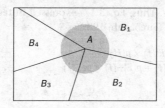

Figure 3.1   The joint probability

If the occurrence of event A depends on only two mutually exclusive events, that is B and NOT B, then Eq. (3.14) becomes

$$p(A) = p(A|B) \times p(B) + p(A|\neg B) \times p(\neg B) \tag{3.15}$$

where $\neg$ is the logical function NOT.

Similarly,

$$p(B) = p(B|A) \times p(A) + p(B|\neg A) \times p(\neg A) \tag{3.16}$$

Let us now substitute Eq. (3.16) into the Bayesian rule (3.11) to yield

$$p(A|B) = \frac{p(B|A) \times p(A)}{p(B|A) \times p(A) + p(B|\neg A) \times p(\neg A)} \tag{3.17}$$

Equation (3.17) provides the background for the application of probability theory to manage uncertainty in expert systems.

3.3 Bayesian reasoning

With Eq. (3.17) we can now leave basic probability theory and turn our attention back to expert systems. Suppose all rules in the knowledge base are represented in the following form:

IF E is true
THEN H is true {with probability p}

This rule implies that if event E occurs, then the probability that event H will occur is p.

What if event E has occurred but we do not know whether event H has occurred? Can we compute the probability that event H has occurred as well?
Equation (3.17) tells us how to do this. We simply use H and E instead of A and B. In expert systems, H usually represents a hypothesis and E denotes evidence to

support this hypothesis. Thus, Eq. (3.17) expressed in terms of hypotheses and evidence looks like this (Firebaugh, 1989):

$$p(H|E) = \frac{p(E|H) \times p(H)}{p(E|H) \times p(H) + p(E|\neg H) \times p(\neg H)} \tag{3.18}$$

where:

$p(H)$ is the prior probability of hypothesis H being true;

$p(E|H)$ is the probability that hypothesis H being true will result in evidence E;

$p(\neg H)$ is the prior probability of hypothesis H being false;

$p(E|\neg H)$ is the probability of finding evidence E even when hypothesis H is false.

Equation (3.18) suggests that the probability of hypothesis H, $p(H)$, has to be defined before any evidence is examined. In expert systems, the probabilities required to solve a problem are provided by experts. An expert determines the prior probabilities for possible hypotheses $p(H)$ and $p(\neg H)$, and also the conditional probabilities for observing evidence E if hypothesis H is true, $p(E|H)$, and if hypothesis H is false, $p(E|\neg H)$. Users provide information about the evidence observed and the expert system computes $p(H|E)$ for hypothesis H in light of the user-supplied evidence E. Probability $p(H|E)$ is called the **posterior probability** of hypothesis H upon observing evidence E.

What if the expert, based on single evidence E, cannot choose a single hypothesis but rather provides multiple hypotheses H_1, H_2, ..., H_m? Or given multiple evidences E_1, E_2, ..., E_n, the expert also produces multiple hypotheses?
We can generalise Eq. (3.18) to take into account both multiple hypotheses $H_1, H_2, \ldots, H_m$ and multiple evidences $E_1, E_2, \ldots, E_n$. But the hypotheses as well as the evidences must be mutually exclusive and exhaustive.

Single evidence E and multiple hypotheses $H_1, H_2, \ldots, H_m$ follow:

$$p(H_i|E) = \frac{p(E|H_i) \times p(H_i)}{\sum_{k=1}^{m} p(E|H_k) \times p(H_k)} \tag{3.19}$$

Multiple evidences $E_1, E_2, \ldots, E_n$ and multiple hypotheses $H_1, H_2, \ldots, H_m$ follow:

$$p(H_i|E_1E_2\ldots E_n) = \frac{p(E_1E_2\ldots E_n|H_i) \times p(H_i)}{\sum_{k=1}^{m} p(E_1E_2\ldots E_n|H_k) \times p(H_k)} \tag{3.20}$$

An application of Eq. (3.20) requires us to obtain the conditional probabilities of all possible combinations of evidences for all hypotheses. This requirement places an enormous burden on the expert and makes his or her task practically impossible. Therefore, in expert systems, subtleties of evidence should be suppressed and conditional independence among different evidences assumed (Ng and Abramson, 1990). Thus, instead of unworkable Eq. (3.20), we attain

$$p(H_i|E_1 E_2 \ldots E_n) = \frac{p(E_1|H_i) \times p(E_2|H_i) \times \ldots \times p(E_n|H_i) \times p(H_i)}{\sum_{k=1}^{m} p(E_1|H_k) \times p(E_2|H_k) \times \ldots \times p(E_n|H_k) \times p(H_k)} \qquad (3.21)$$

How does an expert system compute all posterior probabilities and finally rank potentially true hypotheses?

Let us consider a simple example. Suppose an expert, given three conditionally independent evidences E_1, E_2 and E_3, creates three mutually exclusive and exhaustive hypotheses H_1, H_2 and H_3, and provides prior probabilities for these hypotheses – $p(H_1)$, $p(H_2)$ and $p(H_3)$, respectively. The expert also determines the conditional probabilities of observing each evidence for all possible hypotheses. Table 3.2 illustrates the prior and conditional probabilities provided by the expert.

Assume that we first observe evidence E_3. The expert system computes the posterior probabilities for all hypotheses according to Eq. (3.19):

$$p(H_i|E_3) = \frac{p(E_3|H_i) \times p(H_i)}{\sum_{k=1}^{3} p(E_3|H_k) \times p(H_k)}, \qquad i = 1, 2, 3$$

Thus,

$$p(H_1|E_3) = \frac{0.6 \times 0.40}{0.6 \times 0.40 + 0.7 \times 0.35 + 0.9 \times 0.25} = 0.34$$

$$p(H_2|E_3) = \frac{0.7 \times 0.35}{0.6 \times 0.40 + 0.7 \times 0.35 + 0.9 \times 0.25} = 0.34$$

$$p(H_3|E_3) = \frac{0.9 \times 0.25}{0.6 \times 0.40 + 0.7 \times 0.35 + 0.9 \times 0.25} = 0.32$$

Table 3.2 The prior and conditional probabilities

	Hypothesis		
Probability	**i = 1**	**i = 2**	**i = 3**
$p(H_i)$	0.40	0.35	0.25
$p(E_1|H_i)$	0.3	0.8	0.5
$p(E_2|H_i)$	0.9	0.0	0.7
$p(E_3|H_i)$	0.6	0.7	0.9

As you can see, after evidence E_3 is observed, belief in hypothesis H_1 decreases and becomes equal to belief in hypothesis H_2. Belief in hypothesis H_3 increases and even nearly reaches beliefs in hypotheses H_1 and H_2.

Suppose now that we observe evidence E_1. The posterior probabilities are calculated by Eq. (3.21):

$$p(H_i|E_1E_3) = \frac{p(E_1|H_i) \times p(E_3|H_i) \times p(H_i)}{\sum\limits_{k=1}^{3} p(E_1|H_k) \times p(E_3|H_k) \times p(H_k)}, \quad i = 1,2,3$$

Hence,

$$p(H_1|E_1E_3) = \frac{0.3 \times 0.6 \times 0.40}{0.3 \times 0.6 \times 0.40 + 0.8 \times 0.7 \times 0.35 + 0.5 \times 0.9 \times 0.25} = 0.19$$

$$p(H_2|E_1E_3) = \frac{0.8 \times 0.7 \times 0.35}{0.3 \times 0.6 \times 0.40 + 0.8 \times 0.7 \times 0.35 + 0.5 \times 0.9 \times 0.25} = 0.52$$

$$p(H_3|E_1E_3) = \frac{0.5 \times 0.9 \times 0.25}{0.3 \times 0.6 \times 0.40 + 0.8 \times 0.7 \times 0.35 + 0.5 \times 0.9 \times 0.25} = 0.29$$

Hypothesis H_2 is now considered as the most likely one, while belief in hypothesis H_1 has decreased dramatically.

After observing evidence E_2 as well, the expert system calculates the final posterior probabilities for all hypotheses:

$$p(H_i|E_1E_2E_3) = \frac{p(E_1|H_i) \times p(E_2|H_i) \times p(E_3|H_i) \times p(H_i)}{\sum\limits_{k=1}^{3} p(E_1|H_k) \times p(E_2|H_k) \times p(E_3|H_k) \times p(H_k)}, \quad i = 1,2,3$$

Thus,

$$p(H_1|E_1E_2E_3) = \frac{0.3 \times 0.9 \times 0.6 \times 0.40}{0.3 \times 0.9 \times 0.6 \times 0.40 + 0.8 \times 0.0 \times 0.7 \times 0.35 + 0.5 \times 0.7 \times 0.9 \times 0.25}$$
$$= 0.45$$

$$p(H_2|E_1E_2E_3) = \frac{0.8 \times 0.0 \times 0.7 \times 0.35}{0.3 \times 0.9 \times 0.6 \times 0.40 + 0.8 \times 0.0 \times 0.7 \times 0.35 + 0.5 \times 0.7 \times 0.9 \times 0.25}$$
$$= 0$$

$$p(H_3|E_1E_2E_3) = \frac{0.5 \times 0.7 \times 0.9 \times 0.25}{0.3 \times 0.9 \times 0.6 \times 0.40 + 0.8 \times 0.0 \times 0.7 \times 0.35 + 0.5 \times 0.7 \times 0.9 \times 0.25}$$
$$= 0.55$$

Although the initial ranking provided by the expert was H_1, H_2 and H_3, only hypotheses H_1 and H_3 remain under consideration after all evidences

(E_1, E_2 and E_3) were observed. Hypothesis H_2 can now be completely abandoned. Note that hypothesis H_3 is considered more likely than hypothesis H_1.

PROSPECTOR, an expert system for mineral exploration, was the first system to use Bayesian rules of evidence to compute $p(H|E)$ and propagate uncertainties throughout the system (Duda *et al.*, 1979). To help interpret Bayesian reasoning in expert systems, consider a simple example.

3.4   FORECAST: Bayesian accumulation of evidence

Let us develop an expert system for a real problem such as the weather forecast. Our expert system will be required to work out if it is going to rain tomorrow. It will need some real data, which can be obtained from the weather bureau.

Table 3.3 summarises London weather for March 1982. It gives the minimum and maximum temperatures, rainfall and sunshine for each day. If rainfall is zero it is a dry day.

The expert system should give us two possible outcomes – *tomorrow is rain* and *tomorrow is dry* – and provide their likelihood. In other words, the expert system must determine the conditional probabilities of the two hypotheses *tomorrow is rain* and *tomorrow is dry*.

To apply the Bayesian rule (3.18), we should provide the prior probabilities of these hypotheses.

The first thing to do is to write two basic rules that, with the data provided, could predict the weather for tomorrow.

Rule: 1
IF   today is rain
THEN   tomorrow is rain

Rule: 2
IF   today is dry
THEN   tomorrow is dry

Using these rules we will make only 10 mistakes – every time a wet day precedes a dry one, or a dry day precedes a wet one. Thus, we can accept the prior probabilities of 0.5 for both hypotheses and rewrite our rules in the following form:

Rule: 1
IF   today is rain {LS 2.5 LN .6}
THEN   tomorrow is rain {prior .5}

Rule: 2
IF   today is dry {LS 1.6 LN .4}
THEN   tomorrow is dry {prior .5}

Table 3.3 London weather summary for March 1982

Day of month	Min. temp. °C	Max. temp. °C	Rainfall mm	Sunshine hours	Actual weather	Weather forecast
1	9.4	11.0	17.5	3.2	Rain	–
2	4.2	12.5	4.1	6.2	Rain	Rain
3	7.6	11.2	7.7	1.1	Rain	Rain
4	5.7	10.5	0.0	4.3	Dry	Rain*
5	3.0	12.0	0.0	9.5	Dry	Dry
6	4.4	9.6	0.0	3.5	Dry	Dry
7	4.8	9.4	4.6	10.1	Rain	Rain
8	1.8	9.2	5.5	7.8	Rain	Rain
9	2.4	10.2	4.8	4.1	Rain	Rain
10	5.5	12.7	4.2	3.8	Rain	Rain
11	3.7	10.9	4.4	9.2	Rain	Rain
12	5.9	10.0	4.8	7.1	Rain	Rain
13	3.0	11.9	0.0	8.3	Dry	Rain*
14	5.4	12.1	4.8	1.8	Rain	Dry*
15	8.8	9.1	8.8	0.0	Rain	Rain
16	2.4	8.4	3.0	3.1	Rain	Rain
17	4.3	10.8	0.0	4.3	Dry	Dry
18	3.4	11.1	4.2	6.6	Rain	Rain
19	4.4	8.4	5.4	0.7	Rain	Rain
20	5.1	7.9	3.0	0.1	Rain	Rain
21	4.4	7.3	0.0	0.0	Dry	Dry
22	5.6	14.0	0.0	6.8	Dry	Dry
23	5.7	14.0	0.0	8.8	Dry	Dry
24	2.9	13.9	0.0	9.5	Dry	Dry
25	5.8	16.4	0.0	10.3	Dry	Dry
26	3.9	17.0	0.0	9.9	Dry	Dry
27	3.8	18.3	0.0	8.3	Dry	Dry
28	5.8	15.4	3.2	7.0	Rain	Dry*
29	6.7	8.8	0.0	4.2	Dry	Dry
30	4.5	9.6	4.8	8.8	Rain	Rain
31	4.6	9.6	3.2	4.2	Rain	Rain

* Errors in weather forecast.

The value of LS represents a measure of the expert belief in hypothesis H if evidence E is present. It is called **likelihood of sufficiency**. The likelihood of sufficiency is defined as the ratio of $p(E|H)$ over $p(E|\neg H)$

$$LS = \frac{p(E|H)}{p(E|\neg H)} \tag{3.22}$$

In our case, LS is the probability of getting rain today if we have rain tomorrow, divided by the probability of getting rain today if there is no rain tomorrow:

$$LS = \frac{p(today\ is\ rain\,|\,tomorrow\ is\ rain)}{p(today\ is\ rain\,|\,tomorrow\ is\ dry)}$$

LN, as you may already have guessed, is a measure of discredit to hypothesis *H* if evidence *E* is missing. *LN* is called **likelihood of necessity** and defined as

$$LN = \frac{p(\neg E|H)}{p(\neg E|\neg H)} \tag{3.23}$$

In our weather example, *LN* is the probability of not getting rain today if we have rain tomorrow, divided by the probability of not getting rain today if there is no rain tomorrow:

$$LN = \frac{p(today\ is\ dry\ |\ tomorrow\ is\ rain)}{p(today\ is\ dry\ |\ tomorrow\ is\ dry)}$$

Note that *LN* cannot be derived from *LS*. The domain expert must provide both values independently.

How does the domain expert determine values of the likelihood of sufficiency and the likelihood of necessity? Is the expert required to deal with conditional probabilities?

To provide values for *LS* and *LN*, an expert does not need to determine exact values of conditional probabilities. The expert decides likelihood ratios directly. High values of *LS* ($LS \gg 1$) indicate that the rule strongly supports the hypothesis if the evidence is observed, and low values of *LN* ($0 < LN < 1$) suggest that the rule also strongly opposes the hypothesis if the evidence is missing.

Since the conditional probabilities can be easily computed from the likelihood ratios *LS* and *LN*, this approach can use the Bayesian rule to propagate evidence.

Go back now to the London weather. Rule 1 tells us that if it is raining today, there is a high probability of rain tomorrow ($LS = 2.5$). But even if there is no rain today, or in other words today is dry, there is still some chance of having rain tomorrow ($LN = 0.6$).

Rule 2, on the other hand, clarifies the situation with a dry day. If it is dry today, then the probability of a dry day tomorrow is also high ($LS = 1.6$). However, as you can see, the probability of rain tomorrow if it is raining today is higher than the probability of a dry day tomorrow if it is dry today. Why? The values of *LS* and *LN* are usually determined by the domain expert. In our weather example, these values can also be confirmed from the statistical information published by the weather bureau. Rule 2 also determines the chance of a dry day tomorrow even if today we have rain ($LN = 0.4$).

How does the expert system get the overall probability of a dry or wet day tomorrow?

In the rule-based expert system, the prior probability of the consequent, $p(H)$, is converted into the prior odds:

$$O(H) = \frac{p(H)}{1 - p(H)} \tag{3.24}$$

The prior probability is only used when the uncertainty of the consequent is adjusted for the first time. Then in order to obtain the posterior odds, the prior odds are updated by LS if the antecedent of the rule (in other words, evidence) is true and by LN if the antecedent is false:

$$O(H|E) = LS \times O(H) \tag{3.25}$$

and

$$O(H|\neg E) = LN \times O(H) \tag{3.26}$$

The posterior odds are then used to recover the posterior probabilities:

$$p(H|E) = \frac{O(H|E)}{1 + O(H|E)} \tag{3.27}$$

and

$$p(H|\neg E) = \frac{O(H|\neg E)}{1 + O(H|\neg E)} \tag{3.28}$$

Our London weather example shows how this scheme works. Suppose the user indicates that *today is rain*. Rule 1 is fired and the prior probability of *tomorrow is rain* is converted into the prior odds:

$$O(tomorrow\ is\ rain) = \frac{0.5}{1 - 0.5} = 1.0$$

The evidence *today is rain* increases the odds by a factor of 2.5, thereby raising the probability from 0.5 to 0.71:

$$O(tomorrow\ is\ rain\,|\,today\ is\ rain) = 2.5 \times 1.0 = 2.5$$

$$p(tomorrow\ is\ rain\,|\,today\ is\ rain) = \frac{2.5}{1 + 2.5} = 0.71$$

Rule 2 is also fired. The prior probability of *tomorrow is dry* is converted into the prior odds, but the evidence *today is rain* reduces the odds by a factor of 0.4. This, in turn, diminishes the probability of *tomorrow is dry* from 0.5 to 0.29:

$$O(tomorrow\ is\ dry) = \frac{0.5}{1 - 0.5} = 1.0$$

$$O(tomorrow\ is\ dry\,|\,today\ is\ rain) = 0.4 \times 1.0 = 0.4$$

$$p(tomorrow\ is\ dry\,|\,today\ is\ rain) = \frac{0.4}{1 + 0.4} = 0.29$$

Hence if it is raining today there is a 71 per cent chance of it raining and a 29 per cent chance of it being dry tomorrow.

Further suppose that the user input is *today is dry*. By a similar calculation there is a 62 per cent chance of it being dry and a 38 per cent chance of it raining tomorrow.

Now we have examined the basic principles of Bayesian rules of evidence, we can incorporate some new knowledge in our expert system. To do this, we need to determine conditions when the weather actually did change. Analysis of the data provided in Table 3.3 allows us to develop the following knowledge base (the Leonardo expert system shell is used here).

Knowledge base

/* FORECAST: BAYESIAN ACCUMULATION OF EVIDENCE

control bayes

Rule: 1
if   today is rain {LS 2.5 LN .6}
then   tomorrow is rain {prior .5}

Rule: 2
if   today is dry {LS 1.6 LN .4}
then   tomorrow is dry {prior .5}

Rule: 3
if   today is rain
and   rainfall is low {LS 10 LN 1}
then   tomorrow is dry {prior .5}

Rule: 4
if   today is rain
and   rainfall is low
and   temperature is cold {LS 1.5 LN 1}
then   tomorrow is dry {prior .5}

Rule: 5
if   today is dry
and   temperature is warm {LS 2 LN .9}
then   tomorrow is rain {prior .5}

Rule: 6
if   today is dry
and   temperature is warm
and   sky is overcast {LS 5 LN 1}
then   tomorrow is rain {prior .5}

/* The SEEK directive sets up the goal of the rule set

seek tomorrow

Dialogue

Based on the information provided by the user, the expert system determines whether we can expect a dry day tomorrow. The user's answers are indicated by arrows. We assume that rainfall is low if it is less than 4.1 mm, the temperature is cold if the average daily temperature is lower than or equal to 7.0°C, and warm if it is higher than 7.0°C. Finally, sunshine less than 4.6 hours a day stands for overcast.

What is the weather today?
⇒ **rain**

Rule: 1
if   today is rain {LS 2.5 LN .6}
then   tomorrow is rain {prior .5}

$$O(\text{tomorrow is rain}) = \frac{0.5}{1 - 0.5} = 1.0$$

$$O(\text{tomorrow is rain} \mid \text{today is rain}) = 2.5 \times 1.0 = 2.5$$

$$p(\text{tomorrow is rain} \mid \text{today is rain}) = \frac{2.5}{1 + 2.5} = 0.71$$

tomorrow is rain   {0.71}

Rule: 2
if   today is dry {LS 1.6 LN .4}
then   tomorrow is dry {prior .5}

$$O(\text{tomorrow is dry}) = \frac{0.5}{1 - 0.5} = 1.0$$

$$O(\text{tomorrow is dry} \mid \text{today is rain}) = 0.4 \times 1.0 = 0.4$$

$$p(\text{tomorrow is dry} \mid \text{today is rain}) = \frac{0.4}{1 + 0.4} = 0.29$$

tomorrow is rain   {0.71}
            dry   {0.29}

What is the rainfall today?
⇒ **low**

Rule: 3
if   today is rain
and   rainfall is low {LS 10 LN 1}
then   tomorrow is dry {prior .5}

$$O(\text{tomorrow is dry}) = \frac{0.29}{1 - 0.29} = 0.41$$

$$O(\text{tomorrow is dry} \mid \text{today is rain} \cap \text{rainfall is low}) = 10 \times 0.41 = 4.1$$

$$p(\text{tomorrow is dry} \mid \text{today is rain} \cap \text{rainfall is low}) = \frac{4.1}{1 + 4.1} = 0.80$$

tomorrow is dry {0.80}
          rain {0.71}

What is the temperature today?
⇒ **cold**

Rule: 4
if   today is rain
and   rainfall is low
and   temperature is cold {LS 1.5 LN 1}
then   tomorrow is dry {prior .5}

$$O(\text{tomorrow is dry}) = \frac{0.80}{1 - 0.80} = 4$$

$O(\text{tomorrow is dry} \mid \text{today is rain} \cap \text{rainfall is low} \cap \text{temperature is cold})$
$= 1.50 \times 4 = 6$

$p(\text{tomorrow is dry} \mid \text{today is rain} \cap \text{rainfall is low} \cap \text{temperature is cold})$

$$= \frac{6}{1 + 6} = 0.86$$

tomorrow is dry {0.86}
          rain {0.71}

Rule: 5
if   today is dry
and   temperature is warm {LS 2 LN .9}
then   tomorrow is rain {prior .5}

$$O(\text{tomorrow is rain}) = \frac{0.71}{1 - 0.71} = 2.45$$

$O(\text{tomorrow is rain} \mid \text{today is not dry} \cap \text{temperature is not warm}) = 0.9 \times 2.45 = 2.21$

$$p(\text{tomorrow is rain} \mid \text{today is not dry} \cap \text{temperature is not warm}) = \frac{2.21}{1 + 2.21} = 0.69$$

tomorrow is dry {0.86}
          rain {0.69}

What is the cloud cover today?
⇒ **overcast**

Rule: 6
if   today is dry
and   temperature is warm
and   sky is overcast {LS 5 LN 1}
then   tomorrow is rain {prior .5}

$$O(tomorrow\ is\ rain) = \frac{0.69}{1 - 0.69} = 2.23$$

$O(tomorrow\ is\ rain\ |\ today\ is\ not\ dry \cap temperature\ is\ not\ warm \cap sky\ is\ overcast)$
$= 1.0 \times 2.23 = 2.23$

$p(tomorrow\ is\ rain\ |\ today\ is\ not\ dry \cap temperature\ is\ not\ warm \cap sky\ is\ overcast)$
$$= \frac{2.23}{1 + 2.23} = 0.69$$

tomorrow is dry   {0.86}
            rain   {0.69}

This means that we have two potentially true hypotheses, *tomorrow is dry* and *tomorrow is rain*, but the likelihood of the first one is higher.

From Table 3.3 you can see that our expert system made only four mistakes. This is an 86 per cent success rate, which compares well with the results provided in Naylor (1987) for the same case of the London weather.

3.5 Bias of the Bayesian method

The framework for Bayesian reasoning requires probability values as primary inputs. The assessment of these values usually involves human judgement. However, psychological research shows that humans either cannot elicit probability values consistent with the Bayesian rules or do it badly (Burns and Pearl, 1981; Tversky and Kahneman, 1982). This suggests that the conditional probabilities may be inconsistent with the prior probabilities given by the expert. Consider, for example, a car that does not start and makes odd noises when you press the starter. The conditional probability of the starter being faulty if the car makes odd noises may be expressed as

IF   the symptom is 'odd noises'
THEN   the starter is bad {with probability 0.7}

Apparently the conditional probability that the starter is not bad if the car makes odd noises is

$p(starter\ is\ not\ bad\ |\ odd\ noises) = p(starter\ is\ good\ |\ odd\ noises) = 1 - 0.7 = 0.3$

Therefore, we can obtain a companion rule that states

IF   the symptom is 'odd noises'
THEN   the starter is good {with probability 0.3}

Domain experts do not deal easily with conditional probabilities and quite often deny the very existence of the **hidden implicit probability** (0.3 in our example).

In our case, we would use available statistical information and empirical studies to derive the following two rules:

IF   the starter is bad
THEN   the symptom is 'odd noises' {with probability 0.85}

IF   the starter is bad
THEN   the symptom is not 'odd noises' {with probability 0.15}

To use the Bayesian rule, we still need the prior probability, the probability that the starter is bad if the car does not start. Here we need an expert judgement. Suppose the expert supplies us the value of 5 per cent. Now we can apply the Bayesian rule (3.18) to obtain

$$p(\text{starter is bad} \mid \text{odd noises}) = \frac{0.85 \times 0.05}{0.85 \times 0.05 + 0.15 \times 0.95} = 0.23$$

The number obtained is significantly lower than the expert's estimate of 0.7 given at the beginning of this section.

Why this inconsistency? Did the expert make a mistake?

The most obvious reason for the inconsistency is that the expert made different assumptions when assessing the conditional and prior probabilities. We may attempt to investigate it by working backwards from the posterior probability $p(\text{starter is bad} \mid \text{odd noises})$ to the prior probability $p(\text{starter is bad})$. In our case, we can assume that

$$p(\text{starter is good}) = 1 - p(\text{starter is bad})$$

From Eq. (3.18) we obtain

$$p(H) = \frac{p(H|E) \times p(E|\neg H)}{p(H|E) \times p(E|\neg H) + p(E|H)[1 - p(H|E)]}$$

where:

$p(H) = p(\text{starter is bad})$;

$p(H|E) = p(\text{starter is bad} \mid \text{odd noises})$;

$p(E|H) = p(\text{odd noises} \mid \text{starter is bad})$;

$p(E|\neg H) = p(\text{odd noises} \mid \text{starter is good})$.

If we now take the value of 0.7, $p(\text{starter is bad}|\text{odd noises})$, provided by the expert as the correct one, the prior probability $p(\text{starter is bad})$ would have to be

$$p(H) = \frac{0.7 \times 0.15}{0.7 \times 0.15 + 0.85 \times (1 - 0.7)} = 0.29$$

This value is almost six times larger than the figure of 5 per cent provided by the expert. Thus the expert indeed uses quite different estimates of the prior and conditional probabilities.

In fact, the prior probabilities also provided by the expert are likely to be inconsistent with the likelihood of sufficiency, LS, and the likelihood of necessity, LN. Several methods are proposed to handle this problem (Duda et al., 1976). The most popular technique, first applied in PROSPECTOR, is the use of a piecewise linear interpolation model (Duda et al., 1979).

However, to use the subjective Bayesian approach, we must satisfy many assumptions, including the conditional independence of evidence under both a hypothesis and its negation. As these assumptions are rarely satisfied in real-world problems, only a few systems have been built based on Bayesian reasoning. The best known one is PROSPECTOR, an expert system for mineral exploration (Duda et al., 1979).

3.6 Certainty factors theory and evidential reasoning

Certainty factors theory is a popular alternative to Bayesian reasoning. The basic principles of this theory were first introduced in MYCIN, an expert system for the diagnosis and therapy of blood infections and meningitis (Shortliffe and Buchanan, 1975). The developers of MYCIN found that medical experts expressed the strength of their belief in terms that were neither logical nor mathematically consistent. In addition, reliable statistical data about the problem domain was not available. Therefore, the MYCIN team was unable to use a classical probability approach. Instead they decided to introduce a **certainty factor** (*cf*), a number to measure the expert's belief. The maximum value of the certainty factor was +1.0 (definitely true) and the minimum −1.0 (definitely false). A positive value represented a degree of belief and a negative a degree of disbelief. For example, if the expert stated that some evidence was almost certainly true, a *cf* value of 0.8 would be assigned to this evidence. Table 3.4 shows some uncertain terms interpreted in MYCIN (Durkin, 1994).

In expert systems with certainty factors, the knowledge base consists of a set of rules that have the following syntax:

IF   <evidence>
THEN   <hypothesis> {*cf*}

where *cf* represents belief in hypothesis H given that evidence E has occurred.

The certainty factors theory is based on two functions: measure of belief $MB(H,E)$ and measure of disbelief $MD(H,E)$ (Shortliffe and Buchanan, 1975).

Table 3.4 Uncertain terms and their interpretation

Term	Certainty factor
Definitely not	−1.0
Almost certainly not	−0.8
Probably not	−0.6
Maybe not	−0.4
Unknown	−0.2 to +0.2
Maybe	+0.4
Probably	+0.6
Almost certainly	+0.8
Definitely	+1.0

These functions indicate, respectively, the degree to which belief in hypothesis H would be increased if evidence E were observed, and the degree to which disbelief in hypothesis H would be increased by observing the same evidence E.

The measure of belief and disbelief can be defined in terms of prior and conditional probabilities as follows (Ng and Abramson, 1990):

$$MB(H,E) = \begin{cases} 1 & \text{if } p(H) = 1 \\ \dfrac{max\,[p(H|E), p(H)] - p(H)}{max\,[1,0] - p(H)} & \text{otherwise} \end{cases} \quad (3.29)$$

$$MD(H,E) = \begin{cases} 1 & \text{if } p(H) = 0 \\ \dfrac{min\,[p(H|E), p(H)] - p(H)}{min\,[1,0] - p(H)} & \text{otherwise} \end{cases} \quad (3.30)$$

where:

$p(H)$ is the prior probability of hypothesis H being true;

$p(H|E)$ is the probability that hypothesis H is true given evidence E.

The values of $MB(H,E)$ and $MD(H,E)$ range between 0 and 1. The strength of belief or disbelief in hypothesis H depends on the kind of evidence E observed. Some facts may increase the strength of belief, but some increase the strength of disbelief.

How can we determine the total strength of belief or disbelief in a hypothesis?
To combine them into one number, the certainty factor, the following equation is used:

$$cf = \frac{MB(H,E) - MD(H,E)}{1 - min\,[MB(H,E), MD(H,E)]} \quad (3.31)$$

Thus *cf*, which can range in MYCIN from -1 to $+1$, indicates the total belief in hypothesis *H*.

The MYCIN approach can be illustrated through an example. Consider a simple rule:

IF   *A* is *X*
THEN *B* is *Y*

Quite often, an expert may not be absolutely certain that this rule holds. Also suppose it has been observed that in some cases, even when the IF part of the rule is satisfied and object *A* takes on value *X*, object *B* can acquire some different value *Z*. In other words, we have here the uncertainty of a quasi-statistical kind.

The expert usually can associate a certainty factor with each possible value *B* given that *A* has value *X*. Thus our rule might look as follows:

IF   *A* is *X*
THEN *B* is *Y* {*cf* 0.7};
        B is *Z* {*cf* 0.2}

What does it mean? Where is the other 10 per cent?

It means that, given *A* has received value *X*, *B* will be *Y* 70 per cent and *Z* 20 per cent of the time. The other 10 per cent of the time it could be anything. In such a way the expert might reserve a possibility that object *B* can take not only two known values, *Y* and *Z*, but also some other value that has not yet been observed. Note that we assign multiple values to object *B*.

The certainty factor assigned by a rule is then propagated through the reasoning chain. Propagation of the certainty factor involves establishing the net certainty of the rule consequent when the evidence in the rule antecedent is uncertain. The net certainty for a single antecedent rule, $cf(H,E)$, can be easily calculated by multiplying the certainty factor of the antecedent, $cf(E)$, with the rule certainty factor, *cf*

$$cf(H,E) = cf(E) \times cf \tag{3.32}$$

For example,

IF   the sky is clear
THEN the forecast is sunny {*cf* 0.8}

and the current certainty factor of *sky is clear* is 0.5, then

$$cf(H,E) = 0.5 \times 0.8 = 0.4$$

This result, according to Table 3.4, would read as 'It may be sunny.'

How does an expert system establish the certainty factor for rules with multiple antecedents?

For conjunctive rules such as

> IF   \<evidence E_1\>
> AND   \<evidence E_2\>
>
> .
> .
> .
>
> AND   \<evidence E_n\>
> THEN   \<hypothesis H\> {cf}

the net certainty of the consequent, or in other words the certainty of hypothesis H, is established as follows:

$$cf(H, E_1 \cap E_2 \cap \ldots \cap E_n) = min\,[cf(E_1), cf(E_2), \ldots, cf(E_n)] \times cf \qquad (3.33)$$

For example,

> IF   sky is clear
> AND   the forecast is sunny
> THEN   the action is 'wear sunglasses' {$cf\,0.8$}

and the certainty of *sky is clear* is 0.9 and the certainty of the *forecast is sunny* is 0.7, then

$$cf(H, E_1 \cap E_2) = min\,[0.9, 0.7] \times 0.8 = 0.7 \times 0.8 = 0.56$$

According to Table 3.4, this conclusion might be interpreted as 'Probably it would be a good idea to wear sunglasses today.'

For disjunctive rules such as

> IF   \<evidence E_1\>
> OR   \<evidence E_2\>
>
> .
> .
> .
>
> OR   \<evidence E_n\>
> THEN   \<hypothesis H\> {cf}

the certainty of hypothesis H is determined as follows:

$$cf(H, E_1 \cup E_2 \cup \ldots \cup E_n) = max\,[cf(E_1), cf(E_2), \ldots, cf(E_n)] \times cf \qquad (3.34)$$

For example,

> IF   sky is overcast
> OR   the forecast is rain
> THEN the action is 'take an umbrella' {cf 0.9}

and the certainty of *sky is overcast* is 0.6 and the certainty of the *forecast is rain* is 0.8, then

$$cf(H, E_1 \cup E_2) = max\,[0.6, 0.8] \times 0.9 = 0.8 \times 0.9 = 0.72$$

which can be interpreted as 'Almost certainly an umbrella should be taken today.'

Sometimes two or even more rules can affect the same hypothesis. How does an expert system cope with such situations?

When the same consequent is obtained as a result of the execution of two or more rules, the individual certainty factors of these rules must be merged to give a combined certainty factor for a hypothesis. Suppose the knowledge base consists of the following rules:

> Rule 1:   IF   A is X
>   THEN C is Z {cf 0.8}
>
> Rule 2:   IF   B is Y
>   THEN C is Z {cf 0.6}

What certainty should be assigned to object C having value Z if both Rule 1 and Rule 2 are fired? Our common sense suggests that, if we have two pieces of evidence (A is X and B is Y) from different sources (Rule 1 and Rule 2) supporting the same hypothesis (C is Z), then the confidence in this hypothesis should increase and become stronger than if only one piece of evidence had been obtained.

To calculate a combined certainty factor we can use the following equation (Durkin, 1994):

$$cf(cf_1, cf_2) = \begin{cases} cf_1 + cf_2 \times (1 - cf_1) & \text{if } cf_1 > 0 \text{ and } cf_2 > 0 \\ \dfrac{cf_1 + cf_2}{1 - min\,[|cf_1|, |cf_2|]} & \text{if } cf_1 < 0 \text{ or } cf_2 < 0 \\ cf_1 + cf_2 \times (1 + cf_1) & \text{if } cf_1 < 0 \text{ and } cf_2 < 0 \end{cases} \qquad (3.35)$$

where:

cf_1 is the confidence in hypothesis H established by Rule 1;

cf_2 is the confidence in hypothesis H established by Rule 2;

$|cf_1|$ and $|cf_2|$ are absolute magnitudes of cf_1 and cf_2, respectively.

Thus, if we assume that

$$cf(E_1) = cf(E_2) = 1.0$$

then from Eq. (3.32) we get

$$cf_1(H, E_1) = cf(E_1) \times cf_1 = 1.0 \times 0.8 = 0.8$$
$$cf_2(H, E_2) = cf(E_2) \times cf_2 = 1.0 \times 0.6 = 0.6$$

and from Eq. (3.35) we obtain

$$cf(cf_1, cf_2) = cf_1(H, E_1) + cf_2(H, E_2) \times [1 - cf_1(H, E_1)]$$
$$= 0.8 + 0.6 \times (1 - 0.8) = 0.92$$

This example shows an incremental increase of belief in a hypothesis and also confirms our expectations.

Consider now a case when rule certainty factors have the opposite signs. Suppose that

$$cf(E_1) = 1 \text{ and } cf(E_2) = -1.0$$

then

$$cf_1(H, E_1) = 1.0 \times 0.8 = 0.8$$
$$cf_2(H, E_2) = -1.0 \times 0.6 = -0.6$$

and from Eq. (3.35) we obtain

$$cf(cf_1, cf_2) = \frac{cf_1(H, E_1) + cf_2(H, E_2)}{1 - min\left[|cf_1(H, E_1)|, |cf_2(H, E_2)|\right]} = \frac{0.8 - 0.6}{1 - min\,[0.8, 0.6]} = 0.5$$

This example shows how a combined certainty factor, or in other words net belief, is obtained when one rule, Rule 1, confirms a hypothesis but another, Rule 2, discounts it.

Let us consider now the case when rule certainty factors have negative signs. Suppose that

$$cf(E_1) = cf(E_2) = -1.0$$

then

$$cf_1(H, E_1) = -1.0 \times 0.8 = -0.8$$
$$cf_2(H, E_2) = -1.0 \times 0.6 = -0.6$$

and from Eq. (3.35) we obtain

$$cf(cf_1, cf_2) = cf_1(H, E_1) + cf_2(H, E_2) \times [1 + cf_1(H, E_1)]$$
$$= -0.8 - 0.6 \times (1 - 0.8) = -0.92$$

This example represents an incremental increase of disbelief in a hypothesis.

The certainty factors theory provides a **practical** alternative to Bayesian reasoning. The heuristic manner of combining certainty factors is different from the manner in which they would be combined if they were probabilities. The certainty theory is not 'mathematically pure' but does mimic the thinking process of a human expert.

To illustrate the evidential reasoning and the method of certainty factors propagation through a set of rules, consider again the FORECAST expert system developed in section 3.4.

3.7 FORECAST: an application of certainty factors

The expert system is required to predict whether it will rain tomorrow, or in other words to establish certainty factors for the multivalued object *tomorrow*. To simplify our task, we use the same set of rules as in section 3.4.

Knowledge base

/* FORECAST: AN APPLICATION OF CERTAINTY FACTORS

control cf

control 'threshold 0.01'

Rule: 1
if   today is rain
then   tomorrow is rain {cf 0.5}

Rule: 2
if   today is dry
then   tomorrow is dry {cf 0.5}

Rule: 3
if   today is rain
and   rainfall is low
then   tomorrow is dry {cf 0.6}

Rule: 4
if   today is rain
and   rainfall is low
and   temperature is cold
then   tomorrow is dry {cf 0.7}

Rule: 5
if   today is dry
and   temperature is warm
then   tomorrow is rain {cf 0.65}

Rule: 6
if   today is dry
and   temperature is warm
and   sky is overcast
then   tomorrow is rain {cf 0.55}

seek tomorrow

Dialogue

To apply an inexact reasoning technique based on certainty factors, the expert system prompts the user to input not only the object value but also the certainty associated with this value. For example, using the Leonardo scale from 0 to 1.0, the following dialogue might be obtained:

What is the weather today?
⇒ **rain**

Rule: 1
if   today is rain
then   tomorrow is rain {cf 0.5}

cf(tomorrow is rain, today is rain) $= cf$(today is rain) $\times cf = 1.0 \times 0.5 = 0.5$

tomorrow is rain   {0.50}

What is the rainfall today?
⇒ **low**

To what degree do you believe the rainfall is low? Enter a numeric certainty between 0 and 1.0 inclusive.
⇒ **0.8**

Rule: 3
if   today is rain
and   rainfall is low
then   tomorrow is dry {cf 0.6}

cf(tomorrow is dry, today is rain ∩ rainfall is low)
     $= min\,[cf$(today is rain), cf(rainfall is low)$] \times cf = min\,[1, 0.8] \times 0.6 = 0.48$

tomorrow is rain   {0.50}
            dry   {0.48}

What is the temperature today?
⇒ **cold**

To what degree do you believe the temperature is cold? Enter a numeric certainty between 0 and 1.0 inclusive.
⇒ **0.9**

Rule: 4
if   today is rain
and   rainfall is low
and   temperature is cold
then tomorrow is dry {cf 0.7}

cf (tomorrow is dry, today is rain ∩ rainfall is low ∩ temperature is cold)
$= min$ [cf (today is rain), cf (rainfall is low), cf (temperature is cold)] × cf
$= min$ [1, 0.8, 0.9] × 0.7 = 0.56

tomorrow is dry   {0.56}
          rain   {0.50}

cf ($cf_{Rule:3}$, $cf_{Rule:4}$) = $cf_{Rule:3}$ + $cf_{Rule:4}$ × (1 − $cf_{Rule:3}$)
                      = 0.48 + 0.56 × (1 − 0.48) = 0.77

tomorrow is dry   {0.77}
          rain   {0.50}

Now we would conclude that the probability of having a dry day tomorrow is almost certain; however, we also may expect some rain!

3.8 Comparison of Bayesian reasoning and certainty factors

In the previous sections, we outlined the two most popular techniques for uncertainty management in expert systems. Now we will compare these techniques and determine the kinds of problems that can make effective use of either Bayesian reasoning or certainty factors.

Probability theory is the oldest and best-established technique to deal with inexact knowledge and random data. It works well in such areas as forecasting and planning, where statistical data is usually available and accurate probability statements can be made.

An expert system that applied the Bayesian technique, PROSPECTOR, was developed to aid exploration geologists in their search for ore deposits. It was very successful; for example, using geological, geophysical and geochemical data, PROSPECTOR predicted the existence of molybdenum near Mount Tolman in Washington State (Campbell *et al.*, 1982). But the PROSPECTOR team could rely on valid data about known mineral deposits and reliable statistical information. The probabilities of each event were defined as well. The PROSPECTOR team also could assume the conditional independence of evidence, a constraint that must be satisfied in order to apply the Bayesian approach.

However, in many areas of possible applications of expert systems, reliable statistical information is not available or we cannot assume the conditional independence of evidence. As a result, many researchers have found the Bayesian method unsuitable for their work. For example, Shortliffe and Buchanan could not use a classical probability approach in MYCIN because the medical field often could not provide the required data (Shortliffe and Buchanan, 1975). This dissatisfaction motivated the development of the certainty factors theory.

Although the certainty factors approach lacks the mathematical correctness of the probability theory, it appears to outperform subjective Bayesian reasoning in such areas as diagnostics, particularly in medicine. In diagnostic expert systems like MYCIN, rules and certainty factors come from the expert's knowledge and his or her intuitive judgements. Certainty factors are used in cases where the probabilities are not known or are too difficult or expensive to obtain. The evidential reasoning mechanism can manage incrementally acquired evidence, the conjunction and disjunction of hypotheses, as well as evidences with different degrees of belief. Besides, the certainty factors approach provides better explanations of the control flow through a rule-based expert system.

The Bayesian approach and certainty factors are different from one another, but they share a common problem: finding an expert able to quantify personal, subjective and qualitative information. Humans are easily biased, and therefore the choice of an uncertainty management technique strongly depends on the existing domain expert.

The Bayesian method is likely to be the most appropriate if reliable statistical data exists, the knowledge engineer is able to lead, and the expert is available for serious decision-analytical conversations. In the absence of any of the specified conditions, the Bayesian approach might be too arbitrary and even biased to produce meaningful results. It should also be mentioned that the Bayesian belief propagation is of exponential complexity, and thus is impractical for large knowledge bases.

The certainty factors technique, despite the lack of a formal foundation, offers a simple approach for dealing with uncertainties in expert systems and delivers results acceptable in many applications.

3.9 Summary

In this chapter, we presented two uncertainty management techniques used in expert systems: Bayesian reasoning and certainty factors. We identified the main sources of uncertain knowledge and briefly reviewed probability theory. We considered the Bayesian method of accumulating evidence and developed a simple expert system based on the Bayesian approach. Then we examined the certainty factors theory (a popular alternative to Bayesian reasoning) and developed an expert system based on evidential reasoning. Finally, we compared

Bayesian reasoning and certainty factors, and determined appropriate areas for their applications.

The most important lessons learned in this chapter are:

- Uncertainty is the lack of exact knowledge that would allow us to reach a perfectly reliable conclusion. The main sources of uncertain knowledge in expert systems are: weak implications, imprecise language, missing data and combining the views of different experts.

- Probability theory provides an exact, mathematically correct, approach to uncertainty management in expert systems. The Bayesian rule permits us to determine the probability of a hypothesis given that some evidence has been observed.

- PROSPECTOR, an expert system for mineral exploration, was the first successful system to employ Bayesian rules of evidence to propagate uncertainties throughout the system.

- In the Bayesian approach, an expert is required to provide the prior probability of hypothesis H and values for the likelihood of sufficiency, LS, to measure belief in the hypothesis if evidence E is present, and the likelihood of necessity, LN, to measure disbelief in hypothesis H if the same evidence is missing. The Bayesian method uses rules of the following form:

    IF E is true $\{LS, LN\}$
    THEN H is true $\{prior\ probability\}$

- To employ the Bayesian approach, we must satisfy the conditional independence of evidence. We also should have reliable statistical data and define the prior probabilities for each hypothesis. As these requirements are rarely satisfied in real-world problems, only a few systems have been built based on Bayesian reasoning.

- Certainty factors theory is a popular alternative to Bayesian reasoning. The basic principles of this theory were introduced in MYCIN, a diagnostic medical expert system.

- Certainty factors theory provides a judgemental approach to uncertainty management in expert systems. An expert is required to provide a certainty factor, cf, to represent the level of belief in hypothesis H given that evidence E has been observed. The certainty factors method uses rules of the following form:

    IF E is true
    THEN H is true $\{cf\}$

- Certainty factors are used if the probabilities are not known or cannot be easily obtained. Certainty theory can manage incrementally acquired evidence, the conjunction and disjunction of hypotheses, as well as evidences with different degrees of belief.

- Both Bayesian reasoning and certainty theory share a common problem: finding an expert able to quantify subjective and qualitative information.

Questions for review

1 What is uncertainty? When can knowledge be inexact and data incomplete or inconsistent? Give an example of inexact knowledge.

2 What is probability? Describe mathematically the conditional probability of event A occurring given that event B has occurred. What is the Bayesian rule?

3 What is Bayesian reasoning? How does an expert system rank potentially true hypotheses? Give an example.

4 Why was the PROSPECTOR team able to apply the Bayesian approach as an uncertainty management technique? What requirements must be satisfied before Bayesian reasoning will be effective?

5 What are the likelihood of sufficiency and likelihood of necessity? How does an expert determine values for LS and LN?

6 What is a prior probability? Give an example of the rule representation in the expert system based on Bayesian reasoning.

7 How does a rule-based expert system propagate uncertainties using the Bayesian approach?

8 Why may conditional probabilities be inconsistent with the prior probabilities provided by the expert? Give an example of such an inconsistency.

9 Why is the certainty factors theory considered as a **practical** alternative to Bayesian reasoning? What are the measure of belief and the measure of disbelief? Define a certainty factor.

10 How does an expert system establish the net certainty for conjunctive and disjunctive rules? Give an example for each case.

11 How does an expert system combine certainty factors of two or more rules affecting the same hypothesis? Give an example.

12 Compare Bayesian reasoning and certainty factors. Which applications are most suitable for Bayesian reasoning and which for certainty factors? Why? What is a common problem in both methods?

References

Bhatnagar, R.K. and Kanal, L.N. (1986). Handling uncertain information: a review of numeric and non-numeric methods, *Uncertainty in AI*, L.N. Kanal and J.F. Lemmer, eds, Elsevier North-Holland, New York, pp. 3–26.
Bonissone, P.P. and Tong, R.M. (1985). Reasoning with uncertainty in expert systems, *International Journal on Man–Machine Studies*, 22(3), 241–250.

Burns, M. and Pearl, J. (1981). Causal and diagnostic inferences: a comparison of validity, *Organizational Behaviour and Human Performance*, 28, 379–394.

Campbell, A.N., Hollister, V.F., Duda, R.O. and Hart, P.E. (1982). Recognition of a hidden mineral deposit by an artificial intelligence program, *Science*, 217(3), 927–929.

Duda, R.O., Hart, P.E. and Nilsson, N.L. (1976). Subjective Bayesian methods for a rule-based inference system, *Proceedings of the National Computer Conference (AFIPS)*, vol. 45, pp. 1075–1082.

Duda, R.O., Gaschnig, J. and Hart, P.E. (1979). Model design in the PROSPECTOR consultant system for mineral exploration, *Expert Systems in the Microelectronic Age*, D. Michie, ed., Edinburgh University Press, Edinburgh, Scotland, pp. 153–167.

Durkin, J. (1994). *Expert Systems: Design and Development*. Prentice Hall, Englewood Cliffs, NJ.

Feller, W. (1966). *An Introduction to Probability Theory and its Applications*, vol. 2, John Wiley, New York.

Feller, W. (1968). *An Introduction to Probability Theory and its Applications*, vol. 1, 3rd edn. John Wiley, New York.

Fine, T.L. (1973). *Theories of Probability: An Examination of Foundations*. Academic Press, New York.

Firebaugh, M.W. (1989). *Artificial Intelligence: A Knowledge-based Approach*. PWS-KENT Publishing Company, Boston, MA.

Good, I.J. (1959). Kinds of probability, *Science*, 129(3347), 443–447.

Hakel, M.D. (1968). How often is often? *American Psychologist*, no. 23, 533–534.

Naylor, C. (1987). *Build Your Own Expert System*. Sigma Press, Wilmslow, Cheshire.

Ng, K.-C. and Abramson, B. (1990). Uncertainty management in expert systems, *IEEE Expert*, 5(2), 29–47.

Shortliffe, E.H. and Buchanan, B.G. (1975). A model of inexact reasoning in medicine, *Mathematical Biosciences*, 23(3/4), 351–379.

Simpson, R. (1944). The specific meanings of certain terms indicating differing degrees of frequency, *The Quarterly Journal of Speech*, no. 30, 328–330.

Stephanou, H.E. and Sage, A.P. (1987). Perspectives on imperfect information processing, *IEEE Transactions on Systems, Man, and Cybernetics*, SMC-17(5), 780–798.

Tversky, A. and Kahneman, D. (1982). Causal schemes in judgements under uncertainty, *Judgements Under Uncertainty: Heuristics and Biases*, D. Kahneman, P. Slovic and A. Tversky, eds, Cambridge University Press, New York.

Fuzzy expert systems 4

In which we present fuzzy set theory, consider how to build fuzzy expert systems and illustrate the theory through an example.

4.1 Introduction, or what is fuzzy thinking?

Experts usually rely on **common sense** when they solve problems. They also use vague and ambiguous terms. For example, an expert might say, 'Though the power transformer is **slightly** overloaded, I can keep this load for **a while**.' Other experts have no difficulties with understanding and interpreting this statement because they have the background to hearing problems described like this. However, a knowledge engineer would have difficulties providing a computer with the same level of understanding. How can we represent expert knowledge that uses vague and ambiguous terms in a computer? Can it be done at all?

This chapter attempts to answer these questions by exploring the **fuzzy set theory** (or **fuzzy logic**). We review the philosophical ideas behind fuzzy logic, study its apparatus and then consider how fuzzy logic is used in fuzzy expert systems.

Let us begin with a trivial, but still basic and essential, statement: fuzzy logic is not logic that is fuzzy, but logic that is used to describe fuzziness. Fuzzy logic is the theory of fuzzy sets, sets that calibrate vagueness. Fuzzy logic is based on the idea that all things admit of degrees. Temperature, height, speed, distance, beauty – all come on a sliding scale. The motor is running **really hot**. Tom is a **very tall** guy. Electric cars are **not very fast**. **High**-performance drives require **very rapid** dynamics and **precise** regulation. Hobart is **quite a short** distance from Melbourne. Sydney is a **beautiful** city. Such a sliding scale often makes it impossible to distinguish members of a class from non-members. When does a hill become a mountain?

Boolean or conventional logic uses sharp distinctions. It forces us to draw lines between members of a class and non-members. It makes us draw lines in the sand. For instance, we may say, 'The maximum range of an electric vehicle is short', regarding a range of 300 km or less as short, and a range greater than 300 km as long. By this standard, any electric vehicle that can cover a distance of 301 km (or 300 km and 500 m or even 300 km and 1 m) would be described as long-range. Similarly, we say Tom is tall because his height is 181 cm. If we drew a line at 180 cm, we would find that David, who is 179 cm, is small. Is David really a small man or have we just drawn an arbitrary line in the sand? Fuzzy logic makes it possible to avoid such absurdities.

Fuzzy logic reflects how people think. It attempts to model our sense of words, our decision making and our common sense. As a result, it is leading to new, more human, intelligent systems.

Fuzzy or multi-valued logic was introduced in the 1930s by Jan Lukasiewicz, a Polish logician and philosopher (Lukasiewicz, 1930). He studied the mathematical representation of fuzziness based on such terms as **tall**, **old** and **hot**. While classical logic operates with only two values, 1 (true) and 0 (false), Lukasiewicz introduced logic that extended the range of truth values to all real numbers in the interval between 0 and 1. He used a number in this interval to represent the **possibility** that a given statement was true or false. For example, the possibility that a man 181 cm tall is really tall might be set to a value of 0.86. It is **likely** that the man is tall. This work led to an inexact reasoning technique often called **possibility theory**.

Later, in 1937, Max Black, a philosopher, published a paper called 'Vagueness: an exercise in logical analysis' (Black, 1937). In this paper, he argued that a continuum implies degrees. Imagine, he said, a line of countless 'chairs'. At one end is a Chippendale. Next to it is a near-Chippendale, in fact indistinguishable from the first item. Succeeding 'chairs' are less and less chair-like, until the line ends with a log. When does a **chair** become a **log**? The concept **chair** does not permit us to draw a clear line distinguishing **chair** from **not-chair**. Max Black also stated that if a continuum is discrete, a number can be allocated to each element. This number will indicate a degree. But the question is degree of what? Black used the number to show the percentage of people who would call an element in a line of 'chairs' a **chair**; in other words, he accepted vagueness as a matter of probability.

However, Black's most important contribution was in the paper's appendix. Here he defined the first simple fuzzy set and outlined the basic ideas of fuzzy set operations.

In 1965 Lotfi Zadeh, Professor and Head of the Electrical Engineering Department at the University of California at Berkeley, published his famous paper 'Fuzzy sets'. In fact, Zadeh rediscovered fuzziness, identified and explored it, and promoted and fought for it.

Zadeh extended the work on possibility theory into a formal system of mathematical logic and, even more importantly, he introduced a new concept for applying natural language terms. This new logic for representing and manipulating fuzzy terms was called fuzzy logic, and Zadeh became the Master of fuzzy logic.

Why fuzzy?

As Zadeh said, the term is concrete, immediate and descriptive; we all know what it means. However, many people in the West were repelled by the word fuzzy, because it is usually used in a negative sense.

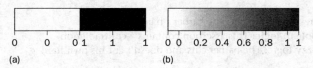

Figure 4.1 Range of logical values in Boolean and fuzzy logic: (a) Boolean logic; (b) multi-valued logic

Why logic?

Fuzziness rests on fuzzy set theory, and fuzzy logic is just a small part of that theory. However, Zadeh used the term 'fuzzy logic' in a broader sense (Zadeh, 1965):

> Fuzzy logic is determined as a set of mathematical principles for knowledge representation based on degrees of membership rather than on crisp membership of classical binary logic.

Unlike two-valued Boolean logic, fuzzy logic is **multi-valued**. It deals with **degrees of membership** and **degrees of truth**. Fuzzy logic uses the continuum of logical values between 0 (completely false) and 1 (completely true). Instead of just black and white, it employs the spectrum of colours, accepting that things can be partly true and partly false at the same time. As can be seen in Figure 4.1, fuzzy logic adds a range of logical values to Boolean logic. Classical binary logic now can be considered as a special case of multi-valued fuzzy logic.

4.2 Fuzzy sets

The concept of a **set** is fundamental to mathematics. However, our own language is the supreme expression of sets. For example, *car* indicates the set of cars. When we say *a car*, we mean one out of the set of cars.

Let X be a classical (**crisp**) set and x an element. Then the element x either belongs to X ($x \in X$) or does not belong to X ($x \notin X$). That is, classical set theory imposes a sharp boundary on this set and gives each member of the set the value of 1, and all members that are not within the set a value of 0. This is known as the **principle of dichotomy**. Let us now dispute this principle.

Consider the following classical paradoxes of logic.

1. Pythagorean School (400 BC):
    Question: Does the Cretan philosopher tell the truth when he asserts that 'All Cretans always lie'?
    Boolean logic: This assertion contains a contradiction.
    Fuzzy logic: The philosopher does and does not tell the truth!

2. Russell's Paradox:
    The barber of a village gives a hair cut only to those who do not cut their hair themselves.

Question: Who cuts the barber's hair?
Boolean logic: This assertion contains a contradiction.
Fuzzy logic: The barber cuts and doesn't cut his own hair!

Crisp set theory is governed by a logic that uses one of only two values: true or false. This logic cannot represent vague concepts, and therefore fails to give the answers on the paradoxes. The basic idea of the fuzzy set theory is that an element belongs to a fuzzy set with a certain degree of membership. Thus, a proposition is not either true or false, but may be partly true (or partly false) to any degree. This degree is usually taken as a real number in the interval [0,1].

The classical example in the fuzzy set theory is *tall men*. The elements of the fuzzy set 'tall men' are all men, but their degrees of membership depend on their height, as shown in Table 4.1. Suppose, for example, Mark at 205 cm tall is given a degree of 1, and Peter at 152 cm is given a degree of 0. All men of intermediate height have intermediate degrees. They are partly tall. Obviously, different people may have different views as to whether a given man should be considered as tall. However, our candidates for *tall men* could have the memberships presented in Table 4.1.

It can be seen that the crisp set asks the question, 'Is the man tall?' and draws a line at, say, 180 cm. *Tall men* are above this height and *not tall men* below. In contrast, the fuzzy set asks, 'How tall is the man?' The answer is the partial membership in the fuzzy set, for example Tom is 0.82 tall.

A fuzzy set is capable of providing a graceful transition across a boundary, as shown in Figure 4.2.

We might consider a few other sets such as 'very short men', 'short men', 'average men' and 'very tall men'.

In Figure 4.2 the horizontal axis represents the **universe of discourse** – the range of all possible values applicable to a chosen variable. In our case, the variable is the human height. According to this representation, the universe of men's heights consists of all tall men. However, there is often room for

Table 4.1 Degree of membership of 'tall men'

Name	Height, cm	Degree of membership	
		Crisp	Fuzzy
Chris	208	1	1.00
Mark	205	1	1.00
John	198	1	0.98
Tom	181	1	0.82
David	179	0	0.78
Mike	172	0	0.24
Bob	167	0	0.15
Steven	158	0	0.06
Bill	155	0	0.01
Peter	152	0	0.00

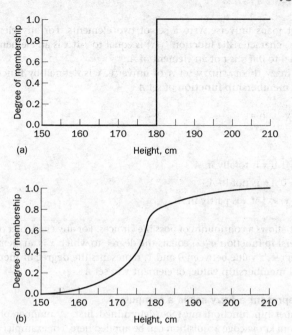

Figure 4.2   Crisp (a) and fuzzy (b) sets of 'tall men'

discretion, since the context of the universe may vary. For example, the set of 'tall men' might be part of the universe of human heights or mammal heights, or even all animal heights.

The vertical axis in Figure 4.2 represents the membership value of the fuzzy set. In our case, the fuzzy set of 'tall men' maps height values into corresponding membership values. As can be seen from Figure 4.2, David, who is 179 cm tall, which is just 2 cm less than Tom, no longer suddenly becomes a *not tall* (or *short*) man (as he would in crisp sets). Now David and other men are gradually removed from the set of 'tall men' according to the decrease of their heights.

What is a fuzzy set?

A fuzzy set can be simply defined as a set with fuzzy boundaries.

Let X be the universe of discourse and its elements be denoted as x. In classical set theory, crisp set A of X is defined as function $f_A(x)$ called the **characteristic function** of A

$$f_A(x) : X \rightarrow \{0, 1\} \tag{4.1}$$

where

$$f_A(x) = \begin{cases} 1, & \text{if } x \in A \\ 0, & \text{if } x \notin A \end{cases}$$

This set maps universe X to a set of two elements. For any element x of universe X, characteristic function $f_A(x)$ is equal to 1 if x is an element of set A, and is equal to 0 if x is not an element of A.

In the fuzzy theory, fuzzy set A of universe X is defined by function $\mu_A(x)$ called the **membership function** of set A

$$\mu_A(x) : X \rightarrow [0,1] \tag{4.2}$$

where

$\mu_A(x) = 1$ if x is totally in A;

$\mu_A(x) = 0$ if x is not in A;

$0 < \mu_A(x) < 1$ if x is partly in A.

This set allows a continuum of possible choices. For any element x of universe X, membership function $\mu_A(x)$ equals the degree to which x is an element of set A. This degree, a value between 0 and 1, represents the **degree of membership**, also called **membership value**, of element x in set A.

How to represent a fuzzy set in a computer?

The membership function must be determined first. A number of methods learned from knowledge acquisition can be applied here. For example, one of the most practical approaches for forming fuzzy sets relies on the knowledge of a single expert. The expert is asked for his or her opinion whether various elements belong to a given set. Another useful approach is to acquire knowledge from multiple experts. A new technique to form fuzzy sets was recently introduced. It is based on artificial neural networks, which learn available system operation data and then derive the fuzzy sets automatically.

Now we return to our 'tall men' example. After acquiring the knowledge for men's heights, we could produce a fuzzy set of *tall men*. In a similar manner, we could obtain fuzzy sets of *short* and *average* men. These sets are shown in Figure 4.3, along with crisp sets. The universe of discourse – the men's heights – consists of three sets: *short*, *average* and *tall men*. In fuzzy logic, as you can see, a man who is 184 cm tall is a member of the *average men* set with a degree of membership of 0.1, and, at the same time, he is also a member of the *tall men* set with a degree of 0.4. This means that a man of 184 cm tall has partial membership in multiple sets.

Now assume that universe of discourse X, also called the **reference super set**, is a crisp set containing five elements $X = \{x_1, x_2, x_3, x_4, x_5\}$. Let A be a crisp subset of X and assume that A consists of only two elements, $A = \{x_2, x_3\}$. Subset A can now be described by $A = \{(x_1, 0), (x_2, 1), (x_3, 1), (x_4, 0), (x_5, 0)\}$, that is as a set of pairs $\{x_i, \mu_A(x_i)\}$, where $\mu_A(x_i)$ is the membership function of element x_i in the subset A.

The question is whether $\mu_A(x)$ can take only two values, either 0 or 1, or any value between 0 and 1. It was also the basic question in fuzzy sets examined by Lotfi Zadeh in 1965 (Zadeh, 1965).

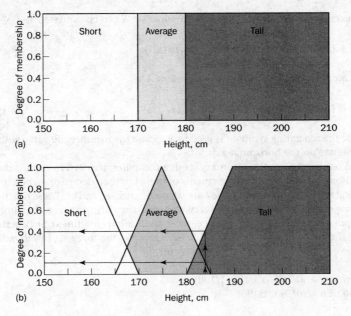

Figure 4.3 Crisp (a) and fuzzy (b) sets of short, average and tall men

If X is the reference super set and A is a subset of X, then A is said to be a fuzzy subset of X if, and only if,

$$A = \{x, \mu_A(x)\} \qquad x \in X, \mu_A(x) : X \to [0, 1] \tag{4.3}$$

In a special case, when $X \to \{0, 1\}$ is used instead of $X \to [0, 1]$, the fuzzy subset A becomes the crisp subset A.

Fuzzy and crisp sets can be also presented as shown in Figure 4.4.

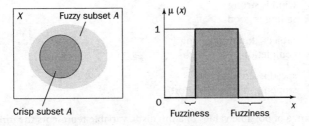

Figure 4.4 Representation of crisp and fuzzy subset of X

Fuzzy subset A of the finite reference super set X can be expressed as

$$A = \{x_1, \mu_A(x_1)\}, \{x_2, \mu_A(x_2)\}, \dots, \{x_n, \mu_A(x_n)\} \tag{4.4}$$

However, it is more convenient to represent A as

$$A = \{\mu_A(x_1)/x_1\}, \{\mu_A(x_2)/x_2\}, \dots, \{\mu_A(x_n)/x_n\}, \tag{4.5}$$

where the separating symbol / is used to associate the membership value with its coordinate on the horizontal axis.

To represent a continuous fuzzy set in a computer, we need to express it as a function and then to map the elements of the set to their degree of membership. Typical functions that can be used are sigmoid, gaussian and pi. These functions can represent the real data in fuzzy sets, but they also increase the time of computation. Therefore, in practice, most applications use **linear fit functions** similar to those shown in Figure 4.3. For example, the fuzzy set of *tall men* in Figure 4.3 can be represented as a **fit-vector,**

tall men = (0/180, 0.5/185, 1/190) or
tall men = (0/180, 1/190)

Fuzzy sets of *short* and *average men* can be also represented in a similar manner,

short men = (1/160, 0.5/165, 0/170) or
short men = (1/160, 0/170)

average men = (0/165, 1/175, 0/185)

4.3 Linguistic variables and hedges

At the root of fuzzy set theory lies the idea of linguistic variables. A linguistic variable is a fuzzy variable. For example, the statement 'John is tall' implies that the linguistic variable *John* takes the linguistic value *tall*. In fuzzy expert systems, linguistic variables are used in fuzzy rules. For example,

IF   wind is strong
THEN   sailing is good

IF   project_duration is long
THEN   completion_risk is high

IF   speed is slow
THEN   stopping_distance is short

The range of possible values of a linguistic variable represents the universe of discourse of that variable. For example, the universe of discourse of the linguistic variable *speed* might have the range between 0 and 220 km per hour and may include such fuzzy subsets as *very slow, slow, medium, fast* and *very fast*. Each fuzzy subset also represents a linguistic value of the corresponding linguistic variable.

A linguistic variable carries with it the concept of fuzzy set qualifiers, called **hedges**. Hedges are terms that modify the shape of fuzzy sets. They include adverbs such as *very, somewhat, quite, more or less* and *slightly*. Hedges can modify verbs, adjectives, adverbs or even whole sentences. They are used as

- All-purpose modifiers, such as *very, quite* or *extremely*.
- Truth values, such as *quite true* or *mostly false*.
- Probabilities, such as *likely* or *not very likely*.
- Quantifiers, such as *most, several* or *few*.
- Possibilities, such as *almost impossible* or *quite possible*.

Hedges act as operations themselves. For instance, *very* performs concentration and creates a new subset. From the set of *tall men*, it derives the subset of *very tall men*. *Extremely* serves the same purpose to a greater extent.

An operation opposite to concentration is dilation. It expands the set. *More or less* performs dilation; for example, the set of *more or less tall men* is broader than the set of *tall men*.

Hedges are useful as operations, but they can also break down continuums into fuzzy intervals. For example, the following hedges could be used to describe temperature: *very cold, moderately cold, slightly cold, neutral, slightly hot, moderately hot* and *very hot*. Obviously these fuzzy sets overlap. Hedges help to reflect human thinking, since people usually cannot distinguish between *slightly hot* and *moderately hot*.

Figure 4.5 illustrates an application of hedges. The fuzzy sets shown previously in Figure 4.3 are now modified mathematically by the hedge *very*. Consider, for example, a man who is 185 cm tall. He is a member of the *tall men* set with a degree of membership of 0.5. However, he is also a member of the set of *very tall men* with a degree of 0.15, which is *fairly* reasonable.

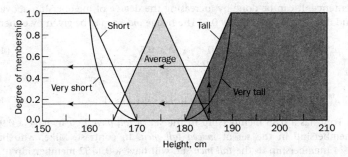

Figure 4.5 Fuzzy sets with *very* hedge

Let us now consider the hedges often used in practical applications:

- *Very,* the operation of concentration, as we mentioned above, narrows a set down and thus reduces the degree of membership of fuzzy elements. This operation can be given as a mathematical square:

$$\mu_A^{very}(x) = [\mu_A(x)]^2 \tag{4.6}$$

Hence, if Tom has a 0.86 membership in the set of *tall men,* he will have a 0.7396 membership in the set of *very tall men.*

- *Extremely* serves the same purpose as *very,* but does it to a greater extent. This operation can be performed by raising $\mu_A(x)$ to the third power:

$$\mu_A^{extremely}(x) = [\mu_A(x)]^3 \tag{4.7}$$

If Tom has a 0.86 membership in the set of *tall men,* he will have a 0.7396 membership in the set of *very tall men* and 0.6361 membership in the set of *extremely tall men.*

- *Very very* is just an extension of concentration. It can be given as a square of the operation of concentration:

$$\mu_A^{very\,very}(x) = [\mu_A^{very}(x)]^2 = [\mu_A(x)]^4 \tag{4.8}$$

For example, Tom, with a 0.86 membership in the *tall men* set and a 0.7396 membership in the *very tall men* set, will have a membership of 0.5470 in the set of *very very tall men.*

- *More or less,* the operation of dilation, expands a set and thus increases the degree of membership of fuzzy elements. This operation is presented as

$$\mu_A^{more\,or\,less}(x) = \sqrt{\mu_A(x)} \tag{4.9}$$

Hence, if Tom has a 0.86 membership in the set of *tall men,* he will have a 0.9274 membership in the set of *more or less tall men.*

- *Indeed,* the operation of intensification intensifies the meaning of the whole sentence. It can be done by increasing the degree of membership above 0.5 and decreasing those below 0.5. The hedge *indeed* may be given by either

$$\mu_A^{indeed}(x) = 2[\mu_A(x)]^2 \qquad \text{if } 0 \leqslant \mu_A(x) \leqslant 0.5 \tag{4.10}$$

or

$$\mu_A^{indeed}(x) = 1 - 2[1 - \mu_A(x)]^2 \qquad \text{if } 0.5 < \mu_A(x) \leqslant 1 \tag{4.11}$$

If Tom has a 0.86 membership in the set of *tall men,* he can have a 0.9608 membership in the set of *indeed tall men.* In contrast, Mike, who has a 0.24 membership in the *tall men* set, will have a 0.1152 membership in the *indeed tall men* set.

Table 4.2 Representation of hedges in fuzzy logic

Hedge	Mathematical expression	Graphical representation
A little	$[\mu_A(x)]^{1.3}$	
Slightly	$[\mu_A(x)]^{1.7}$	
Very	$[\mu_A(x)]^2$	
Extremely	$[\mu_A(x)]^3$	
Very very	$[\mu_A(x)]^4$	
More or less	$\sqrt{\mu_A(x)}$	
Somewhat	$\sqrt{\mu_A(x)}$	
Indeed	$2[\mu_A(x)]^2$ if $0 \leqslant \mu_A \leqslant 0.5$ $1 - 2[1 - \mu_A(x)]^2$ if $0.5 < \mu_A \leqslant 1$	

Mathematical and graphical representations of hedges are summarised in Table 4.2.

4.4 Operations of fuzzy sets

The classical set theory developed in the late 19th century by Georg Cantor describes how crisp sets can interact. These interactions are called **operations**.

Cantor's sets

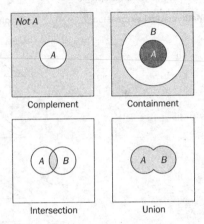

Complement   Containment

Intersection   Union

Figure 4.6   Operations on classical sets

We look at four of them: complement, containment, intersection and union. These operations are presented graphically in Figure 4.6. Let us compare operations of classical and fuzzy sets.

Complement

- Crisp sets: Who does not belong to the set?
- Fuzzy sets: How much do elements not belong to the set?

The complement of a set is an opposite of this set. For example, if we have the set of *tall men*, its complement is the set of *NOT tall men*. When we remove the tall men set from the universe of discourse, we obtain the complement. If A is the fuzzy set, its complement $\neg A$ can be found as follows:

$$\mu_{\neg A}(x) = 1 - \mu_A(x) \qquad (4.12)$$

For example, if we have a fuzzy set of *tall men*, we can easily obtain the fuzzy set of *NOT tall men*:

$$\text{tall men} = (0/180, 0.25/182.5, 0.5/185, 0.75/187.5, 1/190)$$
$$\text{NOT tall men} = (1/180, 0.75/182.5, 0.5/185, 0.25/187.5, 0/190)$$

Containment

- Crisp sets: Which sets belong to which other sets?
- Fuzzy sets: Which sets belong to other sets?

Similar to a Chinese box or Russian doll, a set can contain other sets. The smaller set is called the **subset**. For example, the set of *tall men* contains all tall men. Therefore, *very tall men* is a subset of *tall men*. However, the *tall men* set is just a subset of the set of *men*. In crisp sets, all elements of a subset entirely belong to a larger set and their membership values are equal to 1. In fuzzy sets, however, each element can belong less to the subset than to the larger set. Elements of the fuzzy subset have smaller memberships in it than in the larger set.

$$tall\ men = (0/180, 0.25/182.5, 0.50/185, 0.75/187.5, 1/190)$$
$$very\ tall\ men = (0/180, 0.06/182.5, 0.25/185, 0.56/187.5, 1/190)$$

Intersection

- Crisp sets: Which element belongs to both sets?
- Fuzzy sets: How much of the element is in both sets?

In classical set theory, an intersection between two sets contains the elements shared by these sets. If we have, for example, the set of *tall men* and the set of *fat men*, the intersection is the area where these sets overlap; that is, Tom is in the intersection only if he is tall AND fat. In fuzzy sets, however, an element may partly belong to both sets with different memberships. Thus, a fuzzy intersection is the lower membership in both sets of each element.

The fuzzy operation for creating the intersection of two fuzzy sets A and B on universe of discourse X can be obtained as

$$\mu_{A \cap B}(x) = min\,[\mu_A(x), \mu_B(x)] = \mu_A(x) \cap \mu_B(x), \quad \text{where } x \in X \tag{4.13}$$

Consider, for example, the fuzzy sets of *tall* and *average men*:

$$tall\ men = (0/165, 0/175, 0.0/180, 0.25/182.5, 0.5/185, 1/190)$$
$$average\ men = (0/165, 1/175, 0.5/180, 0.25/182.5, 0.0/185, 0/190)$$

According to Eq. (4.13), the intersection of these two sets is

$$tall\ men \cap average\ men = (0/165, 0/175, 0/180, 0.25/182.5, 0/185, 0/190)$$

or

$$tall\ men \cap average\ men = (0/180, 0.25/182.5, 0/185)$$

This solution is represented graphically in Figure 4.3.

Union

- Crisp sets: Which element belongs to either set?
- Fuzzy sets: How much of the element is in either set?

The union of two crisp sets consists of every element that falls into either set. For example, the union of *tall men* and *fat men* contains all men who are tall OR fat, that is Tom is in the union since he is tall, and it does not matter whether he is fat or not. In fuzzy sets, the union is the reverse of the intersection. That is, the union is the largest membership value of the element in either set.

The fuzzy operation for forming the union of two fuzzy sets A and B on universe X can be given as

$$\mu_{A\cup B}(x) = max\,[\mu_A(x), \mu_B(x)] = \mu_A(x) \cup \mu_B(x), \quad \text{where } x \in X \tag{4.14}$$

Consider again the fuzzy sets of *tall* and *average* men:

$$tall\ men = (0/165, 0/175, 0.0/180, 0.25/182.5, 0.5/185, 1/190)$$
$$average\ men = (0/165, 1/175, 0.5/180, 0.25/182.5, 0.0/185, 0/190)$$

According to Eq. (4.14), the union of these two sets is

$$tall\ men \cup average\ men = (0/165, 1/175, 0.5/180, 0.25/182.5, 0.5/185, 1/190)$$

Diagrams for fuzzy set operations are shown in Figure 4.7.

Crisp and fuzzy sets have the same properties; crisp sets can be considered as just a special case of fuzzy sets. Frequently used properties of fuzzy sets are described below.

Commutativity

$$A \cup B = B \cup A$$
$$A \cap B = B \cap A$$

Example:

tall men OR *short men* = *short men* OR *tall men*
tall men AND *short men* = *short men* AND *tall men*

Associativity

$$A \cup (B \cup C) = (A \cup B) \cup C$$
$$A \cap (B \cap C) = (A \cap B) \cap C$$

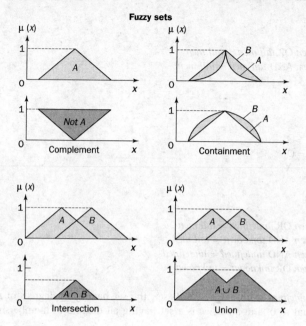

Figure 4.7 Operations of fuzzy sets

Example:

> *tall men* OR (*short men* OR *average men*) = (*tall men* OR *short men*) OR
> *average men*
> *tall men* AND (*short men* AND *average men*) = (*tall men* AND *short men*) AND
> *average men*

Distributivity

$$A \cup (B \cap C) = (A \cup B) \cap (A \cup C)$$
$$A \cap (B \cup C) = (A \cap B) \cup (A \cap C)$$

Example:

> *tall men* OR (*short men* AND *average men*) = (*tall men* OR *short men*) AND
> (*tall men* OR *average men*)
> *tall men* AND (*short men* OR *average men*) = (*tall men* AND *short men*) OR
> (*tall men* AND *average men*)

Idempotency

$$A \cup A = A$$
$$A \cap A = A$$

Example:

> *tall men* OR *tall men* = *tall men*
> *tall men* AND *tall men* = *tall men*

Identity

$$A \cup \emptyset = A$$
$$A \cap X = A$$
$$A \cap \emptyset = \emptyset$$
$$A \cup X = X$$

Example:

> *tall men* OR *undefined* = *tall men*
> *tall men* AND *unknown* = *tall men*
> *tall men* AND *undefined* = *undefined*
> *tall men* OR *unknown* = *unknown*

where *undefined* is an empty (**null**) set, the set having all degrees of membership equal to 0, and *unknown* is a set having all degrees of membership equal to 1.

Involution

$$\neg(\neg A) = A$$

Example:

> NOT (NOT *tall men*) = *tall men*

Transitivity

If $(A \subset B) \cap (B \subset C)$ then $A \subset C$
Every set contains the subsets of its subsets.

Example:

> IF (*extremely tall men* $\subset$ *very tall men*) AND (*very tall men* $\subset$ *tall men*)
> THEN (*extremely tall men* $\subset$ *tall men*)

De Morgan's Laws

$$\neg(A \cap B) = \neg A \cup \neg B$$
$$\neg(A \cup B) = \neg A \cap \neg B$$

Example:

NOT (*tall men* AND *short men*) = NOT *tall men* OR NOT *short men*
NOT (*tall men* OR *short men*) = NOT *tall men* AND NOT *short men*

Using fuzzy set operations, their properties and hedges, we can easily obtain a variety of fuzzy sets from the existing ones. For example, if we have fuzzy set A of *tall men* and fuzzy set B of *short men*, we can derive fuzzy set C of *not very tall men and not very short men* or even set D of *not very very tall and not very very short men* from the following operations:

$$\mu_C(x) = [1 - \mu_A(x)^2] \cap [1 - \mu_B(x)^2]$$
$$\mu_D(x) = [1 - \mu_A(x)^4] \cap [1 - \mu_B(x)^4]$$

Generally, we apply fuzzy operations and hedges to obtain fuzzy sets which can represent linguistic descriptions of our natural language.

4.5 Fuzzy rules

In 1973, Lotfi Zadeh published his second most influential paper (Zadeh, 1973). This paper outlined a new approach to analysis of complex systems, in which Zadeh suggested capturing human knowledge in fuzzy rules.

What is a fuzzy rule?
A fuzzy rule can be defined as a conditional statement in the form

IF x is A
THEN y is B

where x and y are linguistic variables, and A and B are linguistic values determined by fuzzy sets on the universe of discourses X and Y, respectively.

What is the difference between classical and fuzzy rules?
A classical IF-THEN rule uses binary logic, for example

Rule: 1
IF   speed is > 100
THEN   stopping_distance is long

Rule: 2
IF   speed is < 40
THEN   stopping_distance is short

The variable speed can have any numerical value between 0 and 220 km/h, but the linguistic variable *stopping_distance* can take either value *long* or *short*. In other words, classical rules are expressed in the black-and-white language of Boolean logic. However, we can also represent the stopping distance rules in a fuzzy form:

Rule: 1
IF   speed is fast
THEN   stopping_distance is long

Rule: 2
IF   speed is slow
THEN   stopping_distance is short

Here the linguistic variable *speed* also has the range (the universe of discourse) between 0 and 220 km/h, but this range includes fuzzy sets, such as *slow*, *medium* and *fast*. The universe of discourse of the linguistic variable *stopping_distance* can be between 0 and 300 m and may include such fuzzy sets as *short*, *medium* and *long*. Thus fuzzy rules relate to fuzzy sets.

Fuzzy expert systems merge the rules and consequently cut the number of rules by at least 90 per cent.

How to reason with fuzzy rules?

Fuzzy reasoning includes two distinct parts: evaluating the rule antecedent (the IF part of the rule) and *implication* or applying the result to the consequent (the THEN part of the rule).

In classical rule-based systems, if the rule antecedent is true, then the consequent is also true. In fuzzy systems, where the antecedent is a fuzzy statement, all rules fire to some extent, or in other words they fire partially. If the antecedent is true to some degree of membership, then the consequent is also true to that same degree.

Consider, for example, two fuzzy sets, 'tall men' and 'heavy men', represented in Figure 4.8.

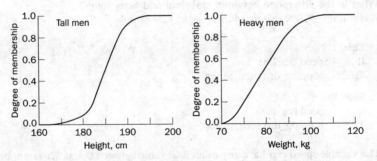

Figure 4.8 Fuzzy sets of *tall* and *heavy* men

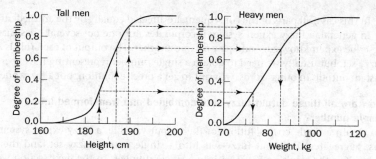

Figure 4.9 Monotonic selection of values for man weight

These fuzzy sets provide the basis for a weight estimation model. The model is based on a relationship between a man's height and his weight, which is expressed as a single fuzzy rule:

IF   height is *tall*
THEN   weight is *heavy*

The value of the output or a truth membership grade of the rule consequent can be estimated directly from a corresponding truth membership grade in the antecedent (Cox, 1999). This form of fuzzy inference uses a method called **monotonic selection**. Figure 4.9 shows how various values of men's weight are derived from different values for men's height.

Can the antecedent of a fuzzy rule have multiple parts?

As a production rule, a fuzzy rule can have multiple antecedents, for example

IF   project_duration is long
AND   project_staffing is large
AND   project_funding is inadequate
THEN   risk is high

IF   service is excellent
OR   food is delicious
THEN   tip is generous

All parts of the antecedent are calculated simultaneously and resolved in a single number, using fuzzy set operations considered in the previous section.

Can the consequent of a fuzzy rule have multiple parts?

The consequent of a fuzzy rule can also include multiple parts, for instance

IF   temperature is hot
THEN   hot_water is reduced;
        cold_water is increased

In this case, all parts of the consequent are affected equally by the antecedent.

In general, a fuzzy expert system incorporates not one but several rules that describe expert knowledge and play off one another. The output of each rule is a fuzzy set, but usually we need to obtain a single number representing the expert system output. In other words, we want to get a precise solution, not a fuzzy one.

How are all these output fuzzy sets combined and transformed into a single number?

To obtain a single crisp solution for the output variable, a fuzzy expert system first aggregates all output fuzzy sets into a single output fuzzy set, and then defuzzifies the resulting fuzzy set into a single number. In the next section we will see how the whole process works from the beginning to the end.

4.6 Fuzzy inference

Fuzzy inference can be defined as a process of mapping from a given input to an output, using the theory of fuzzy sets.

4.6.1 Mamdani-style inference

The most commonly used fuzzy inference technique is the so-called Mamdani method. In 1975, Professor Ebrahim Mamdani of London University built one of the first fuzzy systems to control a steam engine and boiler combination (Mamdani and Assilian, 1975). He applied a set of fuzzy rules supplied by experienced human operators.

The Mamdani-style fuzzy inference process is performed in four steps: fuzzification of the input variables, rule evaluation, aggregation of the rule outputs and finally defuzzification.

To see how everything fits together, we examine a simple two-input, one-output problem that includes three rules:

Rule: 1	Rule: 1
IF x is $A3$	IF *project_funding* is *adequate*
OR y is $B1$	OR *project_staffing* is *small*
THEN z is $C1$	THEN *risk* is *low*
Rule: 2	Rule: 2
IF x is $A2$	IF *project_funding* is *marginal*
AND y is $B2$	AND *project_staffing* is *large*
THEN z is $C2$	THEN *risk* is *normal*
Rule: 3	Rule: 3
IF x is $A1$	IF *project_funding* is *inadequate*
THEN z is $C3$	THEN *risk* is *high*

where x, y and z (*project funding, project staffing* and *risk*) are linguistic variables; $A1$, $A2$ and $A3$ (*inadequate, marginal* and *adequate*) are linguistic values determined by fuzzy sets on universe of discourse X (*project funding*); $B1$ and $B2$ (*small* and *large*) are linguistic values determined by fuzzy sets on universe of discourse Y (*project staffing*); $C1$, $C2$ and $C3$ (*low*, *normal* and *high*) are linguistic values determined by fuzzy sets on universe of discourse Z (*risk*).

The basic structure of Mamdani-style fuzzy inference for our problem is shown in Figure 4.10.

Step 1: *Fuzzification*

The first step is to take the crisp inputs, $x1$ and $y1$ (*project funding* and *project staffing*), and determine the degree to which these inputs belong to each of the appropriate fuzzy sets.

What is a crisp input and how is it determined?

The crisp input is always a numerical value limited to the universe of discourse. In our case, values of $x1$ and $y1$ are limited to the universe of discourses X and Y, respectively. The ranges of the universe of discourses can be determined by expert judgements. For instance, if we need to examine the risk involved in developing the 'fuzzy' project, we can ask the expert to give numbers between 0 and 100 per cent that represent the project funding and the project staffing, respectively. In other words, the expert is required to answer to what extent the project funding and the project staffing are really adequate. Of course, various fuzzy systems use a variety of different crisp inputs. While some of the inputs can be measured directly (height, weight, speed, distance, temperature, pressure, etc.), some of them can be based only on expert estimates.

Once the crisp inputs, $x1$ and $y1$, are obtained, they are fuzzified against the appropriate linguistic fuzzy sets. The crisp input $x1$ (project funding rated by the expert as 35 per cent) corresponds to the membership functions $A1$ and $A2$ (*inadequate* and *marginal*) to the degrees of 0.5 and 0.2, respectively, and the crisp input $y1$ (project staffing rated as 60 per cent) maps the membership functions $B1$ and $B2$ (*small* and *large*) to the degrees of 0.1 and 0.7, respectively. In this manner, each input is fuzzified over all the membership functions used by the fuzzy rules.

Step 2: *Rule evaluation*

The second step is to take the fuzzified inputs, $\mu_{(x=A1)} = 0.5$, $\mu_{(x=A2)} = 0.2$, $\mu_{(y=B1)} = 0.1$ and $\mu_{(y=B2)} = 0.7$, and apply them to the antecedents of the fuzzy rules. If a given fuzzy rule has multiple antecedents, the fuzzy operator (AND or OR) is used to obtain a single number that represents the result of the antecedent evaluation. This number (the truth value) is then applied to the consequent membership function.

To evaluate the disjunction of the rule antecedents, we use the OR fuzzy operation. Typically, fuzzy expert systems make use of the classical fuzzy operation *union* (4.14) shown in Figure 4.10 (Rule 1):

$$\mu_{A \cup B}(x) = max\,[\mu_A(x), \mu_B(x)]$$

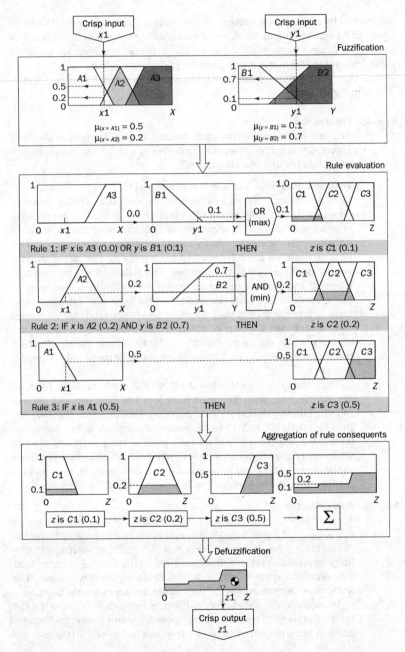

Figure 4.10 The basic structure of Mamdani-style fuzzy inference

However, the OR operation can be easily customised if necessary. For example, the MATLAB Fuzzy Logic Toolbox has two built-in OR methods: *max* and the probabilistic OR method, *probor*. The probabilistic OR, also known as the **algebraic sum**, is calculated as

$$\mu_{A\cup B}(x) = probor\,[\mu_A(x), \mu_B(x)] = \mu_A(x) + \mu_B(x) - \mu_A(x) \times \mu_B(x) \quad (4.15)$$

Similarly, in order to evaluate the conjunction of the rule antecedents, we apply the AND fuzzy operation *intersection* (4.13) also shown in Figure 4.10 (Rule 2):

$$\mu_{A\cap B}(x) = min\,[\mu_A(x), \mu_B(x)]$$

The Fuzzy Logic Toolbox also supports two AND methods: *min* and the product, *prod*. The product is calculated as

$$\mu_{A\cap B}(x) = prod\,[\mu_A(x), \mu_B(x)] = \mu_A(x) \times \mu_B(x) \quad (4.16)$$

Do different methods of the fuzzy operations produce different results?
Fuzzy researchers have proposed and applied several approaches to execute AND and OR fuzzy operators (Cox, 1999) and, of course, different methods may lead to different results. Most fuzzy packages also allow us to customise the AND and OR fuzzy operations and a user is required to make the choice.

Let us examine our rules again.

Rule: 1
IF   x is A3 (0.0)
OR   y is B1 (0.1)
THEN   z is C1 (0.1)

$$\mu_{C1}(z) = max\,[\mu_{A3}(x), \mu_{B1}(y)] = max\,[0.0, 0.1] = 0.1$$

or

$$\mu_{C1}(z) = probor\,[\mu_{A3}(x), \mu_{B1}(y)] = 0.0 + 0.1 - 0.0 \times 0.1 = 0.1$$

Rule: 2
IF   x is A2 (0.2)
AND   y is B2 (0.7)
THEN   z is C2 (0.2)

$$\mu_{C2}(z) = min\,[\mu_{A2}(x), \mu_{B2}(y)] = min\,[0.2, 0.7] = 0.2$$

or

$$\mu_{C2}(z) = prod\,[\mu_{A2}(x), \mu_{B2}(y)] = 0.2 \times 0.7 = 0.14$$

Thus, Rule 2 can be also represented as shown in Figure 4.11.

Now the result of the antecedent evaluation can be applied to the membership function of the consequent. In other words, the consequent membership function is **clipped** or **scaled** to the level of the truth value of the rule antecedent.

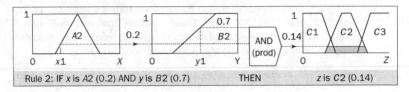

Rule 2: IF x is A2 (0.2) AND y is B2 (0.7)   THEN   z is C2 (0.14)

Figure 4.11 The AND *product* fuzzy operation

What do we mean by 'clipped or scaled'?

The most common method of correlating the rule consequent with the truth value of the rule antecedent is to simply cut the consequent membership function at the level of the antecedent truth. This method is called **clipping** or **correlation minimum**. Since the top of the membership function is sliced, the clipped fuzzy set loses some information. However, clipping is still often preferred because it involves less complex and faster mathematics, and generates an aggregated output surface that is easier to defuzzify.

While clipping is a frequently used method, **scaling** or **correlation product** offers a better approach for preserving the original shape of the fuzzy set. The original membership function of the rule consequent is adjusted by multiplying all its membership degrees by the truth value of the rule antecedent. This method, which generally loses less information, can be very useful in fuzzy expert systems.

Clipped and scaled membership functions are illustrated in Figure 4.12.

Step 3: *Aggregation of the rule outputs*

Aggregation is the process of unification of the outputs of all rules. In other words, we take the membership functions of all rule consequents previously clipped or scaled and combine them into a single fuzzy set. Thus, the input of the aggregation process is the list of clipped or scaled consequent membership functions, and the output is one fuzzy set for each output variable. Figure 4.10 shows how the output of each rule is aggregated into a single fuzzy set for the overall fuzzy output.

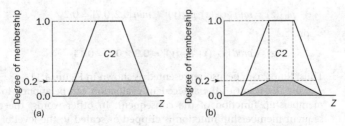

Figure 4.12 Clipped (a) and scaled (b) membership functions

Step 4: *Defuzzification*

The last step in the fuzzy inference process is defuzzification. Fuzziness helps us to evaluate the rules, but the final output of a fuzzy system has to be a crisp number. The input for the defuzzification process is the aggregate output fuzzy set and the output is a single number.

How do we defuzzify the aggregate fuzzy set?

There are several defuzzification methods (Cox, 1999), but probably the most popular one is the **centroid technique**. It finds the point where a vertical line would slice the aggregate set into two equal masses. Mathematically this **centre of gravity** (COG) can be expressed as

$$COG = \frac{\int_a^b \mu_A(x)x\,dx}{\int_a^b \mu_A(x)dx} \tag{4.17}$$

As Figure 4.13 shows, a centroid defuzzification method finds a point representing the centre of gravity of the fuzzy set, A, on the interval, $[a, b]$.

In theory, the centre of gravity is calculated over a continuum of points in the aggregate output membership function, but in practice a reasonable estimate can be obtained by calculating it over a sample of points, as shown in Figure 4.13. In this case, the following formula is applied:

$$COG = \frac{\sum_{x=a}^b \mu_A(x)x}{\sum_{x=a}^b \mu_A(x)} \tag{4.18}$$

Let us now calculate the centre of gravity for our problem. The solution is presented in Figure 4.14.

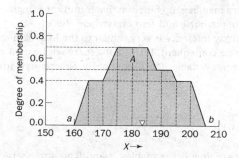

Figure 4.13   The centroid method of defuzzification

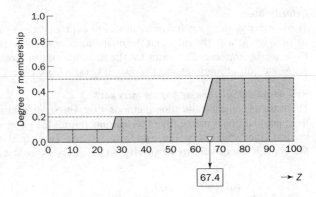

Figure 4.14 Defuzzifying the solution variable's fuzzy set

$$COG = \frac{(0+10+20) \times 0.1 + (30+40+50+60) \times 0.2 + (70+80+90+100) \times 0.5}{0.1+0.1+0.1+0.2+0.2+0.2+0.2+0.5+0.5+0.5+0.5}$$
$$= 67.4$$

Thus, the result of defuzzification, crisp output $z1$, is 67.4. It means, for instance, that the risk involved in our 'fuzzy' project is 67.4 per cent.

4.6.2 Sugeno-style inference

Mamdani-style inference, as we have just seen, requires us to find the centroid of a two-dimensional shape by integrating across a continuously varying function. In general, this process is not computationally efficient.

Could we shorten the time of fuzzy inference?

We can use a single spike, a **singleton**, as the membership function of the rule consequent. This method was first introduced by Michio Sugeno, the 'Zadeh of Japan', in 1985 (Sugeno, 1985). A singleton, or more precisely a fuzzy singleton, is a fuzzy set with a membership function that is unity at a single particular point on the universe of discourse and zero everywhere else.

Sugeno-style fuzzy inference is very similar to the Mamdani method. Sugeno changed only a rule consequent. Instead of a fuzzy set, he used a mathematical function of the input variable. The format of the Sugeno-style fuzzy rule is

IF x is A
AND y is B
THEN z is $f(x,y)$

where x, y and z are linguistic variables; A and B are fuzzy sets on universes of discourse X and Y, respectively; and $f(x,y)$ is a mathematical function.

The most commonly used **zero-order Sugeno fuzzy model** applies fuzzy rules in the following form:

IF x is A
AND y is B
THEN z is k

where k is a constant.

In this case, the output of each fuzzy rule is constant. In other words, all consequent membership functions are represented by singleton spikes. Figure 4.15 shows the fuzzy inference process for a zero-order Sugeno model. Let us compare Figure 4.15 with Figure 4.10. The similarity of the Sugeno and Mamdani methods is quite noticeable. The only distinction is that rule consequents are singletons in Sugeno's method.

How is the result, crisp output, obtained?

As you can see from Figure 4.15, the aggregation operation simply includes all the singletons. Now we can find the **weighted average** (WA) of these singletons:

$$\text{WA} = \frac{\mu(k1) \times k1 + \mu(k2) \times k2 + \mu(k3) \times k3}{\mu(k1) + \mu(k2) + \mu(k3)} = \frac{0.1 \times 20 + 0.2 \times 50 + 0.5 \times 80}{0.1 + 0.2 + 0.5} = 65$$

Thus, a zero-order Sugeno system might be sufficient for our problem's needs. Fortunately, singleton output functions satisfy the requirements of a given problem quite often.

How do we make a decision on which method to apply – Mamdani or Sugeno?

The Mamdani method is widely accepted for capturing expert knowledge. It allows us to describe the expertise in a more intuitive, more human-like manner. However, Mamdani-type fuzzy inference entails a substantial computational burden. On the other hand, the Sugeno method is computationally effective and works well with optimisation and adaptive techniques, which makes it very attractive in control problems, particularly for dynamic non-linear systems.

4.7 Building a fuzzy expert system

To illustrate the design of a fuzzy expert system, we will consider a problem of operating a service centre of spare parts (Turksen *et al.*, 1992).

A service centre keeps spare parts and repairs failed ones. A customer brings a failed item and receives a spare of the same type. Failed parts are repaired, placed on the shelf, and thus become spares. If the required spare is available on the shelf, the customer takes it and leaves the service centre. However, if there is no spare on the shelf, the customer has to wait until the needed item becomes available. The objective here is to advise a manager of the service centre on certain decision policies to keep the customers satisfied.

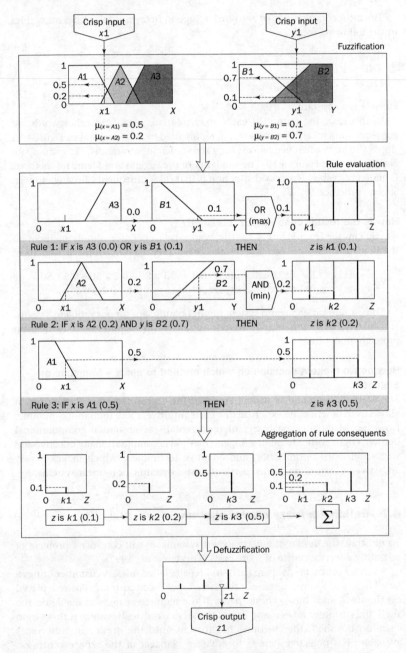

Figure 4.15　The basic structure of Sugeno-style fuzzy inference

A typical process in developing the fuzzy expert system incorporates the following steps:

1. Specify the problem and define linguistic variables.
2. Determine fuzzy sets.
3. Elicit and construct fuzzy rules.
4. Encode the fuzzy sets, fuzzy rules and procedures to perform fuzzy inference into the expert system.
5. Evaluate and tune the system.

Step 1:   *Specify the problem and define linguistic variables*

The first, and probably the most important, step in building any expert system is to specify the problem. We need to describe our problem in terms of knowledge engineering. In other words, we need to determine problem input and output variables and their ranges.

For our problem, there are four main linguistic variables: average waiting time (mean delay) m, repair utilisation factor of the service centre ρ, number of servers s and initial number of spare parts n.

The customer's average waiting time, m, is the most important criterion of the service centre's performance. The actual mean delay in service should not exceed the limits acceptable to customers.

The repair utilisation factor of the service centre, ρ, is the ratio of the customer arrival rate, λ, to the customer departure rate, μ. Magnitudes of λ and μ indicate the rates of an item's failure (failures per unit time) and repair (repairs per unit time), respectively. Apparently, the repair rate is proportional to the number of servers, s. To increase the productivity of the service centre, its manager will try to keep the repair utilisation factor as high as possible.

The number of servers, s, and the initial number of spares, n, directly affect the customer's average waiting time, and thus have a major impact on the centre's performance. By increasing s and n, we achieve lower values of the mean delay, but at the same time we increase the costs of employing new servers, building up the number of spares and expanding the inventory capacities of the service centre for additional spares.

Let us determine the initial number of spares n, given the customer's mean delay m, number of servers s and repair utilisation factor ρ. Thus, in the decision model considered here, we have three inputs – m, s and ρ – and one output – n. In other words, a manager of the service centre wants to determine the number of spares required to maintain the actual mean delay in customer service within an acceptable range.

Now we need to specify the ranges of our linguistic variables. Suppose we obtain the results shown in Table 4.3 where the intervals for m, s and n are normalised to be within the range of [0, 1] by dividing base numerical values by the corresponding maximum magnitudes. Note that, for the customer mean delay m, we consider only three

Table 4.3   Linguistic variables and their ranges

Linguistic variable: Mean delay, m		
Linguistic value	**Notation**	**Numerical range (normalised)**
Very Short	VS	[0, 0.3]
Short	S	[0.1, 0.5]
Medium	M	[0.4, 0.7]
Linguistic variable: Number of servers, s		
Linguistic value	**Notation**	**Numerical range (normalised)**
Small	S	[0, 0.35]
Medium	M	[0.30, 0.70]
Large	L	[0.60, 1]
Linguistic variable: Repair utilisation factor, ρ		
Linguistic value	**Notation**	**Numerical range**
Low	L	[0, 0.6]
Medium	M	[0.4, 0.8]
High	H	[0.6, 1]
Linguistic variable: Number of spares, n		
Linguistic value	**Notation**	**Numerical range (normalised)**
Very Small	VS	[0, 0.30]
Small	S	[0, 0.40]
Rather Small	RS	[0.25, 0.45]
Medium	M	[0.30, 0.70]
Rather Large	RL	[0.55, 0.75]
Large	L	[0.60, 1]
Very Large	VL	[0.70, 1]

linguistic values – *Very Short*, *Short* and *Medium* – because other values such as *Long* and *Very Long* are simply not practical. A manager of the service centre cannot afford to keep customers waiting longer than a medium time.

In practice, all linguistic variables, linguistic values and their ranges are usually chosen by the domain expert.

Step 2:   *Determine fuzzy sets*

Fuzzy sets can have a variety of shapes. However, a triangle or a trapezoid can often provide an adequate representation of the expert knowledge, and at the same time significantly simplifies the process of computation.

Figures 4.16 to 4.19 show the fuzzy sets for all linguistic variables used in our problem. As you may notice, one of the key points here is to maintain sufficient overlap in adjacent fuzzy sets for the fuzzy system to respond smoothly.

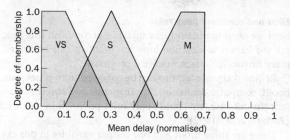

Figure 4.16 Fuzzy sets of mean delay m

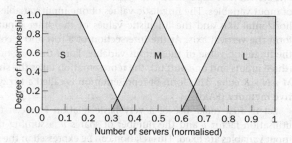

Figure 4.17 Fuzzy sets of number of servers s

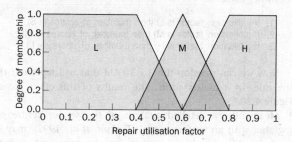

Figure 4.18 Fuzzy sets of repair utilisation factor ρ

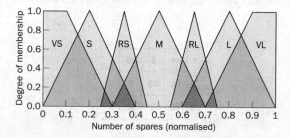

Figure 4.19 Fuzzy sets of number of spares n

Step 3: *Elicit and construct fuzzy rules*

Next we need to obtain fuzzy rules. To accomplish this task, we might ask the expert to describe how the problem can be solved using the fuzzy linguistic variables defined previously.

Required knowledge also can be collected from other sources such as books, computer databases, flow diagrams and observed human behaviour. In our case, we could apply rules provided in the research paper (Turksen *et al.*, 1992).

There are three input and one output variables in our example. It is often convenient to represent fuzzy rules in a matrix form. A two-by-one system (two inputs and one output) is depicted as an $M \times N$ matrix of input variables. The linguistic values of one input variable form the horizontal axis and the linguistic values of the other input variable form the vertical axis. At the intersection of a row and a column lies the linguistic value of the output variable. For a three-by-one system (three inputs and one output), the representation takes the shape of an $M \times N \times K$ cube. This form of representation is called a **fuzzy associative memory** (FAM).

Let us first make use of a very basic relation between the repair utilisation factor ρ and the number of spares n, assuming that other input variables are fixed. This relation can be expressed in the following form: if ρ increases, then n will not decrease. Thus we could write the following three rules:

1. If (utilisation_factor is L) then (number_of_spares is S)
2. If (utilisation_factor is M) then (number_of_spares is M)
3. If (utilisation_factor is H) then (number_of_spares is L)

Now we can develop the 3×3 FAM that will represent the rest of the rules in a matrix form. The results of this effort are shown in Figure 4.20.

Meanwhile, a detailed analysis of the service centre operation, together with an 'expert touch' (Turksen *et al.*, 1992), may enable us to derive 27 rules that represent complex relationships between all variables used in the expert system. Table 4.4 contains these rules and Figure 4.21 shows the cube ($3 \times 3 \times 3$) FAM representation.

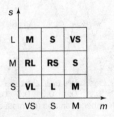

Figure 4.20 The square FAM representation

Table 4.4 The rule table

Rule	m	s	ρ	n	Rule	m	s	ρ	n	Rule	m	s	ρ	n
1	VS	S	L	VS	10	VS	S	M	S	19	VS	S	H	VL
2	S	S	L	VS	11	S	S	M	VS	20	S	S	H	L
3	M	S	L	VS	12	M	S	M	VS	21	M	S	H	M
4	VS	M	L	VS	13	VS	M	M	RS	22	VS	M	H	M
5	S	M	L	VS	14	S	M	M	S	23	S	M	H	M
6	M	M	L	VS	15	M	M	M	VS	24	M	M	H	S
7	VS	L	L	S	16	VS	L	M	M	25	VS	L	H	RL
8	S	L	L	S	17	S	L	M	RS	26	S	L	H	M
9	M	L	L	VS	18	M	L	M	S	27	M	L	H	RS

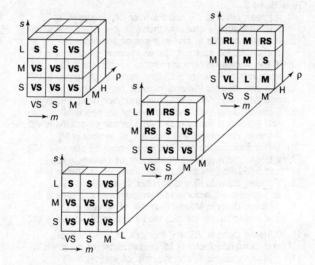

Figure 4.21 Cube FAM and sliced cube FAM representations

First we developed 12 $(3 + 3 \times 3)$ rules, but then we obtained 27 $(3 \times 3 \times 3)$ rules. If we implement both schemes, we can compare results; only the system's performance can tell us which scheme is better.

Rule Base 1
1. If (utilisation_factor is L) then (number_of_spares is S)
2. If (utilisation_factor is M) then (number_of_spares is M)
3. If (utilisation_factor is H) then (number_of_spares is L)

4. If (mean_delay is VS) and (number_of_servers is S) then (number_of_spares is VL)
5. If (mean_delay is S) and (number_of_servers is S) then (number_of_spares is L)

6. If (mean_delay is M) and (number_of_servers is S)
   then (number_of_spares is M)

7. If (mean_delay is VS) and (number_of_servers is M)
   then (number_of_spares is RL)

8. If (mean_delay is S) and (number_of_servers is M)
   then (number_of_spares is RS)

9. If (mean_delay is M) and (number_of_servers is M)
   then (number_of_spares is S)

10. If (mean_delay is VS) and (number_of_servers is L)
    then (number_of_spares is M)

11. If (mean_delay is S) and (number_of_servers is L)
    then (number_of_spares is S)

12. If (mean_delay is M) and (number_of_servers is L)
    then (number_of_spares is VS)

Rule Base 2

1. If (mean_delay is VS) and (number_of_servers is S)
   and (utilisation_factor is L) then (number_of_spares is VS)

2. If (mean_delay is S) and (number_of_servers is S)
   and (utilisation_factor is L) then (number_of_spares is VS)

3. If (mean_delay is M) and (number_of_servers is S)
   and (utilisation_factor is L) then (number_of_spares is VS)

4. If (mean_delay is VS) and (number_of_servers is M)
   and (utilisation_factor is L) then (number_of_spares is VS)

5. If (mean_delay is S) and (number_of_servers is M)
   and (utilisation_factor is L) then (number_of_spares is VS)

6. If (mean_delay is M) and (number_of_servers is M)
   and (utilisation_factor is L) then (number_of_spares is VS)

7. If (mean_delay is VS) and (number_of_servers is L)
   and (utilisation_factor is L) then (number_of_spares is S)

8. If (mean_delay is S) and (number_of_servers is L)
   and (utilisation_factor is L) then (number_of_spares is S)

9. If (mean_delay is M) and (number_of_servers is L)
   and (utilisation_factor is L) then (number_of_spares is VS)

10. If (mean_delay is VS) and (number_of_servers is S)
    and (utilisation_factor is M) then (number_of_spares is S)

11. If (mean_delay is S) and (number_of_servers is S)
    and (utilisation_factor is M) then (number_of_spares is VS)

12. If (mean_delay is M) and (number_of_servers is S)
    and (utilisation_factor is M) then (number_of_spares is VS)

13. If (mean_delay is VS) and (number_of_servers is M)
    and (utilisation_factor is M) then (number_of_spares is RS)

14. If (mean_delay is S) and (number_of_servers is M)
    and (utilisation_factor is M) then (number_of_spares is S)

15. If (mean_delay is M) and (number_of_servers is M)
    and (utilisation_factor is M) then (number_of_spares is VS)

16. If (mean_delay is VS) and (number_of_servers is L)
    and (utilisation_factor is M) then (number_of_spares is M)

17. If (mean_delay is S) and (number_of_servers is L)
    and (utilisation_factor is M) then (number_of_spares is RS)

18. If (mean_delay is M) and (number_of_servers is L)
    and (utilisation_factor is M) then (number_of_spares is S)

19. If (mean_delay is VS) and (number_of_servers is S)
    and (utilisation_factor is H) then (number_of_spares is VL)

20. If (mean_delay is S) and (number_of_servers is S)
    and (utilisation_factor is H) then (number_of_spares is L)
21. If (mean_delay is M) and (number_of_servers is S)
    and (utilisation_factor is H) then (number_of_spares is M)
22. If (mean_delay is VS) and (number_of_servers is M)
    and (utilisation_factor is H) then (number_of_spares is M)
23. If (mean_delay is S) and (number_of_servers is M)
    and (utilisation_factor is H) then (number_of_spares is M)
24. If (mean_delay is M) and (number_of_servers is M)
    and (utilisation_factor is H) then (number_of_spares is S)
25. If (mean_delay is VS) and (number_of_servers is L)
    and (utilisation_factor is H) then (number_of_spares is RL)
26. If (mean_delay is S) and (number_of_servers is L)
    and (utilisation_factor is H) then (number_of_spares is M)
27. If (mean_delay is M) and (number_of_servers is L)
    and (utilisation_factor is H) then (number_of_spares is RS)

Step 4: *Encode the fuzzy sets, fuzzy rules and procedures to perform fuzzy inference into the expert system*

The next task after defining fuzzy sets and fuzzy rules is to encode them, and thus actually build a fuzzy expert system. To accomplish this task, we may choose one of two options: to build our system using a programming language such as C or Pascal, or to apply a fuzzy logic development tool such as MATLAB Fuzzy Logic Toolbox from The MathWorks or Fuzzy Knowledge Builder from Fuzzy Systems Engineering.

Most experienced fuzzy system builders often prefer the C/C++ programming language (Li and Gupta, 1995; Cox, 1999) because it offers greater flexibility. However, for rapid developing and proto-typing a fuzzy expert system, the best choice is a fuzzy logic development tool. Such a tool usually provides complete environments for building and testing fuzzy systems. For example, the MATLAB Fuzzy Logic Toolbox has five integrated graphical editors: the fuzzy inference system editor, the rule editor, the membership function editor, the fuzzy inference viewer and the output surface viewer. All these features make designing fuzzy systems much easier. This option is also prefer-able for novices, who do not have sufficient experience in building fuzzy expert systems. When a fuzzy logic development tool is chosen, the knowledge engineer needs only to encode fuzzy rules in English-like syntax, and define membership functions graphically.

To build our fuzzy expert system, we will use one of the most popular tools, the MATLAB Fuzzy Logic Toolbox. It provides a system-atic framework for computing with fuzzy rules and graphical user interfaces. It is easy to master and convenient to use, even for new fuzzy system builders.

Step 5: *Evaluate and tune the system*

The last, and the most laborious, task is to evaluate and tune the system. We want to see whether our fuzzy system meets the requirements

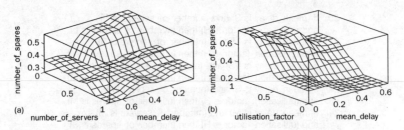

Figure 4.22 Three-dimensional plots for Rule Base 1

specified at the beginning. Several test situations depend on the mean delay, number of servers and repair utilisation factor. The Fuzzy Logic Toolbox can generate surface to help us analyse the system's perform- ance. Figure 4.22 represents three-dimensional plots for the two-input, one-output system.

But our system has three inputs and one output. Can we move beyond three dimensions? When we move beyond three dimensions, we encounter difficulties in displaying the results. Luckily, the Fuzzy Logic Toolbox has a special capability: it can generate a three- dimensional output surface by varying any two of the inputs and keeping other inputs constant. Thus we can observe the performance of our three-input, one-output system on two three-dimensional plots.

Although the fuzzy system works well, we may attempt to improve it by applying Rule Base 2. The results are shown in Figure 4.23. If we compare Figures 4.22 and 4.23, we will see the improvement.

However, even now, the expert might not be satisfied with the system performance. To improve it, he or she may suggest additional sets – *Rather Small* and *Rather Large* – on the universe of discourse *Number of servers* (as shown in Figure 4.24), and to extend the rule base according to the FAM presented in Figure 4.25. The ease with which a fuzzy system can be modified and extended permits us to follow the expert suggestions and quickly obtain results shown in Figure 4.26.

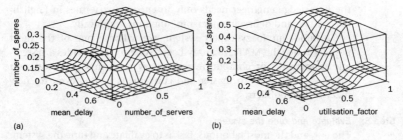

Figure 4.23 Three-dimensional plots for Rule Base 2

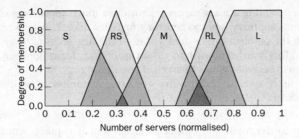

Figure 4.24   Modified fuzzy sets of number of servers *s*

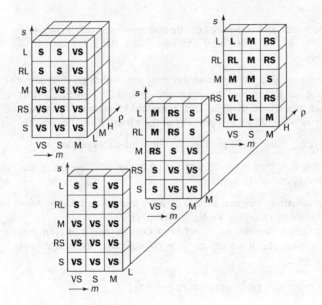

Figure 4.25   Cube FAM of Rule Base 3

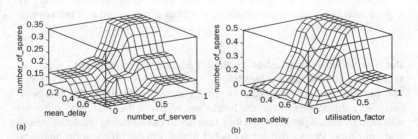

Figure 4.26   Three-dimensional plots for Rule Base 3

In general, tuning a fuzzy expert system takes much more time and effort than determining fuzzy sets and constructing fuzzy rules. Usually a reasonable solution to the problem can be achieved from the first series of fuzzy sets and fuzzy rules. This is an acknowledged advantage of fuzzy logic; however, improving the system becomes rather an art than engineering.

Tuning fuzzy systems may involve executing a number of actions in the following order:

1. Review model input and output variables, and if required redefine their ranges. Pay particular attention to the variable units. Variables used in the same domain must be measured in the same units on the universe of discourse.

2. Review the fuzzy sets, and if required define additional sets on the universe of discourse. The use of wide fuzzy sets may cause the fuzzy system to perform roughly.

3. Provide sufficient overlap between neighbouring sets. Although there is no precise method to determine the optimum amount of overlap, it is suggested that triangle-to-triangle and trapezoid-to-triangle fuzzy sets should overlap between 25 and 50 per cent of their bases (Cox, 1999).

4. Review the existing rules, and if required add new rules to the rule base.

5. Examine the rule base for opportunities to write hedge rules to capture the pathological behaviour of the system.

6. Adjust the rule execution weights. Most fuzzy logic tools allow control of the importance of rules by changing a weight multiplier.

   In the Fuzzy Logic Toolbox, all rules have a default weight of (1.0), but the user can reduce the force of any rule by adjusting its weight. For example, if we specify

   If (utilisation_factor is H) then (number_of_spares is L) (0.6)

   then the rule's force will be reduced by 40 per cent.

7. Revise shapes of the fuzzy sets. In most cases, fuzzy systems are highly tolerant of a shape approximation, and thus a system can still behave well even when the shapes of the fuzzy sets are not precisely defined.

But how about defuzzification methods? Should we try different techniques to tune our system?

The centroid technique appears to provide consistent results. This is a well-balanced method sensitive to the height and width of the total fuzzy region as well as to sparse singletons. Therefore, unless you have a strong reason to believe that your fuzzy system will behave better under other defuzzification methods, the centroid technique is recommended.

4.8 Summary

In this chapter, we introduced fuzzy logic and discussed the philosophical ideas behind it. We presented the concept of fuzzy sets, considered how to represent a fuzzy set in a computer, and examined operations on fuzzy sets. We also defined linguistic variables and hedges. Then we presented fuzzy rules and explained the main differences between these and classical rules. We explored two fuzzy inference techniques – Mamdani and Sugeno – and suggested appropriate areas for their application. Finally, we introduced the main steps in developing a fuzzy expert system, and illustrated the theory through the actual process of building and tuning a fuzzy system.

The most important lessons learned in this chapter are:

- Fuzzy logic is a logic that describes fuzziness. As fuzzy logic attempts to model humans' sense of words, decision making and common sense, it is leading to more human intelligent machines.

- Fuzzy logic was introduced by Jan Lukasiewicz in the 1920s, scrutinised by Max Black in the 1930s, and rediscovered, extended into a formal system of mathematical logic and promoted by Lotfi Zadeh in the 1960s.

- Fuzzy logic is a set of mathematical principles for knowledge representation based on degrees of membership rather than on the crisp membership of classical binary logic. Unlike two-valued Boolean logic, fuzzy logic is multi-valued.

- A fuzzy set is a set with fuzzy boundaries, such as *short*, *average* or *tall* for men's height. To represent a fuzzy set in a computer, we express it as a function and then map the elements of the set to their degree of membership. Typical membership functions used in fuzzy expert systems are triangles and trapezoids.

- A linguistic variable is used to describe a term or concept with vague or fuzzy values. These values are represented in fuzzy sets.

- Hedges are fuzzy set qualifiers used to modify the shape of fuzzy sets. They include adverbs such as *very*, *somewhat*, *quite*, *more or less* and *slightly*. Hedges perform mathematical operations of concentration by reducing the degree of membership of fuzzy elements (e.g. *very* tall men), dilation by increasing the degree of membership (e.g. *more or less* tall men) and intensification by increasing the degree of membership above 0.5 and decreasing those below 0.5 (e.g. *indeed* tall men).

- Fuzzy sets can interact. These relations are called operations. The main operations of fuzzy sets are: complement, containment, intersection and union.

- Fuzzy rules are used to capture human knowledge. A fuzzy rule is a conditional statement in the form

  IF x is A
  THEN y is B

where x and y are linguistic variables and A and B are linguistic values determined by fuzzy sets.

- Fuzzy inference is a process of mapping from a given input to an output by using the theory of fuzzy sets. The fuzzy inference process includes four steps: fuzzification of the input variables, rule evaluation, aggregation of the rule outputs and defuzzification.

- The two fuzzy inference techniques are the Mamdani and Sugeno methods. The Mamdani method is widely accepted in fuzzy expert systems for its ability to capture expert knowledge in fuzzy rules. However, Mamdani-type fuzzy inference entails a substantial computational burden.

- To improve the computational efficiency of fuzzy inference, Sugeno used a single spike, a singleton, as the membership function of the rule consequent. The Sugeno method works well with optimisation and adaptive techniques, which makes it very attractive in control, particularly for dynamic non-linear systems.

- Building a fuzzy expert system is an iterative process that involves defining fuzzy sets and fuzzy rules, evaluating and then tuning the system to meet the specified requirements.

- Tuning is the most laborious and tedious part in building a fuzzy system. It often involves adjusting existing fuzzy sets and fuzzy rules.

Questions for review

1 What is fuzzy logic? Who are the founders of fuzzy logic? Why is fuzzy logic leading to more human intelligent machines?

2 What are a fuzzy set and a membership function? What is the difference between a crisp set and a fuzzy set? Determine possible fuzzy sets on the universe of discourse for *man weights*.

3 Define a linguistic variable and its value. Give an example. How are linguistic variables used in fuzzy rules? Give a few examples of fuzzy rules.

4 What is a hedge? How do hedges modify the existing fuzzy sets? Give examples of hedges performing operations of concentration, dilation and intensification. Provide appropriate mathematical expressions and their graphical representations.

5 Define main operations of fuzzy sets. Provide examples. How are fuzzy set operations, their properties and hedges used to obtain a variety of fuzzy sets from the existing ones?

6 What is a fuzzy rule? What is the difference between classical and fuzzy rules? Give examples.

7 Define fuzzy inference. What are the main steps in the fuzzy inference process?

8 How do we evaluate multiple antecedents of fuzzy rules? Give examples. Can different methods of executing the AND and OR fuzzy operations provide different results? Why?

9   What is clipping a fuzzy set? What is scaling a fuzzy set? Which method best preserves the original shape of the fuzzy set? Why? Give an example.

10 What is defuzzification? What is the most popular defuzzification method? How do we determine the final output of a fuzzy system mathematically and graphically?

11 What are the differences between Mamdani-type and Sugeno-type fuzzy inferences? What is a singleton?

12 What are the main steps in developing a fuzzy expert system? What is the most laborious and tedious part in this process? Why?

References

Chang, A.M. and Hall, L.O. (1992). The validation of fuzzy knowledge-based systems, *Fuzzy Logic for the Management of Uncertainty*, L.A. Zadeh and J. Kacprzyk, eds, John Wiley, New York, pp. 589–604.

Black, M. (1937). Vagueness: An exercise in logical analysis, *Philosophy of Science*, 4, 427–455.

Cox, E. (1999). *The Fuzzy Systems Handbook: A Practitioner's Guide to Building, Using, and Maintaining Fuzzy Systems*, 2nd edn. Academic Press, San Diego, CA.

Li, H. and Gupta, M. (1995). *Fuzzy Logic and Intelligent Systems*. Kluwer Academic Publishers, Boston, MA.

Lukasiewicz, J. (1930). Philosophical remarks on many-valued systems of propositional logic. Reprinted in *Selected Works*, L. Borkowski, ed., Studies in Logic and the Foundations of Mathematics, North-Holland, Amsterdam, 1970, pp. 153–179.

Mamdani, E.H. and Assilian, S. (1975). An experiment in linguistic synthesis with a fuzzy logic controller, *International Journal of Man–Machine Studies*, 7(1), 1–13.

Sugeno, M. (1985). *Industrial Applications of Fuzzy Control*. North-Holland, Amsterdam.

Turksen, I.B., Tian, Y. and Berg, M. (1992). A fuzzy expert system for a service centre of spare parts, *Expert Systems with Applications*, 5, 447–464.

Zadeh, L. (1965). Fuzzy sets, *Information and Control*, 8(3), 338–353.

Zadeh, L. (1973). Outline of a new approach to the analysis of complex systems and decision processes, *IEEE Transactions on Systems, Man, and Cybernetics*, SMC-3(1), 28–44.

Bibliography

Arfi, B. (2010). *Linguistic Fuzzy-Logic Methods in Social Sciences*. Springer-Verlag, Berlin.

Bergmann, M. (2008). *An Introduction to Many-Valued and Fuzzy Logic: Semantics, Algebras, and Derivation Systems*. Cambridge University Press, New York.

Bojadziev, G. and Bojadziev, M. (2007). *Fuzzy Logic for Business, Finance, and Management*. World Scientific, Singapore.

Buckley, J.J. and Eslami, E. (2002). *An Introduction to Fuzzy Logic and Fuzzy Sets*. Physica-Verlag, Heidelberg.

Carlsson, C., Fedrizzi, M. and Fuller, R. (2004). *Fuzzy Logic in Management*, Kluwer Academic Publishers, Norwell, MA.

Engelbrecht, A.P. (2007). *Computational Intelligence: An Introduction*, 2nd edn. John Wiley, Chichester.

Galindo, J., Urrutia, A. and Piattini, M. (2006). *Fuzzy Databases: Modeling, Design and Implementation*. Idea Group Publishing, Hershey, PA.

Hájek, P. (1998). *Metamathematics of Fuzzy Logic*. Kluwer Academic Publishers, Dordrecht.

Jantzen, J. (2007). *Foundations of Fuzzy Control*. John Wiley, Chichester.

Klir, G.J. and Yuan, B. (1996). *Fuzzy Sets, Fuzzy Logic, and Fuzzy Systems: Selected Papers by Lotfi A. Zadeh*, Advances in Fuzzy Systems – Applications and Theory, vol. 6. World Scientific, Singapore.

Kosko, B. (1992). *Fuzzy Associative Memory Systems, Fuzzy Expert Systems*, A. Kandel, ed., CRC Press, Boca Raton, FL, pp. 135–164.

Kosko, B. (1993). *Fuzzy Thinking: The New Science of Fuzzy Logic*. Hyperion, New York.

Kosko, B. (1997). *Fuzzy Engineering*. Prentice Hall, Upper Saddle River, NJ.

Kosko, B. (2000). *Heaven in a Chip: Fuzzy Visions of Society and Science in the Digital Age*. Random House/Three Rivers Press, New York.

Lee, C.C. (1990). Fuzzy logic in control systems: fuzzy logic controller, Part I, *IEEE Transactions on Systems, Man, and Cybernetics*, 20(2), 404–418.

Lee, C.C. (1990). Fuzzy logic in control systems: fuzzy logic controller, Part II, *IEEE Transactions on Systems, Man, and Cybernetics*, 20(2), 419–435.

Lilly, J.H. (2010). *Fuzzy Control and Identification*. John Wiley, Chichester.

Mamdani, E.H. (1974). Application of fuzzy algorithms for control of simple dynamic plant, *Proceedings of the Institute of Electrical Engineers*, 121(12), 1585–1588.

Margaliot, M. and Langholz, G. (2004). Fuzzy control of a benchmark problem: a computing with words approach, *IEEE Transactions on Fuzzy Systems*, 12(2), 230–235.

Mendel, J. and Wu, D. (2010). *Perceptual Computing: Aiding People in Making Subjective Judgments*. John Wiley, Hoboken, NJ.

Mukaidono, M. (2001). *Fuzzy Logic for Beginners*. World Scientific, Singapore.

Negoita, C.V. (1985). *Expert Systems and Fuzzy Systems*. Benjamin/Cummings, Menlo Park, CA.

Negoita, C.V. (2000). *Fuzzy Sets*. New Falcon Publications, Tempe, AZ.

Nguyen, H.T. and Walker, E.A. (2005). *A First Course in Fuzzy Logic*, 3rd edn. Chapman & Hall/CRC Press, London.

Pedrycz, W. and Gomide, F. (2007). *Fuzzy Systems Engineering: Toward Human-Centric Computing*. John Wiley, Hoboken, NJ.

Ross, T. (2010). *Fuzzy Logic with Engineering Applications*, 3rd edn. John Wiley, Chichester.

Siler, W. and Buckley, J.J. (2004). *Fuzzy Expert Systems and Fuzzy Reasoning*. John Wiley, Hoboken, NJ.

Tanaka, K. (1996). *An Introduction to Fuzzy Logic for Practical Applications*. Springer-Verlag, New York.

Terano, T., Asai, K. and Sugeno, M. (1992). *Fuzzy Systems Theory and its Applications*. Academic Press, London.

Von Altrock, C. (1995). *Fuzzy Logic and Neuro Fuzzy Applications Explained*. Prentice Hall, Upper Saddle River, NJ.

Yager, R.R. and Filev, D.P. (1994). *Essentials of Fuzzy Modeling and Control*. John Wiley, New York.

Yager, R.R. and Zadeh, L.A. (1992). *An Introduction to Fuzzy Logic Applications in Intelligent Systems*. Kluwer Academic Publishers, Boston, MA.

Yager, R.R. and Zadeh, L.A. (1994). *Fuzzy Sets, Neural Networks and Soft Computing*. Van Nostrand Reinhold, New York.

Zadeh, L.A. (1975). The concept of a linguistic variable and its applications to approximate reasoning, Part I, *Information Sciences*, 8, 199–249.

Zadeh, L.A. (1975). The concept of a linguistic variable and its applications to approximate reasoning, Part II, *Information Sciences*, 8, 301–357.

Zadeh, L.A. (1975). The concept of a linguistic variable and its applications to approximate reasoning, Part III, *Information Sciences*, 9, 43–80.

Zadeh, L.A. (1999). From computing with numbers to computing with words – from manipulation of measurements to manipulation of perceptions, *IEEE Transactions on Circuits and Systems Science*, 45, 105–119.

Zadeh, L.A. (2004). Precisiated natural language (PNL), *AI Magazine*, 25(3), 74–91.

Zadeh, L.A. (2005). Towards a generalised theory of uncertainty (GTU): an outline, *Information Sciences – Informatics and Computer Science*, 172(1–2), 1–40.

Zadeh, L.A. (2009). Toward extended fuzzy logic – a first step, *Fuzzy Sets and Systems*, 160(21), 3175–3181.

Zimmermann, H.-J. (2001). *Fuzzy Set Theory and its Applications*, 4th edn. Kluwer Academic Publishers, Boston, MA.

Frame-based expert systems 5

In which we introduce frames as one of the common methods used for representing knowledge in expert systems, describe how to develop a frame-based expert system and illustrate the theory through an example.

5.1 Introduction, or what is a frame?

Knowledge in a computer can be represented through several techniques. In the previous chapters, we considered rules. In this chapter, we will use **frames** for the knowledge representation.

What is a frame?

A frame is a data structure with typical knowledge about a particular object or concept. Frames, first proposed by Marvin Minsky in the 1970s (Minsky, 1975), are used to capture and represent knowledge in a frame-based expert system. Boarding passes shown in Figure 5.1 represent typical frames with knowledge about airline passengers. Both frames have the same structure.

Each frame has its own name and a set of **attributes**, or **slots**, associated with it. *Name, weight, height* and *age* are slots in the frame *Person*. *Model, processor, memory* and *price* are slots in the frame *Computer*. Each attribute or slot has a value attached to it. In Figure 5.1(a), for example, slot *Carrier* has value *QANTAS AIRWAYS* and slot *Gate* has value *2*. In some cases, instead of a particular value, a slot may have a procedure that determines the value.

In expert systems, frames are often used in conjunction with production rules.

Why is it necessary to use frames?

Frames provide a natural way for the structured and concise representation of knowledge. In a single entity, a frame combines all necessary knowledge about a particular object or concept. A frame provides a means of organising knowledge in slots to describe various attributes and characteristics of the object.

Earlier we argued that many real-world problems can be naturally expressed by IF-THEN production rules. However, a rule-based expert system using a

QANTAS BOARDING PASS	
Carrier:	QANTAS AIRWAYS
Name:	MR N BLACK
Flight:	QF 612
Date:	29DEC
Seat:	23A
From:	HOBART
To:	MELBOURNE
Boarding:	0620
Gate:	2

AIR NEW ZEALAND BOARDING PASS	
Carrier:	AIR NEW ZEALAND
Name:	MRS J WHITE
Flight:	NZ 0198
Date:	23NOV
Seat:	27K
From:	MELBOURNE
To:	CHRISTCHURCH
Boarding:	1815
Gate:	4

(a)   (b)

Figure 5.1 Boarding pass frames

systematic search technique works with facts scattered throughout the entire knowledge base. It may search through the knowledge that is not relevant to a given problem, and, as a result, the search may take a great deal of time. If, for example, we are searching for knowledge about Qantas frequent flyers, then we want to avoid the search through knowledge about Air New Zealand or British Airways passengers. In this situation, we need frames to collect the relevant facts within a single structure.

Basically, frames are an application of object-oriented programming for expert systems.

What is object-oriented programming?

Object-oriented programming can be defined as a programming method that uses **objects** as a basis for analysis, design and implementation. In object-oriented programming, an object is defined as a concept, abstraction or thing with crisp boundaries and meaning for the problem at hand (Blaha and Rumbaugh, 2004). All objects have identity and are clearly distinguishable. *Michael Black, Audi 5000 Turbo, HP Pavilion P6555A* are examples of objects.

An object combines both data structure and its behaviour in a single entity. This is in sharp contrast to conventional programming, in which data structure and the program behaviour have concealed or vague connections.

Object-oriented programming offers a natural way of representing the real world in a computer, and also illuminates the problem of data dependency, which is inherent in conventional programming (Weisfeld, 2008). When programmers create an object in an object-oriented programming language, they first assign a name to the object, then determine a set of attributes to describe the object's characteristics, and at last write procedures to specify the object's behaviour.

A knowledge engineer refers to an object as a **frame**, the term introduced by Minsky, which has become the AI jargon. Today the terms are used as synonyms.

5.2 Frames as a knowledge representation technique

The concept of a frame is defined by a collection of **slots**. Each slot describes a particular attribute or operation of the frame. In many respects, a frame resembles the traditional 'record' that contains information relevant to typical entities. Slots are used to store values. A slot may contain a default value or a pointer to another frame, a set of rules or procedure by which the slot value is obtained. In general, slots may include such information as:

1. **Frame name**.

2. **Relationship of the frame to the other frames.** The frame *IBM Aptiva S35* might be a member of the class *Computer*, which in turn might belong to the class *Hardware*.

3. **Slot value.** A slot value can be symbolic, numeric or Boolean. For example, in the frames shown in Figure 5.1, the slot *Name* has symbolic values, and the slot *Gate* numeric values. Slot values can be assigned when the frame is created or during a session with the expert system.

4. **Default slot value.** The default value is taken to be true when no evidence to the contrary has been found. For example, a car frame might have four wheels and a chair frame four legs as default values in the corresponding slots.

5. **Range of the slot value.** The range of the slot value determines whether a particular object or concept complies with the stereotype requirements defined by the frame. For example, the cost of a computer might be specified between $750 and $1500.

6. **Procedural information.** A slot can have a procedure (a self-contained arbitrary piece of computer code) attached to it, which is executed if the slot value is changed or needed. There are two types of procedures often attached to slots:
   (a) *WHEN CHANGED* procedure is executed when new information is placed in the slot.
   (b) *WHEN NEEDED* procedure is executed when information is needed for the problem solving, but the slot value is unspecified.

   Such procedural attachments are often called **demons**.

Frame-based expert systems also provide an extension to the slot-value structure through the application of **facets**.

What is a facet?
A facet is a means of providing extended knowledge about an attribute of a frame. Facets are used to establish the attribute value, control end-user queries, and tell the inference engine how to process the attribute.

In general, frame-based expert systems allow us to attach value, prompt and inference facets to attributes. **Value facets** specify default and initial values of an attribute. **Prompt facets** enable the end-user to enter the attribute value on-line during a session with the expert system. And finally, **inference facets** allow us to stop the inference process when the value of a specified attribute changes.

What is the correct level of decomposition of a problem into frames, slots and facets?
Decomposition of a problem into frames, frames into slots and facets depends on the nature of the problem itself and the judgement of the knowledge engineer. There is no predefined 'correct' representation.

Figure 5.2 illustrates frames describing desktop computers. The topmost frame represents the class *Computer* and the frames below describe instances *HP Pavilion P6555A* and *Acer Aspire M3910*. Two types of attributes are used here: *string* [Str] for symbolic information and *numeric* [N] for numeric data. Note default and initial value facets attached to the slots *Optical Drive*, *Keyboard*, *Warranty* and *Stock* in the class *Desktop*. The attribute names, types, default and initial values are the properties inherited by instances.

What are the class and instances?
The word 'frame' often has a vague meaning. The frame may refer to a particular object, for example the desktop *HP Pavilion P6555A*, or to a group of similar objects. To be more precise, we will use the **instance-frame** when referring to a particular object, and the **class-frame** when referring to a group of similar objects.

A class-frame describes a group of objects with common attributes. *Animal*, *person*, *car* and *computer* are all class-frames. In AI, however, the abbreviation 'class' is often used instead of the term 'class-frame'.

Each frame in a frame-based system 'knows' its class. In other words, the frame's class is an implicit property of the frame. For example, instances in Figure 5.2 identify their class in the slot *Class*.

If objects are the basis of the frame-based systems, why bother with classes?
Grouping objects into classes helps us to represent a problem in an abstract form. Minsky himself described frames as 'data structures for representing **stereotyped** situations'. In general, we are less concerned with defining strictly and exhaustively the properties of each object, and more concerned with the salient properties typical for the entire class. Let us take, for example, the class of birds. Can a bird fly? A typical answer is yes. Almost all birds can fly, and thus we think of the ability to fly as being an essential property of the class of birds, even though there are birds, such as ostriches, which cannot fly. In other words, an eagle is a better member of the class *bird* than an ostrich because an eagle is a more typical representative of birds.

Frame-based systems support class inheritance. The fundamental idea of inheritance is that attributes of the class-frame represent things that are *typically* true for all objects in the class. However, slots in the instance-frames can be filled with actual data uniquely specified for each instance.

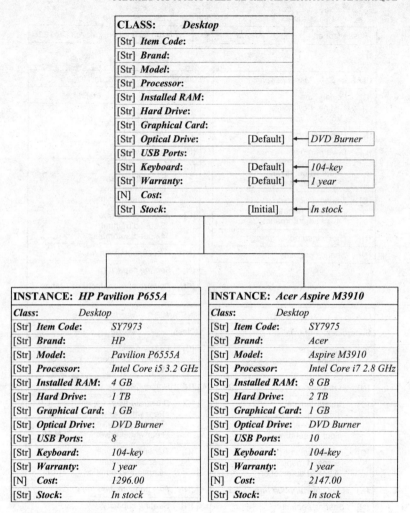

Figure 5.2 *Desktop* class and instances

Consider the simple frame structure represented in Figure 5.3. The class *Passenger car* has several attributes typical for all cars. This class is too heterogeneous to have any of the attributes filled in, even though we can place certain restrictions upon such attributes as *Engine type*, *Drivetrain type* and *Transmission type*. Note that these attributes are declared as *compound* [C]. Compound attributes can assume only one value from a group of symbolic values, for

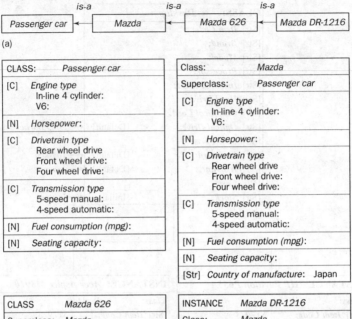

(a)

(b)

Figure 5.3 Inheritance of slot values in a simple frame structure: (a) relations of the car frames; (b) car frames and their slots

example the attribute *Engine type* can assume the value of either *In-line 4 cylinder* or *V6*, but not both.

The class *Mazda* is linked to its superclass *Passenger car* by the 'is-a' relation. The *Mazda* inherits all attributes of the superclass and also declares the attribute *Country of manufacture* with the default value *Japan* attached to it. The class *Mazda 626* introduces three additional attributes: *Model*, *Colour* and *Owner*. Finally, the instance-frame *Mazda DR-1216* inherits its country of manufacture from the *Mazda* frame, as the *Mazda 626* does, and establishes single values for all compound attributes.

Can an instance-frame overwrite attribute values inherited from the class-frame?

An instance-frame can overwrite, or in other words violate, some of the typical attribute values in the hierarchy. For example, the class *Mazda 626* has an average fuel consumption of 22 miles per gallon, but the instance *Mazda DR-1216* has a worse figure because it has done a lot of miles. Thus the *Mazda DR-1216* frame remains the instance of the class *Mazda 626*, with access to the properties further up the hierarchy, even though it violates the typical value in its class.

Relationships between frames in such a hierarchy constitute a process of specialisation. The class-frame on the top of the hierarchy represents some generic concept, class-frames further down stand for a more restricted concept and the instances are closer to exemplification.

How are objects related in a frame-based system? Is the 'is-a' relationship the only one available to us?

In general, there are three types of relationships between objects: generalisation, aggregation and association.

Generalisation denotes 'a-kind-of' or 'is-a' relationship between a superclass and its subclasses. For example, a car *is a* vehicle, or, in other words, *Car* represents a subclass of the more general superclass *Vehicle*. Each subclass inherits all features of the superclass.

Aggregation is 'a-part-of' or 'part-whole' relationship in which several subclasses representing **components** are associated with a superclass representing a **whole**. For example, an engine is *a part of* a car.

Association describes some semantic relationship between different classes which are unrelated otherwise. For example, Mr Black owns a house, a car and a computer. Such classes as *House*, *Car* and *Computer* are mutually independent, but they are linked with the frame *Mr Black* through the semantic association.

Unlike generalisation and aggregation relationships, associations usually appear as verbs and are inherently bidirectional.

Does a computer own Mr Black? Of course, the name of a bidirectional association reads in a particular direction (Mr Black *owns* a computer), but this direction can be changed to the opposite. The inverse of *owns* is *belongs to*, and thus we can anticipate that a computer *belongs to* Mr Black. In fact, both directions are equally meaningful and refer to the same association.

Figure 5.4 illustrates all three types of relationships between different objects.

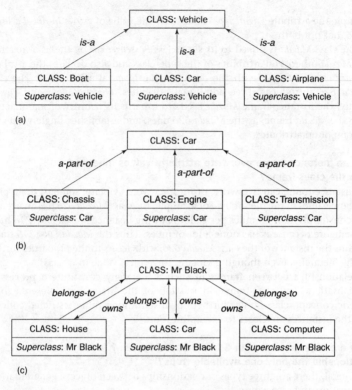

Figure 5.4   Three types of relationships among objects: (a) generalisation;
(b) aggregation; (c) association

5.3   Inheritance in frame-based systems

Inheritance is an essential feature of frame-based systems. Inheritance can be defined as the process by which all characteristics of a class-frame are assumed by the instance-frame.

A common use of inheritance is to impose default features on all instance-frames. We can create just one class-frame that contains generic characteristics of some object or concept, and then obtain several instance-frames without encoding the class-level characteristics.

A hierarchical arrangement of a frame-based system can be viewed as a tree that is turned over. The highest level of abstraction is represented at the top by the root of the tree. Branches below the root illustrate lower levels of abstraction, and leaves at the bottom appear as instance-frames. Each frame inherits characteristics of all related frames at the higher levels.

Figure 5.5 shows a hierarchy of frames representing zero-emission (ZE) vehicles. The root, *ZE vehicle*, has three branches: *Electric vehicle*, *Solar vehicle*

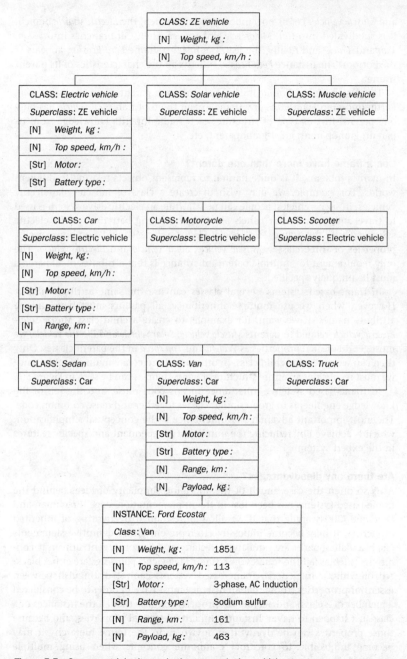

Figure 5.5 One-parent inheritance in the zero-emission vehicle structure

and *Muscle vehicle*. Let us now follow just one branch, the *Electric vehicle* branch. It is subdivided into *Car*, *Motorcycle* and *Scooter*. Then *Car* branches into *Sedan*, *Van* and *Truck*, and finally, the leaf, the instance-frame *Ford Ecostar*, appears at the bottom. The instance *Ford Ecostar* inherits all the characteristics of its **parent frame**.

The instance *Ford Ecostar* indeed has only one parent, the class-frame *Van*. Furthermore, in Figure 5.5, any frame except the root frame *ZE vehicle* has only one parent. In this type of structure, each frame inherits knowledge from its parent, grandparent, great-grandparent, etc.

Can a frame have more than one parent?

In many problems, it is quite natural to represent objects relating to different worlds. For example, we may wish to create a class of muscle-solar-electric vehicles. In such vehicles, people can pedal, while an electric drive system is used to travel uphill, and solar panels assist in recharging batteries for the electric system. Thus, the frame *Muscle-Solar-Electric vehicle* should combine specific properties of three classes, *Muscle vehicle*, *Solar vehicle* and *Electric vehicle*. The only requirement for multiple parent inheritance is that attributes of all parents must be uniquely specified.

In frame-based systems, several classes can use the same attribute names. However, when we use multiple inheritance, all parents must have unique attribute names. If we want, for example, to create a child class *Muscle-Solar-Electric vehicle* related to parents *Muscle vehicle*, *Solar vehicle* and *Electric vehicle*, we must get rid of such properties as *Weight* and *Top speed* in the parent classes. Only then can we create the child class. In other words, to create multiple inheritance we must reconsider an entire structure of our system, as can be seen in Figure 5.6.

In frame-based systems, inheritance means code reuse, and the job of the knowledge engineer is to group similar classes together and reuse common code. The most important advantage of inheritance is the conceptual simplification, which is achieved by reducing the number of independent and specific features in the expert system.

Are there any disadvantages?

As is so often the case, much of the appealing simplicity of ideas behind the frame-based systems has been lost in the implementation stage. Brachman and Levesque (2004) argue that if we allow unrestrained overwriting of inherited properties, it may become impossible to represent either definitive statements (such as 'all squares are equilateral rectangles') or contingent universal conditions (such as 'all the squares on Kasimir Malevich's paintings are either black, red or white'). In general, frame-based systems cannot distinguish between **essential properties** (those that an instance must have in order to be considered a member of a class) and **accidental properties** (those that all the instances of a class just happen to have). Instances inherit all **typical** properties, and because those properties can be overwritten anywhere in the frame hierarchy it may become impossible to construct composite concepts when using multiple inheritance.

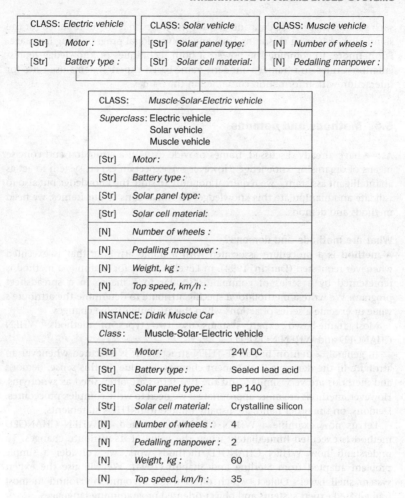

Figure 5.6   Multiple inheritance

This appears to undermine the whole idea of the frame knowledge representation. However, frames offer us a powerful tool for combining declarative and procedural knowledge, although they leave the knowledge engineer with difficult decisions to make about the hierarchical structure of the system and its inheritance paths. Appeals to so-called 'typical' properties do not always work, because they may lead us to unexpected results. Thus, although we may use frames to represent the fact that an ostrich is a bird, it is certainly not a typical bird, in the way that an eagle is. Frame-based expert systems, such as Level5 Object, provide no safeguards against creating incoherent structures. However, such systems do provide data and control structures that are more suited for the simulation of human reasoning than any conventional programming language. Furthermore, to combine the power of both techniques of knowledge representation – rules and frames – modern frame-based expert systems use rules for interaction with information contained in the frames.

5.4 Methods and demons

As we have already discussed, frames provide us with a structural and concise means of organising knowledge. However, we expect an expert system to act as an intelligent assistant – we require it not only to store the knowledge but also to validate and manipulate this knowledge. To add actions to our frames, we need methods and demons.

What are methods and demons?
A **method** is a procedure associated with a frame attribute that is executed whenever requested (Durkin, 1994). In Level5 Object, for example, a method is represented by a series of commands similar to a macro in a spreadsheet program. We write a method for a specific attribute to determine the attribute's value or execute a series of actions when the attribute's value changes.

Most frame-based expert systems use two types of methods: WHEN CHANGED and WHEN NEEDED.

In general, a **demon** has an IF-THEN structure. It is executed whenever an attribute in the demon's IF statement changes its value. In this sense, demons and methods are very similar, and the two terms are often used as synonyms. However, methods are more appropriate if we need to write complex procedures. Demons, on the other hand, are usually limited to IF-THEN statements.

Let us now examine a WHEN CHANGED method. A WHEN CHANGED method is executed immediately when the value of its attribute changes. To understand how WHEN CHANGED methods work, we consider a simple problem adapted from Sterling and Shapiro (1994). We will use the expert system shell Level5 Object, which offers features commonly found in most frame-based expert systems and object-oriented programming languages.

The expert system is required to assist a loan officer in evaluating credit requests from small business ventures. A credit request is to be classified into one of three categories, 'Give credit', 'Deny credit' or 'Consult a superior', based on the collateral and financial rating of the business, and the bank's expected yield from the loan. When a loan officer provides a qualitative rating of the expected yield from the loan, the expert system compares the business collateral with the amount of credit requested, evaluates a financial rating based on a weighted sum of the business's net worth to assets, last year's sales growth, gross profit on sales and short-term debt to sales, and finally determines a category for the credit request.

The expert system is expected to provide details of any business venture and evaluate the credit request for the business selected by the user (a loan officer).

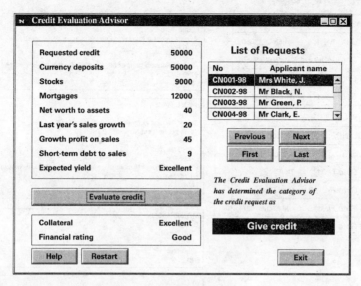

Figure 5.7 Input display for the request selection

The input display for the request selection is shown in Figure 5.7. The data on the display changes depending on which business is selected.

The class *Action Data*, shown in Figure 5.8, is used to control the input display. The user can move to the next, previous, first or last request in the list of requests and examine the business data. The WHEN CHANGED methods here allow us to advance through a list of requests. Note that all attributes in Figure 5.8 are declared as *simple* [S]. Simple attributes can assume either a value of TRUE or FALSE. Let us examine the WHEN CHANGED method attached to the attribute *Goto Next*.

How does this method work?

In Level5 Object, any method begins with the reserved words WHEN CHANGED or WHEN NEEDED, which are followed by the reserved word BEGIN and a series of commands to be executed. The reserved word END completes a method. To refer to a particular attribute in a method, we must specify the class name as well as the attribute name. The syntax is

    <attribute name> OF <class name>

For example, the statement *Goto Next OF Action Data* refers to the attribute *Goto Next* of the class *Action Data*.

The *Next* pushbutton on the input display is attached to the attribute *Goto Next* of the class *Action Data*. When we select this pushbutton at run time, the attribute *Goto Next* receives a value of TRUE, causing the WHEN CHANGED method attached to it to execute. The method's first command assigns the

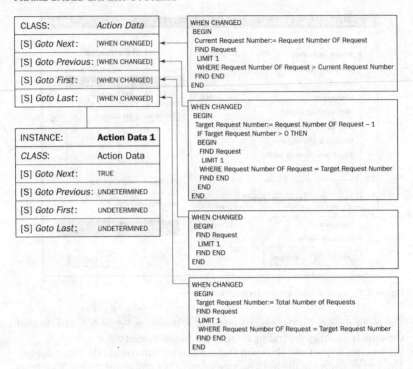

CLASS:	Action Data
[S] *Goto Next*:	[WHEN CHANGED]
[S] *Goto Previous*:	[WHEN CHANGED]
[S] *Goto First*:	[WHEN CHANGED]
[S] *Goto Last*:	[WHEN CHANGED]

```
WHEN CHANGED
BEGIN
  Current Request Number:= Request Number OF Request
  FIND Request
  LIMIT 1
    WHERE Request Number OF Request > Current Request Number
  FIND END
END
```

INSTANCE:	**Action Data 1**
CLASS:	Action Data
[S] *Goto Next*:	TRUE
[S] *Goto Previous*:	UNDETERMINED
[S] *Goto First*:	UNDETERMINED
[S] *Goto Last*:	UNDETERMINED

```
WHEN CHANGED
BEGIN
  Target Request Number:= Request Number OF Request - 1
  IF Target Request Number > 0 THEN
  BEGIN
    FIND Request
    LIMIT 1
      WHERE Request Number OF Request = Target Request Number
    FIND END
  END
END
```

```
WHEN CHANGED
BEGIN
  FIND Request
  LIMIT 1
  FIND END
END
```

```
WHEN CHANGED
BEGIN
  Target Request Number:= Total Number of Requests
  FIND Request
  LIMIT 1
    WHERE Request Number OF Request = Target Request Number
  FIND END
END
```

Figure 5.8 The class *Action Data* and WHEN CHANGED methods

number of the currently selected instance of the class *Request* to the attribute *Current Request Number*, which is used as a reference point. The FIND command uses the number stored in *Current Request Number* to determine the next request in the list. The LIMIT 1 command tells Level5 Object to find the first instance that matches the search condition. The WHERE clause

WHERE Request Number OF Request > Current Request Number

locates the first instance of the class *Request* whose number is greater than the value of *Current Request Number*. The request list is maintained in increasing order to ensure that the proper instance is retrieved. If, for example, the current instance number is 6, then the FIND command will retrieve the instance with the number 7.

Let us now consider the class *Request* and its instances represented in Figure 5.9. The instances, *Request 1* and *Request 2*, have the same attributes as the class *Request*, but each instance holds specific values for these attributes. To show the attribute values on the input display, we have to create value-boxes (display items that show data) and then attach these value-boxes to the appropriate attributes. When we run the application, the value-boxes show the attribute values of the

CLASS: *Request*	
[Str]	*Applicant's name:*
[Str]	*Application no.:*
[N]	*Requested credit:*
[N]	*Currency deposits:*
[N]	*Stocks:*
[N]	*Mortgages:*
[N]	*Net worth to assets:*
[N]	*Last year's sales growth:*
[N]	*Gross profits on sales:*
[N]	*Short-term debt to sales:*
[C]	*Expected yield:* Excellent: Reasonable: Poor:
[N]	*Request Number:*

INSTANCE: **Request 1**	
CLASS: *Request*	
[Str] *Applicant's name:*	Mrs White, J.
[Str] *Application no.:*	CN001-98
[N] *Requested credit:*	50000
[N] *Currency deposits:*	50000
[N] *Stocks:*	9000
[N] *Mortgages:*	12000
[N] *Net worth to assets:*	40
[N] *Last year's sales growth:*	20
[N] *Gross profits on sales:*	45
[N] *Short-term debt to sales:*	9
[C] *Expected yield:* Excellent: TRUE Reasonable: FALSE Poor: FALSE	
[N] *Request Number:*	1

INSTANCE: **Request 2**	
CLASS: *Request*	
[Str] *Applicant's name:*	Mr Black, N.
[Str] *Application no.:*	CN002-98
[N] *Requested credit:*	75000
[N] *Currency deposits:*	45000
[N] *Stocks:*	10000
[N] *Mortgages:*	20000
[N] *Net worth to assets:*	45
[N] *Last year's sales growth:*	25
[N] *Gross profits on sales:*	35
[N] *Short-term debt to sales:*	10
[C] *Expected yield:* Excellent: FALSE Reasonable: TRUE Poor: FALSE	
[N] *Request Number:*	2

Figure 5.9 Class *Request* and its instances

currently selected instance of the class *Request* and WHEN CHANGED methods cause actions to occur.

When are WHEN NEEDED methods to be used?
In many applications, an attribute is assigned to some initial or default value. However, in some applications, a WHEN NEEDED method can be used to obtain the attribute value only when it is needed. In other words, a WHEN NEEDED method is executed when information associated with a particular attribute is needed for solving the problem, but the attribute value is undetermined. We will return to this method when we discuss rules for our credit evaluation example.

5.5 Interaction of frames and rules

Most frame-based expert systems allow us to use a set of rules to evaluate information contained in frames.

Are there any specific differences between rules used in rule-based expert systems and those used in frame-based systems?
Every rule has an IF-THEN structure, and every rule relates given information or facts in its IF part to some action in its THEN part. In this sense, there are no differences between rules used in a rule-based expert system and those used in a frame-based system. However, in frame-based systems, rules often use **pattern matching** clauses. These clauses contain variables that are used for finding matching conditions among all instance-frames.

How does an inference engine work in a frame-based system? What causes rules to fire?
Let us again compare rule-based and frame-based expert systems. In a rule-based expert system, the inference engine links the rules contained in the knowledge base with data given in the database. When the goal is set up – or in other words when an expert system receives the instruction to determine a value for the specified object – the inference engine searches the knowledge base to find a rule that has the goal in its consequent (THEN part). If such a rule is found and its antecedent (IF part) matches data in the database, the rule is fired and the specified object, the goal, obtains its value. If no rules are found that can derive a value for the goal, the system queries the user to supply that value.

In a frame-based system, the inference engine also searches for the goal, or in other terms for the specified attribute, until its value is obtained.

In a rule-based expert system, the goal is defined for the rule base. In a frame-based system, rules play an auxiliary role. Frames represent here a major source of knowledge, and both methods and demons are used to add actions to the frames. Thus, we might expect that the goal in a frame-based system can be established either in a method or in a demon. Let us return to our credit evaluation example.

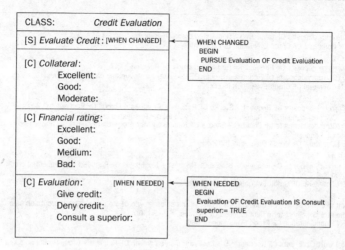

CLASS:	Credit Evaluation

[S] *Evaluate Credit* : [WHEN CHANGED]

```
WHEN CHANGED
BEGIN
    PURSUE Evaluation OF Credit Evaluation
END
```

[C] *Collateral* :
    Excellent:
    Good:
    Moderate:

[C] *Financial rating* :
    Excellent:
    Good:
    Medium:
    Bad:

[C] *Evaluation* :   [WHEN NEEDED]
    Give credit:
    Deny credit:
    Consult a superior:

```
WHEN NEEDED
BEGIN
    Evaluation OF Credit Evaluation IS Consult
    superior:= TRUE
END
```

Figure 5.10 The *Credit Evaluation* class, WHEN CHANGED and WHEN NEEDED methods

Suppose we want to evaluate the credit request selected by the user. The expert system is expected to begin the evaluation when the user clicks on the *Evaluate Credit* pushbutton on the input display. This pushbutton is attached to the attribute *Evaluate Credit* of the class *Credit Evaluation* shown in Figure 5.10. The attribute *Evaluate Credit* has the WHEN CHANGED method attached to it, and when we select the *Evaluate Credit* pushbutton at run time, the attribute *Evaluate Credit* receives a new value, a value of TRUE. This change causes the WHEN CHANGED method to execute. The PURSUE command tells *Level5 Object* to establish the value of the attribute *Evaluation* of the class *Credit Evaluation*. A simple set of rules shown in Figure 5.11 is used to determine the attribute's value.

How does the inference engine work here?

Based on the goal, *Evaluation OF Credit Evaluation*, the inference engine finds those rules whose consequents contain the goal of interest and examines them one at a time in the order in which they appear in the rule base. That is, the inference engine starts with RULE 9 and attempts to establish whether the attribute *Evaluation* receives the *Give credit* value. This is done by examining the validity of each antecedent of the rule. In other words, the inference engine attempts to determine first whether the attribute *Collateral* has the value of *Excellent*, and next whether the attribute *Financial rating* is *Excellent*. To determine whether *Collateral OF Credit Evaluation* is *Excellent*, the inference engine examines RULE 1 and RULE 2, and to determine whether *Financial rating OF Credit Evaluation* is *Excellent*, it looks at RULE 8. If all of the rule antecedents are valid, then the inference engine will conclude that *Evaluation OF Credit Evaluation* is *Give credit*. However, if any of the antecedents are invalid, then the conclusion is invalid. In this case, the inference engine will examine the next rule, RULE 10, which can establish a value for the attribute *Evaluation*.

RULE 1
IF Currency deposits OF Request >= Requested credit OF Request
THEN Collateral OF Credit Evaluation IS Excellent

RULE 2
IF Currency deposits OF Request >= Requested credit OF Request * 0.7
AND (Currency deposits OF Request + Stocks OF Request) >= Requested credit OF Request
THEN Collateral OF Credit Evaluation IS Excellent

RULE 3
IF (Currency deposits OF Request + Stocks OF Request) > Requested credit OF Request * 0.6
AND (Currency deposits OF Request + Stocks OF Request) < Requested credit OF Request * 0.7
AND (Currency deposits OF Request + Stocks OF Request + Mortgages OF Request) >= Requested credit OF Request
THEN Collateral OF Credit Evaluation IS Good

RULE 4
IF (Currency deposits OF Request + Stocks OF Request + Mortgages OF Request) <= Requested credit OF Request
THEN Collateral OF Credit Evaluation IS Moderate

RULE 5
IF Net worth to assets OF Request * 5 + Last year's sales growth OF Request + Gross profits on sales OF Request * 5 + Short term debt to sales OF Request * 2 <= -500
THEN Financial rating OF Credit Evaluation IS Bad

RULE 6
IF Net worth to assets OF Request * 5 + Last year's sales growth OF Request + Gross Profits on sales OF Request * 5 + Short term debt to sales OF Request * 2 >= -500
AND Net worth to assets OF Request * 5 + Last year's sales growth OF Request + Gross profits on sales OF Request * 5 + Short term debt to sales OF Request * 2 <= 150
THEN Financial rating OF Credit Evaluation IS Medium

RULE 7
IF Net worth to assets OF Request * 5 + Last year's sales growth OF Request + Gross Profits on sales OF Request * 5 + Short term debt to sales OF Request * 2 >= 150
AND Net worth to assets OF Request * 5 + Last year's sales growth OF Request + Gross profits on sales OF Request * 5 + Short term debt to sales OF Request * 2 <= 1000
THEN Financial rating OF Credit Evaluation IS Good

RULE 8
IF Net worth to assets OF Request * 5 + Last year's sales growth OF Request + Gross Profits on sales OF Request * 5 + Short term debt to sales OF Request * 2 > 1000
THEN Financial rating OF Credit Evaluation IS Excellent

RULE 9
IF Collateral OF Credit Evaluation IS Excellent
AND Financial rating OF Credit Evaluation IS Excellent
THEN Evaluation OF Credit Evaluation IS Give Credit

RULE 10
IF Collateral OF Credit Evaluation IS Excellent
AND Financial rating OF Credit Evaluation IS Good
THEN Evaluation OF Credit Evaluation IS Give Credit

RULE 11
IF Collateral OF Credit Evaluation IS Moderate
AND Financial rating OF Credit Evaluation IS Medium
THEN Evaluation OF Credit Evaluation IS Deny Credit

RULE 12
IF Collateral OF Credit Evaluation IS Moderate
AND Financial rating OF Credit Evaluation IS Bad
THEN Evaluation OF Credit Evaluation IS Deny Credit

Figure 5.11 Rules for credit evaluation

What happens if *Collateral OF Credit Evaluation* is *Good*?

Based on the set of rules provided for credit evaluation, the inference engine cannot establish the value of the attribute *Evaluation* in some cases. This is especially true when the collateral is good and the financial rating of the business is excellent or good. In fact, if we have a look at Figure 5.10, we find cases that are not represented in the rule base. However, it is not necessary always to rely on a set of rules. We can use the WHEN NEEDED method to establish the attribute value.

The WHEN NEEDED method shown in Figure 5.10 is attached to the attribute *Evaluation*. The inference engine executes this method when it needs to determine the value of *Evaluation*. When the WHEN NEEDED method is executed, the attribute *Evaluation* receives the value *Consult a superior*.

How does the inference engine know where, and in what order, to obtain the value of an attribute?
In our case, if the WHEN NEEDED method were executed first, the attribute *Evaluation* would always receive the value *Consult a superior*, and no rules would ever be fired. Thus, the inference engine has to obtain the value from the WHEN NEEDED method only if it has not been determined from the rule base. In other words, the search order for the attribute value has to be determined first. It can be done, for example, by means of the SEARCH ORDER facet attached to an attribute that tells the inference engine where, and in what order, to obtain the value of this attribute.

In Level5 Object, a search order can be specified for every attribute, and in our credit evaluation example, we set the search order for the *Evaluation* value to RULES, WHEN NEEDED. It makes certain that the inference engine starts the search from the rule base.

5.6 Buy Smart: a frame-based expert system

To illustrate the ideas discussed above, we consider a simple frame-based expert system, Buy Smart, which advises property buyers.

We will review the main steps in developing frame-based systems, and show how to use methods and demons to bring frames to life. To aid us in this effort we will use the Level5 Object expert system shell.

Are there any differences between the main steps in building a rule-based expert system and a frame-based one?
The basic steps are essentially the same. First, the knowledge engineer needs to obtain a general understanding of the problem and the overall knowledge structure. He or she then decides which expert system tool to use for developing a prototype system. Then the knowledge engineer actually creates the knowledge base and tests it by running a number of consultations. And finally, the expert system is expanded, tested and revised until it does what the user wants it to do.

The principal difference between the design of a rule-based expert system and a frame-based one lies in how the knowledge is viewed and represented in the system.

In a rule-based system, a set of rules represents the domain knowledge useful for problem solving. Each rule captures some heuristic of the problem, and each new rule adds some new knowledge and thus makes the system smarter. The rule-based system can easily be modified by changing, adding or subtracting rules.

In a frame-based system, the problem is viewed in a different manner. Here, the overall hierarchical structure of the knowledge is decided first. Classes and their attributes are identified, and hierarchical relationships between frames are established. The architecture of a frame-based system should not only provide a natural description of the problem, but also allow us to add actions to the frames through methods and demons.

The development of a frame-based system typically involves the following steps:

1. Specify the problem and define the scope of the system.
2. Determine classes and their attributes.
3. Define instances.
4. Design displays.
5. Define WHEN CHANGED and WHEN NEEDED methods, and demons.
6. Define rules.
7. Evaluate and expand the system.

Step 1: *Specify the problem and define the scope of the system*

In our Buy Smart example, we start by collecting some information about properties for sale in our region. We can identify relevant details such as the property type, location, number of bedrooms and bathrooms and, of course, the property price. We also should provide a short description and a nice photo for each property.

We expect that some of the properties will be sold and new properties will appear on the market. Thus, we need to build a database that can be easily modified and then accessed from the expert system. Level5 Object allows us to access, modify, delete and perform other actions on data within a dBASE III database.

Can we store descriptions and pictures of the properties within a database?

Property descriptions and pictures should be stored separately, descriptions as text files (*.txt) and pictures as bit-map files (*.bmp). If we then set up a display that includes a text-box and a picture-box, we will be able to view a property description and its picture in this display by reading the text file into the text-box and the bit-map file into the picture-box, respectively.

Now we create an external database file, *house.dbf*, using dBASE III or Microsoft Excel, as shown in Table 5.1.

The next step is to list all possible queries we might think of:

- What is the maximum amount you want to spend on a property?
- What type of property do you prefer?
- Which suburb would you like to live in?
- How many bedrooms do you want?
- How many bathrooms do you want?

Table 5.1 The property database *house.dbf*

Area	Suburb	Price	Type	Bedrooms
Central Suburbs	New Town	164000	House	3
Central Suburbs	Taroona	150000	House	3
Southern Suburbs	Kingston	225000	Townhouse	4
Central Suburbs	North Hobart	127000	House	3
Northern Suburbs	West Moonah	89500	Unit	2
Central Suburbs	Taroona	110000	House	3
Central Suburbs	Lenah Valley	145000	House	3
Eastern Shore	Old Beach	79500	Unit	2
Central Suburbs	South Hobart	140000	House	3
Central Suburbs	South Hobart	115000	House	3
Eastern Shore	Cambridge	94500	Unit	2
Northern Suburbs	Glenorchy	228000	Townhouse	4
.	.	.	.	.
.	.	.	.	.
.	.	.	.	.

Bathrooms	Construction	Phone	Pictfile	Textfile
1	Weatherboard	(03) 6226 4212	house01.bmp	house01.txt
1	Brick	(03) 6226 1416	house02.bmp	house02.txt
2	Brick	(03) 6229 4200	house03.bmp	house03.txt
1	Brick	(03) 6226 8620	house04.bmp	house04.txt
1	Weatherboard	(03) 6225 4666	house05.bmp	house05.txt
1	Brick	(03) 6229 5316	house06.bmp	house06.txt
1	Brick	(03) 6278 2317	house07.bmp	house07.txt
1	Brick	(03) 6249 7298	house08.bmp	house08.txt
1	Brick	(03) 6228 5460	house09.bmp	house09.txt
1	Brick	(03) 6227 8937	house10.bmp	house10.txt
1	Brick	(03) 6248 1459	house11.bmp	house11.txt
2	Weatherboard	(03) 6271 6347	house12.bmp	house12.txt
.	.	.	.	.
.	.	.	.	.
.	.	.	.	.

Once these queries are answered, the expert system is expected to provide a list of suitable properties.

Step 2: *Determine classes and their attributes*

Here, we identify the problem's principal classes. We begin with the general or conceptual type of classes. For example, we can talk about the concept of a **property** and describe general features that are common to most properties. We can characterise each property by its location, price, type, number of bedrooms and bathrooms, construction, picture and description. We also need to present contact details of the property, such as its address or phone number. Thus, the class

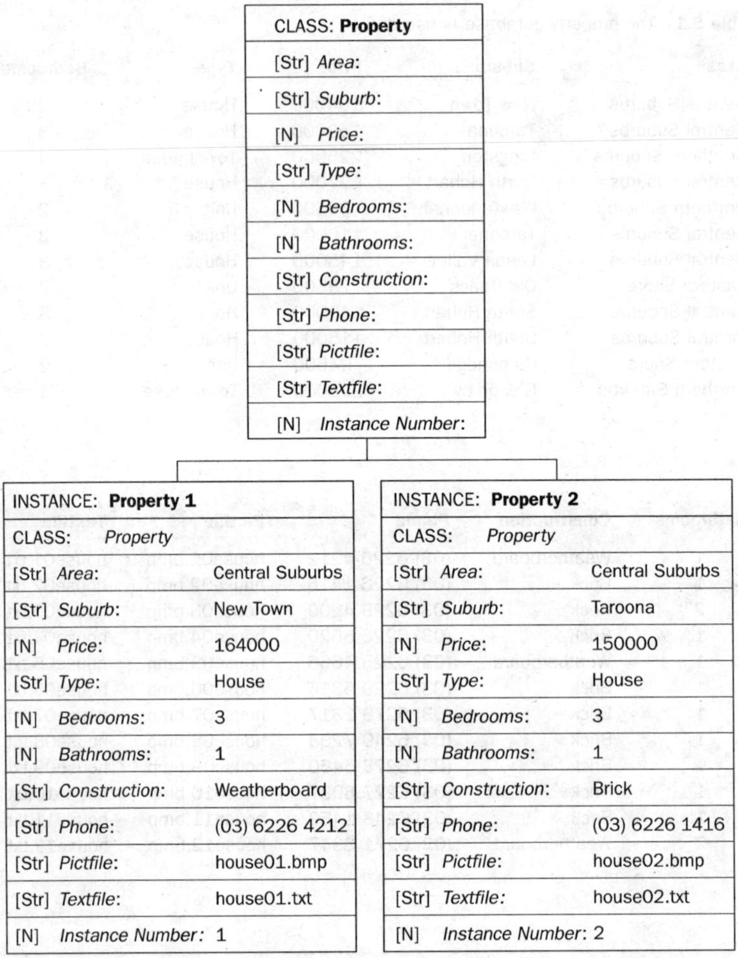

CLASS: **Property**
[Str] *Area*:
[Str] *Suburb*:
[N] *Price*:
[Str] *Type*:
[N] *Bedrooms*:
[N] *Bathrooms*:
[Str] *Construction*:
[Str] *Phone*:
[Str] *Pictfile*:
[Str] *Textfile*:
[N] *Instance Number*:

INSTANCE: **Property 1**	
CLASS:	*Property*
[Str] *Area*:	Central Suburbs
[Str] *Suburb*:	New Town
[N] *Price*:	164000
[Str] *Type*:	House
[N] *Bedrooms*:	3
[N] *Bathrooms*:	1
[Str] *Construction*:	Weatherboard
[Str] *Phone*:	(03) 6226 4212
[Str] *Pictfile*:	house01.bmp
[Str] *Textfile*:	house01.txt
[N] *Instance Number*:	1

INSTANCE: **Property 2**	
CLASS:	*Property*
[Str] *Area*:	Central Suburbs
[Str] *Suburb*:	Taroona
[N] *Price*:	150000
[Str] *Type*:	House
[N] *Bedrooms*:	3
[N] *Bathrooms*:	1
[Str] *Construction*:	Brick
[Str] *Phone*:	(03) 6226 1416
[Str] *Pictfile*:	house02.bmp
[Str] *Textfile:*	house02.txt
[N] *Instance Number*:	2

Figure 5.12 Class *Property* and its instances

Property can be presented as shown in Figure 5.12. Note that we added the attribute *Instance Number* as well. This attribute does not characterise the property but will assist Level5 Object in accessing the external database.

Step 3: *Define instances*

Once we determined the class-frame *Property*, we can easily create its instances by using data stored in the dBASE III database. For most frame-based expert systems like Level5 Object, this task requires us to tell the system that we want a new instance to be created. For example, to create a new instance of the class *Property*, we can use the following code:

```
MAKE Property
      WITH Area := area OF dB3 HOUSE 1
      WITH Suburb := suburb OF dB3 HOUSE 1
      WITH Price := price OF dB3 HOUSE 1
      WITH Type := type OF dB3 HOUSE 1
      WITH Bedrooms := bedrooms OF dB3 HOUSE 1
      WITH Bathrooms := bathrooms OF dB3 HOUSE 1
      WITH Construction := construct OF dB3 HOUSE 1
      WITH Phone := phone OF dB3 HOUSE 1
      WITH Pictfile := pictfile OF dB3 HOUSE 1
      WITH Textfile := textfile OF dB3 HOUSE 1
      WITH Instance Number := Current Instance Number
```

Here, the class *dB3 HOUSE 1* is used to represent the structure of the external database file *house.dbf*. Each row in the property database, shown in Table 5.1, represents an instance of the class *Property*, and each column represents an attribute. A newly created instance-frame receives the values of the current record of the database. Figure 5.12 shows instances that are created from the external database. These instances are linked to the class *Property*, and they inherit all attributes of this class.

Step 4: *Design displays*

Once the principal classes and their attributes are determined, we can design major displays for our application. We need the *Application Title Display* to present some general information to the user at the beginning of each application. This display may consist of the application title, general description of the problem, representative graphics and also copyright information. An example of the *Application Title Display* is shown in Figure 5.13.

The next display we can think of is the *Query Display*. This display should allow us to indicate our preferences by answering the queries presented by the expert system. The *Query Display* may look like a display shown in Figure 5.14. Here, the user is asked to select the most important things he or she is looking for in the property. Based on these selections, the expert system will then come up with a complete list of suitable properties.

And finally, we should design the *Property Information Display*. This display has to provide us with the list of suitable properties, an opportunity to move to the next, previous, first or last property in the list, and also a chance to look at the property picture and its description. Such a display may look like the one presented in Figure 5.15. Note that the picture-box and text-box are included in the display.

Figure 5.13 The *Application Title Display*

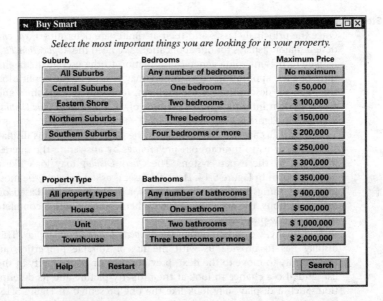

Figure 5.14 The *Query Display*

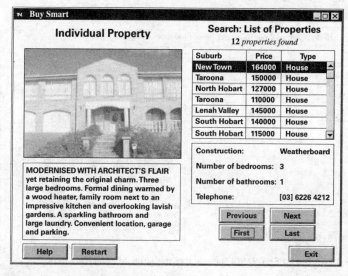

Figure 5.15 The *Property Information Display*

How are these displays linked?

Level5 Object allows us to link these displays by attaching the *Continue* pushbutton on the *Application Title Display* to the *Query Display*, and the *Search* pushbutton on the *Query Display* to the *Property Information Display*. When we run the application, clicking on either the *Continue* or *Search* pushbutton will cause a new display to appear.

Now we have to bring these displays to life.

Step 5: *Define WHEN CHANGED and WHEN NEEDED methods, and demons*

At this point, we have already created the problem principal classes and their attributes. We also determined the class instances, and established the mechanism for creating these instances from the external database. And finally, we designed static displays for presenting information to the user. We must now develop a way to bring our application to life. There are two ways to accomplish this task. The first one relies on WHEN CHANGED and WHEN NEEDED methods, and demons. The second approach involves pattern matching rules. In frame-based systems, we always first consider an application of methods and demons.

What we need now is to decide when to create instances of the class *Property*. There are two possible solutions. The first one is to create all instances at once when the user clicks on the *Continue* pushbutton on the *Application Title Display*, and then remove inappropriate instances step by step based on the user's preferences when he or she selects pushbuttons on the *Query Display*.

The second approach is to create only relevant instances after the user has made all selections on the *Query Display*. This approach

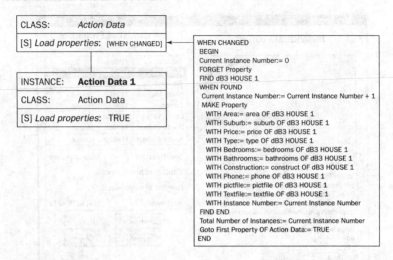

Figure 5.16 The WHEN CHANGED method of the attribute *Load properties*

illuminates the necessity to remove inappropriate instances of the class *Property*, but may add to the complexity of the system's design.

In our design here, we give preference to the first approach. It will provide us with an opportunity to use demons instead of rules. However, you could use the other approach.

Let us now create an additional class, the class *Action Data*, shown in Figure 5.16. The WHEN CHANGED method attached to the attribute *Load Properties* allows us to create all instances of the class *Property*.

How do we make this method work?

To make it work, we attach the *Continue* pushbutton on the *Application Title Display* to the attribute *Load Properties*. Now when we select this pushbutton at run time, the attribute *Load Properties* receives a value of TRUE, causing its WHEN CHANGED method to execute and create all instances of the class *Property*. The number of the instances created equals the number of records in the external database.

Now the *Query Display* appears (remember that we attach the *Continue* pushbutton of the *Application Title Display* to the *Query Display*), and the user is required to choose the most desirable features of the property by selecting appropriate pushbuttons. Each pushbutton here is associated with a demon that removes inappropriate instances of the class *Properties*. A set of demons is shown in Figure 5.17.

How do demons work here?

A demon does not go into action until something happens. In our application, it means that a demon is fired only if the user selects a corresponding pushbutton.

```
DEMON 1
IF selected OF Central Suburbs pushbutton
THEN FIND Property
    WHERE Area OF Property <> "Central Suburbs"
    WHEN FOUND
        FORGET CURRENT Property
    FIND END

DEMON 2
IF selected OF Eastern Shore pushbutton
THEN FIND Property
    WHERE Area OF Property <> "Eastern Shore"
    WHEN FOUND
        FORGET CURRENT Property
    FIND END
                    :
                    :
DEMON 5
IF selected OF House pushbutton
THEN FIND Property
    WHERE Type OF Property <> "House"
    WHEN FOUND
        FORGET CURRENT Property
    FIND END
                    :
                    :
DEMON 9
IF selected OF One bedroom pushbutton
THEN FIND Property
    WHERE Bedrooms OF Property <> 1
    WHEN FOUND
        FORGET CURRENT Property
    FIND END
                    :
                    :
DEMON 12
IF selected OF One bathroom pushbutton
THEN FIND Property
    WHERE Bathrooms OF Property <> 1
    WHEN FOUND
        FORGET CURRENT Property
    FIND END
                    :
                    :
DEMON 15
IF selected OF $50000 pushbutton
THEN FIND Property
    WHERE Price OF Property > 50000
    WHEN FOUND
        FORGET CURRENT Property
    FIND END
```

Figure 5.17 Demons for the *Query Display*

Let us consider, for example, DEMON 1 associated with the *Central Suburbs* pushbutton. When the user clicks on the *Central Suburbs* pushbutton on the *Query Display*, DEMON 1 is fired. The first command of the demon consequent tells Level5 Object to find the class *Property*. The WHERE clause

WHERE Area OF Property <> "Central Suburbs"

finds all instances of the class *Property* that do not match the user selection. It looks for any instance where the value of the attribute

Area is not equal to *Central Suburbs*. Then, the FORGET CURRENT command removes the current instance of the class *Property* from the application.

Once the property features are selected, the user clicks on the *Search* pushbutton on the *Query Display* to obtain a list of properties with these features. This list will appear on the *Property Information Display* (recall that the *Search* pushbutton is attached to the *Property Information Display*).

Can we view pictures and descriptions of the properties?

Let us first create two more attributes, *Load Instance Number* and *Goto First Property*, for the class *Action Data* as shown in Figure 5.18. Let us also attach the *Search* pushbutton on the *Query Display* to the attribute *Load Instance Number*. Now when we click on the *Search* pushbutton at run time, the attribute *Load Instance Number* will receive a value of TRUE, causing its WHEN CHANGED method to execute. This method determines the total number of instances left in the class *Property*. It also assigns the attribute *Goto First Property* a value of TRUE, subsequently causing its WHEN CHANGED method to execute.

The method attached to the attribute *Goto First Property* ensures that we are always positioned at the first property when we enter the *Property Information Display*. It also loads the value of the attribute *Pictfile* into the display's picture-box and the value of *Textfile* into the text-box. As a result, we can see the property picture and its description as shown in Figure 5.15.

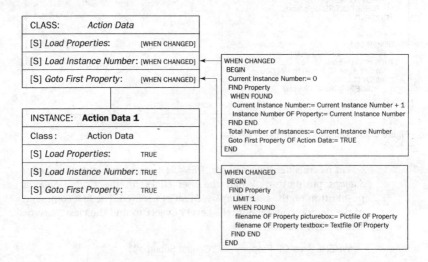

Figure 5.18 The WHEN CHANGED methods of the attributes *Load Instance Number* and *Goto First Property*

Step 6: *Define rules*

When we design a frame-based expert system, one of the most important and difficult decisions is whether to use rules or manage with methods and demons instead. This decision is usually based on the personal preferences of the designer. In our application, we use methods and demons because they offer us a powerful but simple way of representing procedures. On the other hand, in the credit evaluation example considered earlier, we applied a set of rules. In general, however, rules are not effective at dealing with procedural knowledge.

Step 7: *Evaluate and expand the system*

We have now completed the initial design of our Buy Smart expert system. The next task is to evaluate it. We want to make sure that the system's performance meets our expectations. In other words, we want to run a test case.

1. To begin the test, we click on the *Continue* pushbutton on the *Application Title Display*. The attribute *Load Properties* of the class *Action Data* receives a value of TRUE. The WHEN CHANGED method attached to *Load Properties* is executed, and all instances of the class *Property* are created.

2. The *Query Display* appears, and we make our selections, for example:

⇒ *Central Suburbs*

```
DEMON 1
IF selected OF Central Suburbs pushbutton
THEN FIND Property
    WHERE Area OF Property <> "Central Suburbs"
    WHEN FOUND
        FORGET CURRENT Property
FIND END
```

⇒ *House*

```
DEMON 5
IF selected OF House pushbutton
THEN FIND Property
    WHERE Type OF Property <> "House"
    WHEN FOUND
        FORGET CURRENT Property
FIND END
```

⇒ *Three bedrooms*

```
DEMON 10
IF selected OF Three bedroom pushbutton
THEN FIND Property
    WHERE Bedrooms OF Property <> 3
    WHEN FOUND
        FORGET CURRENT Property
FIND END
```

⇒ *One bathroom*

DEMON 12
IF selected OF One bathroom pushbutton
THEN FIND Property
   WHERE Bathrooms OF Property <> 1
   WHEN FOUND
      FORGET CURRENT Property
FIND END

⇒ *$ 200,000*

DEMON 18
IF selected OF $200,000 pushbutton
THEN FIND Property
   WHERE Price OF Property > 200000
   WHEN FOUND
      FORGET CURRENT Property
FIND END

The demons remove those *Property* instances whose features do not match our selections.

3. Now we click on the *Search* pushbutton. The attribute *Load Instance Number* of the class *Action Data* receives a value of TRUE. The WHEN CHANGED method attached to *Load Instance Number* is executed. It determines the number of instances left in the class *Property*, and also assigns the attribute *Goto First Property* a value of TRUE. Now the WHEN CHANGED method attached to *Goto First Property* is executed. It finds the first *Property* instance, and assigns the attribute *filename* of the *Property picturebox* a value of house01.bmp, and the attribute *filename* of the *Property textbox* a value of house01.txt (recall that both the *Property picturebox* and *Property textbox* have been created on the *Property Information Display*).

4. The *Property Information Display* appears. In the example shown in Figure 5.15, we can examine 12 properties that satisfy our requirements. Note that we are positioned at the first property in the property list, the property picture appears in the picture-box and the property description in the text-box. However, we cannot move to the next, previous or last property in the property list by using the pushbuttons assigned on the display. To make them functional, we need to create additional attributes in the class *Action Data*, and then attach WHEN CHANGED methods as shown in Figure 5.19.

Now the Buy Smart expert system is ready for expansion, and we can add new properties to the external database.

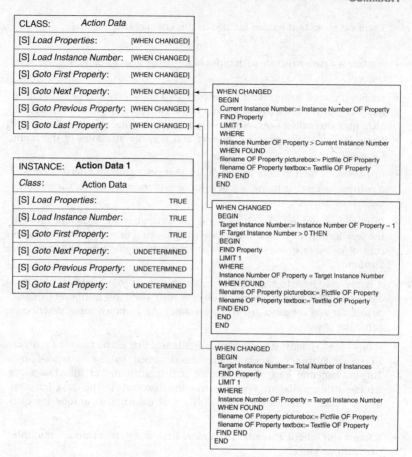

Figure 5.19   The WHEN CHANGED methods of the attributes *Goto Next Property*, *Goto Previous Property* and *Goto Last Property*

5.7   Summary

In this chapter, we presented an overview of frame-based expert systems. We considered the concept of a frame and discussed how to use frames for knowledge representation. We found that inheritance is an essential feature of the frame-based systems. We examined the application of methods, demons and rules. Finally, we considered the development of a frame-based expert system through an example.

The most important lessons learned in this chapter are:

- A frame is a data structure with typical knowledge about a particular object or concept.

- Frames are used to represent knowledge in a frame-based expert system. A frame contains knowledge of a given object, including its name and a set of attributes also called slots. *Name, weight, height* and *age* are attributes of the frame *Person. Model, processor, memory* and *price* are attributes of the frame *Computer*.

- Attributes are used to store values. An attribute may contain a default value or a pointer to another frame, set of rules or procedure by which the attribute value is obtained.

- Frame-based systems can also extend the attribute-value structure through the application of facets. Facets are used to establish the attribute value, control end-user queries, and tell the inference engine how to process the attribute.

- A frame may refer to a group of similar objects, or to a particular object. A class-frame describes a group of objects with common attributes. *Animal, person, car* and *computer* are all class-frames. An instance-frame describes a particular object.

- Frame-based systems support class inheritance, that is the process by which all characteristics of a class-frame are assumed by the instance-frame. The fundamental idea of inheritance is that attributes of the class-frame represent things that are **typically** true for all objects in the class, but slots in the instance-frames are filled with actual data that is unique for each instance.

- A frame can inherit attributes from more than one parent through multiple-parent inheritance.

- Frames communicate with each other by methods and demons. A method is a procedure associated with a frame attribute; it is executed whenever requested. Most frame-based expert systems use two types of methods: WHEN CHANGED and WHEN NEEDED. The WHEN CHANGED method is executed when new information is placed in the slot, and the WHEN NEEDED method is executed when information is needed for solving the problem but the slot value is unspecified.

- Demons are similar to methods, and the terms are often used as synonyms. However, methods are more appropriate if we need to write complex procedures. Demons, on the other hand, are usually limited to IF-THEN statements.

- In frame-based expert systems, rules often use **pattern matching** clauses. These clauses contain variables that are used for locating matching conditions among all instance-frames.

- Although frames provide a powerful tool for combining declarative and procedural knowledge, they leave the knowledge engineer with difficult decisions about the hierarchical structure of the system and its inheritance paths.

Questions for review

1 What is a frame? What are the class and instances? Give examples.

2 Design the class-frame for the object *Student*, determine its attributes and define several instances for this class.

3 What is a facet? Give examples of various types of facets.

4 What is the correct level of decomposition of a problem into frames, slots and facets? Justify your answer through an example.

5 How are objects related in frame-based systems? What are the 'a-kind-of' and 'a-part-of' relationships? Give examples.

6 Define inheritance in frame-based systems. Why is inheritance an essential feature of the frame-based systems?

7 Can a frame inherit attributes from more than one parent? Give an example.

8 What is a method? What are the most popular types of methods used in frame-based expert systems?

9 What is a demon? What are the differences between demons and methods?

10 What are the differences, if any, between rules used in rule-based expert systems and those used in frame-based systems?

11 What are the main steps in developing a frame-based expert system?

12 List some advantages of frame-based expert systems. What are the difficulties involved in developing a frame-based expert system?

References

Blaha, M. and Rumbaugh, J. (2004). *Object-Oriented Modeling and Design with UML*, 2nd edn. Prentice Hall, Englewood Cliffs, NJ.

Brachman, R.J. and Levesque, H.J. (2004). *Knowledge Representation and Reasoning*. Elsevier, Amsterdam.

Durkin, J. (1994). *Expert Systems: Design and Development*. Prentice Hall, Englewood Cliffs, NJ.

Minsky, M. (1975). A framework for representing knowledge, *The Psychology of Computer Vision*, P. Winston, ed., McGraw-Hill, New York, pp. 211–277.

Sterling, L. and Shapiro E. (1994). *The Art of Prolog: Advanced Programming Techniques*, 2nd edn. MIT Press, Cambridge, MA.

Weisfeld, M. (2008). *The Object-Oriented Thought Process*, 3rd edn. Addison-Wesley, Upper Saddle River, NJ.

Bibliography

Aikens, J.S. (1984). A representation scheme using both frames and rules, *Rule-Based Expert Systems*, B.G. Buchanan and E.H. Shortliffe, eds, Addison-Wesley, Reading, MA, pp. 424–440.

Alpert, S.R., Woyak, S.W., Shrobe, H.J. and Arrowood, L.F. (1990). Guest Editors Introduction: Object-oriented programming in AI, *IEEE Expert*, 5(6), 6–7.

Booch G., Maksimchuk, R.A., Engel, M.W., Young, B.J., Conallen, J. and Houston, K.A. (2007). *Object-Oriented Analysis and Design with Applications*, 3rd edn. Addison-Wesley, Reading, MA.

Coppin, B. (2004). *Artificial Intelligence Illuminated*. Jones and Bartlett, Sudbury, MA.

Fikes, R. and Kehler, T. (1985). The role of frame-based representation in reasoning, *Communications of the ACM*, 28(9), 904–920.

Goldstein, I. and Papert, S. (1977). Artificial intelligence, language, and the study of knowledge, *Cognitive Science*, 1(1), 84–123.

Jackson, P. (1999). *Introduction to Expert Systems*, 3rd edn. Addison-Wesley, Harlow.

Keogh, J. and Giannini, M. (2004). *OOP Demystified*. McGraw-Hill, New York.

Kordon, A.K. (2010). *Applying Computational Intelligence: How to Create Value*. Springer-Verlag, Berlin.

Levesque, H.J. and Brachman, R.J. (1985). A fundamental trade-off in knowledge representation and reasoning, *Readings in Knowledge Representation*, R.J. Brachman and H.J. Levesque, eds, Morgan Kaufmann, Los Altos, CA.

Luger, G.F. (2008). *Artificial Intelligence: Structures and Strategies for Complex Problem Solving*, 6th edn. Addison-Wesley, Harlow.

Poo, D., Kiong, D. and Ashok, S. (2008). *Object-Oriented Programming and Java*, 2nd edn. Springer-Verlag, London.

Rosson, M.B. and Alpert, S.R. (1990). The cognitive consequences of object-oriented design, *Human–Computer Interaction*, 5(4), 345–379.

Stefik, M.J. (1995). *Introduction to Knowledge Systems*. Morgan Kaufmann, San Francisco.

Stefik, M.J. and Bobrow, D.G. (1986). Object-oriented programming: themes and variations, *AI Magazine*, 6(4), 40–62.

Touretzky, D.S. (1986). *The Mathematics of Inheritance Systems*. Morgan Kaufmann, Los Altos, CA.

Waterman, D.A. (1986). *A Guide to Expert Systems*. Addison-Wesley, Reading, MA.

Winston, P.H. (1977). Representing knowledge in frames, Chapter 7 of *Artificial Intelligence*, Addison-Wesley, Reading, MA, pp. 181–187.

Wu, C.T. (2009). *An Introduction to Object-Oriented Programming with Java*, 5th edn. McGraw-Hill, New York.

Artificial neural networks   6

In which we consider how our brains work and how to build and train artificial neural networks.

6.1 Introduction, or how the brain works

'The computer hasn't proved anything yet,' angry Garry Kasparov, the world chess champion, said after his defeat in New York in May 1997. 'If we were playing a real competitive match, I would tear down Deep Blue into pieces.'

But Kasparov's efforts to downplay the significance of his defeat in the six-game match was futile. The fact that Kasparov – probably the greatest chess player the world has seen – was beaten by a computer marked a turning point in the quest for intelligent machines.

The IBM supercomputer called Deep Blue was capable of analysing 200 million positions a second, and it appeared to be displaying intelligent thoughts. At one stage Kasparov even accused the machine of cheating!

> There were many, many discoveries in this match, and one of them was that sometimes the computer plays very, very human moves.
>
> It deeply understands positional factors. And that is an outstanding scientific achievement.

Traditionally, it has been assumed that to beat an expert in a chess game, a computer would have to formulate a strategy that goes beyond simply doing a great number of 'look-ahead' moves per second. Chess-playing programs must be able to improve their performance with experience or, in other words, a machine must be capable of learning.

What is machine learning?

In general, machine learning involves adaptive mechanisms that enable computers to learn from experience, learn by example and learn by analogy. Learning capabilities can improve the performance of an intelligent system over time. Machine learning mechanisms form the basis for adaptive systems. The most popular approaches to machine learning are **artificial neural networks** and **genetic algorithms**. This chapter is dedicated to neural networks.

What is a neural network?

A neural network can be defined as a model of reasoning based on the human brain. The brain consists of a densely interconnected set of nerve cells, or basic information-processing units, called **neurons**. The human brain incorporates nearly 10 billion neurons and 60 trillion connections, **synapses**, between them (Shepherd and Koch, 1990). By using multiple neurons simultaneously, the brain can perform its functions much faster than the fastest computers in existence today.

Although each neuron has a very simple structure, an army of such elements constitutes a tremendous processing power. A neuron consists of a cell body, **soma**, a number of fibres called **dendrites**, and a single long fibre called the **axon**. While dendrites branch into a network around the soma, the axon stretches out to the dendrites and somas of other neurons. Figure 6.1 is a schematic drawing of a neural network.

Signals are propagated from one neuron to another by complex electro-chemical reactions. Chemical substances released from the synapses cause a change in the electrical potential of the cell body. When the potential reaches its threshold, an electrical pulse, **action potential**, is sent down through the axon. The pulse spreads out and eventually reaches synapses, causing them to increase or decrease their potential. However, the most interesting finding is that a neural network exhibits **plasticity**. In response to the stimulation pattern, neurons demonstrate long-term changes in the strength of their connections. Neurons also can form new connections with other neurons. Even entire collections of neurons may sometimes migrate from one place to another. These mechanisms form the basis for learning in the brain.

Our brain can be considered as a highly complex, non-linear and parallel information-processing system. Information is stored and processed in a neural network simultaneously throughout the whole network, rather than at specific locations. In other words, in neural networks, both data and its processing are **global** rather than local.

Owing to the plasticity, connections between neurons leading to the 'right answer' are strengthened while those leading to the 'wrong answer' weaken. As a result, neural networks have the ability to learn through experience.

Learning is a fundamental and essential characteristic of biological neural networks. The ease and naturalness with which they can learn led to attempts to emulate a biological neural network in a computer.

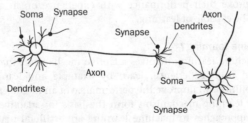

Figure 6.1 Biological neural network

Although a present-day artificial neural network (ANN) resembles the human brain much as a paper plane resembles a supersonic jet, it is a big step forward. ANNs are capable of 'learning'; that is, they use experience to improve their performance. When exposed to a sufficient number of samples, ANNs can generalise to others they have not yet encountered. They can recognise handwritten characters, identify words in human speech, and detect explosives at airports. Moreover, ANNs can observe patterns that human experts fail to recognise. For example, Chase Manhattan Bank used a neural network to examine an array of information about the use of stolen credit cards – and discovered that the most suspicious sales were for women's shoes costing between $40 and $80.

How do artificial neural nets model the brain?

An ANN consists of a number of very simple and highly interconnected processors, also called neurons, which are analogous to the biological neurons in the brain. The neurons are connected by weighted links passing signals from one neuron to another. Each neuron receives a number of input signals through its connections; however, it never produces more than a single output signal. The output signal is transmitted through the neuron's outgoing connection (corresponding to the biological axon). The outgoing connection, in turn, splits into a number of branches that transmit the same signal (the signal is not divided among these branches in any way). The outgoing branches terminate at the incoming connections of other neurons in the network. Figure 6.2 represents connections of a typical ANN, and Table 6.1 shows the analogy between biological and artificial neural networks (Medsker and Liebowitz, 1994).

How does an artificial neural network 'learn'?

The neurons are connected by **links**, and each link has a **numerical weight** associated with it. Weights are the basic means of long-term memory in ANNs. They express the strength, or in other words importance, of each neuron input. A neural network 'learns' through repeated adjustments of these weights.

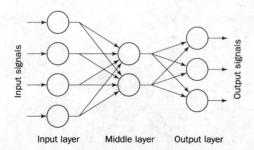

Figure 6.2 Architecture of a typical artificial neural network

Table 6.1 Analogy between biological and artificial neural networks

Biological neural network	Artificial neural network
Soma	Neuron
Dendrite	Input
Axon	Output
Synapse	Weight

But does the neural network know how to adjust the weights?

As shown in Figure 6.2, a typical ANN is made up of a hierarchy of layers, and the neurons in the networks are arranged along these layers. The neurons connected to the external environment form input and output layers. The weights are modified to bring the network input/output behaviour into line with that of the environment.

Each neuron is an elementary information-processing unit. It has a means of computing its **activation level** given the inputs and numerical weights.

To build an ANN, we must decide first how many neurons are to be used and how the neurons are to be connected to form a network. In other words, we must first choose the network architecture. Then we decide which learning algorithm to use. And finally we train the neural network; that is, we initialise the weights of the network and update the weights from a set of training examples.

Let us begin with a neuron, the basic building element of an ANN.

6.2 The neuron as a simple computing element

A neuron receives several signals from its input links, computes a new activation level and sends it as an output signal through the output links. The input signal can be raw data or outputs of other neurons. The output signal can be either a final solution to the problem or an input to other neurons. Figure 6.3 shows a typical neuron.

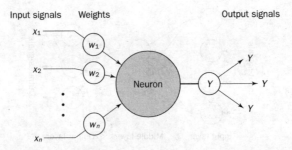

Figure 6.3 Diagram of a neuron

How does the neuron determine its output?

In 1943, Warren McCulloch and Walter Pitts proposed a very simple idea that is still the basis for most ANNs.

The neuron computes the weighted sum of the input signals and compares the result with a threshold value, θ. If the net input is less than the threshold, the neuron output is -1. But if the net input is greater than or equal to the threshold, the neuron becomes activated and its output attains a value $+1$ (McCulloch and Pitts, 1943).

In other words, the neuron uses the following transfer or **activation function**:

$$X = \sum_{i=1}^{n} x_i w_i$$

$$Y = \begin{cases} +1 & \text{if } X \geqslant \theta \\ -1 & \text{if } X < \theta \end{cases} \tag{6.1}$$

where X is the net weighted input to the neuron, x_i is the value of input i, w_i is the weight of input i, n is the number of neuron inputs, and Y is the output of the neuron.

This type of activation function is called a **sign function**.

Thus the actual output of the neuron with a sign activation function can be represented as

$$Y = sign\left[\sum_{i=1}^{n} x_i w_i - \theta\right] \tag{6.2}$$

Is the sign function the only activation function used by neurons?

Many activation functions have been tested, but only a few have found practical applications. Four common choices – the step, sign, linear and sigmoid functions – are illustrated in Figure 6.4.

The **step** and **sign** activation functions, also called **hard-limit functions**, are often used in decision-making neurons for classification and pattern recognition tasks.

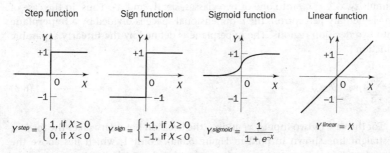

Figure 6.4   Activation functions of a neuron

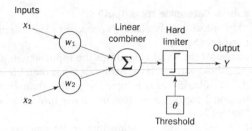

Figure 6.5 Single-layer two-input perceptron

The **sigmoid function** transforms the input, which can have any value between plus and minus infinity, into a reasonable value in the range between 0 and 1. Neurons with this function are used in the back-propagation networks.

The **linear activation function** provides an output equal to the neuron weighted input. Neurons with the linear function are often used for linear approximation.

Can a single neuron learn a task?

In 1958, Frank Rosenblatt introduced a training algorithm that provided the first procedure for training a simple ANN: a **perceptron** (Rosenblatt, 1958). The perceptron is the simplest form of a neural network. It consists of a single neuron with **adjustable** synaptic weights and a **hard limiter**. A single-layer two-input perceptron is shown in Figure 6.5.

6.3 The perceptron

The operation of Rosenblatt's perceptron is based on the McCulloch and Pitts neuron model. The model consists of a linear combiner followed by a hard limiter. The weighted sum of the inputs is applied to the hard limiter, which produces an output equal to $+1$ if its input is positive and -1 if it is negative. The aim of the perceptron is to classify inputs, or in other words externally applied stimuli $x_1, x_2, \ldots, x_n$, into one of two classes, say A_1 and A_2. Thus, in the case of an elementary perceptron, the n-dimensional space is divided by a **hyperplane** into two decision regions. The hyperplane is defined by the **linearly separable** function

$$\sum_{i=1}^{n} x_i w_i - \theta = 0 \tag{6.3}$$

For the case of two inputs, x_1 and x_2, the decision boundary takes the form of a straight line shown in bold in Figure 6.6(a). Point 1, which lies above the boundary line, belongs to class A_1; and point 2, which lies below the line, belongs to class A_2. The threshold θ can be used to shift the decision boundary.

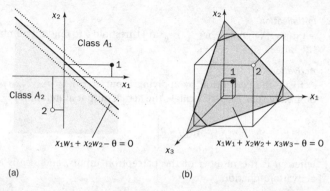

Figure 6.6   Linear separability in the perceptrons: (a) two-input perceptron;
(b) three-input perceptron

With three inputs the hyperplane can still be visualised. Figure 6.6(b) shows
three dimensions for the three-input perceptron. The separating plane here is
defined by the equation

$$x_1 w_1 + x_2 w_2 + x_3 w_3 - \theta = 0$$

But how does the perceptron learn its classification tasks?

This is done by making small adjustments in the weights to reduce the difference
between the actual and desired outputs of the perceptron. The initial weights are
randomly assigned, usually in the range $[-0.5, 0.5]$, and then updated to obtain
the output consistent with the training examples. For a perceptron, the process
of weight updating is particularly simple. If at iteration p, the actual output is
$Y(p)$ and the desired output is $Y_d(p)$, then the error is given by

$$e(p) = Y_d(p) - Y(p) \qquad \text{where } p = 1, 2, 3, \ldots \tag{6.4}$$

Iteration p here refers to the pth training example presented to the perceptron.

If the error, $e(p)$, is positive, we need to increase perceptron output $Y(p)$, but if
it is negative, we need to decrease $Y(p)$. Taking into account that each
perceptron input contributes $x_i(p) \times w_i(p)$ to the total input $X(p)$, we find that
if input value $x_i(p)$ is positive, an increase in its weight $w_i(p)$ tends to increase
perceptron output $Y(p)$, whereas if $x_i(p)$ is negative, an increase in $w_i(p)$ tends to
decrease $Y(p)$. Thus, the following **perceptron learning rule** can be established:

$$w_i(p+1) = w_i(p) + \alpha \times x_i(p) \times e(p) \tag{6.5}$$

where α is the **learning rate**, a positive constant less than unity.

The perceptron learning rule was first proposed by Rosenblatt in 1960
(Rosenblatt, 1960). Using this rule we can derive the perceptron training
algorithm for classification tasks.

Step 1: *Initialisation*

Set initial weights $w_1, w_2, \ldots, w_n$ and threshold θ to random numbers in the range $[-0.5, 0.5]$.

Step 2: *Activation*

Activate the perceptron by applying inputs $x_1(p), x_2(p), \ldots, x_n(p)$ and desired output $Y_d(p)$. Calculate the actual output at iteration $p = 1$

$$Y(p) = step \left[\sum_{i=1}^{n} x_i(p) w_i(p) - \theta \right] \tag{6.6}$$

where n is the number of the perceptron inputs, and *step* is a step activation function.

Step 3: *Weight training*

Update the weights of the perceptron

$$w_i(p+1) = w_i(p) + \Delta w_i(p) \tag{6.7}$$

where $\Delta w_i(p)$ is the weight correction at iteration p.

The weight correction is computed by the **delta rule**:

$$\Delta w_i(p) = \alpha \times x_i(p) \times e(p) \tag{6.8}$$

Step 4: *Iteration*

Increase iteration p by one, go back to Step 2 and repeat the process until convergence.

Can we train a perceptron to perform basic logical operations such as AND, OR or Exclusive-OR?

The truth tables for the operations AND, OR and Exclusive-OR are shown in Table 6.2. The table presents all possible combinations of values for two variables, x_1 and x_2, and the results of the operations. The perceptron must be trained to classify the input patterns.

Let us first consider the operation AND. After completing the initialisation step, the perceptron is activated by the sequence of four input patterns representing an **epoch**. The perceptron weights are updated after each activation. This process is repeated until all the weights converge to a uniform set of values. The results are shown in Table 6.3.

Table 6.2 Truth tables for the basic logical operations

Input variables		AND	OR	Exclusive-OR
x_1	x_2	$x_1 \cap x_2$	$x_1 \cup x_2$	$x_1 \oplus x_2$
0	0	0	0	0
0	1	0	1	1
1	0	0	1	1
1	1	1	1	0

Table 6.3 Example of perceptron learning: the logical operation AND

Epoch	Inputs x_1	Inputs x_2	Desired output Y_d	Initial weights w_1	Initial weights w_2	Actual output Y	Error e	Final weights w_1	Final weights w_2
1	0	0	0	0.3	−0.1	0	0	0.3	−0.1
	0	1	0	0.3	−0.1	0	0	0.3	−0.1
	1	0	0	0.3	−0.1	1	−1	0.2	−0.1
	1	1	1	0.2	−0.1	0	1	0.3	0.0
2	0	0	0	0.3	0.0	0	0	0.3	0.0
	0	1	0	0.3	0.0	0	0	0.3	0.0
	1	0	0	0.3	0.0	1	−1	0.2	0.0
	1	1	1	0.2	0.0	1	0	0.2	0.0
3	0	0	0	0.2	0.0	0	0	0.2	0.0
	0	1	0	0.2	0.0	0	0	0.2	0.0
	1	0	0	0.2	0.0	1	−1	0.1	0.0
	1	1	1	0.1	0.0	0	1	0.2	0.1
4	0	0	0	0.2	0.1	0	0	0.2	0.1
	0	1	0	0.2	0.1	0	0	0.2	0.1
	1	0	0	0.2	0.1	1	−1	0.1	0.1
	1	1	1	0.1	0.1	1	0	0.1	0.1
5	0	0	0	0.1	0.1	0	0	0.1	0.1
	0	1	0	0.1	0.1	0	0	0.1	0.1
	1	0	0	0.1	0.1	0	0	0.1	0.1
	1	1	1	0.1	0.1	1	0	0.1	0.1

Threshold: $\theta = 0.2$; learning rate: $\alpha = 0.1$.

In a similar manner, the perceptron can learn the operation OR. However, a single-layer perceptron cannot be trained to perform the operation Exclusive-OR.

A little geometry can help us to understand why this is. Figure 6.7 represents the AND, OR and Exclusive-OR functions as two-dimensional plots based on the values of the two inputs. Points in the input space where the function output is 1 are indicated by black dots, and points where the output is 0 are indicated by white dots.

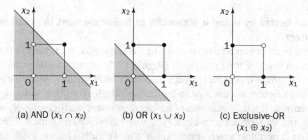

(a) AND $(x_1 \cap x_2)$ (b) OR $(x_1 \cup x_2)$ (c) Exclusive-OR $(x_1 \oplus x_2)$

Figure 6.7 Two-dimensional plots of basic logical operations

In Figures 6.7(a) and (b), we can draw a line so that black dots are on one side and white dots on the other, but dots shown in Figure 6.7(c) are not separable by a single line. A perceptron is able to represent a function only if there is some line that separates all the black dots from all the white dots. Such functions are called **linearly separable**. Therefore, a perceptron can learn the operations AND and OR, but not Exclusive-OR.

But why can a perceptron learn only linearly separable functions?

The fact that a perceptron can learn only linearly separable functions directly follows from Eq. (6.1). The perceptron output Y is 1 only if the total weighted input X is greater than or equal to the threshold value θ. This means that the entire input space is divided in two along a boundary defined by $X = \theta$. For example, a separating line for the operation AND is defined by the equation

$$x_1 w_1 + x_2 w_2 = \theta$$

If we substitute values for weights w_1 and w_2 and threshold θ given in Table 6.3, we obtain one of the possible separating lines as

$$0.1 x_1 + 0.1 x_2 = 0.2$$

or

$$x_1 + x_2 = 2$$

Thus, the region below the boundary line, where the output is 0, is given by

$$x_1 + x_2 - 2 < 0$$

and the region above this line, where the output is 1, is given by

$$x_1 + x_2 - 2 \geqslant 0$$

The fact that a perceptron can learn only linear separable functions is rather bad news, because there are not many such functions.

Can we do better by using a sigmoidal or linear element in place of the hard limiter?

Single-layer perceptrons make decisions in the same way, regardless of the activation function used by the perceptron (Shynk, 1990; Shynk and Bershad, 1992). It means that a single-layer perceptron can classify only linearly separable patterns, regardless of whether we use a hard-limit or soft-limit activation function.

The computational limitations of a perceptron were mathematically analysed in Minsky and Papert's famous book *Perceptrons* (Minsky and Papert, 1969). They proved that Rosenblatt's perceptron cannot make global generalisations on the basis of examples learned locally. Moreover, Minsky and Papert concluded that the limitations of a single-layer perceptron would also hold true for multilayer neural networks. This conclusion certainly did not encourage further research on ANNs.

How do we cope with problems which are not linearly separable?
To cope with such problems we need multilayer neural networks. In fact, history has proved that the limitations of Rosenblatt's perceptron can be overcome by advanced forms of neural networks, for example multilayer perceptrons trained with the back-propagation algorithm.

6.4 Multilayer neural networks

A multilayer perceptron is a feedforward neural network with one or more hidden layers. Typically, the network consists of an **input layer** of source neurons, at least one middle or **hidden layer** of computational neurons and an **output layer** of computational neurons. The input signals are propagated in a forward direction on a layer-by-layer basis. A multilayer perceptron with two hidden layers is shown in Figure 6.8.

But why do we need a hidden layer?
Each layer in a multilayer neural network has its own specific function. The input layer accepts input signals from the outside world and redistributes these signals to all neurons in the hidden layer. Actually, the input layer rarely includes computing neurons, and thus does not process input patterns. The output layer accepts output signals, or in other words a stimulus pattern, from the hidden layer and establishes the output pattern of the entire network.

Neurons in the hidden layer detect the features; the weights of the neurons represent the features hidden in the input patterns. These features are then used by the output layer in determining the output pattern.

With one hidden layer, we can represent any continuous function of the input signals, and with two hidden layers even discontinuous functions can be represented.

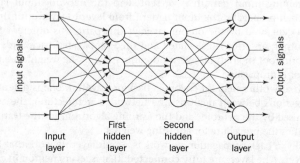

Figure 6.8 Multilayer perceptron with two hidden layers

Why is a middle layer in a multilayer network called a 'hidden' layer? What does this layer hide?
A hidden layer 'hides' its desired output. Neurons in the hidden layer cannot be observed through the input/output behaviour of the network. There is no obvious way to know what the desired output of the hidden layer should be. In other words, the desired output of the hidden layer is determined by the layer itself.

Can a neural network include more than two hidden layers?
Commercial ANNs incorporate three and sometimes four layers, including one or two hidden layers. Each layer can contain from 10 to 1000 neurons. Experimental neural networks may have five or even six layers, including three or four hidden layers, and utilise millions of neurons, but most practical applications use only three layers, because each additional layer increases the computational burden exponentially.

How do multilayer neural networks learn?
More than 100 different learning algorithms are available, but the most popular method is back-propagation. This method was first proposed in 1969 (Bryson and Ho, 1969), but was ignored because of its demanding computations. Only in the mid-1980s was the back-propagation learning algorithm rediscovered.

Learning in a multilayer network proceeds the same way as for a perceptron. A training set of input patterns is presented to the network. The network computes its output pattern, and if there is an error – or in other words a difference between actual and desired output patterns – the weights are adjusted to reduce this error.

In a perceptron, there is only one weight for each input and only one output. But in the multilayer network, there are many weights, each of which contributes to more than one output.

How can we assess the blame for an error and divide it among the contributing weights?
In a back-propagation neural network, the learning algorithm has two phases. First, a training input pattern is presented to the network input layer. The network then propagates the input pattern from layer to layer until the output pattern is generated by the output layer. If this pattern is different from the desired output, an error is calculated and then propagated backwards through the network from the output layer to the input layer. The weights are modified as the error is propagated.

As with any other neural network, a back-propagation one is determined by the connections between neurons (the network's architecture), the activation function used by the neurons, and the learning algorithm (or the learning law) that specifies the procedure for adjusting weights.

Typically, a back-propagation network is a multilayer network that has three or four layers. The layers are **fully connected**: that is, every neuron in each layer is connected to every other neuron in the adjacent forward layer.

A neuron determines its output in a manner similar to Rosenblatt's perceptron. First, it computes the net weighted input as before:

$$X = \sum_{i=1}^{n} x_i w_i - \theta$$

where n is the number of inputs, and θ is the threshold applied to the neuron.

Next, this input value is passed through the activation function. However, unlike a percepron, neurons in the back-propagation network use a sigmoid activation function:

$$Y^{sigmoid} = \frac{1}{1+e^{-X}} \tag{6.9}$$

The derivative of this function is easy to compute. It also guarantees that the neuron output is bounded between 0 and 1.

What about the learning law used in the back-propagation networks?

To derive the back-propagation learning law, let us consider the three-layer network shown in Figure 6.9. The indices i, j and k here refer to neurons in the input, hidden and output layers, respectively.

Input signals, $x_1, x_2, \ldots, x_n$, are propagated through the network from left to right, and error signals, $e_1, e_2, \ldots, e_l$, from right to left. The symbol w_{ij} denotes the weight for the connection between neuron i in the input layer and neuron j in the hidden layer, and the symbol w_{jk} the weight between neuron j in the hidden layer and neuron k in the output layer.

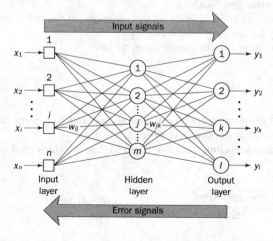

Figure 6.9 Three-layer back-propagation neural network

To propagate error signals, we start at the output layer and work backwards to the hidden layer. The error signal at the output of neuron k at iteration p is defined by

$$e_k(p) = y_{d,k}(p) - y_k(p) \tag{6.10}$$

where $y_{d,k}(p)$ is the desired output of neuron k at iteration p.

Neuron k, which is located in the output layer, is supplied with a desired output of its own. Hence, we may use a straightforward procedure to update weight w_{jk}. In fact, the rule for updating weights at the output layer is similar to the perceptron learning rule of Eq. (6.7):

$$w_{jk}(p+1) = w_{jk}(p) + \Delta w_{jk}(p) \tag{6.11}$$

where $\Delta w_{jk}(p)$ is the weight correction.

When we determined the weight correction for the perceptron, we used input signal x_i. But in the multilayer network, the inputs of neurons in the output layer are different from the inputs of neurons in the input layer.

As we cannot apply input signal x_i, what should we use instead?

We use the output of neuron j in the hidden layer, y_j, instead of input x_i. The weight correction in the multilayer network is computed by (Fu, 1994)

$$\Delta w_{jk}(p) = \alpha \times y_j(p) \times \delta_k(p) \tag{6.12}$$

where $\delta_k(p)$ is the error gradient at neuron k in the output layer at iteration p.

What is the error gradient?

The error gradient is determined as the derivative of the activation function multiplied by the error at the neuron output.

Thus, for neuron k in the output layer, we have

$$\delta_k(p) = \frac{\partial y_k(p)}{\partial X_k(p)} \times e_k(p) \tag{6.13}$$

where $y_k(p)$ is the output of neuron k at iteration p, and $X_k(p)$ is the net weighted input to neuron k at the same iteration.

For a sigmoid activation function, Eq. (6.13) can be represented as

$$\delta_k(p) = \frac{\partial\left\{ \dfrac{1}{1 + \exp[-X_k(p)]} \right\}}{\partial X_k(p)} \times e_k(p) = \frac{\exp[-X_k(p)]}{\{1 + \exp[-X_k(p)]\}^2} \times e_k(p)$$

Thus, we obtain

$$\delta_k(p) = y_k(p) \times [1 - y_k(p)] \times e_k(p) \qquad (6.14)$$

where

$$y_k(p) = \frac{1}{1 + \exp[-X_k(p)]}$$

How can we determine the weight correction for a neuron in the hidden layer?

To calculate the weight correction for the hidden layer, we can apply the same equation as for the output layer:

$$\Delta w_{ij}(p) = \alpha \times x_i(p) \times \delta_j(p) \qquad (6.15)$$

where $\delta_j(p)$ represents the error gradient at neuron j in the hidden layer:

$$\delta_j(p) = y_j(p) \times [1 - y_j(p)] \times \sum_{k=1}^{l} \delta_k(p) w_{jk}(p)$$

where l is the number of neurons in the output layer;

$$y_j(p) = \frac{1}{1 + e^{-X_j(p)}}$$

$$X_j(p) = \sum_{i=1}^{n} x_i(p) \times w_{ij}(p) - \theta_j$$

and n is the number of neurons in the input layer.

Now we can derive the back-propagation training algorithm.

Step 1:   *Initialisation*

Set all the weights and threshold levels of the network to random numbers uniformly distributed inside a small range (Haykin, 2008):

$$\left(-\frac{2.4}{F_i}, +\frac{2.4}{F_i} \right)$$

where F_i is the total number of inputs of neuron i in the network. The weight initialisation is done on a neuron-by-neuron basis.

Step 2:   *Activation*

Activate the back-propagation neural network by applying inputs $x_1(p), x_2(p), \ldots, x_n(p)$ and desired outputs $y_{d,1}(p), y_{d,2}(p), \ldots, y_{d,n}(p)$.

(a) Calculate the actual outputs of the neurons in the hidden layer:

$$y_j(p) = sigmoid\left[\sum_{i=1}^{n} x_i(p) \times w_{ij}(p) - \theta_j \right]$$

where n is the number of inputs of neuron j in the hidden layer, and *sigmoid* is the sigmoid activation function.

(b) Calculate the actual outputs of the neurons in the output layer:

$$y_k(p) = sigmoid \left[\sum_{j=1}^{m} x_{jk}(p) \times w_{jk}(p) - \theta_k \right]$$

where m is the number of inputs of neuron k in the output layer.

Step 3: *Weight training*

Update the weights in the back-propagation network propagating backwards the errors associated with output neurons.

(a) Calculate the error gradient for the neurons in the output layer:

$$\delta_k(p) = y_k(p) \times [1 - y_k(p)] \times e_k(p)$$

where

$$e_k(p) = y_{d,k}(p) - y_k(p)$$

Calculate the weight corrections:

$$\Delta w_{jk}(p) = \alpha \times y_j(p) \times \delta_k(p)$$

Update the weights at the output neurons:

$$w_{jk}(p + 1) = w_{jk}(p) + \Delta w_{jk}(p)$$

(b) Calculate the error gradient for the neurons in the hidden layer:

$$\delta_j(p) = y_j(p) \times [1 - y_j(p)] \times \sum_{k=1}^{l} \delta_k(p) \times w_{jk}(p)$$

Calculate the weight corrections:

$$\Delta w_{ij}(p) = \alpha \times x_i(p) \times \delta_j(p)$$

Update the weights at the hidden neurons:

$$w_{ij}(p + 1) = w_{ij}(p) + \Delta w_{ij}(p)$$

Step 4: *Iteration*

Increase iteration p by one, go back to Step 2 and repeat the process until the selected error criterion is satisfied.

As an example, we may consider the three-layer back-propagation network shown in Figure 6.10. Suppose that the network is required to perform logical operation Exclusive-OR. Recall that a single-layer perceptron could not do this operation. Now we will apply the three-layer net.

Neurons 1 and 2 in the input layer accept inputs x_1 and x_2, respectively, and redistribute these inputs to the neurons in the hidden layer without any processing:

$$x_{13} = x_{14} = x_1 \text{ and } x_{23} = x_{24} = x_2$$

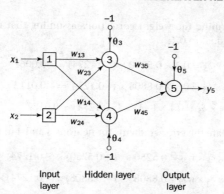

Figure 6.10 Three-layer network for solving the Exclusive-OR operation

The effect of the threshold applied to a neuron in the hidden or output layer is represented by its weight, θ, connected to a fixed input equal to -1.
The initial weights and threshold levels are set randomly as follows:

$w_{13} = 0.5$, $w_{14} = 0.9$, $w_{23} = 0.4$, $w_{24} = 1.0$, $w_{35} = -1.2$, $w_{45} = 1.1$, $\theta_3 = 0.8$, $\theta_4 = -0.1$ and $\theta_5 = 0.3$

Consider a training set where inputs x_1 and x_2 are equal to 1 and desired output $y_{d,5}$ is 0. The actual outputs of neurons 3 and 4 in the hidden layer are calculated as

$$y_3 = sigmoid\,(x_1 w_{13} + x_2 w_{23} - \theta_3) = 1/[1 + e^{-(1\times0.5+1\times0.4-1\times0.8)}] = 0.5250$$
$$y_4 = sigmoid\,(x_1 w_{14} + x_2 w_{24} - \theta_4) = 1/[1 + e^{-(1\times0.9+1\times1.0+1\times0.1)}] = 0.8808$$

Now the actual output of neuron 5 in the output layer is determined as

$$y_5 = sigmoid\,(y_3 w_{35} + y_4 w_{45} - \theta_5) = 1/[1 + e^{-(-0.5250\times1.2+0.8808\times1.1-1\times0.3)}] = 0.5097$$

Thus, the following error is obtained:

$$e = y_{d,5} - y_5 = 0 - 0.5097 = -0.5097$$

The next step is weight training. To update the weights and threshold levels in our network, we propagate the error, e, from the output layer backwards to the input layer.
First, we calculate the error gradient for neuron 5 in the output layer:

$$\delta_5 = y_5(1 - y_5)e = 0.5097 \times (1 - 0.5097) \times (-0.5097) = -0.1274$$

Then we determine the weight corrections assuming that the learning rate parameter, α, is equal to 0.1:

$$\Delta w_{35} = \alpha \times y_3 \times \delta_5 = 0.1 \times 0.5250 \times (-0.1274) = -0.0067$$

$$\Delta w_{45} = \alpha \times y_4 \times \delta_5 = 0.1 \times 0.8808 \times (-0.1274) = -0.0112$$

$$\Delta \theta_5 = \alpha \times (-1) \times \delta_5 = 0.1 \times (-1) \times (-0.1274) = 0.0127$$

Next we calculate the error gradients for neurons 3 and 4 in the hidden layer:

$$\delta_3 = y_3(1-y_3) \times \delta_5 \times w_{35} = 0.5250 \times (1-0.5250) \times (-0.1274) \times (-1.2) = 0.0381$$

$$\delta_4 = y_4(1-y_4) \times \delta_5 \times w_{45} = 0.8808 \times (1-0.8808) \times (-0.1274) \times 1.1 = -0.0147$$

We then determine the weight corrections:

$$\Delta w_{13} = \alpha \times x_1 \times \delta_3 = 0.1 \times 1 \times 0.0381 = 0.0038$$

$$\Delta w_{23} = \alpha \times x_2 \times \delta_3 = 0.1 \times 1 \times 0.0381 = 0.0038$$

$$\Delta \theta_3 = \alpha \times (-1) \times \delta_3 = 0.1 \times (-1) \times 0.0381 = -0.0038$$

$$\Delta w_{14} = \alpha \times x_1 \times \delta_4 = 0.1 \times 1 \times (-0.0147) = -0.0015$$

$$\Delta w_{24} = \alpha \times x_2 \times \delta_4 = 0.1 \times 1 \times (-0.0147) = -0.0015$$

$$\Delta \theta_4 = \alpha \times (-1) \times \delta_4 = 0.1 \times (-1) \times (-0.0147) = 0.0015$$

At last, we update all weights and threshold levels in our network:

$$w_{13} = w_{13} + \Delta w_{13} = 0.5 + 0.0038 = 0.5038$$

$$w_{14} = w_{14} + \Delta w_{14} = 0.9 - 0.0015 = 0.8985$$

$$w_{23} = w_{23} + \Delta w_{23} = 0.4 + 0.0038 = 0.4038$$

$$w_{24} = w_{24} + \Delta w_{24} = 1.0 - 0.0015 = 0.9985$$

$$w_{35} = w_{35} + \Delta w_{35} = -1.2 - 0.0067 = -1.2067$$

$$w_{45} = w_{45} + \Delta w_{45} = 1.1 - 0.0112 = 1.0888$$

$$\theta_3 = \theta_3 + \Delta \theta_3 = 0.8 - 0.0038 = 0.7962$$

$$\theta_4 = \theta_4 + \Delta \theta_4 = -0.1 + 0.0015 = -0.0985$$

$$\theta_5 = \theta_5 + \Delta \theta_5 = 0.3 + 0.0127 = 0.3127$$

The training process is repeated until the sum of squared errors is less than 0.001.

Why do we need to sum the squared errors?

The **sum of the squared errors** is a useful indicator of the network's performance. The back-propagation training algorithm attempts to minimise this criterion. When the value of the sum of squared errors in an entire pass through all

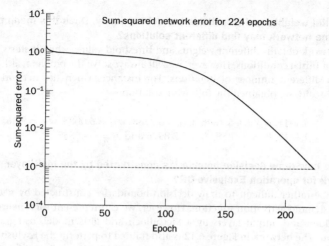

Figure 6.11 Learning curve for operation Exclusive-OR

training sets, or epoch, is **sufficiently small**, a network is considered to have **converged**. In our example, the sufficiently small sum of squared errors is defined as less than 0.001. Figure 6.11 represents a learning curve: the sum of squared errors plotted versus the number of epochs used in training. The learning curve shows how fast a network is learning.

It took 224 epochs or 896 iterations to train our network to perform the Exclusive-OR operation. The following set of final weights and threshold levels satisfied the chosen error criterion:

$$w_{13} = 4.7621,\ w_{14} = 6.3917,\ w_{23} = 4.7618,\ w_{24} = 6.3917,\ w_{35} = -10.3788,$$
$$w_{45} = 9.7691,\ \theta_3 = 7.3061,\ \theta_4 = 2.8441\ \text{and}\ \theta_5 = 4.5589$$

The network has solved the problem! We may now test our network by presenting all training sets and calculating the network's output. The results are shown in Table 6.4.

Table 6.4 Final results of three-layer network learning: the logical operation Exclusive-OR

Inputs		Desired output	Actual output	Error	Sum of squared
x_1	x_2	y_d	y_5	e	errors
1	1	0	0.0155	−0.0155	0.0010
0	1	1	0.9849	0.0151	
1	0	1	0.9849	0.0151	
0	0	0	0.0175	−0.0175	

The initial weights and thresholds are set randomly. Does this mean that the same network may find different solutions?

The network obtains different weights and threshold values when it starts from different initial conditions. However, we will always solve the problem, although using a different number of iterations. For instance, when the network was trained again, we obtained the following solution:

$$w_{13} = -6.3041, \ w_{14} = -5.7896, \ w_{23} = 6.2288, \ w_{24} = 6.0088, \ w_{35} = 9.6657,$$
$$w_{45} = -9.4242, \ \theta_3 = 3.3858, \ \theta_4 = -2.8976 \text{ and } \theta_5 = -4.4859$$

Can we now draw decision boundaries constructed by the multilayer network for operation Exclusive-OR?

It may be rather difficult to draw decision boundaries constructed by neurons with a sigmoid activation function. However, we can represent each neuron in the hidden and output layers by a McCulloch and Pitts model, using a sign function. The network in Figure 6.12 is also trained to perform the Exclusive-OR operation (Touretzky and Pomerlean, 1989; Haykin, 2008).

The positions of the decision boundaries constructed by neurons 3 and 4 in the hidden layer are shown in Figures 6.13(a) and (b), respectively. Neuron 5 in the output layer performs a linear combination of the decision boundaries formed by the two hidden neurons, as shown in Figure 6.13(c). The network in Figure 6.12 does indeed separate black and white dots and thus solves the Exclusive-OR problem.

Is back-propagation learning a good method for machine learning?

Although widely used, back-propagation learning is not immune from problems. For example, the back-propagation learning algorithm does not seem to function in the biological world (Stork, 1989). Biological neurons do not work backwards to adjust the strengths of their interconnections, synapses, and thus back-propagation learning cannot be viewed as a process that emulates brain-like learning.

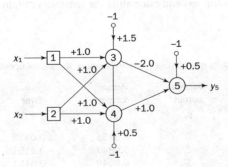

Figure 6.12 Network represented by McCulloch–Pitts model for solving the Exclusive-OR operation

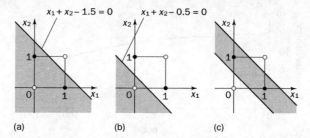

Figure 6.13 (a) Decision boundary constructed by hidden neuron 3 of the network in Figure 6.12; (b) decision boundary constructed by hidden neuron 4; (c) decision boundaries constructed by the complete three-layer network

Another apparent problem is that the calculations are extensive and, as a result, training is slow. In fact, a pure back-propagation algorithm is rarely used in practical applications.

There are several possible ways to improve the computational efficiency of the back-propagation algorithm (Jacobs, 1988; Stubbs, 1990; Caudill, 1991). Some of them are discussed below.

6.5 Accelerated learning in multilayer neural networks

A multilayer network, in general, learns much faster when the sigmoidal activation function is represented by a **hyperbolic tangent**,

$$Y^{tanh} = \frac{2a}{1 + e^{-bX}} - a \tag{6.16}$$

where a and b are constants.

Suitable values for a and b are: $a = 1.716$ and $b = 0.667$ (Guyon, 1991).

We also can accelerate training by including a **momentum term** in the delta rule of Eq. (6.12) (Rumelhart *et al.*, 1986):

$$\Delta w_{jk}(p) = \beta \times \Delta w_{jk}(p-1) + \alpha \times y_j(p) \times \delta_k(p) \tag{6.17}$$

where β is a positive number $(0 \leqslant \beta < 1)$ called the momentum constant. Typically, the momentum constant is set to 0.95.

Equation (6.17) is called the **generalised delta rule**. In a special case, when $\beta = 0$, we obtain the delta rule of Eq. (6.12).

Why do we need the momentum constant?

According to the observations made in Watrous (1987) and Jacobs (1988), the inclusion of momentum in the back-propagation algorithm has a **stabilising effect** on training. In other words, the inclusion of momentum tends to

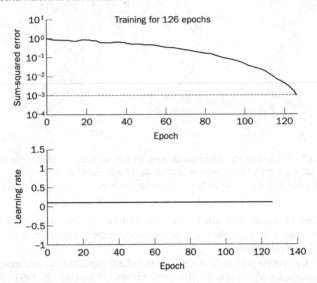

Figure 6.14 Learning with momentum

accelerate descent in the steady downhill direction, and to slow down the process when the learning surface exhibits peaks and valleys.

Figure 6.14 represents learning with momentum for operation Exclusive-OR. A comparison with a pure back-propagation algorithm shows that we reduced the number of epochs from 224 to 126.

In the delta and generalised delta rules, we use a constant and rather small value for the learning rate parameter, α. Can we increase this value to speed up training?

One of the most effective means to accelerate the convergence of back-propagation learning is to adjust the learning rate parameter during training. The small learning rate parameter, α, causes small changes to the weights in the network from one iteration to the next, and thus leads to the smooth learning curve. On the other hand, if the learning rate parameter, α, is made larger to speed up the training process, the resulting larger changes in the weights may cause instability and, as a result, the network may become oscillatory.

To accelerate the convergence and yet avoid the danger of instability, we can apply two heuristics (Jacobs, 1988):

- **Heuristic 1**. If the change of the sum of squared errors has the same algebraic sign for several consequent epochs, then the learning rate parameter, α, should be increased.

- **Heuristic 2**. If the algebraic sign of the change of the sum of squared errors alternates for several consequent epochs, then the learning rate parameter, α, should be decreased.

Adapting the learning rate requires some changes in the back-propagation algorithm. First, the network outputs and errors are calculated from the initial learning rate parameter. If the sum of squared errors at the current epoch exceeds the previous value by more than a predefined ratio (typically 1.04), the learning rate parameter is decreased (typically by multiplying by 0.7) and new weights and thresholds are calculated. However, if the error is less than the previous one, the learning rate is increased (typically by multiplying by 1.05).

Figure 6.15 represents an example of back-propagation training with adaptive learning rate. It demonstrates that adapting the learning rate can indeed decrease the number of iterations.

Learning rate adaptation can be used together with learning with momentum. Figure 6.16 shows the benefits of applying simultaneously both techniques.

The use of momentum and adaptive learning rate significantly improves the performance of a multilayer back-propagation neural network and minimises the chance that the network can become oscillatory.

Neural networks were designed on an analogy with the brain. The brain's memory, however, works by association. For example, we can recognise a familiar face even in an unfamiliar environment within 100–200 ms. We can also recall a complete sensory experience, including sounds and scenes, when we hear only a few bars of music. The brain routinely associates one thing with another.

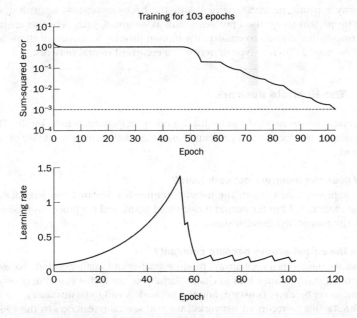

Figure 6.15 Learning with adaptive learning rate

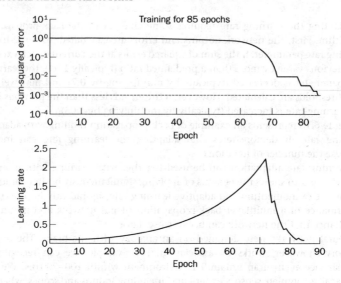

Figure 6.16 Learning with momentum and adaptive learning rate

Can a neural network simulate associative characteristics of the human memory?

Multilayer neural networks trained with the back-propagation algorithm are used for pattern recognition problems. But, as we noted, such networks are not intrinsically intelligent. To emulate the human memory's associative characteristics we need a different type of network: a **recurrent neural network**.

6.6 The Hopfield network

A recurrent neural network has feedback loops from its outputs to its inputs. The presence of such loops has a profound impact on the learning capability of the network.

How does the recurrent network learn?

After applying a new input, the network output is calculated and fed back to adjust the input. Then the output is calculated again, and the process is repeated until the output becomes constant.

Does the output always become constant?

Successive iterations do not always produce smaller and smaller output changes, but on the contrary may lead to chaotic behaviour. In such a case, the network output never becomes constant, and the network is said to be **unstable**.

The stability of recurrent networks intrigued several researchers in the 1960s and 1970s. However, none was able to predict which network would be stable,

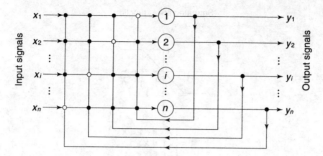

Figure 6.17 Single-layer n-neuron Hopfield network

and some researchers were pessimistic about finding a solution at all. The problem was solved only in 1982, when John Hopfield formulated the physical principle of storing information in a dynamically stable network (Hopfield, 1982).

Figure 6.17 shows a single-layer Hopfield network consisting of n neurons. The output of each neuron is fed back to the inputs of all other neurons (there is no self-feedback in the Hopfield network).

The Hopfield network usually uses McCulloch and Pitts neurons with the **sign activation function** as its computing element.

How does this function work here?

It works in a similar way to the sign function represented in Figure 6.4. If the neuron's weighted input is less than zero, the output is -1; if the input is greater than zero, the output is $+1$. However, if the neuron's weighted input is exactly zero, its output remains unchanged – in other words, a neuron remains in its previous state, regardless of whether it is $+1$ or -1.

$$
Y^{sign} = \begin{cases} +1, & \text{if } X > 0 \\ -1, & \text{if } X < 0 \\ Y, & \text{if } X = 0 \end{cases} \tag{6.18}
$$

The sign activation function may be replaced with a **saturated linear function**, which acts as a pure linear function within the region $[-1, 1]$ and as a sign function outside this region. The saturated linear function is shown in Figure 6.18.

The current state of the network is determined by the current outputs of all neurons, $y_1, y_2, \ldots, y_n$. Thus, for a single-layer n-neuron network, the state can be defined by the **state vector** as

$$
\mathbf{Y} = \begin{bmatrix} y_1 \\ y_2 \\ \vdots \\ y_n \end{bmatrix} \tag{6.19}
$$

Saturated linear function

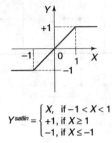

$$Y^{satlin} = \begin{cases} X, & \text{if } -1 < X < 1 \\ +1, & \text{if } X \geq 1 \\ -1, & \text{if } X \leq -1 \end{cases}$$

Figure 6.18   The saturated linear activation function

In the Hopfield network, synaptic weights between neurons are usually represented in matrix form as follows:

$$\mathbf{W} = \sum_{m=1}^{M} \mathbf{Y}_m \mathbf{Y}_m^T - M\mathbf{I} \tag{6.20}$$

where M is the number of states to be memorised by the network, $\mathbf{Y}_m$ is the n-dimensional binary vector, $\mathbf{I}$ is $n \times n$ identity matrix, and superscript T denotes a matrix transposition.

An operation of the Hopfield network can be represented geometrically. Figure 6.19 shows a three-neuron network represented as a cube in the three-dimensional space. In general, a network with n neurons has 2^n possible states and is associated with an n-dimensional hypercube. In Figure 6.19, each state is represented by a vertex. When a new input vector is applied, the network moves from one state-vertex to another until it becomes stable.

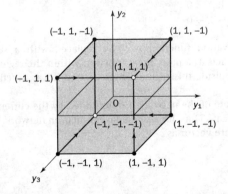

Figure 6.19   Cube representation of the possible states for the three-neuron Hopfield network

What determines a stable state-vertex?

The stable state-vertex is determined by the weight matrix **W**, the current input vector **X** and the threshold matrix θ. If the input vector is partially incorrect or incomplete, the initial state will converge into the stable state-vertex after a few iterations.

Suppose, for instance, that our network is required to memorise two opposite states, $(1, 1, 1)$ and $(-1, -1, -1)$. Thus,

$$Y_1 = \begin{bmatrix} 1 \\ 1 \\ 1 \end{bmatrix} \text{ and } Y_2 = \begin{bmatrix} -1 \\ -1 \\ -1 \end{bmatrix}$$

where Y_1 and Y_2 are the three-dimensional vectors.

We also can represent these vectors in the row, or *transposed*, form

$$Y_1^T = \begin{bmatrix} 1 & 1 & 1 \end{bmatrix} \text{ and } Y_2^T = \begin{bmatrix} -1 & -1 & -1 \end{bmatrix}$$

The 3×3 identity matrix **I** is

$$I = \begin{bmatrix} 1 & 0 & 0 \\ 0 & 1 & 0 \\ 0 & 0 & 1 \end{bmatrix}$$

Thus, we can now determine the weight matrix as follows:

$$W = Y_1 Y_1^T + Y_2 Y_2^T - 2I$$

or

$$W = \begin{bmatrix} 1 \\ 1 \\ 1 \end{bmatrix} \begin{bmatrix} 1 & 1 & 1 \end{bmatrix} + \begin{bmatrix} -1 \\ -1 \\ -1 \end{bmatrix} \begin{bmatrix} -1 & -1 & -1 \end{bmatrix} - 2 \begin{bmatrix} 1 & 0 & 0 \\ 0 & 1 & 0 \\ 0 & 0 & 1 \end{bmatrix} = \begin{bmatrix} 0 & 2 & 2 \\ 2 & 0 & 2 \\ 2 & 2 & 0 \end{bmatrix}$$

Next, the network is tested by the sequence of input vectors, X_1 and X_2, which are equal to the output (or target) vectors Y_1 and Y_2, respectively. We want to see whether our network is capable of recognising familiar patterns.

How is the Hopfield network tested?

First, we activate it by applying the input vector **X**. Then, we calculate the actual output vector **Y**, and finally, we compare the result with the initial input vector **X**.

$$Y_m = sign(W X_m - \theta), \quad m = 1, 2, \ldots, M \tag{6.21}$$

where θ is the threshold matrix.

In our example, we may assume all thresholds to be zero. Thus,

$$\mathbf{Y}_1 = sign \left\{ \begin{bmatrix} 0 & 2 & 2 \\ 2 & 0 & 2 \\ 2 & 2 & 0 \end{bmatrix} \begin{bmatrix} 1 \\ 1 \\ 1 \end{bmatrix} - \begin{bmatrix} 0 \\ 0 \\ 0 \end{bmatrix} \right\} = \begin{bmatrix} 1 \\ 1 \\ 1 \end{bmatrix}$$

and

$$\mathbf{Y}_2 = sign \left\{ \begin{bmatrix} 0 & 2 & 2 \\ 2 & 0 & 2 \\ 2 & 2 & 0 \end{bmatrix} \begin{bmatrix} -1 \\ -1 \\ -1 \end{bmatrix} - \begin{bmatrix} 0 \\ 0 \\ 0 \end{bmatrix} \right\} = \begin{bmatrix} -1 \\ -1 \\ -1 \end{bmatrix}$$

As we see, $\mathbf{Y}_1 = \mathbf{X}_1$ and $\mathbf{Y}_2 = \mathbf{X}_2$. Thus, both states, $(1, 1, 1)$ and $(-1, -1, -1)$, are said to be *stable*.

How about other states?

With three neurons in the network, there are eight possible states. The remaining six states are all unstable. However, stable states (also called **fundamental memories**) are capable of attracting states that are close to them. As shown in Table 6.5, the fundamental memory $(1, 1, 1)$ attracts unstable states $(-1, 1, 1)$, $(1, -1, 1)$ and $(1, 1, -1)$. Each of these unstable states represents a single error, compared to the fundamental memory $(1, 1, 1)$. On the other hand, the

Table 6.5 Operation of the three-neuron Hopfield network

Possible state	Iteration	Inputs			Outputs			Fundamental memory
		x_1	x_2	x_3	y_1	y_2	y_3	
1 1 1	0	1	1	1	1	1	1	1 1 1
−1 1 1	0	−1	1	1	1	1	1	
	1	1	1	1	1	1	1	1 1 1
1 −1 1	0	1	−1	1	1	1	1	
	1	1	1	1	1	1	1	1 1 1
1 1 −1	0	1	1	−1	1	1	1	
	1	1	1	1	1	1	1	1 1 1
−1 −1 −1	0	−1	−1	−1	−1	−1	−1	−1 −1 −1
−1 −1 1	0	−1	−1	1	−1	−1	−1	
	1	−1	−1	−1	−1	−1	−1	−1 −1 −1
−1 1 −1	0	−1	1	−1	−1	−1	−1	
	1	−1	−1	−1	−1	−1	−1	−1 −1 −1
1 −1 −1	0	1	−1	−1	−1	−1	−1	
	1	−1	−1	−1	−1	−1	−1	−1 −1 −1

fundamental memory $(-1, -1, -1)$ attracts unstable states $(-1, -1, 1)$, $(-1, 1, -1)$ and $(1, -1, -1)$. Here again, each of the unstable states represents a single error, compared to the fundamental memory. Thus, the Hopfield network can indeed act as an **error correction network**. Let us now summarise the Hopfield network training algorithm.

Step 1: *Storage*

The n-neuron Hopfield network is required to store a set of M fundamental memories, $\mathbf{Y}_1, \mathbf{Y}_2, \ldots, \mathbf{Y}_M$. The synaptic weight from neuron i to neuron j is calculated as

$$w_{ij} = \begin{cases} \displaystyle\sum_{m=1}^{M} y_{m,i}\, y_{m,j}, & i \neq j \\ 0, & i = j \end{cases} \qquad (6.22)$$

where $y_{m,i}$ and $y_{m,j}$ are the ith and the jth elements of the fundamental memory $\mathbf{Y}_m$, respectively. In matrix form, the synaptic weights between neurons are represented as

$$\mathbf{W} = \sum_{m=1}^{M} \mathbf{Y}_m \mathbf{Y}_m^T - M\mathbf{I}$$

The Hopfield network can store a set of fundamental memories if the weight matrix is symmetrical, with zeros in its main diagonal (Cohen and Grossberg, 1983). That is,

$$\mathbf{W} = \begin{bmatrix} 0 & w_{12} & \cdots & w_{1i} & \cdots & w_{1n} \\ w_{21} & 0 & \cdots & w_{2i} & \cdots & w_{2n} \\ \vdots & \vdots & & \vdots & & \vdots \\ w_{i1} & w_{i2} & \cdots & 0 & \cdots & w_{in} \\ \vdots & \vdots & & \vdots & & \vdots \\ w_{n1} & w_{n2} & \cdots & w_{ni} & \cdots & 0 \end{bmatrix} \qquad (6.23)$$

where $w_{ij} = w_{ji}$.

Once the weights are calculated, they remain fixed.

Step 2: *Testing*

We need to confirm that the Hopfield network is capable of recalling all fundamental memories. In other words, the network must recall any fundamental memory $\mathbf{Y}_m$ when presented with it as an input. That is,

$$x_{m,i} = y_{m,i}, \qquad i = 1, 2, \ldots, n; \qquad m = 1, 2, \ldots, M$$

$$y_{m,i} = sign\left(\sum_{j=1}^{n} w_{ij}\, x_{m,j} - \theta_i\right)$$

where $y_{m,i}$ is the ith element of the actual output vector $\mathbf{Y}_m$, and $x_{m,j}$ is the jth element of the input vector $\mathbf{X}_m$. In matrix form,

$$\mathbf{X}_m = \mathbf{Y}_m, \qquad m = 1, 2, \ldots, M$$
$$\mathbf{Y}_m = sign\,(\mathbf{W}\mathbf{X}_m - \boldsymbol{\theta})$$

If all fundamental memories are recalled perfectly we may proceed to the next step.

Step 3: *Retrieval*

Present an unknown n-dimensional vector (probe), $\mathbf{X}$, to the network and retrieve a stable state. Typically, the probe represents a corrupted or incomplete version of the fundamental memory, that is

$$\mathbf{X} \neq \mathbf{Y}_m, \qquad m = 1, 2, \ldots, M$$

(a) Initialise the retrieval algorithm of the Hopfield network by setting

$$x_j(0) = x_j \qquad j = 1, 2, \ldots, n$$

and calculate the initial state for each neuron

$$y_i(0) = sign\left(\sum_{j=1}^{n} w_{ij}\, x_j(0) - \theta_i\right), \qquad i = 1, 2, \ldots, n$$

where $x_j(0)$ is the jth element of the probe vector $\mathbf{X}$ at iteration $p = 0$, and $y_i(0)$ is the state of neuron i at iteration $p = 0$.

In matrix form, the state vector at iteration $p = 0$ is presented as

$$\mathbf{Y}(0) = sign\,[\mathbf{W}\mathbf{X}(0) - \boldsymbol{\theta}]$$

(b) Update the elements of the state vector, $\mathbf{Y}(p)$, according to the following rule:

$$y_i(p + 1) = sign\left(\sum_{j=1}^{n} w_{ij}\, x_j(p) - \theta_i\right)$$

Neurons for updating are selected **asynchronously**, that is randomly and one at a time.

Repeat the iteration until the state vector becomes unchanged, or in other words a stable state is achieved. The condition for stability can be defined as

$$y_i(p + 1) = sign\left(\sum_{j=1}^{n} w_{ij}\, y_j(p) - \theta_i\right), \qquad i = 1, 2, \ldots, n \qquad (6.24)$$

or, in matrix form,

$$\mathbf{Y}(p + 1) = sign\,[\mathbf{W}\mathbf{Y}(p) - \boldsymbol{\theta}] \qquad (6.25)$$

The Hopfield network will always converge to a stable state if the retrieval is done asynchronously (Haykin, 2008). However, this stable state does not necessarily represent one of the fundamental memories, and if it is a fundamental memory it is not necessarily the closest one.

Suppose, for example, we wish to store three fundamental memories in the five-neuron Hopfield network:

$$X_1 = (+1, +1, +1, +1, +1)$$
$$X_2 = (+1, -1, +1, -1, +1)$$
$$X_3 = (-1, +1, -1, +1, -1)$$

The weight matrix is constructed from Eq. (6.20),

$$
\mathbf{W} = \begin{bmatrix}
0 & -1 & 3 & -1 & 3 \\
-1 & 0 & -1 & 3 & -1 \\
3 & -1 & 0 & -1 & 3 \\
-1 & 3 & -1 & 0 & -1 \\
3 & -1 & 3 & -1 & 0
\end{bmatrix}
$$

Assume now that the probe vector is represented by

$$X = (+1, +1, -1, +1, +1)$$

If we compare this probe with the fundamental memory X_1, we find that these two vectors differ only in a single bit. Thus, we may expect that the probe X will converge to the fundamental memory X_1. However, when we apply the Hopfield network training algorithm described above, we obtain a different result. The pattern produced by the network recalls the memory X_3, a false memory.

This example reveals one of the problems inherent to the Hopfield network.

Another problem is the **storage capacity**, or the largest number of fundamental memories that can be stored and retrieved correctly. Hopfield showed experimentally (Hopfield, 1982) that the maximum number of fundamental memories M_{max} that can be stored in the n-neuron recurrent network is limited by

$$M_{max} = 0.15n \qquad (6.26)$$

We also may define the storage capacity of a Hopfield network on the basis that **most** of the fundamental memories are to be retrieved perfectly (Amit, 1989):

$$M_{max} = \frac{n}{2\ln n} \qquad (6.27)$$

What if we want all the fundamental memories to be retrieved perfectly?
It can be shown that to retrieve **all** the fundamental memories perfectly, their number must be halved (Amit, 1989):

$$M_{max} = \frac{n}{4 \ln n} \tag{6.28}$$

As we can see now, the storage capacity of a Hopfield network has to be kept rather small for the fundamental memories to be retrievable. This is a major limitation of the Hopfield network.

Strictly speaking, a Hopfield network represents an **autoassociative** type of memory. In other words, a Hopfield network can retrieve a corrupted or incomplete memory but cannot associate it with another different memory.

In contrast, human memory is essentially associative. One thing may remind us of another, and that of another, and so on. We use a chain of mental associations to recover a lost memory. If we, for example, forget where we left an umbrella, we try to recall where we last had it, what we were doing, and who we were talking to. Thus, we attempt to establish a chain of associations, and thereby to restore a lost memory.

Why can't a Hopfield network do this job?
The Hopfield network is a single-layer network, and thus the output pattern appears on the same set of neurons to which the input pattern was applied. To associate one memory with another, we need a recurrent neural network capable of accepting an input pattern on one set of neurons and producing a related, but different, output pattern on another set of neurons. In fact, we need a two-layer recurrent network, the **bidirectional associative memory**.

6.7 Bidirectional associative memory

Bidirectional associative memory (BAM), first proposed by Bart Kosko, is a heteroassociative network (Kosko, 1987; 1988). It associates patterns from one set, set A, to patterns from another set, set B, and vice versa. Like a Hopfield network, the BAM can generalise and also produce correct outputs despite corrupted or incomplete inputs. The basic BAM architecture is shown in Figure 6.20. It consists of two fully connected layers: an input layer and an output layer.

How does the BAM work?
The input vector $X(p)$ is applied to the transpose of weight matrix W^T to produce an output vector $Y(p)$, as illustrated in Figure 6.20(a). Then, the output vector $Y(p)$ is applied to the weight matrix W to produce a new input vector $X(p+1)$, as in Figure 6.20(b). This process is repeated until input and output vectors become unchanged, or in other words the BAM reaches a stable state.

The basic idea behind the BAM is to store pattern pairs so that when n-dimensional vector X from set A is presented as input, the BAM recalls

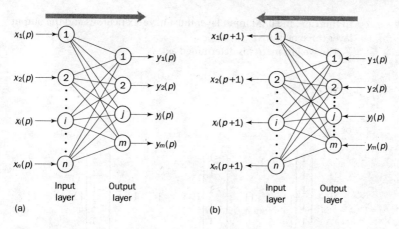

Figure 6.20 BAM operation: (a) forward direction; (b) backward direction

m-dimensional vector $\mathbf{Y}$ from set B, but when $\mathbf{Y}$ is presented as input, the BAM recalls $\mathbf{X}$.

To develop the BAM, we need to create a correlation matrix for each pattern pair we want to store. The correlation matrix is the matrix product of the input vector $\mathbf{X}$ and the transpose of the output vector $\mathbf{Y}^T$. The BAM weight matrix is the sum of all correlation matrices, that is

$$\mathbf{W} = \sum_{m=1}^{M} \mathbf{X}_m \mathbf{Y}_m^T \tag{6.29}$$

where M is the number of pattern pairs to be stored in the BAM.

Like a Hopfield network, the BAM usually uses McCulloch and Pitts neurons with the sign activation function.

The BAM training algorithm can be presented as follows.

Step 1: *Storage*

The BAM is required to store M pairs of patterns. For example, we may wish to store four pairs:

$$\text{Set } A\text{: } \mathbf{X}_1 = \begin{bmatrix} 1 \\ 1 \\ 1 \\ 1 \\ 1 \\ 1 \end{bmatrix} \quad \mathbf{X}_2 = \begin{bmatrix} -1 \\ -1 \\ -1 \\ -1 \\ -1 \\ -1 \end{bmatrix} \quad \mathbf{X}_3 = \begin{bmatrix} 1 \\ 1 \\ -1 \\ -1 \\ 1 \\ 1 \end{bmatrix} \quad \mathbf{X}_4 = \begin{bmatrix} -1 \\ -1 \\ 1 \\ 1 \\ -1 \\ -1 \end{bmatrix}$$

$$\text{Set } B\text{: } \mathbf{Y}_1 = \begin{bmatrix} 1 \\ 1 \\ 1 \end{bmatrix} \quad \mathbf{Y}_2 = \begin{bmatrix} -1 \\ -1 \\ -1 \end{bmatrix} \quad \mathbf{Y}_3 = \begin{bmatrix} 1 \\ -1 \\ 1 \end{bmatrix} \quad \mathbf{Y}_4 = \begin{bmatrix} -1 \\ 1 \\ -1 \end{bmatrix}$$

In this case, the BAM input layer must have six neurons and the output layer three neurons.

The weight matrix is determined as

$$W = \sum_{m=1}^{4} X_m Y_m^T$$

or

$$W = \begin{bmatrix} 1 \\ 1 \\ 1 \\ 1 \\ 1 \\ 1 \end{bmatrix} [1 \quad 1 \quad 1] + \begin{bmatrix} -1 \\ -1 \\ -1 \\ -1 \\ -1 \\ -1 \end{bmatrix} [-1 \quad -1 \quad -1] + \begin{bmatrix} 1 \\ 1 \\ -1 \\ -1 \\ 1 \\ 1 \end{bmatrix} [1 \quad -1 \quad 1]$$

$$+ \begin{bmatrix} -1 \\ -1 \\ 1 \\ 1 \\ -1 \\ -1 \end{bmatrix} [-1 \quad 1 \quad -1] = \begin{bmatrix} 4 & 0 & 4 \\ 4 & 0 & 4 \\ 0 & 4 & 0 \\ 0 & 4 & 0 \\ 4 & 0 & 4 \\ 4 & 0 & 4 \end{bmatrix}$$

Step 2: *Testing*

The BAM should be able to receive any vector from set A and retrieve the associated vector from set B, and receive any vector from set B and retrieve the associated vector from set A. Thus, first we need to confirm that the BAM is able to recall Y_m when presented with X_m. That is,

$$Y_m = sign\,(W^T X_m), \qquad m = 1, 2, \dots, M \tag{6.30}$$

For instance,

$$Y_1 = sign\,(W^T X_1) = sign\left\{ \begin{bmatrix} 4 & 4 & 0 & 0 & 4 & 4 \\ 0 & 0 & 4 & 4 & 0 & 0 \\ 4 & 4 & 0 & 0 & 4 & 4 \end{bmatrix} \begin{bmatrix} 1 \\ 1 \\ 1 \\ 1 \\ 1 \\ 1 \end{bmatrix} \right\} = \begin{bmatrix} 1 \\ 1 \\ 1 \end{bmatrix}$$

Then, we confirm that the BAM recalls X_m when presented with Y_m. That is,

$$X_m = sign\,(W Y_m), \qquad m = 1, 2, \dots, M \tag{6.31}$$

For instance,

$$X_3 = sign\,(W\,Y_3) = sign\left\{\begin{bmatrix} 4 & 0 & 4 \\ 4 & 0 & 4 \\ 0 & 4 & 0 \\ 0 & 4 & 0 \\ 4 & 0 & 4 \\ 4 & 0 & 4 \end{bmatrix}\begin{bmatrix} 1 \\ -1 \\ 1 \end{bmatrix}\right\} = \begin{bmatrix} 1 \\ 1 \\ -1 \\ -1 \\ 1 \\ 1 \end{bmatrix}$$

In our example, all four pairs are recalled perfectly, and we can proceed to the next step.

Step 3: *Retrieval*

Present an unknown vector (probe) X to the BAM and retrieve a stored association. The probe may present a corrupted or incomplete version of a pattern from set A (or from set B) stored in the BAM. That is,

$$X \neq X_m, \qquad m = 1, 2, \ldots, M$$

(a) Initialise the BAM retrieval algorithm by setting

$$X(0) = X, \qquad p = 0$$

and calculate the BAM output at iteration p

$$Y(p) = sign\,[W^T\,X(p)]$$

(b) Update the input vector $X(p)$:

$$X(p+1) = sign\,[W\,Y(p)]$$

and repeat the iteration until equilibrium, when input and output vectors remain unchanged with further iterations. The input and output patterns will then represent an associated pair.

The BAM is unconditionally stable (Kosko, 1992). This means that any set of associations can be learned without risk of instability. This important quality arises from the BAM using the transpose relationship between weight matrices in forward and backward directions.

Let us now return to our example. Suppose we use vector X as a probe. It represents a single error compared with the pattern X_1 from set A:

$$X = (-1, +1, +1, +1, +1, +1)$$

This probe applied as the BAM input produces the output vector Y_1 from set B. The vector Y_1 is then used as input to retrieve the vector X_1 from set A. Thus, the BAM is indeed capable of error correction.

There is also a close relationship between the BAM and the Hopfield network. If the BAM weight matrix is square and symmetrical, then $W = W^T$. In this case, input and output layers are of the same size, and the BAM can be reduced to the autoassociative Hopfield network. Thus, the Hopfield network can be considered as a BAM special case.

The constraints imposed on the storage capacity of the Hopfield network can also be extended to the BAM. In general, the maximum number of associations to be stored in the BAM should not exceed the number of neurons in the smaller layer. Another, even more serious, problem is incorrect convergence. The BAM may not always produce the closest association. In fact, a stable association may be only slightly related to the initial input vector.

The BAM still remains the subject of intensive research. However, despite all its current problems and limitations, the BAM promises to become one of the most useful ANNs.

Can a neural network learn without a 'teacher'?

The main property of a neural network is an ability to learn from its environment, and to improve its performance through learning. So far we have considered **supervised** or **active learning** – learning with an external 'teacher' or a supervisor who presents a training set to the network. But another type of learning also exists: **unsupervised learning**.

In contrast to supervised learning, unsupervised or **self-organised learning** does not require an external teacher. During the training session, the neural network receives a number of different input patterns, discovers significant features in these patterns and learns how to classify input data into appropriate categories. Unsupervised learning tends to follow the neuro-biological organisation of the brain.

Unsupervised learning algorithms aim to learn rapidly. In fact, self-organising neural networks learn much faster than back-propagation networks, and thus can be used in real time.

6.8 Self-organising neural networks

Self-organising neural networks are effective in dealing with unexpected and changing conditions. In this section, we consider Hebbian and competitive learning, which are based on self-organising networks.

6.8.1 Hebbian learning

In 1949, neuropsychologist Donald Hebb proposed one of the key ideas in biological learning, commonly known as Hebb's Law (Hebb, 1949). Hebb's Law states that if neuron i is near enough to excite neuron j and repeatedly participates in its activation, the synaptic connection between these two neurons is strengthened and neuron j becomes more sensitive to stimuli from neuron i.

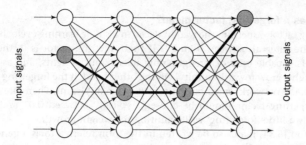

Figure 6.21   Hebbian learning in a neural network

We can represent Hebb's Law in the form of two rules as follows (Stent, 1973):

1. If two neurons on either side of a connection are activated synchronously, then the weight of that connection is increased.

2. If two neurons on either side of a connection are activated asynchronously, then the weight of that connection is decreased.

Hebb's Law provides the basis for learning without a teacher. Learning here is a local phenomenon occurring without feedback from the environment. Figure 6.21 shows Hebbian learning in a neural network.

Using Hebb's Law we can express the adjustment applied to the weight w_{ij} at iteration p in the following form:

$$\Delta w_{ij}(p) = F[y_j(p), x_i(p)] \tag{6.32}$$

where $F[y_j(p), x_i(p)]$ is a function of both postsynaptic and presynaptic activities. As a special case, we can represent Hebb's Law as follows (Haykin, 2008):

$$\Delta w_{ij}(p) = \alpha y_j(p) x_i(p) \tag{6.33}$$

where α is the learning rate parameter.

This equation is referred to as the **activity product rule**. It shows how a change in the weight of the synaptic connection between a pair of neurons is related to a product of the incoming and outgoing signals.

Hebbian learning implies that weights can only increase. In other words, Hebb's Law allows the strength of a connection to increase, but it does not provide a means to decrease the strength. Thus, repeated application of the input signal may drive the weight w_{ij} into saturation. To resolve this problem, we might impose a limit on the growth of synaptic weights. It can be done by introducing a non-linear **forgetting factor** into Hebb's Law in Eq. (6.33) as follows (Kohonen, 1989):

$$\Delta w_{ij}(p) = \alpha y_j(p) x_i(p) - \phi y_j(p) w_{ij}(p) \tag{6.34}$$

where ϕ is the forgetting factor.

What does a forgetting factor mean?

Forgetting factor ϕ specifies the weight decay in a single learning cycle. It usually falls in the interval between 0 and 1. If the forgetting factor is 0, the neural network is capable only of strengthening its synaptic weights, and as a result these weights grow towards infinity. On the other hand, if the forgetting factor is close to 1, the network remembers very little of what it learns. Therefore, a rather small forgetting factor should be chosen, typically between 0.01 and 0.1, to allow only a little 'forgetting' while limiting the weight growth.

Equation (6.34) may also be written in the form referred to as a **generalised activity product rule**

$$\Delta w_{ij}(p) = \phi y_j(p)[\lambda x_i(p) - w_{ij}(p)] \tag{6.35}$$

where $\lambda = \alpha/\phi$.

The generalised activity product rule implies that, if the presynaptic activity (input of neuron i) at iteration p, $x_i(p)$, is less than $w_{ij}(p)/\lambda$, then the modified synaptic weight at iteration $(p+1)$, $w_{ij}(p+1)$, will decrease by an amount proportional to the postsynaptic activity (output of neuron j) at iteration p, $y_j(p)$. On the other hand, if $x_i(p)$ is greater than $w_{ij}(p)/\lambda$, then the modified synaptic weight at iteration $(p+1)$, $w_{ij}(p+1)$, will increase also in proportion to the output of neuron j, $y_j(p)$. In other words, we can determine the **activity balance point** for modifying the synaptic weight as a variable equal to $w_{ij}(p)/\lambda$. This approach solves the problem of an infinite increase of the synaptic weights.

Let us now derive the generalised Hebbian learning algorithm.

Step 1:   *Initialisation*

Set initial synaptic weights and thresholds to small random values, say in an interval [0, 1]. Also assign small positive values to the learning rate parameter α and forgetting factor ϕ.

Step 2:   *Activation*

Compute the neuron output at iteration p

$$y_j(p) = \sum_{i=1}^{n} x_i(p) w_{ij}(p) - \theta_j$$

where n is the number of neuron inputs, and θ_j is the threshold value of neuron j.

Step 3:   *Learning*

Update the weights in the network:

$$w_{ij}(p+1) = w_{ij}(p) + \Delta w_{ij}(p)$$

where $\Delta w_{ij}(p)$ is the weight correction at iteration p.

The weight correction is determined by the generalised activity product rule:

$$\Delta w_{ij}(p) = \phi y_j(p)[\lambda x_i(p) - w_{ij}(p)]$$

Step 4: *Iteration*

Increase iteration p by one, go back to Step 2 and continue until the synaptic weights reach their steady-state values.

To illustrate Hebbian learning, consider a fully connected feedforward network with a single layer of five computation neurons, as shown in Figure 6.22(a). Each neuron is represented by a McCulloch and Pitts model with the sign activation function. The network is trained with the generalised activity product rule on the following set of input vectors:

$$\mathbf{X}_1 = \begin{bmatrix} 0 \\ 0 \\ 0 \\ 0 \\ 0 \end{bmatrix} \quad \mathbf{X}_2 = \begin{bmatrix} 0 \\ 1 \\ 0 \\ 0 \\ 1 \end{bmatrix} \quad \mathbf{X}_3 = \begin{bmatrix} 0 \\ 0 \\ 0 \\ 1 \\ 0 \end{bmatrix} \quad \mathbf{X}_4 = \begin{bmatrix} 0 \\ 0 \\ 1 \\ 0 \\ 0 \end{bmatrix} \quad \mathbf{X}_5 = \begin{bmatrix} 0 \\ 1 \\ 0 \\ 0 \\ 1 \end{bmatrix}$$

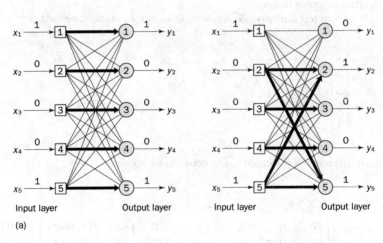

(a)

(b)

Figure 6.22 Unsupervised Hebbian learning in a single-layer network: (a) initial and final states of the network; (b) initial and final weight matrices

Here, the input vector X_1 is the null vector. As you may also notice, input signals x_4 (in the vector X_3) and x_3 (in the vector X_4) are the only unity components in the corresponding vectors, while unity signals x_2 and x_5 always come together, as seen in the vectors X_2 and X_5.

In our example, the initial weight matrix is represented by the 5×5 identity matrix I. Thus, in the initial state, each of the neurons in the input layer is connected to the neuron in the same position in the output layer with a synaptic weight of 1, and to the other neurons with weights of 0. The thresholds are set to random numbers in the interval between 0 and 1. The learning rate parameter α and forgetting factor ϕ are taken as 0.1 and 0.02, respectively.

After training, as can be seen from Figure 6.22(b), the weight matrix becomes different from the initial identity matrix I. The weights between neuron 2 in the input layer and neuron 5 in the output layer, and neuron 5 in the input layer and neuron 2 in the output layer, have increased from 0 to 2.0204. Our network has learned new associations. At the same time, the weight between neuron 1 in the input layer and neuron 1 in the output layer has become 0. The network has forgotten this association.

Let us now test our network. A test input vector, or probe, is defined as

$$X = \begin{bmatrix} 1 \\ 0 \\ 0 \\ 0 \\ 1 \end{bmatrix}$$

When this probe is presented to the network, we obtain

$$Y = sign\,(W\,X - \theta)$$

$$Y = sign \left\{ \begin{bmatrix} 0 & 0 & 0 & 0 & 0 \\ 0 & 2.0204 & 0 & 0 & 2.0204 \\ 0 & 0 & 1.0200 & 0 & 0 \\ 0 & 0 & 0 & 0.9996 & 0 \\ 0 & 2.0204 & 0 & 0 & 2.0204 \end{bmatrix} \begin{bmatrix} 1 \\ 0 \\ 0 \\ 0 \\ 1 \end{bmatrix} - \begin{bmatrix} 0.4940 \\ 0.2661 \\ 0.0907 \\ 0.9478 \\ 0.0737 \end{bmatrix} \right\} = \begin{bmatrix} 0 \\ 1 \\ 0 \\ 0 \\ 1 \end{bmatrix}$$

Sure enough, the network has associated input x_5 with outputs y_2 and y_5 because inputs x_2 and x_5 were coupled during training. But the network cannot associate input x_1 with output y_1 any more because unity input x_1 did not appear during training and our network has lost the ability to recognise it.

Thus, a neural network really can learn to associate stimuli commonly presented together, and, most important, the network can learn without a 'teacher'.

6.8.2 Competitive learning

Another popular type of unsupervised learning is **competitive learning**. In competitive learning, neurons compete among themselves to be activated. While in Hebbian learning, several output neurons can be activated simultaneously, in competitive learning only a single output neuron is active at any time. The output neuron that wins the 'competition' is called the **winner-takes-all** neuron.

The basic idea of competitive learning was introduced in the early 1970s (Grossberg, 1972; von der Malsburg, 1973; Fukushima, 1975). However, competitive learning did not attract much interest until the late 1980s, when Teuvo Kohonen introduced a special class of ANNs called **self-organising feature maps** (Kohonen, 1989). These maps are based on competitive learning.

What is a self-organising feature map?

Our brain is dominated by the cerebral cortex, a very complex structure of billions of neurons and hundreds of billions of synapses. The cortex is neither uniform nor homogeneous. It includes areas, identified by the thickness of their layers and the types of neurons within them, that are responsible for different human activities (motor, visual, auditory, somatosensory, etc.), and thus associated with different sensory inputs. We can say that each sensory input is mapped into a corresponding area of the cerebral cortex; in other words, the cortex is a self-organising computational map in the human brain.

Can we model the self-organising map?

Kohonen formulated the **principle of topographic map formation** (Kohonen, 1990). This principle states that the spatial location of an output neuron in the topographic map corresponds to a particular feature of the input pattern. Kohonen also proposed the feature-mapping model shown in Figure 6.23 (Kohonen, 1982). This model captures the main features of self-organising maps in the brain and yet can be easily represented in a computer.

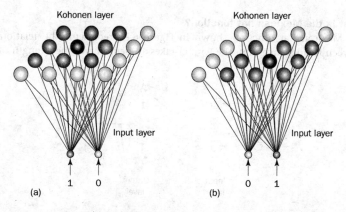

Figure 6.23   Feature-mapping Kohonen model

The Kohonen model provides a topological mapping, placing a fixed number of input patterns from the input layer into a higher-dimensional output or Kohonen layer. In Figure 6.23, the Kohonen layer consists of a two-dimensional lattice made up of 4-by-4 neurons, with each neuron having two inputs. The winning neuron is shown in black and its neighbours in grey. Here, the winner's neighbours are neurons in close physical proximity to the winner.

How close is 'close physical proximity'?

How close physical proximity is, is determined by the network designer. The winner's neighbourhood may include neurons within one, two or even three positions on either side. For example, Figure 6.23 depicts the winner's neighbourhood of size one. Generally, training in the Kohonen network begins with the winner's neighbourhood of a fairly large size. Then, as training proceeds, the neighbourhood size gradually decreases.

The Kohonen network consists of a single layer of computation neurons, but it has two different types of connections. There are **forward connections** from the neurons in the input layer to the neurons in the output layer, and also **lateral connections** between neurons in the output layer, as shown in Figure 6.24. The lateral connections are used to create a competition between neurons. The neuron with the largest activation level among all neurons in the output layer becomes the winner (the winner-takes-all neuron). This neuron is the only neuron that produces an output signal. The activity of all other neurons is suppressed in the competition.

When an input pattern is presented to the network, each neuron in the Kohonen layer receives a full copy of the input pattern, modified by its path through the weights of the synaptic connections between the input layer and the Kohonen layer. The lateral feedback connections produce excitatory or inhibitory effects, depending on the distance from the winning neuron. This is achieved by the use of a **Mexican hat function** which describes synaptic weights between neurons in the Kohonen layer.

What is the Mexican hat function?

The Mexican hat function shown in Figure 6.25 represents the relationship between the distance from the winner-takes-all neuron and the strength of the

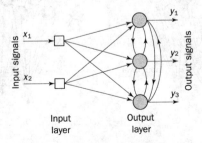

Figure 6.24 Architecture of the Kohonen network

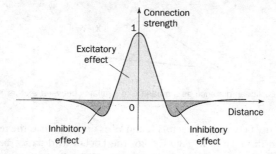

Figure 6.25   The Mexican hat function of lateral connection

connections within the Kohonen layer. According to this function, the near neighbourhood (a short-range lateral excitation area) has a strong excitatory effect, remote neighbourhood (an inhibitory penumbra) has a mild inhibitory effect and very remote neighbourhood (an area surrounding the inhibitory penumbra) has a weak excitatory effect, which is usually neglected.

In the Kohonen network, a neuron learns by shifting its weights from inactive connections to active ones. Only the winning neuron and its neighbourhood are allowed to learn. If a neuron does not respond to a given input pattern, then learning cannot occur in that particular neuron.

The output signal, y_j, of the winner-takes-all neuron j is set equal to one and the output signals of all the other neurons (the neurons that lose the competition) are set to zero.

The **standard competitive learning rule** (Haykin, 2008) defines the change Δw_{ij} applied to synaptic weight w_{ij} as

$$\Delta w_{ij} = \begin{cases} \alpha(x_i - w_{ij}), & \text{if neuron } j \text{ wins the competition} \\ 0, & \text{if neuron } j \text{ loses the competition} \end{cases} \quad (6.36)$$

where x_i is the input signal and α is the **learning rate parameter**. The learning rate parameter lies in the range between 0 and 1.

The overall effect of the competitive learning rule resides in moving the synaptic weight vector $\mathbf{W}_j$ of the winning neuron j towards the input pattern $\mathbf{X}$. The matching criterion is equivalent to the minimum **Euclidean distance** between vectors.

What is the Euclidean distance?

The Euclidean distance between a pair of n-by-1 vectors $\mathbf{X}$ and $\mathbf{W}_j$ is defined by

$$d = \|\mathbf{X} - \mathbf{W}_j\| = \left[\sum_{i=1}^{n} (x_i - w_{ij})^2 \right]^{1/2} \quad (6.37)$$

where x_i and w_{ij} are the ith elements of the vectors $\mathbf{X}$ and $\mathbf{W}_j$, respectively.

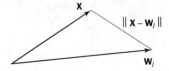

Figure 6.26 Euclidean distance as a measure of similarity between vectors **X** and **W**_j

The similarity between the vectors X and $\mathbf{W}_j$ is determined as the reciprocal of the Euclidean distance d. In Figure 6.26, the Euclidean distance between the vectors X and $\mathbf{W}_j$ is presented as the length of the line joining the tips of those vectors. Figure 6.26 clearly demonstrates that the smaller the Euclidean distance is, the greater will be the similarity between the vectors X and $\mathbf{W}_j$.

To identify the winning neuron, $j_{\mathbf{X}}$, that best matches the input vector X, we may apply the following condition (Haykin, 2008):

$$j_{\mathbf{X}} = \min_j \|\mathbf{X} - \mathbf{W}_j\|, \qquad j = 1, 2, \dots, m \tag{6.38}$$

where m is the number of neurons in the Kohonen layer.

Suppose, for instance, that the two-dimensional input vector X is presented to the three-neuron Kohonen network,

$$\mathbf{X} = \begin{bmatrix} 0.52 \\ 0.12 \end{bmatrix}$$

The initial weight vectors, $\mathbf{W}_j$, are given by

$$\mathbf{W}_1 = \begin{bmatrix} 0.27 \\ 0.81 \end{bmatrix} \quad \mathbf{W}_2 = \begin{bmatrix} 0.42 \\ 0.70 \end{bmatrix} \quad \mathbf{W}_3 = \begin{bmatrix} 0.43 \\ 0.21 \end{bmatrix}$$

We find the winning (best-matching) neuron $j_{\mathbf{X}}$ using the minimum-distance Euclidean criterion:

$$d_1 = \sqrt{(x_1 - w_{11})^2 + (x_2 - w_{21})^2} = \sqrt{(0.52 - 0.27)^2 + (0.12 - 0.81)^2} = 0.73$$

$$d_2 = \sqrt{(x_1 - w_{12})^2 + (x_2 - w_{22})^2} = \sqrt{(0.52 - 0.42)^2 + (0.12 - 0.70)^2} = 0.59$$

$$d_3 = \sqrt{(x_1 - w_{13})^2 + (x_2 - w_{23})^2} = \sqrt{(0.52 - 0.43)^2 + (0.12 - 0.21)^2} = 0.13$$

Thus, neuron 3 is the winner and its weight vector $\mathbf{W}_3$ is to be updated according to the competitive learning rule described in Eq. (6.36). Assuming that the learning rate parameter α is equal to 0.1, we obtain

$$\Delta w_{13} = \alpha(x_1 - w_{13}) = 0.1(0.52 - 0.43) = 0.01$$

$$\Delta w_{23} = \alpha(x_2 - w_{23}) = 0.1(0.12 - 0.21) = -0.01$$

The updated weight vector $\mathbf{W}_3$ at iteration $(p+1)$ is determined as

$$\mathbf{W}_3(p+1) = \mathbf{W}_3(p) + \Delta\mathbf{W}_3(p) = \begin{bmatrix} 0.43 \\ 0.21 \end{bmatrix} + \begin{bmatrix} 0.01 \\ -0.01 \end{bmatrix} = \begin{bmatrix} 0.44 \\ 0.20 \end{bmatrix}$$

The weight vector $\mathbf{W}_3$ of the winning neuron 3 becomes closer to the input vector $\mathbf{X}$ with each iteration.

Let us now summarise the competitive learning algorithm as follows (Kohonen, 1989):

Step 1: *Initialisation*
Set initial synaptic weights to small random values, say in an interval $[0, 1]$, and assign a small positive value to the learning rate parameter α.

Step 2: *Activation and similarity matching*
Activate the Kohonen network by applying the input vector $\mathbf{X}$, and find the winner-takes-all (best-matching) neuron $j_{\mathbf{X}}$ at iteration p, using the minimum-distance Euclidean criterion

$$j_{\mathbf{X}}(p) = \min_{j} \|\mathbf{X} - \mathbf{W}_j(p)\| = \left\{ \sum_{i=1}^{n} [x_i - w_{ij}(p)]^2 \right\}^{1/2}, \quad j = 1, 2, \ldots, m$$

where n is the number of neurons in the input layer, and m is the number of neurons in the output or Kohonen layer.

Step 3: *Learning*
Update the synaptic weights

$$w_{ij}(p+1) = w_{ij}(p) + \Delta w_{ij}(p)$$

where $\Delta w_{ij}(p)$ is the weight correction at iteration p.

The weight correction is determined by the competitive learning rule

$$\Delta w_{ij}(p) = \begin{cases} \alpha[x_i - w_{ij}(p)], & j \in \Lambda_j(p) \\ 0, & j \notin \Lambda_j(p) \end{cases} \tag{6.39}$$

where α is the learning rate parameter, and $\Lambda_j(p)$ is the neighbourhood function centred around the winner-takes-all neuron $j_{\mathbf{X}}$ at iteration p.

The neighbourhood function Λ_j usually has a constant amplitude. It implies that all the neurons located inside the topological neighbourhood are activated simultaneously, and the relationship among those neurons is independent of their distance from the winner-takes-all neuron $j_{\mathbf{X}}$. This simple form of a neighbourhood function is shown in Figure 6.27.

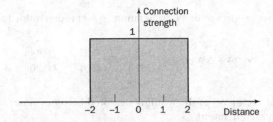

Figure 6.27 Rectangular neighbourhood function

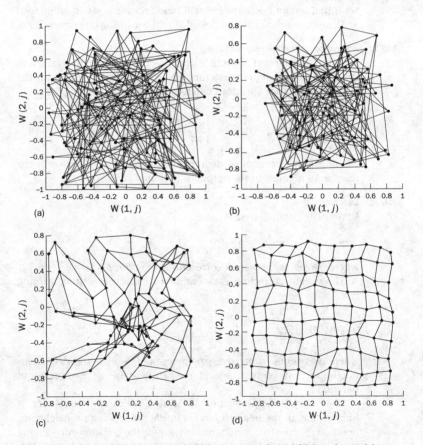

Figure 6.28 Competitive learning in the Kohonen network: (a) initial random weights; (b) network after 100 iterations; (c) network after 1000 iterations; (d) network after 10,000 iterations

The rectangular neighbourhood function Λ_j takes on a binary character. Thus, identifying the neuron outputs, we may write

$$y_j = \begin{cases} 1, & j \in \Lambda_j(p) \\ 0, & j \notin \Lambda_j(p) \end{cases} \tag{6.40}$$

Step 4: *Iteration*

Increase iteration p by one, go back to Step 2 and continue until the minimum-distance Euclidean criterion is satisfied, or no noticeable changes occur in the feature map.

To illustrate competitive learning, consider the Kohonen network with 100 neurons arranged in the form of a two-dimensional lattice with 10 rows and 10 columns. The network is required to classify two-dimensional input vectors. In other words, each neuron in the network should respond only to the input vectors occurring in its region.

The network is trained with 1000 two-dimensional input vectors generated randomly in a square region in the interval between -1 and $+1$. Initial synaptic weights are also set to random values in the interval between -1 and $+1$, and the learning rate parameter α is equal to 0.1.

Figure 6.28 demonstrates different stages in the process of network learning. Each neuron is represented by a black dot at the location of its two weights, w_{1j} and w_{2j}. Figure 6.28(a) shows the initial synaptic weights randomly distributed in the square region. Figures 6.28(b), (c) and (d) present the weight vectors in the input space after 100, 1000 and 10,000 iterations, respectively.

The results shown in Figure 6.28 demonstrate the self-organisation of the Kohonen network that characterises unsupervised learning. At the end of the learning process, the neurons are mapped in the correct order and the map itself spreads out to fill the input space. Each neuron now is able to identify input vectors in its own input space.

To see how neurons respond, let us test our network by applying the following input vectors:

$$\mathbf{X}_1 = \begin{bmatrix} 0.2 \\ 0.9 \end{bmatrix} \quad \mathbf{X}_2 = \begin{bmatrix} 0.6 \\ -0.2 \end{bmatrix} \quad \mathbf{X}_3 = \begin{bmatrix} -0.7 \\ -0.8 \end{bmatrix}$$

As illustrated in Figure 6.29, neuron 6 responds to the input vector $\mathbf{X}_1$, neuron 69 responds to the input vector $\mathbf{X}_2$ and neuron 92 to the input vector $\mathbf{X}_3$. Thus, the feature map displayed in the input space in Figure 6.29 is topologically ordered and the spatial location of a neuron in the lattice corresponds to a particular feature of input patterns.

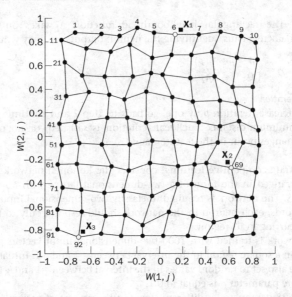

Figure 6.29 Topologically ordered feature map displayed in the input space

6.9 Summary

In this chapter, we introduced artificial neural networks and discussed the basic ideas behind machine learning. We presented the concept of a perceptron as a simple computing element and considered the perceptron learning rule. We explored multilayer neural networks and discussed how to improve the computational efficiency of the back-propagation learning algorithm. Then we introduced recurrent neural networks, considered the Hopfield network training algorithm and bidirectional associative memory (BAM). Finally, we presented self-organising neural networks and explored Hebbian and competitive learning.

The most important lessons learned in this chapter are:

- Machine learning involves adaptive mechanisms that enable computers to learn from experience, learn by example and learn by analogy. Learning capabilities can improve the performance of an intelligent system over time. One of the most popular approaches to machine learning is artificial neural networks.

- An artificial neural network consists of a number of very simple and highly interconnected processors, called neurons, which are analogous to the biological neurons in the brain. The neurons are connected by weighted links that pass signals from one neuron to another. Each link has a numerical weight associated with it. Weights are the basic means of long-term memory in ANNs. They express the strength, or importance, of each neuron input. A neural network 'learns' through repeated adjustments of these weights.

- In the 1940s, Warren McCulloch and Walter Pitts proposed a simple neuron model that is still the basis for most ANNs. The neuron computes the weighted sum of the input signals and compares the result with a threshold value. If the net input is less than the threshold, the neuron output is -1. But if the net input is greater than or equal to the threshold, the neuron becomes activated and its output attains a value $+1$.

- Frank Rosenblatt suggested the simplest form of a neural network, which he called a perceptron. The operation of the perceptron is based on the McCulloch and Pitts neuron model. It consists of a single neuron with adjustable synaptic weights and a hard limiter. The perceptron learns its task by making small adjustments in the weights to reduce the difference between the actual and desired outputs. The initial weights are randomly assigned and then updated to obtain the output consistent with the training examples.

- A perceptron can learn only linearly separable functions and cannot make global generalisations on the basis of examples learned locally. The limitations of Rosenblatt's perceptron can be overcome by advanced forms of neural networks, such as multilayer perceptrons trained with the back-propagation algorithm.

- A multilayer perceptron is a feedforward neural network with an input layer of source neurons, at least one middle or hidden layer of computational neurons, and an output layer of computational neurons. The input layer accepts input signals from the outside world and redistributes these signals to all neurons in the hidden layer. The hidden layer detects the feature. The weights of the neurons in the hidden layer represent the features in the input patterns. The output layer establishes the output pattern of the entire network.

- Learning in a multilayer network proceeds in the same way as in a perceptron. The learning algorithm has two phases. First, a training input pattern is presented to the network input layer. The network propagates the input pattern from layer to layer until the output pattern is generated by the output layer. If it is different from the desired output, an error is calculated and then propagated backwards through the network from the output layer to the input layer. The weights are modified as the error is propagated.

- Although widely used, back-propagation learning is not without problems. Because the calculations are extensive and, as a result, training is slow, a pure back-propagation algorithm is rarely used in practical applications. There are several possible ways to improve computational efficiency. A multilayer network learns much faster when the sigmoidal activation function is represented by a hyperbolic tangent. The use of momentum and adaptive learning rate also significantly improves the performance of a multilayer back-propagation neural network.

- While multilayer back-propagation neural networks are used for pattern recognition problems, the associative memory of humans is emulated by a different type of network called a recurrent network, which has feedback loops from its outputs to its inputs. John Hopfield formulated the physical principle of storing information in a dynamically stable network, and also proposed a single-layer recurrent network using McCulloch and Pitts neurons with the sign activation function.

- The Hopfield network training algorithm has two basic phases: storage and retrieval. In the first phase, the network is required to store a set of states, or fundamental memories, determined by the current outputs of all neurons. This is achieved by calculating the network's weight matrix. Once the weights are calculated, they remain fixed. In the second phase, an unknown corrupted or incomplete version of the fundamental memory is presented to the network. The network output is calculated and fed back to adjust the input. This process is repeated until the output becomes constant. For the fundamental memories to be retrievable, the storage capacity of the Hopfield network has to be kept small.

- The Hopfield network represents an autoassociative type of memory. It can retrieve a corrupted or incomplete memory but cannot associate one memory with another. To overcome this limitation, Bart Kosko proposed the bidirectional associative memory (BAM). The BAM is a heteroassociative network. It associates patterns from one set to patterns from another set and vice versa. As with a Hopfield network, the BAM can generalise and produce correct outputs despite corrupted or incomplete inputs. The basic BAM architecture consists of two fully connected layers – an input layer and an output layer.

- The idea behind the BAM is to store pattern pairs so that when n-dimensional vector X from set A is presented as input, the BAM recalls m-dimensional vector Y from set B, but when Y is presented as input, the BAM recalls X. The constraints on the storage capacity of the Hopfield network can also be extended to the BAM. The number of associations to be stored in the BAM should not exceed the number of neurons in the smaller layer. Another problem is incorrect convergence, that is the BAM may not always produce the closest association.

- In contrast to supervised learning, or learning with an external 'teacher' who presents a training set to the network, unsupervised or self-organised learning does not require a teacher. During a training session, the neural network receives a number of different input patterns, discovers significant features in these patterns and learns how to classify input.

- Hebb's Law, introduced by Donald Hebb in the late 1940s, states that if neuron i is near enough to excite neuron j and repeatedly participates in its activation, the synaptic connection between these two neurons is strengthened and neuron j becomes more sensitive to stimuli from neuron i. This law provides the basis for learning without a teacher. Learning here is a local phenomenon occurring without feedback from the environment.

- Another popular type of unsupervised learning is competitive learning. In competitive learning, neurons compete among themselves to become active. The output neuron that wins the 'competition' is called the winner-takes-all neuron. Although competitive learning was proposed in the early 1970s, it was largely ignored until the late 1980s, when Teuvo Kohonen introduced a special class of ANNs called self-organising feature maps. He also formulated the principle of topographic map formation which states that the spatial location of an output neuron in the topographic map corresponds to a particular feature of the input pattern.

- The Kohonen network consists of a single layer of computation neurons, but it has two different types of connections. There are forward connections from the neurons in the input layer to the neurons in the output layer, and lateral connections between neurons in the output layer. The lateral connections are used to create a competition between neurons. In the Kohonen network, a neuron learns by shifting its weights from inactive connections to active ones. Only the winning neuron and its neighbourhood are allowed to learn. If a neuron does not respond to a given input pattern, then learning does not occur in that neuron.

Questions for review

1 How does an artificial neural network model the brain? Describe two major classes of learning paradigms: supervised learning and unsupervised (self-organised) learning. What are the features that distinguish these two paradigms from each other?

2 What are the problems with using a perceptron as a biological model? How does the perceptron learn? Demonstrate perceptron learning of the binary logic function OR. Why can the perceptron learn only linearly separable functions?

3 What is a fully connected multilayer perceptron? Construct a multilayer perceptron with an input layer of six neurons, a hidden layer of four neurons and an output layer of two neurons. What is a hidden layer for, and what does it hide?

4 How does a multilayer neural network learn? Derive the back-propagation training algorithm. Demonstrate multilayer network learning of the binary logic function Exclusive-OR.

5 What are the main problems with the back-propagation learning algorithm? How can learning be accelerated in multilayer neural networks? Define the generalised delta rule.

6 What is a recurrent neural network? How does it learn? Construct a single six-neuron Hopfield network and explain its operation. What is a fundamental memory?

7 Derive the Hopfield network training algorithm. Demonstrate how to store three fundamental memories in the six-neuron Hopfield network.

8 The delta rule and Hebb's rule represent two different methods of learning in neural networks. Explain the differences between these two rules.

9 What is the difference between autoassociative and heteroassociative types of memory? What is the bidirectional associative memory (BAM)? How does the BAM work?

10 Derive the BAM training algorithm. What constraints are imposed on the storage capacity of the BAM? Compare the BAM storage capacity with the storage capacity of the Hopfield network.

11 What does Hebb's Law represent? Derive the activity product rule and the generalised activity product rule. What is the meaning of the forgetting factor? Derive the generalised Hebbian learning algorithm.

12 What is competitive learning? What are the differences between Hebbian and competitive learning paradigms? Describe the feature-mapping Kohonen model. Derive the competitive learning algorithm.

References

Amit, D.J. (1989). *Modelling Brain Functions: The World of Attractor Neural Networks.* Cambridge University Press, New York.

Bryson, A.E. and Ho, Y.C. (1969). *Applied Optimal Control.* Blaisdell, New York.

Caudill, M. (1991). Neural network training tips and techniques, *AI Expert*, January, 56–61.

Cohen, M.H. and Grossberg, S. (1983). Absolute stability of global pattern formation and parallel memory storage by competitive networks, *IEEE Transactions on Systems, Man, and Cybernetics*, SMC-13, 815–826.

Fu, L.M. (1994). *Neural Networks in Computer Intelligence.* McGraw-Hill, Singapore.

Fukushima, K. (1975). Cognition: a self-organizing multilayered neural network, *Biological Cybernetics*, 20, 121–136.

Grossberg, S. (1972). Neural expectation: cerebellar and retinal analogs of cells fired by learnable or unlearned pattern classes, *Kybernetik*, 10, 49–57.

Guyon, I.P. (1991). Applications of neural networks to character recognition, *International Journal of Pattern Recognition and Artificial Intelligence*, 5, 353–382.

Haykin, S. (2008). *Neural Networks and Learning Machines*, 3rd edn. Prentice Hall, Englewood Cliffs, NJ.

Hebb, D.O. (1949). *The Organisation of Behaviour: A Neuropsychological Theory.* John Wiley, New York.

Hopfield, J.J. (1982). Neural networks and physical systems with emergent collective computational abilities, *Proceedings of the National Academy of Sciences of the USA*, 79, 2554–2558.

Jacobs, R.A. (1988). Increased rates of convergence through learning rate adaptation, *Neural Networks*, 1, 295–307.

Kohonen, T. (1982). Self-organized formation of topologically correct feature maps, *Biological Cybernetics*, 43, 59–69.

Kohonen, T. (1989). *Self-Organization and Associative Memory*, 3rd edn. Springer-Verlag, Berlin, Heidelberg.

Kohonen, T. (1990). The self-organizing map, *Proceedings of the IEEE*, 78, 1464–1480.

Kosko, B. (1987). Adaptive bidirectional associative memories, *Applied Optics*, 26(23), 4947–4960.

Kosko, B. (1988). Bidirectional associative memories, *IEEE Transactions on Systems, Man, and Cybernetics*, SMC-18, 49–60.

Kosko, B. (1992). *Neural Networks and Fuzzy Systems: A Dynamical Systems Approach to Machine Intelligence.* Prentice Hall, Englewood Cliffs, NJ.

McCulloch, W.S. and Pitts, W. (1943). A logical calculus of the ideas immanent in nervous activity, *Bulletin of Mathematical Biophysics*, 5, 115–137.

Medsker, L.R. and Liebowitz, J. (1994). *Design and Development of Expert Systems and Neural Computing*. Macmillan College Publishing, New York.

Minsky, M.L. and Papert, S.A. (1969). *Perceptrons*. MIT Press, Cambridge, MA.

Rosenblatt, F. (1958). The perceptron: a probabilistic model for information storage and organization in the brain, *Psychological Review*, 65, 386–408.

Rosenblatt, F. (1960). Perceptron simulation experiments, *Proceedings of the Institute of Radio Engineers*, 48, 301–309.

Rumelhart, D.E., Hinton, G.E. and Williams, R.J. (1986). Learning representations by back-propagating errors, *Nature (London)*, 323, 533–536.

Shepherd, G.M. and Koch, C. (1990). Introduction to synaptic circuits, *The Synaptic Organisation of the Brain*, G.M. Shepherd, ed., Oxford University Press, New York, pp. 3–31.

Shynk, J.J. (1990). Performance surfaces of a single-layer perceptron, *IEEE Transactions on Neural Networks*, 1, 268–274.

Shynk, J.J. and Bershad, N.J. (1992). Stationary points and performance surfaces of a perceptron learning algorithm for a nonstationary data model, *Proceedings of the International Joint Conference on Neural Networks*, Baltimore, MD, vol. 2, pp. 133–139.

Stent, G.S. (1973). A physiological mechanism for Hebb's postulate of learning, *Proceedings of the National Academy of Sciences of the USA*, 70, 997–1001.

Stork, D. (1989). Is backpropagation biologically plausible? *Proceedings of the International Joint Conference on Neural Networks*, Washington, DC, vol. 2, pp. 241–246.

Stubbs, D.F. (1990). Six ways to improve back-propagation results, *Journal of Neural Network Computing*, Spring, 64–67.

Touretzky, D.S. and Pomerlean, D.A. (1989). What is hidden in the hidden layers? *Byte*, 14, 227–233.

Von der Malsburg, C. (1973). Self-organisation of orientation sensitive cells in the striate cortex, *Kybernetik*, 14, 85–100.

Watrous, R.L. (1987). Learning algorithms for connectionist networks: applied gradient methods of nonlinear optimisation, *Proceedings of the First IEEE International Conference on Neural Networks*, San Diego, CA, vol. 2, pp. 619–627.

Evolutionary computation 7

In which we consider the field of evolutionary computation, including genetic algorithms, evolution strategies and genetic programming, and their applications to machine learning.

7.1 Introduction, or can evolution be intelligent?

Intelligence can be defined as the capability of a system to adapt its behaviour to an ever-changing environment. According to Alan Turing (Turing, 1950), the form or appearance of a system is irrelevant to its intelligence. However, from our everyday experience we know that evidences of intelligent behaviour are easily observed in humans. But we are products of evolution, and thus by modelling the process of evolution, we might expect to create intelligent behaviour. Evolutionary computation simulates evolution on a computer. The result of such a simulation is a series of optimisation algorithms, usually based on a simple set of rules. Optimisation iteratively improves the quality of solutions until an optimal, or at least feasible, solution is found.

But is evolution really intelligent? We can consider the behaviour of an individual organism as an inductive inference about some yet unknown aspects of its environment (Fogel *et al.*, 1966). Then if, over successive generations, the organism survives, we can say that this organism is capable of learning to predict changes in its environment. Evolution is a tortuously slow process from the human perspective, but the simulation of evolution on a computer does not take billions of years!

The evolutionary approach to machine learning is based on computational models of natural selection and genetics. We call them **evolutionary computation**, an umbrella term that combines **genetic algorithms, evolution strategies** and **genetic programming**. All these techniques simulate evolution by using the processes of **selection, mutation** and **reproduction**.

7.2 Simulation of natural evolution

On 1 July 1858, Charles Darwin presented his theory of evolution before the Linnean Society of London. This day marks the beginning of a revolution in biology. Darwin's classical theory of evolution, together with Weismann's theory of natural selection and Mendel's concept of genetics, now represent the neo-Darwinian paradigm (Mayr, 1988; Gould and Keeton, 1996).

Neo-Darwinism is based on processes of reproduction, mutation, competition and selection. The power to reproduce appears to be an essential property of life. The power to mutate is also guaranteed in any living organism that reproduces itself in a continuously changing environment. Processes of competition and selection normally take place in the natural world, where expanding populations of different species are limited by a finite space.

If the process of evolution is to be emulated on a computer, what is being optimised by evolution in natural life? Evolution can be seen as a process leading to the maintenance or increase of a population's ability to survive and reproduce in a specific environment (Conner and Hartl, 2004). This ability is called **evolutionary fitness**. Although fitness cannot be measured directly, it can be estimated on the basis of the ecology and functional morphology of the organism in its environment (Hoffman, 1989). Evolutionary fitness can also be viewed as a measure of the organism's ability to anticipate changes in its environment (Atmar, 1994). Thus, the fitness, or the quantitative measure of the ability to predict environmental changes and respond adequately, can be considered as the quality that is being optimised in natural life.

To illustrate fitness, we can use the concept of **adaptive topology** (Wright, 1932). We can represent a given environment by a landscape where each peak corresponds to the optimised fitness of a species. As evolution takes place, each species of a given population moves up the slopes of the landscape towards the peaks. Environmental conditions change over time, and thus the species have to continuously adjust their routes. As a result, only the fittest can reach the peaks.

Adaptive topology is a continuous function; it simulates the fact that the environment, or natural topology, is not static. The shape of the topology changes over time, and all species continually undergo selection. The goal of evolution is to generate a population of individuals with increasing fitness.

But how is a population with increasing fitness generated? Michalewicz (1996) suggests a simple explanation based on a population of rabbits. Some rabbits are faster than others, and we may say that these rabbits possess superior fitness because they have a greater chance of avoiding foxes, surviving and then breeding. Of course, some of the slower rabbits may survive too. As a result, some slow rabbits breed with fast rabbits, some fast with other fast rabbits, and some slow rabbits with other slow rabbits. In other words, the breeding generates a mixture of rabbit genes. If two parents have superior fitness, there is a good chance that a combination of their genes will produce an offspring with even higher fitness. Over time the entire population of rabbits becomes faster to meet their environmental challenges in the face of foxes. However, environmental conditions could change in favour of, say, fat but smart rabbits. To optimise survival, the genetic structure of the rabbit population will change accordingly. At the same time, faster and smarter rabbits encourage the breeding of faster and smarter foxes. Natural evolution is a continuous, never-ending process.

Can we simulate the process of natural evolution in a computer?

Several different methods of evolutionary computation are now known. They all simulate natural evolution, generally by creating a population of individuals, evaluating their fitness, generating a new population through genetic operations, and repeating this process a number of times. However, there are different ways of performing evolutionary computation. We will start with **genetic algorithms** (GAs) as most of the other evolutionary algorithms can be viewed as variations of GAs.

In the early 1970s, John Holland, one of the founders of evolutionary computation, introduced the concept of genetic algorithms (Holland, 1975). His aim was to make computers do what nature does. As a computer scientist, Holland was concerned with algorithms that manipulate strings of binary digits. He viewed these algorithms as an abstract form of natural evolution. Holland's GA can be represented by a sequence of procedural steps for moving from one population of artificial 'chromosomes' to a new population. It uses 'natural' selection and genetics-inspired techniques known as crossover and mutation. Each chromosome consists of a number of 'genes', and each gene is represented by 0 or 1, as shown in Figure 7.1.

Nature has an ability to adapt and learn without being told what to do. In other words, nature finds good chromosomes blindly. GAs do the same. Two mechanisms link a GA to the problem it is solving: **encoding** and **evaluation**.

In Holland's work, encoding is carried out by representing chromosomes as strings of ones and zeros. Although many other types of encoding techniques have been invented (Goldberg and Sastry, 2010), no one type works best for all problems. We will use bit strings as the most popular technique.

An evaluation function is used to measure the chromosome's performance, or fitness, for the problem to be solved (an evaluation function in GAs plays the same role the environment plays in natural evolution). The GA uses a measure of fitness of individual chromosomes to carry out reproduction. As reproduction takes place, the crossover operator exchanges parts of two single chromosomes, and the mutation operator changes the gene value in some randomly chosen location of the chromosome. As a result, after a number of successive reproductions, the less fit chromosomes become extinct, while those best able to survive gradually come to dominate the population. It is a simple approach, yet even crude reproduction mechanisms display highly complex behaviour and are capable of solving some difficult problems.

Let us now discuss genetic algorithms in more detail.

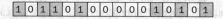

Figure 7.1   A 16-bit binary string of an artificial chromosome

7.3 Genetic algorithms

We start with a definition: genetic algorithms are a class of stochastic search algorithms based on biological evolution. Given a clearly defined problem to be solved and a binary string representation for candidate solutions, a basic GA can be represented as in Figure 7.2. A GA applies the following major steps (Davis, 1991; Mitchell, 1996):

Step 1: Represent the problem variable domain as a chromosome of a fixed length, choose the size of a chromosome population N, the crossover probability p_c and the mutation probability p_m.

Step 2: Define a fitness function to measure the performance, or fitness, of an individual chromosome in the problem domain. The fitness function establishes the basis for selecting chromosomes that will be mated during reproduction.

Step 3: Randomly generate an initial population of chromosomes of size N:

$$x_1, x_2, \ldots, x_N$$

Step 4: Calculate the fitness of each individual chromosome:

$$f(x_1), f(x_2), \ldots, f(x_N)$$

Step 5: Select a pair of chromosomes for mating from the current population. Parent chromosomes are selected with a probability related to their fitness. Highly fit chromosomes have a higher probability of being selected for mating than less fit chromosomes.

Step 6: Create a pair of offspring chromosomes by applying the genetic operators – crossover and mutation.

Step 7: Place the created offspring chromosomes in the new population.

Step 8: Repeat Step 5 until the size of the new chromosome population becomes equal to the size of the initial population, N.

Step 9: Replace the initial (parent) chromosome population with the new (offspring) population.

Step 10: Go to Step 4, and repeat the process until the termination criterion is satisfied.

As we see, a GA represents an iterative process. Each iteration is called a **generation**. A typical number of generations for a simple GA can range from 50 to over 500 (Mitchell, 1996). The entire set of generations is called a **run**. At the end of a run, we expect to find one or more highly fit chromosomes.

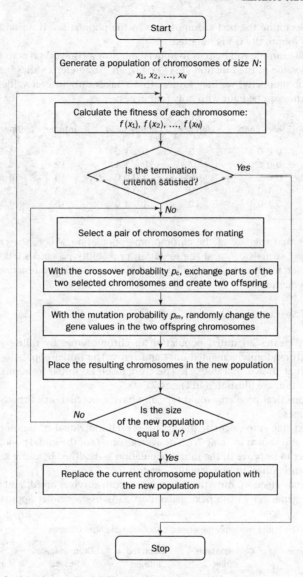

Figure 7.2 A basic genetic algorithm

Are any conventional termination criteria used in genetic algorithms?

Because GAs use a stochastic search method, the fitness of a population may remain stable for a number of generations before a superior chromosome appears. This makes applying conventional termination criteria problematic. A common practice is to terminate a GA after a specified number of generations and then examine the best chromosomes in the population. If no satisfactory solution is found, the GA is restarted.

A simple example will help us to understand how a GA works. Let us find the maximum value of the function $(15x - x^2)$ where parameter x varies between 0 and 15. For simplicity, we may assume that x takes only integer values. Thus, chromosomes can be built with only four genes:

Integer	Binary code	Integer	Binary code	Integer	Binary code
1	0 0 0 1	6	0 1 1 0	11	1 0 1 1
2	0 0 1 0	7	0 1 1 1	12	1 1 0 0
3	0 0 1 1	8	1 0 0 0	13	1 1 0 1
4	0 1 0 0	9	1 0 0 1	14	1 1 1 0
5	0 1 0 1	10	1 0 1 0	15	1 1 1 1

Suppose that the size of the chromosome population N is 6, the crossover probability p_c equals 0.7, and the mutation probability p_m equals 0.001. (The values chosen for p_c and p_m are fairly typical in GAs.) The fitness function in our example is defined by

$$f(x) = 15x - x^2$$

The GA creates an initial population of chromosomes by filling six 4-bit strings with randomly generated ones and zeros. The initial population might look like that shown in Table 7.1. The chromosomes' initial locations on the fitness function are illustrated in Figure 7.3(a).

A real practical problem would typically have a population of thousands of chromosomes.

The next step is to calculate the fitness of each individual chromosome. The results are also shown in Table 7.1. The average fitness of the initial population is 36. In order to improve it, the initial population is modified by using selection, crossover and mutation, the genetic operators.

In natural selection, only the fittest species can survive, breed, and thereby pass their genes on to the next generation. GAs use a similar approach, but

Table 7.1 The initial randomly generated population of chromosomes

Chromosome label	Chromosome string	Decoded integer	Chromosome fitness	Fitness ratio, %
X1	1 1 0 0	12	36	16.5
X2	0 1 0 0	4	44	20.2
X3	0 0 0 1	1	14	6.4
X4	1 1 1 0	14	14	6.4
X5	0 1 1 1	7	56	25.7
X6	1 0 0 1	9	54	24.8

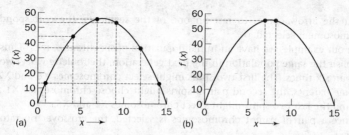

Figure 7.3 The fitness function and chromosome locations: (a) chromosome initial locations; (b) chromosome final locations

unlike nature, the size of the chromosome population remains unchanged from one generation to the next.

How can we maintain the size of the population constant, and at the same time improve its average fitness?

The last column in Table 7.1 shows the ratio of the individual chromosome's fitness to the population's total fitness. This ratio determines the chromosome's chance of being selected for mating. Thus, the chromosomes X5 and X6 stand a fair chance, while the chromosomes X3 and X4 have a very low probability of being selected. As a result, the chromosome's average fitness improves from one generation to the next.

One of the most commonly used chromosome selection techniques is the **roulette wheel selection** (Goldberg, 1989; Davis, 1991). Figure 7.4 illustrates the roulette wheel for our example. As you can see, each chromosome is given a slice of a circular roulette wheel. The area of the slice within the wheel is equal to the chromosome fitness ratio (see Table 7.1). For instance, the chromosomes X5 and X6 (the most fit chromosomes) occupy the largest areas, whereas the chromosomes X3 and X4 (the least fit) have much smaller segments in the roulette wheel. To select a chromosome for mating, a random number is generated in the interval [0, 100], and the chromosome whose segment spans the random number is selected. It is like spinning a roulette wheel where each chromosome has a segment on the wheel proportional to its fitness. The roulette wheel is spun, and

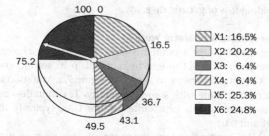

Figure 7.4 Roulette wheel selection

when the arrow comes to rest on one of the segments, the corresponding chromosome is selected.

In our example, we have an initial population of six chromosomes. Thus, to establish the same population in the next generation, the roulette wheel would be spun six times. The first two spins might select chromosomes X6 and X2 to become parents, the second pair of spins might choose chromosomes X1 and X5, and the last two spins might select chromosomes X2 and X5.

Once a pair of parent chromosomes is selected, the crossover operator is applied.

How does the crossover operator work?

First, the crossover operator randomly chooses a crossover point where two parent chromosomes 'break', and then exchanges the chromosome parts after that point. As a result, two new offspring are created. For example, the chromosomes X6 and X2 could be crossed over after the second gene in each to produce the two offspring, as shown in Figure 7.5.

If a pair of chromosomes does not cross over, then chromosome **cloning** takes place, and the offspring are created as exact copies of each parent. For example, the parent chromosomes X2 and X5 may not cross over. Instead, they create the offspring that are their exact copies, as shown in Figure 7.5.

A value of 0.7 for the crossover probability generally produces good results. After selection and crossover, the average fitness of the chromosome population has improved and gone from 36 to 42.

What does mutation represent?

Mutation, which is rare in nature, represents a change in the gene. It may lead to a significant improvement in fitness, but more often has rather harmful results.

So why use mutation at all? Holland introduced mutation as a background operator (Holland, 1975). Its role is to provide a guarantee that the search algorithm is not trapped on a local optimum. The sequence of selection and crossover operations may stagnate at any homogeneous set of solutions. Under such conditions, all chromosomes are identical, and thus the average fitness of the population cannot be improved. However, the solution might appear to become optimal, or rather locally optimal, only because the search algorithm is not able to proceed any further. Mutation is equivalent to a random search, and aids us in avoiding loss of genetic diversity.

How does the mutation operator work?

The mutation operator flips a randomly selected gene in a chromosome. For example, the chromosome X1' might be mutated in its second gene, and the chromosome X2 in its third gene, as shown in Figure 7.5. Mutation can occur at any gene in a chromosome with some probability. The mutation probability is quite small in nature, and is kept quite low for GAs, typically in the range between 0.001 and 0.01.

GAs assure the continuous improvement of the average fitness of the population, and after a number of generations (typically several hundred)

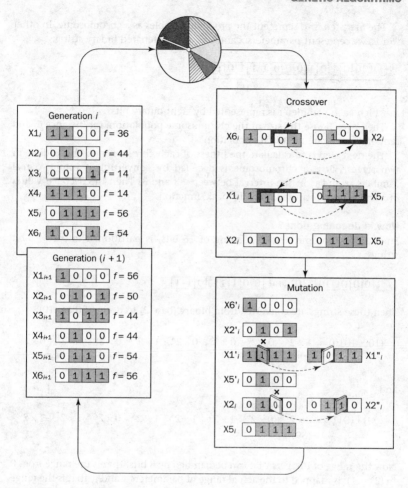

Figure 7.5 The GA cycle

the population evolves to a **near-optimal** solution. In our example, the
final population would consist of only chromosomes $\boxed{0}\boxed{1}\boxed{1}\boxed{1}$ and $\boxed{1}\boxed{0}\boxed{0}\boxed{0}$.
The chromosome's final locations on the fitness function are illustrated in
Figure 7.3(b).

In this example, the problem has only one variable. It is easy to represent. But
suppose it is desired to find the maximum of the 'peak' function of two variables:

$$f(x,y) = (1-x)^2 e^{-x^2-(y+1)^2} - (x-x^3-y^3)e^{-x^2-y^2}$$

where parameters x and y vary between -3 and 3.

The first step is to represent the problem variables as a chromosome. In other words, we represent parameters x and y as a concatenated binary string:

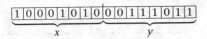

in which each parameter is represented by eight binary bits.

Then, we choose the size of the chromosome population, for instance 6, and randomly generate an initial population.

The next step is to calculate the fitness of each chromosome. This is done in two stages. First, a chromosome is decoded by converting it into two real numbers, x and y, in the interval between -3 and 3. Then the decoded values of x and y are substituted into the 'peak' function.

How is decoding done?

First, a chromosome, that is a string of 16 bits, is partitioned into two 8-bit strings:

$\boxed{1\,0\,0\,0\,1\,0\,1\,0}$ and $\boxed{0\,0\,1\,1\,1\,0\,1\,1}$

Then these strings are converted from binary (base 2) to decimal (base 10):

$$(10001010)_2 = 1 \times 2^7 + 0 \times 2^6 + 0 \times 2^5 + 0 \times 2^4 + 1 \times 2^3 + 0 \times 2^2 + 1 \times 2^1 + 0 \times 2^0$$
$$= (138)_{10}$$

and

$$(00111011)_2 = 0 \times 2^7 + 0 \times 2^6 + 1 \times 2^5 + 1 \times 2^4 + 1 \times 2^3 + 0 \times 2^2 + 1 \times 2^1 + 1 \times 2^0$$
$$= (59)_{10}$$

Now the range of integers that can be handled by 8 bits, that is the range from 0 to $(2^8 - 1)$, is mapped to the actual range of parameters x and y, that is the range from -3 to 3:

$$\frac{6}{256 - 1} = 0.0235294$$

To obtain the actual values of x and y, we multiply their decimal values by 0.0235294 and subtract 3 from the results:

$$x = (138)_{10} \times 0.0235294 - 3 = 0.2470588$$

and

$$y = (59)_{10} \times 0.0235294 - 3 = -1.6117647$$

When necessary, we can also apply other decoding techniques, such as **Gray coding** (Caruana and Schaffer, 1988).

Using decoded values of x and y as inputs in the mathematical function, the GA calculates the fitness of each chromosome.

To find the maximum of the 'peak' function, we will use crossover with the probability equal to 0.7 and mutation with the probability equal to 0.001. As we mentioned earlier, a common practice in GAs is to specify the number of generations. Suppose the desired number of generations is 100. That is, the GA will create 100 generations of six chromosomes before stopping.

Figure 7.6(a) shows the initial locations of the chromosomes on the surface and contour plot of the 'peak' function. Each chromosome here is represented by a sphere. The initial population consists of randomly generated individuals that are dissimilar or **heterogeneous**. However, starting from the second generation, crossover begins to recombine features of the best chromosomes, and the population begins to converge on the peak containing the maximum, as shown in Figure 7.6(b). From then until the final generation, the GA is searching around this peak with mutation, resulting in diversity. Figure 7.6(c) shows the final chromosome generation. However, the population has converged on a chromosome lying on a local maximum of the 'peak' function.

But we are looking for the global maximum, so can we be sure the search is for the optimal solution? The most serious problem in the use of GAs is concerned with the quality of the results, in particular whether or not an optimal solution is

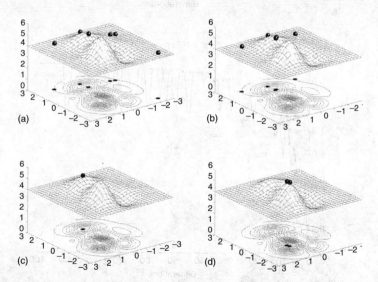

Figure 7.6 Chromosome locations on the surface and contour plot of the 'peak' function: (a) initial population; (b) first generation; (c) local maximum solution; (d) global maximum solution

being reached. One way of providing some degree of insurance is to compare results obtained under different rates of mutation. Let us, for example, increase the mutation rate to 0.01 and rerun the GA. The population might now converge on the chromosomes shown in Figure 7.6(d). However, to be sure of steady results we must increase the size of the chromosome population.

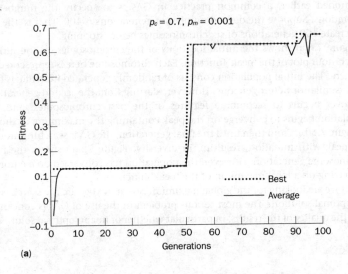

(a)

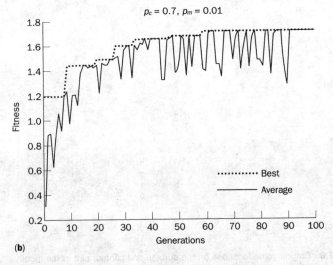

(b)

Figure 7.7 Performance graphs for 100 generations of six chromosomes: (a) local maximum solution and (b) global maximum solution of the 'peak' function

A surface of a mathematical function of the sort given in Figure 7.6 is a convenient medium for displaying the GA's performance. However, fitness functions for real-world problems cannot be easily represented graphically. Instead, we can use **performance graphs**.

What is a performance graph?

Since GAs are stochastic, their performance usually varies from generation to generation. As a result, a curve showing the average performance of the entire population of chromosomes as well as a curve showing the performance of the best individual in the population is a useful way of examining the behaviour of a GA over the chosen number of generations.

Figures 7.7(a) and (b) show plots of the best and average values of the fitness function across 100 generations. The x-axis of the performance graph indicates how many generations have been created and evaluated at the particular point in the run, and the y-axis displays the value of the fitness function at that point.

The erratic behaviour of the average performance curves is due to mutation. The mutation operator allows a GA to explore the landscape in a random manner. Mutation may lead to significant improvement in the population fitness, but more often decreases it. To ensure diversity and at the same time to reduce the harmful effects of mutation, we can increase the size of the chromosome population. Figure 7.8 shows performance graphs for 20 generations of 60 chromosomes. The best and average curves represented here are typical for GAs. As you can see, the average curve rises rapidly at the beginning of the run, but then as the population converges on the nearly optimal solution, it rises more slowly, and finally flattens at the end.

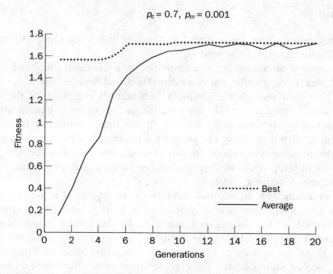

Figure 7.8 Performance graphs for 20 generations of 60 chromosomes

7.4 Why genetic algorithms work

The GA techniques have a solid theoretical foundation (Holland, 1975; Goldberg, 1989; Rawlins, 1991; Whitley, 1993). That foundation is based on the **Schema Theorem**.

John Holland introduced the notation of **schema** (Holland, 1975), which came from the Greek word meaning 'form'. A schema is a set of bit strings of ones, zeros and asterisks, where each asterisk can assume either value 1 or 0. The ones and zeros represent the fixed positions of a schema, while asterisks represent 'wild cards'. For example, the schema $\boxed{1\,|\,*\,|\,*\,|\,0}$ stands for a set of 4-bit strings. Each string in this set begins with 1 and ends with 0. These strings are called **instances** of the schema.

What is the relationship between a schema and a chromosome?

It is simple. A chromosome matches a schema when the fixed positions in the schema match the corresponding positions in the chromosome. For example, the schema H

$$\boxed{1\,|\,*\,|\,*\,|\,0}$$

matches the following set of 4-bit chromosomes:

$$\boxed{1\,|\,1\,|\,1\,|\,0}$$
$$\boxed{1\,|\,1\,|\,0\,|\,0}$$
$$\boxed{1\,|\,0\,|\,1\,|\,0}$$
$$\boxed{1\,|\,0\,|\,0\,|\,0}$$

Each chromosome here begins with 1 and ends with 0. These chromosomes are said to be instances of the schema H.

The number of defined bits (non-asterisks) in a schema is called the **order**. The schema H, for example, has two defined bits, and thus its order is 2.

In short, GAs manipulate **schemata** (schemata is the plural of the word schema) when they run. If GAs use a technique that makes the probability of reproduction proportional to chromosome fitness, then according to the Schema Theorem (Holland, 1975), we can predict the presence of a given schema in the next chromosome generation. In other words, we can describe the GA's behaviour in terms of the increase or decrease in the number of instances of a given schema (Goldberg, 1989).

Let us assume that at least one instance of the schema H is present in the chromosome initial generation i. Now let $m_H(i)$ be the number of instances of the schema H in the generation i, and $\hat{f}_H(i)$ be the average fitness of these instances. We want to calculate the number of instances in the next generation, $m_H(i+1)$. As the probability of reproduction is proportional to chromosome fitness, we can easily calculate the expected number of offspring of a chromosome x in the next generation:

$$m_x(i+1) = \frac{f_x(i)}{\hat{f}(i)} \tag{7.1}$$

where $f_x(i)$ is the fitness of the chromosome x, and $\hat{f}(i)$ is the average fitness of the chromosome initial generation i.

Then, assuming that the chromosome x is an instance of the schema H, we obtain

$$m_H(i+1) = \frac{\sum_{x=1}^{x=m_H(i)} f_x(i)}{\hat{f}(i)}, \quad x \in H \tag{7.2}$$

Since, by definition,

$$\hat{f}_H(i) = \frac{\sum_{x=1}^{x=m_H(i)} f_x(i)}{m_H(i)}$$

we obtain

$$m_H(i+1) = \frac{\hat{f}_H(i)}{\hat{f}(i)} m_H(i) \tag{7.3}$$

Thus, a schema with above-average fitness will indeed tend to occur more frequently in the next generation of chromosomes, and a schema with below-average fitness will tend to occur less frequently.

How about effects caused by crossover and mutation?
Crossover and mutation can both create and destroy instances of a schema. Here we will consider only destructive effects, that is effects that decrease the number of instances of the schema H. Let us first quantify the destruction caused by the crossover operator. The schema will survive after crossover if at least one of its offspring is also its instance. This is the case when crossover does not occur within the defining length of the schema.

What is the defining length of a schema?
The distance between the outermost defined bits of a schema is called **defining length**. For example, the defining length of $\boxed{*}\boxed{*}\boxed{*}\boxed{*}\boxed{*}\boxed{1}\boxed{0}\boxed{1}\boxed{1}$ is 3, of $\boxed{*}\boxed{0}\boxed{*}\boxed{1}\boxed{*}\boxed{1}\boxed{0}\boxed{*}$ is 5 and of $\boxed{1}\boxed{*}\boxed{*}\boxed{*}\boxed{*}\boxed{*}\boxed{*}\boxed{0}$ is 7.

If crossover takes place within the defining length, the schema H can be destroyed and offspring that are not instances of H can be created. (Although the schema H will not be destroyed if two identical chromosomes cross over, even when crossover occurs within the defining length.)

Thus, the probability that the schema H will survive after crossover can be defined as

$$P_H^{(c)} = 1 - p_c\left(\frac{l_d}{l-1}\right) \tag{7.4}$$

where p_c is the crossover probability, and l and l_d are, respectively, the length and the defining length of the schema H.

It is clear that the probability of survival under crossover is higher for short schemata rather than for long ones.

Now consider the destructive effects of mutation. Let p_m be the mutation probability for any bit of the schema H, and n be the order of the schema H. Then $(1 - p_m)$ represents the probability that the bit will not be mutated, and thus the probability that the schema H will survive after mutation is determined as

$$P_H^{(m)} = (1 - p_m)^n \tag{7.5}$$

It is also clear that the probability of survival under mutation is higher for low-order schemata than for high-order ones.

We can now amend Eq. (7.3) to take into account the destructive effects of crossover and mutation:

$$m_H(i+1) = \frac{\hat{f}_H(i)}{\hat{f}(i)}\, m_H(i)\left[1 - p_c\left(\frac{l_d}{l-1}\right)\right](1 - p_m)^n \tag{7.6}$$

This equation describes the growth of a schema from one generation to the next. It is known as the Schema Theorem. Because Eq. (7.6) considers only the destructive effects of crossover and mutation, it gives us a lower bound on the number of instances of the schema H in the next generation.

Despite crossover arguably representing a major advantage of GAs, there is as yet no theoretical basis to support the view that a GA will outperform other search and optimisation techniques just because crossover allows the combination of partial solutions.

GAs are a very powerful tool, but need to be applied intelligently. For example, coding the problem as a bit string may change the nature of the problem being investigated. In other words, there is a danger that the coded representation becomes a problem that is different from the one we wanted to solve.

To illustrate the ideas discussed above, we consider a simple application of the GA to problems of scheduling resources.

7.5   Case study: maintenance scheduling with genetic algorithms

One of the most successful areas for GA applications includes the problem of scheduling resources. Scheduling problems are complex and difficult to solve. They are usually approached with a combination of search techniques and heuristics.

Why are scheduling problems so difficult?

First, scheduling belongs to NP-complete problems. Such problems are likely to be unmanageable and cannot be solved by combinatorial search techniques. Moreover, heuristics alone cannot guarantee the best solution.

Second, scheduling problems involve a competition for limited resources; as a result, they are complicated by many constraints. The key to the success of the GA lies in defining a fitness function that incorporates all these constraints.

The problem we discuss here is the maintenance scheduling in modern power systems. This task has to be carried out under several constraints and uncertainties, such as failures and forced outages of power equipment and delays in obtaining spare parts. The schedule often has to be revised at short notice. Human experts usually work out the maintenance scheduling by hand, and there is no guarantee that the optimum or even near-optimum schedule is produced.

A typical process of the GA development includes the following steps:

1.   Specify the problem, define constraints and optimum criteria.

2.   Represent the problem domain as a chromosome.

3.   Define a fitness function to evaluate the chromosome performance.

4.   Construct the genetic operators.

5.   Run the GA and tune its parameters.

Step 1:   *Specify the problem, define constraints and optimum criteria*
This is probably the most important step in developing a GA, because if it is not correct and complete a viable schedule cannot be obtained.

Power system components are made to operate continuously throughout their life by means of preventive maintenance. The purpose of maintenance scheduling is to find the sequence of outages of power units over a given period of time (normally a year) such that the security of a power system is maximised.

Any outage in a power system is associated with some loss in security. The security margin is determined by the system's net reserve. The net reserve, in turn, is defined as the total installed generating capacity of the system *minus* the power lost due to a scheduled outage and *minus* the maximum load forecast during the maintenance period. For instance, if we assume that the total installed capacity is 150 MW

Table 7.2 Power units and their maintenance requirements

Unit number	Unit capacity, MW	Number of intervals required for unit maintenance during one year
1	20	2
2	15	2
3	35	1
4	40	1
5	15	1
6	15	1
7	10	1

and a unit of 20 MW is scheduled for maintenance during the period when the maximum load is predicted to be 100 MW, then the net reserve will be 30 MW. Maintenance scheduling must ensure that sufficient net reserve is provided for secure power supply during any maintenance period.

Suppose, there are seven power units to be maintained in four equal intervals. The maximum loads expected during these intervals are 80, 90, 65 and 70 MW. The unit capacities and their maintenance requirements are presented in Table 7.2.

The constraints for this problem can be specified as follows:

• Maintenance of any unit starts at the beginning of an interval and finishes at the end of the same or adjacent interval. The maintenance cannot be aborted or finished earlier than scheduled.

• The net reserve of the power system must be greater than or equal to zero at any interval.

The optimum criterion here is that the net reserve must be at the maximum during any maintenance period.

Step 2: *Represent the problem domain as a chromosome*

Our scheduling problem is essentially an ordering problem, requiring us to list the tasks in a particular order. A complete schedule may consist of a number of overlapping tasks, but not all orderings are legal, since they may violate the constraints. Our job is to represent a complete schedule as a chromosome of a fixed length.

An obvious coding scheme that comes to mind is to assign each unit a binary number and to let the chromosome be a sequence of these binary numbers. However, an ordering of the units in a sequence is not yet a schedule. Some units can be maintained simultaneously, and we must also incorporate the time required for unit maintenance into the schedule. Thus, rather than ordering units in a sequence, we might build a sequence of maintenance schedules of individual units. The unit schedule can be easily represented as a 4-bit string, where each bit is a maintenance interval. If a unit is to be maintained in a particular interval, the corresponding bit assumes value 1, otherwise it is 0. For example, the string $\boxed{0\,|\,1\,|\,0\,|\,0}$ presents a schedule for a unit to be maintained in the second interval. It also shows that the number of intervals required for maintenance of this unit is equal to 1. Thus, a complete maintenance schedule for our problem can be represented as a 28-bit chromosome.

However, crossover and mutation operators could easily create binary strings that call for maintaining some units more than once and others not at all. In addition, we could call for maintenance periods that would exceed the number of intervals really required for unit maintenance.

A better approach is to change the chromosome syntax. As already discussed, a chromosome is a collection of elementary parts called genes. Traditionally, each gene is represented by only 1 bit and cannot be broken into smaller elements. For our problem, we can adopt the same concept, but represent a gene by 4 bits. In other words, the smallest indivisible part of our chromosome is a 4-bit string. This representation allows crossover and mutation operators to act according to the theoretical grounding of GAs. What remains to be done is to produce a pool of genes for each unit:

Unit 1:	$\boxed{1\ 1\ 0\ 0}$	$\boxed{0\ 1\ 1\ 0}$	$\boxed{0\ 0\ 1\ 1}$	
Unit 2:	$\boxed{1\ 1\ 0\ 0}$	$\boxed{0\ 1\ 1\ 0}$	$\boxed{0\ 0\ 1\ 1}$	
Unit 3:	$\boxed{1\ 0\ 0\ 0}$	$\boxed{0\ 1\ 0\ 0}$	$\boxed{0\ 0\ 1\ 0}$	$\boxed{0\ 0\ 0\ 1}$
Unit 4:	$\boxed{1\ 0\ 0\ 0}$	$\boxed{0\ 1\ 0\ 0}$	$\boxed{0\ 0\ 1\ 0}$	$\boxed{0\ 0\ 0\ 1}$
Unit 5:	$\boxed{1\ 0\ 0\ 0}$	$\boxed{0\ 1\ 0\ 0}$	$\boxed{0\ 0\ 1\ 0}$	$\boxed{0\ 0\ 0\ 1}$
Unit 6:	$\boxed{1\ 0\ 0\ 0}$	$\boxed{0\ 1\ 0\ 0}$	$\boxed{0\ 0\ 1\ 0}$	$\boxed{0\ 0\ 0\ 1}$
Unit 7:	$\boxed{1\ 0\ 0\ 0}$	$\boxed{0\ 1\ 0\ 0}$	$\boxed{0\ 0\ 1\ 0}$	$\boxed{0\ 0\ 0\ 1}$

The GA can now create an initial population of chromosomes by filling seven-gene chromosomes with genes randomly selected from the corresponding pools. A sample of such a chromosome is shown in Figure 7.9.

Step 3: *Define a fitness function to evaluate the chromosome performance*
The chromosome evaluation is a crucial part of the GA, because chromosomes are selected for mating based on their fitness. The fitness function must capture what makes a maintenance schedule either good or bad for the user. For our problem we apply a fairly simple function concerned with constraint violations and the net reserve at each interval.

Unit 1	Unit 2	Unit 3	Unit 4	Unit 5	Unit 6	Unit 7
0 1 1 0	0 0 1 1	0 0 0 1	1 0 0 0	0 1 0 0	0 0 1 0	1 0 0 0

Figure 7.9 A chromosome for the scheduling problem

The evaluation of a chromosome starts with the sum of capacities of the units scheduled for maintenance at each interval. For the chromosome shown in Figure 7.9, we obtain

Interval 1: $0 \times 20 + 0 \times 15 + 0 \times 35 + 1 \times 40 + 0 \times 15 + 0 \times 15 + 1 \times 10$
$= 50$

Interval 2: $1 \times 20 + 0 \times 15 + 0 \times 35 + 0 \times 40 + 1 \times 15 + 0 \times 15 + 0 \times 10$
$= 35$

Interval 3: $1 \times 20 + 1 \times 15 + 0 \times 35 + 0 \times 40 + 0 \times 15 + 1 \times 15 + 0 \times 10$
$= 50$

Interval 4: $0 \times 20 + 1 \times 15 + 1 \times 35 + 0 \times 40 + 0 \times 15 + 0 \times 15 + 0 \times 10$
$= 50$

Then these values are subtracted from the total installed capacity of the power system (in our case, 150 MW):

Interval 1: $150 - 50 = 100$
Interval 2: $150 - 35 = 115$
Interval 3: $150 - 50 = 100$
Interval 4: $150 - 50 = 100$

And finally, by subtracting the maximum loads expected at each interval, we obtain the respective net reserves:

Interval 1: $100 - 80 = 20$
Interval 2: $115 - 90 = 25$
Interval 3: $100 - 65 = 35$
Interval 4: $100 - 70 = 30$

Since all the results are positive, this particular chromosome does not violate any constraint, and thus represents a legal schedule. The chromosome's fitness is determined as the lowest of the net reserves; in our case it is 20.

If, however, the net reserve at any interval is negative, the schedule is illegal, and the fitness function returns zero.

At the beginning of a run, a randomly built initial population might consist of all illegal schedules. In this case, chromosome fitness values remain unchanged, and selection takes place in accordance with the actual fitness values.

Step 4:   *Construct the genetic operators*
Constructing genetic operators is challenging and we must experiment to make crossover and mutation work correctly. The chromosome has to be broken up in a way that is legal for our problem. Since we have already changed the chromosome syntax for this, we can use the GA operators in their classical forms. Each gene in a chromosome is represented by a 4-bit indivisible string, which consists of a possible maintenance schedule for a particular unit. Thus, any random mutation

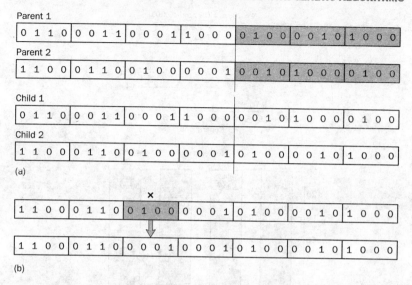

Figure 7.10 Genetic operators for the scheduling problem: (a) the crossover operator; (b) the mutation operator

of a gene or recombination of several genes from two parent chromosomes may result only in changes of the maintenance schedules for individual units, but cannot create 'unnatural' chromosomes.

Figure 7.10(a) shows an example of the crossover application during a run of the GA. The children are made by cutting the parents at the randomly selected point denoted by the vertical line and exchanging parental genes after the cut. Figure 7.10(b) demonstrates an example of mutation. The mutation operator randomly selects a 4-bit gene in a chromosome and replaces it by a gene randomly selected from the corresponding pool. In the example shown in Figure 7.10(b), the chromosome is mutated in its third gene, which is replaced by the gene $\boxed{0\,0\,0\,1}$ chosen from the pool of genes for the Unit 3.

Step 5: *Run the GA and tune its parameters*

It is time to run the GA. First, we must choose the population size and the number of generations to be run. Common sense suggests that a larger population can achieve better solutions than a smaller one, but will work more slowly. In fact, however, the most effective population size depends on the problem being solved, particularly on the problem coding scheme (Goldberg, 1989). The GA can run only a finite number of generations to obtain a solution. Perhaps we could choose a very large population and run it only once, or we could choose a smaller population and run it several times. In any case, only experimentation can give us the answer.

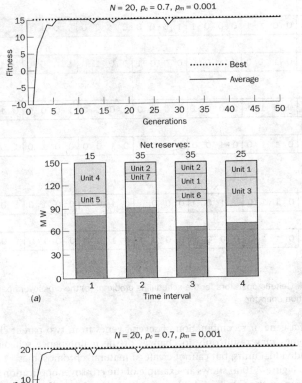

(a)

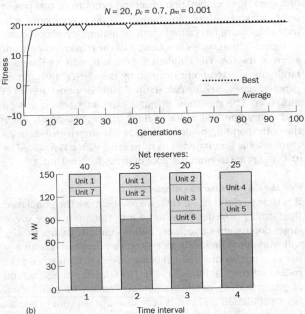

(b)

Figure 7.11 Performance graphs and the best maintenance schedules created in a population of 20 chromosomes: (a) 50 generations; (b) 100 generations

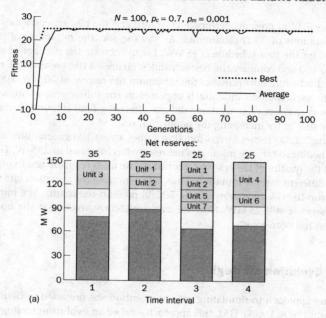

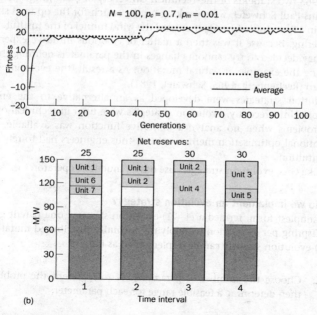

Figure 7.12 Performance graphs and the best maintenance schedules created in a population of 100 chromosomes: (a) mutation rate is 0.001; (b) mutation rate is 0.01

Figure 7.11(a) presents performance graphs and the best schedule created by 50 generations of 20 chromosomes. As you can see, the minimum of the net reserves for the best schedule is 15 MW. Let us increase the number of generations to 100 and compare the best schedules. Figure 7.11(b) presents the results. The best schedule now provides the minimum net reserve of 20 MW. However, in both cases, the best individuals appeared in the initial generation, and the increasing number of generations did not affect the final solution. It indicates that we should try increasing the population size.

Figure 7.12(a) shows fitness function values across 100 generations, and the best schedule so far. The minimum net reserve has increased to 25 MW. To make sure of the quality of the best-so-far schedule, we must compare results obtained under different rates of mutation. Thus, let us increase the mutation rate to 0.01 and rerun the GA once more. Figure 7.12(b) presents the results. The minimum net reserve is still 25 MW. Now we can confidently argue that the optimum solution has been found.

7.6 Evolution strategies

Another approach to simulating natural evolution was proposed in Germany in the early 1960s. Unlike GAs, this approach – called an **evolution strategy** – was designed to solve technical optimisation problems.

In 1963 two students of the Technical University of Berlin, Ingo Rechenberg and Hans-Paul Schwefel, were working on the search for the optimal shapes of bodies in a flow. In their work, they used the wind tunnel of the Institute of Flow Engineering. Because it was then a matter of laborious intuitive experimentation, they decided to try random changes in the parameters defining the shape following the example of natural mutation. As a result, the evolution strategy was born (Rechenberg, 1965; Schwefel, 1981).

Evolution strategies were developed as an alternative to the engineer's intuition. Until recently, evolution strategies were used in technical optimisation problems when no analytical objective function was available, and no conventional optimisation method existed, thus engineers had to rely only on their intuition.

Unlike GAs, evolution strategies use only a mutation operator.

How do we implement an evolution strategy?

In its simplest form, termed a $(1 + 1)$-evolution strategy, one parent generates one offspring per generation by applying **normally distributed** mutation. The $(1 + 1)$-evolution strategy can be implemented as follows:

Step 1: Choose the number of parameters N to represent the problem, and then determine a feasible range for each parameter:

$$\{x_{1min}, x_{1max}\}, \{x_{2min}, x_{2max}\}, \ldots, \{x_{Nmin}, x_{Nmax}\},$$

Define a standard deviation for each parameter and the function to be optimised.

Step 2: Randomly select an initial value for each parameter from the respective feasible range. The set of these parameters will constitute the initial population of parent parameters:

$$x_1, x_2, \ldots, x_N$$

Step 3: Calculate the solution associated with the parent parameters:

$$X = f(x_1, x_2, \ldots, x_N)$$

Step 4: Create a new (offspring) parameter by adding a normally distributed random variable a with mean zero and pre-selected deviation δ to each parent parameter:

$$x_i' = x_i + a(0, \delta), \qquad i = 1, 2, \ldots, N \tag{7.7}$$

Normally distributed mutations with mean zero reflect the natural process of evolution where smaller changes occur more frequently than larger ones.

Step 5: Calculate the solution associated with the offspring parameters:

$$X' = f(x_1', x_2', \ldots, x_N')$$

Step 6: Compare the solution associated with the offspring parameters with the one associated with the parent parameters. If the solution for the offspring is better than that for the parents, replace the parent population with the offspring population. Otherwise, keep the parent parameters.

Step 7: Go to Step 4, and repeat the process until a satisfactory solution is reached, or a specified number of generations is considered.

The $(1 + 1)$-evolution strategy can be represented as a block-diagram shown in Figure 7.13.

Why do we vary all the parameters simultaneously when generating a new solution?

An evolution strategy here reflects the nature of a chromosome. In fact, a single gene may simultaneously affect several characteristics of the living organism. On the other hand, a single characteristic of an individual may be determined by the simultaneous interactions of several genes. The natural selection acts on a collection of genes, not on a single gene in isolation.

Evolution strategies can solve a wide range of constrained and unconstrained non-linear optimisation problems and produce better results than many conventional, highly complex, non-linear optimisation techniques (Schwefel, 1995). Experiments also suggest that the simplest version of evolution strategies that uses a single parent–single offspring search works best.

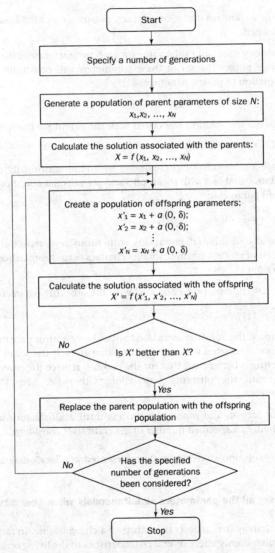

Figure 7.13 Block-diagram of the $(1 + 1)$-evolution strategy

What are the differences between genetic algorithms and evolution strategies?

The principal difference between a GA and an evolution strategy is that the former uses both crossover and mutation whereas the latter uses only mutation. In addition, when we use an evolution strategy we do not need to represent the problem in a coded form.

Which method works best?

An evolution strategy uses a purely numerical optimisation procedure, similar to a focused Monte Carlo search. GAs are capable of more general applications, but the hardest part of applying a GA is coding the problem. In general, to answer the question as to which method works best, we have to experiment to find out. It is application dependent.

7.7 Genetic programming

One of the central problems in computer science is how to make computers solve problems without being explicitly programmed to do so. Genetic programming offers a solution through the evolution of computer programs by methods of natural selection. In fact, genetic programming is an extension of the conventional GA, but the goal of genetic programming is not just to evolve a bit-string representation of some problem but the computer code that solves the problem. In other words, genetic programming creates computer programs as the solution, while GAs create a string of binary numbers that represent the solution.

Genetic programming is a recent development in the area of evolutionary computation. It was greatly stimulated in the 1990s by John Koza (Koza, 1992; 1994).

How does genetic programming work?

According to Koza, genetic programming searches the space of possible computer programs for a program that is highly fit for solving the problem at hand (Koza, 1992).

Any computer program is a sequence of operations (functions) applied to values (arguments), but different programming languages may include different types of statements and operations, and have different syntactic restrictions. Since genetic programming manipulates programs by applying genetic operators, a programming language should permit a computer program to be manipulated as data and the newly created data to be executed as a program. For these reasons, LISP was chosen as the main language for genetic programming (Koza, 1992).

What is LISP?

LISP, or **List Processor**, is one of the oldest high-level programming languages (FORTRAN is just two years older than LISP). LISP, which was written by John McCarthy in the late 1950s, has become one of the standard languages for artificial intelligence.

LISP has a highly symbol-oriented structure. Its basic data structures are **atoms** and **lists**. An atom is the smallest indivisible element of the LISP syntax. The number *21*, the symbol *X* and the string *'This is a string'* are examples of LISP atoms. A list is an object composed of atoms and/or other lists. LISP lists are written as an ordered collection of items inside a pair of parentheses. For example, the list

(−(∗ A B) C)

calls for the application of the subtraction function (−) to two arguments, namely the list (∗A B) and the atom C. First, LISP applies the multiplication function (∗) to the atoms A and B. Once the list (∗ A B) is evaluated, LISP applies the subtraction function (−) to the two arguments, and thus evaluates the entire list (−(∗ A B) C).

Both atoms and lists are called symbolic expressions or **S-expressions**. In LISP, all data and all programs are S-expressions. This gives LISP the ability to operate on programs as if they were data. In other words, LISP programs can modify themselves or even write other LISP programs. This remarkable property of LISP makes it very attractive for genetic programming.

Any LISP S-expression can be depicted as a rooted point-labelled tree with ordered branches. Figure 7.14 shows the tree corresponding to the S-expression (−(∗A B) C). This tree has five points, each of which represents either a function or a terminal. The two internal points of the tree are labelled with functions (−) and (∗). Note that the root of the tree is the function appearing just inside the leftmost opening parenthesis of the S-expression. The three external points of the tree, also called leaves, are labelled with terminals A, B and C. In the graphical representation, the branches are ordered because the order of the arguments in many functions directly affects the results.

How do we apply genetic programming to a problem?
Before applying genetic programming to a problem, we must accomplish **five preparatory steps** (Koza, 1994):

1. Determine the set of terminals.

2. Select the set of primitive functions.

3. Define the fitness function.

4. Decide on the parameters for controlling the run.

5. Choose the method for designating a result of the run.

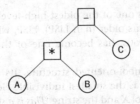

Figure 7.14 Graphical representation of the LISP S-expression (−(∗A B)C)

Table 7.3 Ten fitness cases for the Pythagorean Theorem

Side a	Side b	Hypotenuse c	Side a	Side b	Hypotenuse c
3	5	5.830952	12	10	15.620499
8	14	16.124515	21	6	21.840330
18	2	18.110770	7	4	8.062258
32	11	33.837849	16	24	28.844410
4	3	5.000000	2	9	9.219545

The Pythagorean Theorem helps us to illustrate these preparatory steps and demonstrate the potential of genetic programming. The theorem says that the hypotenuse, c, of a right triangle with short sides a and b is given by

$$c = \sqrt{a^2 + b^2}$$

The aim of genetic programming is to discover a program that matches this function. To measure the performance of the as-yet-undiscovered computer program, we will use a number of different **fitness cases**. The fitness cases for the Pythagorean Theorem are represented by the samples of right triangles in Table 7.3. These fitness cases are chosen at random over a range of values of variables a and b.

Step 1: **Determine the set of terminals**
The terminals correspond to the inputs of the computer program to be discovered. Our program takes two inputs, a and b.

Step 2: **Select the set of primitive functions**
The functions can be presented by standard arithmetic operations, standard programming operations, standard mathematical functions, logical functions or domain-specific functions. Our program will use four standard arithmetic operations +, --, * and /, and one mathematical function *sqrt*.

Terminals and primitive functions together constitute the building blocks from which genetic programming constructs a computer program to solve the problem.

Step 3: **Define the fitness function**
A fitness function evaluates how well a particular computer program can solve the problem. The choice of the fitness function depends on the problem, and may vary greatly from one problem to the next. For our problem, the fitness of the computer program can be measured by the error between the actual result produced by the program and the correct result given by the fitness case. Typically, the error is not measured over just one fitness case, but instead calculated as a sum of the absolute errors over a number of fitness cases. The closer this sum is to zero, the better the computer program.

Step 4:   *Decide on the parameters for controlling the run*

For controlling a run, genetic programming uses the same primary parameters as those used for GAs. They include the population size and the maximum number of generations to be run.

Step 5:   *Choose the method for designating a result of the run*

It is common practice in genetic programming to designate the best-so-far generated program as the result of a run.

Once these five steps are complete, a run can be made. The run of genetic programming starts with a random generation of an initial population of computer programs. Each program is composed of functions $+$, $-$, $*$, $/$ and *sqrt*, and terminals a and b.

In the initial population, all computer programs usually have poor fitness, but some individuals are fitter than others. Just as a fitter chromosome is more likely to be selected for reproduction, so a fitter computer program is more likely to survive by copying itself into the next generation.

Is the crossover operator capable of operating on computer programs?

In genetic programming, the crossover operator operates on two computer programs which are selected on the basis of their fitness. These programs can have different sizes and shapes. The two offspring programs are composed by recombining randomly chosen parts of their parents. For example, consider the following two LISP S-expressions:

$$(/ \, (- \, (sqrt \, (+ \, (* \, a \, a) \, (- \, a \, b))) \, a) \, (* \, a \, b))$$

which is equivalent to

$$\frac{\sqrt{a^2 + (a - b)} - a}{ab}$$

and

$$(+ \, (- \, (sqrt \, (- \, (* \, b \, b) \, a)) \, b) \, (sqrt \, (/ \, a \, b)))$$

which is equivalent to

$$\left(\sqrt{b^2 - a} - b\right) + \sqrt{\frac{a}{b}}$$

These two S-expressions can be presented as rooted, point-labelled trees with ordered branches as shown in Figure 7.15(a). Internal points of the trees correspond to functions and external points correspond to terminals.

Any point, internal or external, can be chosen as a crossover point. Suppose that the crossover point for the first parent is the function $(*)$, and the crossover

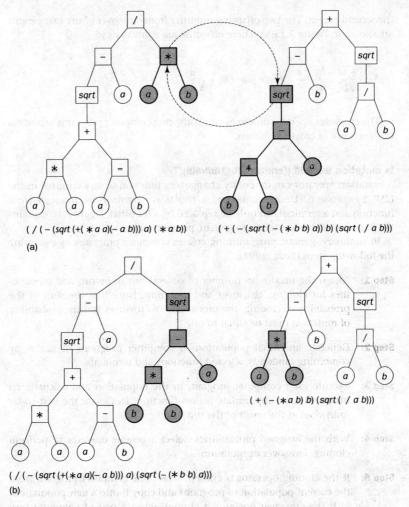

(/ (– (sqrt (+(✳ a a)(– a b))) a) (✳ a b))   (+ (– (sqrt (– (✳ b b) a)) b) (sqrt (/ a b)))

(a)

(/ (– (sqrt (+(✳ a a)(– a b))) a) (sqrt (– (✳ b b) a)))

(b)

(+ (– (✳ a b) b) (sqrt (/ a b)))

Figure 7.15 Crossover in genetic programming: (a) two parental S-expressions; (b) two offspring S-expressions

point for the second parent is the function *sqrt*. As a result, we obtain the two **crossover fragments** rooted at the chosen crossover points as shown in Figure 7.15(a). The crossover operator creates two offspring by exchanging the crossover fragments of two parents. Thus, the first offspring is created by inserting the crossover fragment of the second parent into the place of the crossover fragment of the first parent. Similarly, the second offspring is created by inserting the crossover fragment of the first parent into the place of the crossover fragment of the second parent. The two offspring resulting from crossover of the two parents are shown in Figure 7.15(b). These offspring are equivalent to

$$\frac{\sqrt{a^2 + (a - b)} - a}{\sqrt{b^2 - a}} \quad \text{and} \quad (ab - b) + \sqrt{\frac{a}{b}}$$

The crossover operator produces valid offspring computer programs regardless of the choice of crossover points.

Is mutation used in genetic programming?

A mutation operator can randomly change any function or any terminal in the LISP S-expression. Under mutation, a function can only be replaced by a function and a terminal can only be replaced by a terminal. Figure 7.16 explains the basic concept of mutation in genetic programming.

In summary, genetic programming creates computer programs by executing the following steps (Koza, 1994):

Step 1: Assign the maximum number of generations to be run and probabilities for cloning, crossover and mutation. Note that the sum of the probability of cloning, the probability of crossover and the probability of mutation must be equal to one.

Step 2: Generate an initial population of computer programs of size N by combining randomly selected functions and terminals.

Step 3: Execute each computer program in the population and calculate its fitness with an appropriate fitness function. Designate the best-so-far individual as the result of the run.

Step 4: With the assigned probabilities, select a genetic operator to perform cloning, crossover or mutation.

Step 5: If the cloning operator is chosen, select one computer program from the current population of programs and copy it into a new population.

If the crossover operator is chosen, select a pair of computer programs from the current population, create a pair of offspring programs and place them into the new population.

If the mutation operator is chosen, select one computer program from the current population, perform mutation and place the mutant into the new population.

All programs are selected with a probability based on their fitness (i.e. the higher the fitness, the more likely the program is to be selected).

Step 6: Repeat Step 4 until the size of the new population of computer programs becomes equal to the size of the initial population, N.

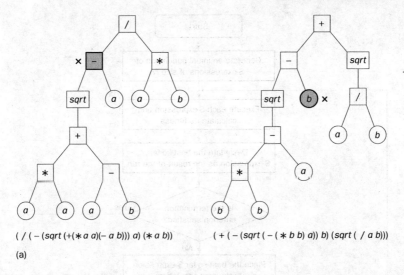

(/ (− (sqrt (+(∗ a a)(− a b))) a) (∗ a b))
(a)

(+ (− (sqrt (− (∗ b b) a)) b) (sqrt (/ a b)))

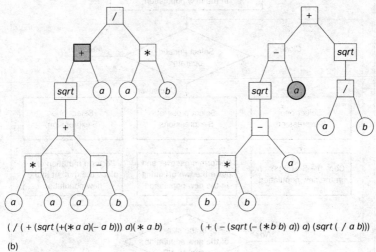

(/ (+ (sqrt (+(∗ a a)(− a b))) a)(∗ a b)
(b)

(+ (− (sqrt (− (∗ b b) a)) a) (sqrt (/ a b)))

Figure 7.16 Mutation in genetic programming: (a) original S-expressions;
(b) mutated S-expressions

Step 7: Replace the current (parent) population with the new (offspring) population.

Step 8: Go to Step 3 and repeat the process until the termination criterion is satisfied.

Figure 7.17 is a flowchart representing the above steps of genetic programming.

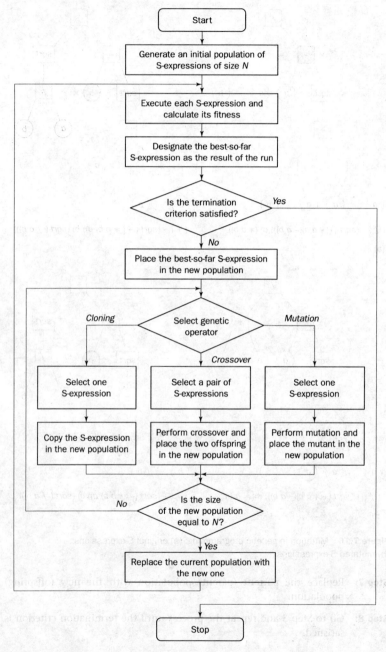

Figure 7.17 Flowchart for genetic programming

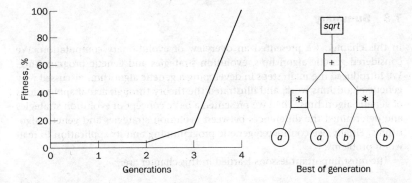

Figure 7.18   Fitness history of the best S-expression

Let us now return to the Pythagorean Theorem. Figure 7.18 shows the fitness history of the best S-expression in a population of 500 computer programs. As you can see, in the randomly generated initial population, even the best S-expression has very poor fitness. But fitness improves very rapidly, and at the fourth generation the correct S-expression is reproduced. This simple example demonstrates that genetic programming offers a general and robust method of evolving computer programs.

In the Pythagorean Theorem example we used LISP S-expressions, but there is no reason to restrict genetic programming only to LISP S-expressions. It can also be implemented in C, C++, Pascal, FORTRAN, Mathematica, Smalltalk and other programming languages, and can be applied more generally.

What are the main advantages of genetic programming compared with genetic algorithms?

Genetic programming applies the same evolutionary approach as a GA does. However, genetic programming is no longer breeding bit strings that represent coded solutions but complete computer programs that solve a particular problem. The fundamental difficulty of GAs lies in the problem representation, that is in the fixed-length coding. A poor representation limits the power of a GA, and, even worse, may lead to a false solution.

A fixed-length coding is rather artificial. As it cannot provide a dynamic variability in length, such a coding often causes considerable redundancy and reduces the efficiency of genetic search. In contrast, genetic programming uses high-level building blocks of variable length. Their size and complexity can change during breeding. Genetic programming works well in a large number of different cases (Koza, 1994) and has many potential applications.

Are there any difficulties?

Despite many successful applications, there is still no proof that genetic programming will scale up to more complex problems that require larger computer programs. And even if it scales up, extensive computer run times may be needed.

7.8 Summary

In this chapter, we presented an overview of evolutionary computation. We considered genetic algorithms, evolution strategies and genetic programming. We introduced the main steps in developing a genetic algorithm, discussed why genetic algorithms work, and illustrated the theory through actual applications of genetic algorithms. Then we presented a basic concept of evolution strategies and determined the differences between evolution strategies and genetic algorithms. Finally, we considered genetic programming and its application to real-world problems.

The most important lessons learned in this chapter are:

- The evolutionary approach to artificial intelligence is based on the computational models of natural selection and genetics known as evolutionary computation. Evolutionary computation combines genetic algorithms, evolution strategies and genetic programming.

- All methods of evolutionary computation work as follows: create a population of individuals, evaluate their fitness, generate a new population by applying genetic operators, and repeat this process a number of times.

- Genetic algorithms were invented by John Holland in the early 1970s. Holland's genetic algorithm is a sequence of procedural steps for moving from one generation of artificial 'chromosomes' to another. It uses 'natural' selection and genetics-inspired techniques known as crossover and mutation. Each chromosome consists of a number of 'genes', and each gene is represented by 0 or 1.

- Genetic algorithms use fitness values of individual chromosomes to carry out reproduction. As reproduction takes place, the crossover operator exchanges parts of two single chromosomes, and the mutation operator changes the gene value in some randomly chosen location of the chromosome. After a number of successive reproductions, the less fit chromosomes become extinct, while those best fit gradually come to dominate the population.

- Genetic algorithms work by discovering and recombining schemata – good 'building blocks' of candidate solutions. The genetic algorithm does not need knowledge of the problem domain, but it requires the fitness function to evaluate the fitness of a solution.

- Solving a problem using genetic algorithms involves defining constraints and optimum criteria, encoding the problem solutions as chromosomes, defining a fitness function to evaluate a chromosome's performance, and creating appropriate crossover and mutation operators.

- Genetic algorithms are a very powerful tool. However, coding the problem as a bit string may change the nature of the problem being investigated. There is always a danger that the coded representation represents a problem that is different from the one we want to solve.

- Evolution strategies were developed by Ingo Rechenberg and Hans-Paul Schwefel in the early 1960s as an alternative to the engineer's intuition. Evolution strategies are used in technical optimisation problems when no analytical objective function is available, and no conventional optimisation method exists – only the engineer's intuition.

- An evolution strategy is a purely numerical optimisation procedure that is similar to a focused Monte Carlo search. Unlike genetic algorithms, evolution strategies use only a mutation operator. In addition, the representation of a problem in a coded form is not required.

- Genetic programming is a recent development in the area of evolutionary computation. It was greatly stimulated in the 1990s by John Koza. Genetic programming applies the same evolutionary approach as genetic algorithms. However, genetic programming is no longer breeding bit strings that represent coded solutions but complete computer programs that solve a problem at hand.

- Solving a problem by genetic programming involves determining the set of arguments, selecting the set of functions, defining a fitness function to evaluate the performance of created computer programs, and choosing the method for designating a result of the run.

- Since genetic programming manipulates programs by applying genetic operators, a programming language should permit a computer program to be manipulated as data and the newly created data to be executed as a program. For these reasons, LISP was chosen as the main language for genetic programming.

Questions for review

1 Why are genetic algorithms called genetic? Who was the 'father' of genetic algorithms?

2 What are the main steps of a genetic algorithm? Draw a flowchart that implements these steps. What are termination criteria used in genetic algorithms?

3 What is the roulette wheel selection technique? How does it work? Give an example.

4 How does the crossover operator work? Give an example using fixed-length bit strings. Give another example using LISP S-expressions.

5 What is mutation? Why is it needed? How does the mutation operator work? Give an example using fixed-length bit strings. Give another example using LISP S-expressions.

6 Why do genetic algorithms work? What is a schema? Give an example of a schema and its instances. Explain the relationship between a schema and a chromosome. What is the Schema Theorem?

7 Describe a typical process of the development of a genetic algorithm for solving a real problem. What is the fundamental difficulty of genetic algorithms?

8 What is an evolution strategy? How is it implemented? What are the differences between evolution strategies and genetic algorithms?

9   Draw a block-diagram of the $(1+1)$-evolution strategy. Why do we vary all the parameters simultaneously when generating a new solution?

10 What is genetic programming? How does it work? Why has LISP become the main language for genetic programming?

11 What is a LISP S-expression? Give an example and represent it as a rooted point-labelled tree with ordered branches. Show terminals and functions on the tree.

12 What are the main steps in genetic programming? Draw a flowchart that implements these steps. What are the advantages of genetic programming?

References

Atmar, W. (1994). Notes on the simulation of evolution, *IEEE Transactions on Neural Networks*, 5(1), 130–148.

Caruana, R.A. and Schaffer, J.D. (1988). Representation and hidden bias: gray vs. binary coding for genetic algorithms, *Proceedings of the Fifth International Conference on Machine Learning*, J. Laird, ed., Morgan Kaufmann, San Mateo, CA.

Conner, J.K. and Hartl, L.D. (2004). *A Primer of Ecological Genetics*. Sinauer Associates, Sunderland, MA.

Davis, L. (1991). *Handbook on Genetic Algorithms*. Van Nostrand Reinhold, New York.

Fogel, L.J., Owens, A.J. and Walsh, M.J. (1966). *Artificial Intelligence Through Simulated Evolution*. Morgan Kaufmann, Los Altos, CA.

Goldberg, D.E. (1989). *Genetic Algorithms in Search, Optimisation and Machine Learning*. Addison-Wesley, Reading, MA.

Goldberg, D. and Sastry, K. (2010). *Genetic Algorithms: The Design of Innovation*, 2nd edn. Springer-Verlag, Berlin.

Gould, J.L. and Keeton, W.T. (1996). *Biological Science*, 6th edn. R.S. Means, New York.

Hoffman, A. (1989). *Arguments on Evolution: A Paleontologist's Perspective*. Oxford University Press, New York.

Holland, J.H. (1975). *Adaptation in Natural and Artificial Systems*. University of Michigan Press, Ann Arbor.

Koza, J.R. (1992). *Genetic Programming: On the Programming of the Computers by Means of Natural Selection*. MIT Press, Cambridge, MA.

Koza, J.R. (1994). *Genetic Programming II: Automatic Discovery of Reusable Programs*. MIT Press, Cambridge, MA.

Mayr, E. (1988). *Towards a New Philosophy of Biology: Observations of an Evolutionist*. Belknap Press, Cambridge, MA.

Michalewicz, Z. (1996). *Genetic Algorithms + Data Structures = Evolutionary Programs*, 3rd edn. Springer-Verlag, New York.

Mitchell, M. (1996). *An Introduction to Genetic Algorithms*. MIT Press, Cambridge, MA.

Rawlins, G. (1991). *Foundations of Genetic Algorithms*. Morgan Kaufmann, San Francisco.

Rechenberg, I. (1965). *Cybernetic Solution Path of an Experimental Problem*. Ministry of Aviation, Royal Aircraft Establishment, Library Translation No. 1122, August.

Schwefel, H.-P. (1981). *Numerical Optimization of Computer Models*. John Wiley, Chichester.

Schwefel, H.-P. (1995). *Evolution and Optimum Seeking*. John Wiley, New York.

Turing, A.M. (1950). Computing machinery and intelligence, *Mind*, 59, 433–460.

Whitley, L.D. (1993). *Foundations of Genetic Algorithms 2*. Morgan Kaufmann, San Francisco.

Wright, S. (1932). The roles of mutation, inbreeding, crossbreeding, and selection in evolution, *Proceedings of the 6th International Congress on Genetics*, Ithaca, NY, vol. 1, pp. 356–366.

Bibliography

Affenzeller, M., Winkler, S., Wagner, S. and Beham, A. (2009). *Genetic Algorithms and Genetic Programming: Modern Concepts and Practical Applications*. Chapman & Hall/CRC Press, Boca Raton, FL.

Arnold, D.V. and Beyer, H.-G. (2002). *Noisy Optimization with Evolution Strategies*. Kluwer Academic Publishers, Boston, MA.

Banzhaf, W., Harding, S., Langdon, W.B. and Wilson, G. (2008). Accelerating genetic programming through graphics processing units, *Genetic Programming Theory and Practice VI*, R. Riolo, T. Soule, and B. Worzel, eds, Springer-Verlag, Berlin, pp. 1–19.

Beyer, H.-G. (2001). *The Theory of Evolution Strategies*. Springer-Verlag, Heidelberg.

Brameier, M. and Banzhaf, W. (2007). *Linear Genetic Programming*, Springer-Verlag, New York.

Cantu-Paz, E. (2000). *Designing Efficient Parallel Genetic Algorithms*. Kluwer Academic Publishers, Boston, MA.

Cevallos, F. (2009). *A Genetic Algorithm Approach to Bus Transfers Synchronization: Minimizing Transfer Times in a Public Transit System*. VDM-Verlag, Saarbrücken.

Christian, J. (2001). *Illustrating Evolutionary Computation with Mathematica*. Morgan Kaufmann, San Francisco.

Coello Coello, C.A., Lamont, G.B. and van Veldhuizen, D.A. (2007). *Evolutionary Algorithms for Solving Multi-Objective Problems*, 2nd edn. Springer-Verlag, Berlin.

Crosby, J.L. (1973). *Computer Simulation in Genetics*. John Wiley, London.

Eiben, A.E. and Smith, J.E. (2003). *Introduction to Evolutionary Computing*. Springer-Verlag, Berlin.

Floreano, D. and Mattiussi, C. (2008). *Bio-Inspired Artificial Intelligence: Theories, Methods, and Technologies*. MIT Press, Cambridge, MA.

Fogel, D.B. (2005). *Evolutionary Computation: Toward a New Philosophy of Machine Intelligence*, 3rd edn. Wiley–IEEE Press, Hoboken, NJ.

Ghanea-Hercock, R. (2003). *Applied Evolutionary Algorithms in Java*. Springer-Verlag, New York.

Haupt, R.L. and Haupt, S.E. (1998). *Practical Genetic Algorithms*, 2nd edn. John Wiley, New York.

Haupt, R.L. and Werner, D.H. (2007). *Genetic Algorithms in Electromagnetics*. Wiley–IEEE Press, Hoboken, NJ.

Haupt, S.E., Pasini, A. and Marzban, C. (2009). *Artificial Intelligence Methods in the Environmental Sciences*. Springer Science+Business Media, Berlin.

Jamshidi, M., Coelho, L.S., Krohling, R.A. and Fleming, P.J. (2003). *Robust Control Systems with Genetic Algorithms*. CRC Press, London.

Kolhe, M. (2008). *Wind Energy Forecasting by Using Artificial Neural Network – Genetic Algorithm*, VDM-Verlag, Saarbrücken.

Koza, J.R., Bennett III, F.H., Andre, D. and Keane, M.A. (1999). *Genetic Programming III: Darwinian Invention and Problem Solving*. Morgan Kaufmann, San Francisco.

Koza, J.R., Keane, M.A., Streeter, M.J., Mydlowec, W., Yu, J. and Lanza, G. (2005). *Genetic Programming IV: Routine Human-Competitive Machine Intelligence*. Springer-Verlag, Berlin.

Langdon, W.B. (1998). *Genetic Programming and Data Structures: Genetic Programming + Data Structures = Automatic Programming!* Kluwer Academic Publishers, Amsterdam.

Langdon, W.B. and Poli, R. (2010). *Foundations of Genetic Programming*. Springer-Verlag, Berlin.

Lowen, R. (2008). *Foundations of Generic Optimization Applications of Fuzzy Control, Genetic Algorithms and Neural Networks*. Springer-Verlag, Berlin.

Pappa, G.L. and Freitas, A. (2009). *Automating the Design of Data Mining Algorithms: An Evolutionary Computation Approach*, Springer-Verlag, Berlin.

Poli, R., Langdon, W.B. and McPhee, N.F. (2008). *A Field Guide to Genetic Programming*. Lulu Enterprises Inc.

Sivanandam, S.N. and Deepa, S.N. (2009). *Introduction to Genetic Algorithms*. Springer-Verlag, Berlin.

Steeb, W.-H. (2008). *The Nonlinear Workbook: Chaos, Fractals, Cellular Automata, Neural Networks, Genetic Algorithms, Gene Expression Programming, Support Vector Machine, Wavelets, Hidden Markov Models, Fuzzy Logic with C++, Java and SymbolicC++ Programs*, 4th edn. World Scientific, Singapore.

Hybrid intelligent systems 8

In which we consider the combination of expert systems, fuzzy logic, neural networks and evolutionary computation, and discuss the emergence of hybrid intelligent systems.

8.1 Introduction, or how to combine German mechanics with Italian love

In previous chapters, we considered several intelligent technologies, including probabilistic reasoning, fuzzy logic, neural networks and evolutionary computation. We discussed the strong and weak points of these technologies, and noticed that in many real-world applications we would need not only to acquire knowledge from various sources, but also to combine different intelligent technologies. The need for such a combination has led to the emergence of **hybrid intelligent systems**.

A hybrid intelligent system is one that combines at least two intelligent technologies. For example, combining a neural network with a fuzzy system results in a hybrid neuro-fuzzy system.

The combination of probabilistic reasoning, fuzzy logic, neural networks and evolutionary computation forms the core of **soft computing** (SC), an emerging approach to building hybrid intelligent systems capable of reasoning and learning in an uncertain and imprecise environment.

The potential of soft computing was first realised by Lotfi Zadeh, the 'father' of fuzzy logic. In March 1991, he established the Berkeley Initiative in Soft Computing. This group includes students, professors, employees of private and government organisations, and other individuals interested in soft computing. The rapid growth of the group suggests that the impact of soft computing on science and technology will be increasingly felt in coming years.

What do we mean by 'soft' computing?

While traditional or 'hard' computing uses **crisp values**, or numbers, soft computing deals with **soft values**, or fuzzy sets. Soft computing is capable of operating with uncertain, imprecise and incomplete information in a manner that reflects human thinking. In real life, humans normally use soft data represented by words rather than numbers. Our sensory organs deal with soft information, our brain makes soft associations and inferences in uncertain and imprecise environments, and we have a remarkable ability to reason and make decisions without using numbers. Humans use words, and soft computing attempts to model our sense of words in decision making.

Can we succeed in solving complex problems using words?

Words are inherently less precise than numbers but precision carries a high cost. We use words when there is a tolerance for imprecision. Likewise, soft computing exploits the tolerance for uncertainty and imprecision to achieve greater tractability and robustness, and lower the cost of solutions (Zadeh, 1996).

We also use words when the available data is not precise enough to use numbers. This is often the case with complex problems, and while 'hard' computing fails to produce any solution, soft computing is still capable of finding good solutions.

What is the difference between soft computing and artificial intelligence?

Conventional artificial intelligence attempts to express human knowledge in symbolic terms. Its corner-stones are its rigid theory for symbol manipulation and its exact reasoning mechanisms, including forward and backward chaining. The most successful product of conventional artificial intelligence is the expert system. But an expert system is good only if explicit knowledge is acquired and represented in the knowledge base. This substantially limits the field of practical applications for such systems.

However, during the last few years, the domain of artificial intelligence has expanded rapidly to include artificial neural networks, genetic algorithms and even fuzzy set theory (Russell and Norvig, 2009). This makes the boundaries between modern artificial intelligence and soft computing vague and elusive. The objective of this chapter, however, is not to argue when one becomes part of the other, but to provide the reader with an understanding of the main principles of building hybrid intelligent systems.

What exactly are we trying to combine in a hybrid system?

Lotfi Zadeh is reputed to have said that a good hybrid would be 'British Police, German Mechanics, French Cuisine, Swiss Banking and Italian Love'. But 'British Cuisine, German Police, French Mechanics, Italian Banking and Swiss Love' would be a bad one. Likewise, a hybrid intelligent system can be good or bad – it depends on which components constitute the hybrid. So our goal is to select the right components for building a good hybrid system.

Each component has its own strengths and weaknesses. Probabilistic reasoning is mainly concerned with uncertainty, fuzzy logic with imprecision, neural networks with learning, and evolutionary computation with optimisation. Table 8.1 presents a comparison of different intelligent technologies. A good hybrid system brings the advantages of these technologies together. Their synergy allows a hybrid system to accommodate common sense, extract knowledge from raw data, use human-like reasoning mechanisms, deal with uncertainty and imprecision, and learn to adapt to a rapidly changing and unknown environment.

Table 8.1 Comparison of expert systems (ESs), fuzzy systems (FSs), neural networks (NNs) and genetic algorithms (GAs)

	ESs	FSs	NNs	GAs
Knowledge representation	○	●	□	■
Uncertainty tolerance	○	●	●	●
Imprecision tolerance	□	●	●	●
Adaptability	□	■	●	●
Learning ability	□	□	●	●
Explanation ability	●	●	□	■
Knowledge discovery and data mining	□	■	●	○
Maintainability	□	○	●	○

The terms used for grading are: □ bad, ■ rather bad, ○ rather good and ● good.

8.2 Neural expert systems

Expert systems and neural networks, as intelligent technologies, share common goals. They both attempt to imitate human intelligence and eventually create an intelligent machine. However, they use very different means to achieve their goals. While expert systems rely on logical inferences and decision trees and focus on modelling human reasoning, neural networks rely on parallel data processing and focus on modelling a human brain. Expert systems treat the brain as a black box, whereas neural networks look at its structure and functions, particularly at its ability to learn. These fundamental differences are reflected in the knowledge representation and data processing techniques used in expert systems and neural networks.

Knowledge in a rule-based expert system is represented by IF-THEN production rules collected by observing or interviewing human experts. This task, called knowledge acquisition, is difficult and expensive. In addition, once the rules are stored in the knowledge base, they cannot be modified by the expert system itself. Expert systems cannot learn from experience or adapt to new environments. Only a human can manually modify the knowledge base by adding, changing or deleting some rules.

Knowledge in neural networks is stored as synaptic weights between neurons. This knowledge is obtained during the learning phase when a training set of data is presented to the network. The network propagates the input data from layer to layer until the output data is generated. If it is different from the desired output, an error is calculated and propagated backwards through the network. The synaptic weights are modified as the error is propagated. Unlike expert systems, neural networks learn without human intervention.

However, in expert systems, knowledge can be divided into individual rules and the user can see and understand the piece of knowledge applied by the system. In contrast, in neural networks, one cannot select a single synaptic weight as a discrete piece of knowledge. Here knowledge is embedded in the

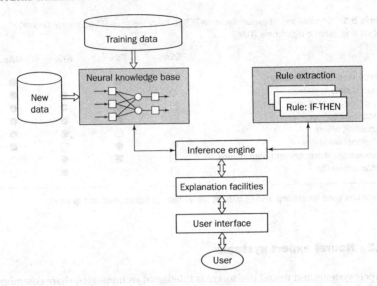

Figure 8.1 Basic structure of a neural expert system

entire network; it cannot be broken into individual pieces, and any change of a synaptic weight may lead to unpredictable results. A neural network is, in fact, a black box for its user.

An expert system cannot learn, but can explain how it arrives at a particular solution. A neural network can learn, but acts as a black box. Thus by combining the advantages of each technology we can create a more powerful and effective expert system. A hybrid system that combines a neural network and a rule-based expert system is called a **neural expert system** (or a **connectionist expert system**). Learning, generalisation, robustness and parallel information processing make neural networks a 'right' component for building a new breed of expert systems.

Figure 8.1 shows the basic structure of a neural expert system. Unlike a rule-based expert system, the knowledge base in the neural expert system is represented by a trained neural network.

A neural expert system can extract IF-THEN rules from the neural network, which enables it to justify and explain its conclusion.

The heart of a neural expert system is the **inference engine**. This controls the information flow in the system and initiates inference over the neural knowledge base. A neural inference engine also ensures approximate reasoning.

What is approximate reasoning?

In a rule-based expert system, the inference engine compares the condition part of each rule with data given in the database. When the IF part of the rule matches the data in the database, the rule is fired and its THEN part is executed.

In rule-based expert systems, the **precise** matching is required. As a result, the inference engine cannot cope with noisy or incomplete data.

Neural expert systems use a trained neural network in place of the knowledge base. The neural network is capable of generalisation. In other words, the new input data does not have to precisely match the data that was used in network training. This allows neural expert systems to deal with noisy and incomplete data. This ability is called approximate reasoning.

The **rule extraction** unit examines the neural knowledge base and produces the rules **implicitly** 'buried' in the trained neural network.

The **explanation facilities** explain to the user how the neural expert system arrives at a particular solution when working with the new input data.

The **user interface** provides the means of communication between the user and the neural expert system.

How does a neural expert system extract rules that justify its inference?

Neurons in the network are connected by links, each of which has a numerical weight attached to it. The weights in a trained neural network determine the strength or importance of the associated neuron inputs; this characteristic is used for extracting rules (Gallant, 1993; Nikolopoulos, 1997; Sestito and Dillon, 1991).

Let us consider a simple example to illustrate how a neural expert system works. This example is an object classification problem. The object to be classified belongs to either birds, planes or gliders. A neural network used for this problem is shown in Figure 8.2. It is a three-layer network fully connected between the first and the second layers. All neurons are labelled according to the concepts they represent.

The first layer is the **input layer**. Neurons in the input layer simply transmit external signals to the next layer. The second layer is the **conjunction layer**. The neurons in this layer apply a sign activation function given by

$$Y^{sign} = \begin{cases} +1, & \text{if } X \geqslant 0 \\ -1, & \text{if } X < 0 \end{cases} \tag{8.1}$$

where X is the net weighted input to the neuron,

$$X = \sum_{i=1}^{n} x_i w_i$$

x_i and w_i are the value of input i and its weight, respectively, and n is the number of neuron inputs.

The third layer is the **output layer**. In our example, each output neuron receives an input from a single conjunction neuron. The weights between the second and the third layers are set to unity.

You might notice that IF-THEN rules are mapped quite naturally into a three-layer neural network where the third (disjunction) layer represents the consequent parts of the rules. Furthermore, the strength of a given rule, or its

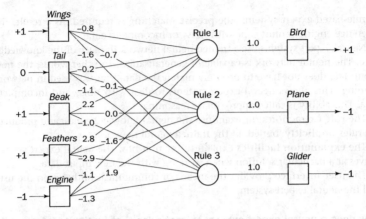

Figure 8.2   The neural knowledge base

certainty factor, can be associated with the weight between respective conjunction and disjunction neurons (Fu, 1993; Kasabov, 2007). We will discuss specific aspects of mapping rules into a neural network later, but now we shall return to our example.

The neural knowledge base was trained with a set of training examples; Figure 8.2 shows the actual numerical weights obtained between the first and the second layers. If we now set each input of the input layer to either +1 (true), −1 (false), or 0 (unknown), we can give a semantic interpretation for the activation of any output neuron. For example, if the object has *Wings* (+1), *Beak* (+1) and *Feathers* (+1), but does not have *Engine* (−1), then we can conclude that this object is *Bird* (+1):

$$X_{Rule1} = 1 \times (-0.8) + 0 \times (-0.2) + 1 \times 2.2 + 1 \times 2.8 + (-1) \times (-1.1)$$
$$= 5.3 > 0$$
$$Y_{Rule1} = Y_{Bird} = +1$$

We can similarly conclude that this object is not *Plane*,

$$X_{Rule2} = 1 \times (-0.7) + 0 \times (-0.1) + 1 \times 0.0 + 1 \times (-1.6) + (-1) \times 1.9$$
$$= -4.2 < 0$$
$$Y_{Rule2} = Y_{Plane} = -1$$

and not *Glider*,

$$X_{Rule3} = 1 \times (-0.6) + 0 \times (-1.1) + 1 \times (-1.0) + 1 \times (-2.9) + (-1) \times (-1.3)$$
$$= -4.2 < 0$$
$$Y_{Rule3} = Y_{Glider} = -1$$

Now by attaching a corresponding question to each input neuron,

Neuron: *Wings*   Question: Does the object have wings?
Neuron: *Tail*   Question: Does the object have a tail?
Neuron: *Beak*   Question: Does the object have a beak?
Neuron: *Feathers*   Question: Does the object have feathers?
Neuron: *Engine*   Question: Does the object have an engine?

we can enable the system to prompt the user for initial values of the input variables. The system's goal is to obtain the most important information first and to draw a conclusion as quickly as possible.

How does the system know what the most important information is, and whether it has enough information to draw a conclusion?

The importance of a particular neuron input is determined by the absolute value of the weight attached to this input. For example, for neuron *Rule* 1, the input *Feathers* has a much greater importance than the input *Wings*. Thus, we might establish the following dialogue with the system:

PURSUING:
> Bird
ENTER INITIAL VALUE FOR THE INPUT FEATHERS:
> +1

Our task now is to see whether the acquired information is sufficient to draw a conclusion. The following heuristic can be applied here (Gallant, 1993):

An inference can be made if the known net weighted input to a neuron is greater than the sum of the absolute values of the weights of the unknown inputs.

This heuristic can be expressed mathematically as follows:

$$\sum_{i=1}^{n} x_i w_i > \sum_{j=1}^{n} |w_j| \tag{8.2}$$

where $i \in$ KNOWN, $j \notin$ KNOWN and n is the number of neuron inputs.
In our example, when the input *Feathers* becomes known, we obtain

KNOWN = $1 \times 2.8 = 2.8$
UNKNOWN = $|-0.8| + |-0.2| + |2.2| + |-1.1| = 4.3$
KNOWN < UNKNOWN

Thus, the inference for neuron *Rule* 1 cannot be made yet, and the user is asked to provide a value for the next most important input, input *Beak*:

ENTER INITIAL VALUE FOR THE INPUT BEAK:
> +1

Now we have

KNOWN $= 1 \times 2.8 + 1 \times 2.2 = 5.0$
UNKNOWN $= |-0.8| + |-0.2| + |-1.1| = 2.1$
KNOWN > UNKNOWN

And thus, according to the heuristic (8.2), the following inference can be made:

CONCLUDE: BIRD IS TRUE

While KNOWN gives the acquired net weighted input to neuron *Rule* 1, UNKNOWN indicates how this net input might change based upon the worst possible combination of values of the unknown inputs. In our example, the net weighted input cannot change more than ±2.1. Therefore, the output of neuron *Rule* 1 will be greater than 0 regardless of the values of the known inputs, and we can make the inference that *Bird* must be true.

Now it is time to examine how a single rule can be extracted to justify an inference. We will use a simple algorithm concerned only with neurons directly connected to the neuron in question (Gallant, 1988). Let us again consider the example shown in Figure 8.2 and justify the inference that *Bird* is true. Because all neurons in the first layer are directly connected to neuron *Rule* 1, we might expect that the rule to be extracted may involve all five neurons – *Wings, Tail, Beak, Feathers* and *Engine*.

First, we determine all contributing inputs and the size of each contribution (Gallant, 1993). An input *i* is considered to be contributing if it does not move the net weighted input in the opposite direction. The size of this contribution is determined by the absolute value of the weight $|w_i|$ of the contributing input *i*.

Now we arrange all contributing inputs according to their sizes in a descending order. In our example, the list of inputs contributing to the inference *Bird is true* looks as follows:

Input: *Feathers*   Size: 2.8
Input: *Beak*   Size: 2.2
Input: *Engine*   Size: 1.1
Input: *Tail*   Size: 0.2

This list enables us to create a rule in which the condition part is represented by the contributing input with the largest contribution:

IF   *Feathers* is true
THEN   *Bird* is true

The next step is to verify this rule. In other words, we need to make sure that the rule passes the validity test. It can be done by applying the heuristic (8.2):

KNOWN $= 1 \times 2.8 = 2.8$
UNKNOWN $= |-0.8| + |-0.2| + |2.2| + |-1.1| = 4.3$
KNOWN < UNKNOWN

The rule is not valid yet, and thus we need to add the 'second best' contributing input as a clause in the condition part of our rule:

IF   *Feathers* is true
AND   *Beak* is true
THEN *Bird* is true

Now we have

$$\text{KNOWN} = 1 \times 2.8 + 1 \times 2.2 = 5.0$$
$$\text{UNKNOWN} = |-0.8| + |-0.2| + | \quad 1.1| = 2.1$$
$$\text{KNOWN} > \text{UNKNOWN}$$

This rule has passed the validity test. It is also a maximally general rule, that is a removal of any condition clause results in an invalid rule.

Similarly, we can obtain rules to justify the inferences that *Plane* is false, and *Glider* is false:

IF   *Engine* is false
AND   *Feathers* is true
THEN *Plane* is false

IF   *Feathers* is true
AND   *Wings* is true
THEN *Glider* is false

This example also illustrates that the neural expert system can make useful deductions even when the data is incomplete (for instance, *Tail* is unknown in our example).

In our example, we assume that the neural expert system has a properly trained neural knowledge base. In the real world, however, the training data is not always adequate. We also assume that we do not have any prior knowledge about the problem domain. In fact, we might have some knowledge, although not often perfect. Can we determine an initial structure of the neural knowledge base by using domain knowledge, train it with a given set of training data, and then interpret the trained neural network as a set of IF-THEN rules?

As we mentioned before, a set of IF-THEN rules that represent domain knowledge can be mapped into a multilayer neural network. Figure 8.3 illustrates a set of rules mapped into a five-layer neural network. The weights between conjunction and disjunction layers indicate the strengths of the rules, and thus can be regarded as certainty factors of the associated rules.

As soon as we have established the initial structure of the neural knowledge base, we can train the network according to a given set of training data. This can be done by using an appropriate training algorithm such as back-propagation. When the training phase is completed, we can examine the neural network knowledge base, extract and, if necessary, refine the set of initial

Rule 1:
IF $a1$ AND $a3$ THEN $b1$ (0.8)

Rule 2:
IF $a1$ AND $a4$ THEN $b1$ (0.2)

Rule 3:
IF $a2$ AND $a5$ THEN $b2$ (−0.1)

Rule 4:
IF $a3$ AND $a4$ THEN $b3$ (0.9)

Rule 5:
IF $a5$ THEN $b3$ (0.6)

Rule 6:
IF $a1$ AND $b3$ THEN $c1$ (0.7)

Rule 7:
IF $b2$ THEN $c1$ (0.1)

Rule 8:
IF $b2$ AND $b3$ THEN $c2$ (0.9)

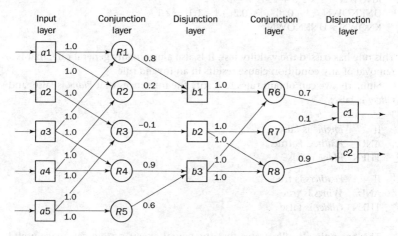

Figure 8.3   An example of a multilayer knowledge base

IF-THEN rules. Thus, neural expert systems can use domain knowledge represented as IF-THEN rules as well as a set of numerical data. In fact, neural
expert systems provide a bidirectional link between neural networks and rule-
based systems.

Unfortunately, neural expert systems still suffer from the limitations of
Boolean logic, and any attempt to represent continuous input variables may
lead to an infinite increase in the number of rules. This might significantly limit
the area of application for neural expert systems. The natural way of overcoming
this limitation is to use fuzzy logic.

8.3   Neuro-fuzzy systems

Fuzzy logic and neural networks are natural complementary tools in building intelligent systems. While neural networks are low-level computational

structures that perform well when dealing with raw data, fuzzy logic deals with reasoning on a higher level, using linguistic information acquired from domain experts. However, fuzzy systems lack the ability to learn and cannot adjust themselves to a new environment. On the other hand, although neural networks can learn, they are opaque to the user. The merger of a neural network with a fuzzy system into one integrated system therefore offers a promising approach to building intelligent systems. Integrated neuro-fuzzy systems can combine the parallel computation and learning abilities of neural networks with the human-like knowledge representation and explanation abilities of fuzzy systems. As a result, neural networks become more transparent, while fuzzy systems become capable of learning.

A neuro-fuzzy system is, in fact, a neural network that is functionally equivalent to a fuzzy inference model. It can be trained to develop IF-THEN fuzzy rules and determine membership functions for input and output variables of the system. Expert knowledge can be easily incorporated into the structure of the neuro-fuzzy system. At the same time, the connectionist structure avoids fuzzy inference, which entails a substantial computational burden.

How does a neuro-fuzzy system look?

The structure of a neuro-fuzzy system is similar to a multilayer neural network. In general, a neuro-fuzzy system has input and output layers, and three hidden layers that represent membership functions and fuzzy rules.

Figure 8.4 shows a Mamdani fuzzy inference model, and Figure 8.5 a neuro-fuzzy system that corresponds to this model. For simplicity, we assume that the fuzzy system has two inputs – $x1$ and $x2$ – and one output – y. Input $x1$ is represented by fuzzy sets $A1$, $A2$ and $A3$; input $x2$ by fuzzy sets $B1$, $B2$ and $B3$; and output y by fuzzy sets $C1$ and $C2$.

Each layer in the neuro-fuzzy system is associated with a particular step in the fuzzy inference process.

Layer 1 is the **input layer**. Each neuron in this layer transmits external crisp signals directly to the next layer. That is,

$$y_i^{(1)} = x_i^{(1)} \tag{8.3}$$

where $x_i^{(1)}$ is the input and $y_i^{(1)}$ is the output of input neuron i in Layer 1.

Layer 2 is the **input membership** or **fuzzification layer**. Neurons in this layer represent fuzzy sets used in the antecedents of fuzzy rules. A fuzzification neuron receives a crisp input and determines the degree to which this input belongs to the neuron's fuzzy set, as follows.

The activation function of a membership neuron is set to the function that specifies the neuron's fuzzy set. In the example presented in Figure 8.4, we use triangular sets. Therefore, the activation functions for the neurons in Layer 2 are set to the triangular membership functions (although fuzzification neurons may have any of the membership functions normally used in fuzzy systems). A

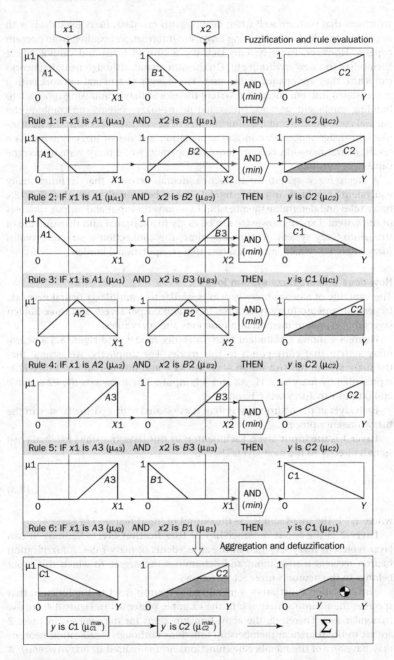

Figure 8.4 Mamdani fuzzy inference system

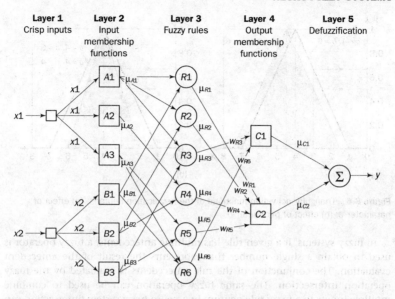

Figure 8.5 Neuro-fuzzy equivalent system

triangular membership function can be specified by two parameters $\{a, b\}$ as follows:

$$
y_i^{(2)} = \begin{cases} 0, & \text{if } x_i^{(2)} \leqslant a - \dfrac{b}{2} \\[2mm] 1 - \dfrac{2|x_i^{(2)} - a|}{b}, & \text{if } a - \dfrac{b}{2} < x_i^{(2)} < a + \dfrac{b}{2} \\[2mm] 0, & \text{if } x_i^{(2)} \geqslant a + \dfrac{b}{2} \end{cases} \tag{8.4}
$$

where a and b are parameters that control the centre and the width of the triangle, respectively, $x_i^{(2)}$ is the input and $y_i^{(2)}$ is the output of fuzzification neuron i in Layer 2.

Figure 8.6 illustrates a triangular function and the effect caused by the variation of parameters a and b. As we can see, the output of a fuzzification neuron depends not only on its input, but also on the centre, a, and the width, b, of the triangular activation function. The neuron input may remain constant, but the output will vary with the change of parameters a and b. In other words, parameters a and b of the fuzzification neurons can play the same role in a neuro-fuzzy system as synaptic weights in a neural network.

Layer 3 is the **fuzzy rule layer**. Each neuron in this layer corresponds to a single fuzzy rule. A fuzzy rule neuron receives inputs from the fuzzification neurons that represent fuzzy sets in the rule antecedents. For instance, neuron $R1$, which corresponds to Rule 1, receives inputs from neurons $A1$ and $B1$.

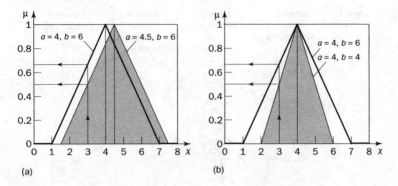

Figure 8.6 Triangular activation functions of the fuzzification neurons: (a) effect of parameter a; (b) effect of parameter b

In fuzzy systems, if a given rule has multiple antecedents, a fuzzy operator is used to obtain a single number that represents the result of the antecedent evaluation. The conjunction of the rule antecedents is evaluated by the fuzzy operation **intersection**. The same fuzzy operation can be used to combine multiple inputs to a fuzzy rule neuron. In a neuro-fuzzy system, intersection can be implemented by the product operator. Thus, the output of neuron i in Layer 3 is obtained as

$$y_i^{(3)} = x_{1i}^{(3)} \times x_{2i}^{(3)} \times \ldots \times x_{ki}^{(3)} \tag{8.5}$$

where $x_{1i}^{(3)}, x_{2i}^{(3)}, \ldots, x_{ki}^{(3)}$ are the inputs and $y_i^{(3)}$ is the output of fuzzy rule neuron i in Layer 3. For example,

$$y_{R1}^{(3)} = \mu_{A1} \times \mu_{B1} = \mu_{R1}$$

The value of μ_{R1} represents the firing strength of fuzzy rule neuron $R1$.

The weights between Layer 3 and Layer 4 represent the **normalised degrees of confidence** (known as certainty factors) of the corresponding fuzzy rules. These weights are adjusted during training of a neuro-fuzzy system.

What is the normalised degree of confidence of a fuzzy rule?
Different rules represented in a neuro-fuzzy system may be associated with different degrees of confidence. In Figure 8.4, an expert may attach the degree of confidence to each fuzzy IF-THEN rule by setting the corresponding weights within the range of $[0, 1]$. During training, however, these weights can change. To keep them within the specified range, the weights are normalised by dividing their respective values by the highest weight magnitude obtained at each iteration.

Layer 4 is the **output membership layer**. Neurons in this layer represent fuzzy sets used in the consequent of fuzzy rules. An output membership neuron receives inputs from the corresponding fuzzy rule neurons and combines them by using the fuzzy operation **union**. This operation can be implemented by the probabilistic OR (also known as the algebraic sum). That is,

$$y_i^{(4)} = x_{1i}^{(4)} \oplus x_{2i}^{(4)} \oplus \ldots \oplus x_{li}^{(4)} \tag{8.6}$$

where $x_{1i}^{(4)}, x_{2i}^{(4)}, \ldots, x_{li}^{(4)}$ are the inputs, and $y_i^{(4)}$ is the output of output membership neuron i in Layer 4. For example,

$$y_{C1}^{(4)} = \mu_{R3} \oplus \mu_{R6} = \mu_{C1}$$

The value of μ_{C1} represents the integrated firing strength of fuzzy rule neurons $R3$ and $R6$. In fact, firing strengths of neurons in the output membership layer are combined in the same way as truth values of the fuzzy rules in Figure 8.4.

In the Mamdani fuzzy system, output fuzzy sets are clipped by the truth values of the corresponding fuzzy rules. In the neuro-fuzzy system, we clip activation functions of the output membership neurons. For example, the membership function of neuron $C1$ is clipped by the integrated firing strength μ_{C1}.

Layer 5 is the **defuzzification layer**. Each neuron in this layer represents a single output of the neuro-fuzzy system. It takes the output fuzzy sets clipped by the respective integrated firing strengths and combines them into a single fuzzy set.

The output of the neuro-fuzzy system is crisp, and thus a combined output fuzzy set must be defuzzified. Neuro-fuzzy systems can apply standard defuzzification methods, including the centroid technique. In our example, we will use the **sum–product composition** method (Jang et al., 1997), which offers a computational shortcut for the Mamdani-style inference.

The sum–product composition calculates the crisp output as the weighted average of the centroids of all output membership functions. For example, the weighted average of the centroids of the clipped fuzzy sets $C1$ and $C2$ is calculated as

$$y = \frac{\mu_{C1} \times a_{C1} \times b_{C1} + \mu_{C2} \times a_{C2} \times b_{C2}}{\mu_{C1} \times b_{C1} + \mu_{C2} \times b_{C2}} \tag{8.7}$$

where a_{C1} and a_{C2} are the centres, and b_{C1} and b_{C2} are the widths of fuzzy sets $C1$ and $C2$, respectively.

How does a neuro-fuzzy system learn?

A neuro-fuzzy system is essentially a multilayer neural network, and thus it can apply standard learning algorithms developed for neural networks, including the back-propagation algorithm (Lin and Lee, 1996; Nauck et al., 1997; Von Altrock, 1997; Kasabov, 2007). When a training input/output example is presented to the system, the back-propagation algorithm computes the system output and compares it with the desired output of the training example. The difference (also called the error) is propagated backwards through the network from the output

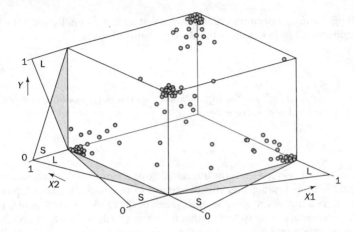

Figure 8.7 Training patterns in the three-dimensional input/output space

layer to the input layer. The neuron activation functions are modified as the error is propagated. To determine the necessary modifications, the back-propagation algorithm differentiates the activation functions of the neurons.

Let us demonstrate how a neuro-fuzzy system works on a simple example. Figure 8.7 shows the distribution of 100 training patterns in the three-dimensional input/output space $X1 \times X2 \times Y$. Each training pattern here is determined by three variables: two inputs $x1$ and $x2$, and one output y. Input and output variables are represented by two linguistic values: *small* (S) and *large* (L).

The data set of Figure 8.7 is used for training the five-rule neuro-fuzzy system shown in Figure 8.8(a). Suppose that fuzzy IF-THEN rules incorporated into the system structure are supplied by a domain expert. **Prior** or existing knowledge can dramatically expedite the system training. Besides, if the quality of training data is poor, the expert knowledge may be the only way to come to a solution at all. However, experts do occasionally make mistakes, and thus some rules used in a neuro-fuzzy system may be false or redundant (e.g. in Figure 8.8(a), either Rule 1 or Rule 2 is wrong because they have exactly the same IF parts, while their THEN parts are different). Therefore, a neuro-fuzzy system should also be capable of identifying bad rules.

In Figure 8.8(a), initial weights between Layer 3 and Layer 4 are set to unity. During training the neuro-fuzzy system uses the back-propagation algorithm to adjust the weights and to modify input and output membership functions. The training continues until the sum of squared errors is less than 0.001. As can be seen from Figure 8.8(b), weight w_{R2} becomes equal to 0 while other weights remain high. This indicates that Rule 2 is certainly false and can be removed without any harm to the neuro-fuzzy system. It leaves the system with four rules that, as you may notice, represent the behaviour of the Exclusive-OR (XOR) operation.

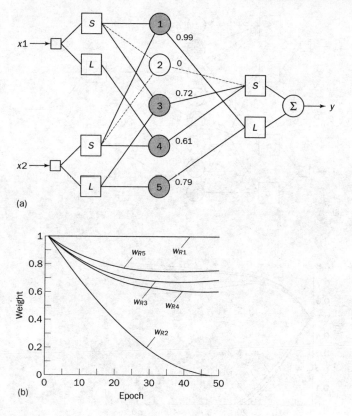

Figure 8.8 Five-rule neuro-fuzzy system for the Exclusive-OR operation: (a) five-rule system; (b) training for 50 epochs

The training data used in this example includes a number of 'bad' patterns inconsistent with the XOR operation. However, the neuro-fuzzy system is still capable of identifying the false rule.

In the XOR example, an expert gives us five fuzzy rules, one of which is wrong. On top of that, we cannot be sure that the 'expert' has not left out a few rules. What can we do to reduce our dependence on the expert knowledge? Can a neuro-fuzzy system extract rules directly from numerical data?

Given input and output linguistic values, a neuro-fuzzy system can automatically generate a complete set of fuzzy IF-THEN rules. Figure 8.9 demonstrates the system created for the XOR example. This system consists of $2^2 \times 2 = 8$ rules. Because expert knowledge is not embodied in the system this time, we set all initial weights between Layer 3 and Layer 4 to 0.5. After training we can eliminate all rules whose certainty factors are less than some sufficiently small number, say 0.1. As a result, we obtain the same set of four fuzzy IF-THEN rules that represents

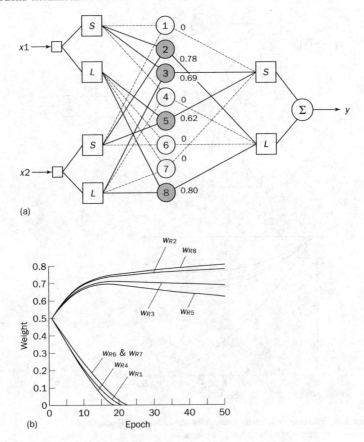

Figure 8.9 Eight-rule neuro-fuzzy system for the Exclusive-OR operation:
(a) eight-rule system; (b) training for 50 epochs

the XOR operation. This simple example demonstrates that a neuro-fuzzy system can indeed extract fuzzy rules directly from numerical data.

The combination of fuzzy logic and neural networks constitutes a powerful means for designing intelligent systems. Domain knowledge can be put into a neuro-fuzzy system by human experts in the form of linguistic variables and fuzzy rules. When a representative set of examples is available, a neuro-fuzzy system can automatically transform it into a robust set of fuzzy IF-THEN rules, and thereby reduce our dependence on expert knowledge when building intelligent systems.

So far we have discussed a neuro-fuzzy system that implements the Mamdani fuzzy inference model. However, the Sugeno model is by far the most popular candidate for data-based fuzzy modelling.

Roger Jang from the Tsing Hua University, Taiwan, China, proposed a neural network that is functionally equal to a Sugeno fuzzy inference model (Jang, 1993). He called it an **adaptive neuro-fuzzy inference system** or ANFIS.

8.4   ANFIS: Adaptive Neuro-Fuzzy Inference System

The Sugeno fuzzy model was proposed for a systematic approach to generating fuzzy rules from a given input/output data set. A typical Sugeno fuzzy rule can be expressed in the following form:

IF x_1 is A_1
AND x_2 is A_2
$\vdots$
AND x_m is A_m
THEN $y = f(x_1, x_2, \ldots, x_m)$

where $x_1, x_2, \ldots, x_m$ are input variables; $A_1, A_2, \ldots, A_m$ are fuzzy sets; and y is either a constant or a linear function of the input variables. When y is a constant, we obtain a zero-order Sugeno fuzzy model in which the consequent of a rule is specified by a singleton. When y is a first-order polynomial, that is

$$y = k_0 + k_1 x_1 + k_2 x_2 + \ldots + k_m x_m$$

we obtain a first-order Sugeno fuzzy model.

Jang's ANFIS is normally represented by a six-layer feedforward neural network. Figure 8.10 shows the ANFIS architecture that corresponds to the first-order Sugeno fuzzy model. For simplicity, we assume that the ANFIS has two inputs – $x1$ and $x2$ – and one output – y. Each input is represented by two fuzzy

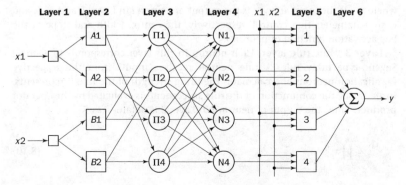

Figure 8.10   Adaptive neuro-fuzzy inference system (ANFIS)

sets, and the output by a first-order polynomial. The ANFIS implements four rules:

Rule 1:		Rule 2:	
IF	$x1$ is $A1$	IF	$x1$ is $A2$
AND	$x2$ is $B1$	AND	$x2$ is $B2$
THEN	$y = f_1 = k_{10} + k_{11}x1 + k_{12}x2$	THEN	$y = f_2 = k_{20} + k_{21}x1 + k_{22}x2$

Rule 3:		Rule 4:	
IF	$x1$ is $A2$	IF	$x1$ is $A1$
AND	$x2$ is $B1$	AND	$x2$ is $B2$
THEN	$y = f_3 = k_{30} + k_{31}x1 + k_{32}x2$	THEN	$y = f_4 = k_{40} + k_{41}x1 + k_{42}x2$

where $x1$, $x2$ are input variables; $A1$ and $A2$ are fuzzy sets on the universe of discourse $X1$; $B1$ and $B2$ are fuzzy sets on the universe of discourse $X2$; and k_{i0}, k_{i1} and k_{i2} are a set of parameters specified for rule i.

Let us now discuss the purpose of each layer in Jang's ANFIS.

Layer 1 is the **input layer**. Neurons in this layer simply pass external crisp signals to Layer 2. That is,

$$y_i^{(1)} = x_i^{(1)} \tag{8.8}$$

where $x_i^{(1)}$ is the input and $y_i^{(1)}$ is the output of input neuron i in Layer 1.

Layer 2 is the **fuzzification layer**. Neurons in this layer perform fuzzification. In Jang's model, fuzzification neurons have a **bell activation function**.

A bell activation function, which has a regular bell shape, is specified as

$$y_i^{(2)} = \frac{1}{1 + \left(\dfrac{x_i^{(2)} - a_i}{c_i} \right)^{2b_i}} \tag{8.9}$$

where $x_i^{(2)}$ is the input and $y_i^{(2)}$ is the output of neuron i in Layer 2; and a_i, b_i and c_i are parameters that control, respectively, the centre, width and slope of the bell activation function of neuron i.

Layer 3 is the **rule layer**. Each neuron in this layer corresponds to a single Sugeno-type fuzzy rule. A rule neuron receives inputs from the respective fuzzification neurons and calculates the firing strength of the rule it represents. In an ANFIS, the conjunction of the rule antecedents is evaluated by the operator **product**. Thus, the output of neuron i in Layer 3 is obtained as

$$y_i^{(3)} = \prod_{j=1}^{k} x_{ji}^{(3)} \tag{8.10}$$

where $x_{ji}^{(3)}$ are the inputs and $y_i^{(3)}$ is the output of rule neuron i in Layer 3.

For example

$$y_{\text{III}}^{(3)} = \mu_{A1} \times \mu_{B1} = \mu_1$$

where the value of μ_1 represents the firing strength, or the truth value, of Rule 1.

Layer 4 is the **normalisation layer**. Each neuron in this layer receives inputs from all neurons in the rule layer, and calculates the **normalised firing strength** of a given rule.

The normalised firing strength is the ratio of the firing strength of a given rule to the sum of firing strengths of all rules. It represents the contribution of a given rule to the final result.

Thus, the output of neuron i in Layer 4 is determined as

$$y_i^{(4)} = \frac{x_{ii}^{(4)}}{\displaystyle\sum_{j=1}^{n} x_{ji}^{(4)}} = \frac{\mu_i}{\displaystyle\sum_{j=1}^{n} \mu_j} = \bar{\mu}_i \qquad (8.11)$$

where $x_{ji}^{(4)}$ is the input from neuron j located in Layer 3 to neuron i in Layer 4, and n is the total number of rule neurons. For example,

$$y_{\text{N1}}^{(4)} = \frac{\mu_1}{\mu_1 + \mu_2 + \mu_3 + \mu_4} = \bar{\mu}_1$$

Layer 5 is the **defuzzification layer**. Each neuron in this layer is connected to the respective normalisation neuron, and also receives initial inputs, x_1 and x_2. A defuzzification neuron calculates the weighted consequent value of a given rule as

$$y_i^{(5)} = x_i^{(5)} [k_{i0} + k_{i1}x1 + k_{i2}x2] = \bar{\mu}_i [k_{i0} + k_{i1}x1 + k_{i2}x2] \qquad (8.12)$$

where $x_i^{(5)}$ is the input and $y_i^{(5)}$ is the output of defuzzification neuron i in Layer 5, and k_{i0}, k_{i1} and k_{i2} is a set of consequent parameters of rule i.

Layer 6 is represented by a single **summation neuron**. This neuron calculates the sum of outputs of all defuzzification neurons and produces the overall ANFIS output, y,

$$y = \sum_{i=1}^{n} x_i^{(6)} = \sum_{i=1}^{n} \bar{\mu}_i [k_{i0} + k_{i1}x1 + k_{i2}x2] \qquad (8.13)$$

Thus, the ANFIS shown in Figure 8.10 is indeed functionally equivalent to a first-order Sugeno fuzzy model.

However, it is often difficult or even impossible to specify a rule consequent in a polynomial form. Conveniently, it is not necessary to have any prior knowledge of rule consequent parameters for an ANFIS to deal with a problem. An ANFIS learns these parameters and tunes membership functions.

How does an ANFIS learn?

An ANFIS uses a hybrid learning algorithm that combines the least-squares estimator and the gradient descent method (Jang, 1993). First, initial activation functions are assigned to each membership neuron. The function centres of the neurons connected to input x_i are set so that the domain of x_i is divided equally, and the widths and slopes are set to allow sufficient overlapping of the respective functions.

In the ANFIS training algorithm, each epoch is composed from a forward pass and a backward pass. In the forward pass, a training set of input patterns (an input vector) is presented to the ANFIS, neuron outputs are calculated on the layer-by-layer basis, and rule consequent parameters are identified by the least-squares estimator. In the Sugeno-style fuzzy inference, an output, y, is a linear function. Thus, given the values of the membership parameters and a training set of P input/output patterns, we can form P linear equations in terms of the consequent parameters as

$$
\begin{cases}
y_d(1) = \bar{\mu}_1(1)f_1(1) + \bar{\mu}_2(1)f_2(1) + \ldots + \bar{\mu}_n(1)f_n(1) \\
y_d(2) = \bar{\mu}_1(2)f_1(2) + \bar{\mu}_2(2)f_2(2) + \ldots + \bar{\mu}_n(2)f_n(2) \\
\quad\vdots \\
y_d(p) = \bar{\mu}_1(p)f_1(p) + \bar{\mu}_2(p)f_2(p) + \ldots + \bar{\mu}_n(p)f_n(p) \\
\quad\vdots \\
y_d(P) = \bar{\mu}_1(P)f_1(P) + \bar{\mu}_2(P)f_2(P) + \ldots + \bar{\mu}_n(P)f_n(P)
\end{cases}
\tag{8.14}
$$

or

$$
\begin{cases}
y_d(1) = \bar{\mu}_1(1)[k_{10} + k_{11}x_1(1) + k_{12}x_2(1) + \ldots + k_{1m}x_m(1)] \\
\qquad + \bar{\mu}_2(1)[k_{20} + k_{21}x_1(1) + k_{22}x_2(1) + \ldots + k_{2m}x_m(1)] + \ldots \\
\qquad + \bar{\mu}_n(1)[k_{n0} + k_{n1}x_1(1) + k_{n2}x_2(1) + \ldots + k_{nm}x_m(1)] \\
y_d(2) = \bar{\mu}_1(2)[k_{10} + k_{11}x_1(2) + k_{12}x_2(2) + \ldots + k_{1m}x_m(2)] \\
\qquad + \bar{\mu}_2(2)[k_{20} + k_{21}x_1(2) + k_{22}x_2(2) + \ldots + k_{2m}x_m(2)] + \ldots \\
\qquad + \bar{\mu}_n(2)[k_{n0} + k_{n1}x_1(2) + k_{n2}x_2(2) + \ldots + k_{nm}x_m(2)] \\
\quad\vdots \\
y_d(p) = \bar{\mu}_1(p)[k_{10} + k_{11}x_1(p) + k_{12}x_2(p) + \ldots + k_{1m}x_m(p)] \\
\qquad + \bar{\mu}_2(p)[k_{20} + k_{21}x_1(p) + k_{22}x_2(p) + \ldots + k_{2m}x_m(p)] + \ldots \\
\qquad + \bar{\mu}_n(p)[k_{n0} + k_{n1}x_1(p) + k_{n2}x_2(p) + \ldots + k_{nm}x_m(p)] \\
\quad\vdots \\
y_d(P) = \bar{\mu}_1(P)[k_{10} + k_{11}x_1(P) + k_{12}x_2(P) + \ldots + k_{1m}x_m(P)] \\
\qquad + \bar{\mu}_2(P)[k_{20} + k_{21}x_1(P) + k_{22}x_2(P) + \ldots + k_{2m}x_m(P)] + \ldots \\
\qquad + \bar{\mu}_n(P)[k_{n0} + k_{n1}x_1(P) + k_{n2}x_2(P) + \ldots + k_{nm}x_m(P)]
\end{cases}
\tag{8.15}
$$

where m is the number of input variables, n is the number of neurons in the rule layer, and $y_d(p)$ is the desired overall output of the ANFIS when inputs $x_1(p)$, $x_2(p), \ldots, x_m(p)$ are presented to it.

In the matrix notation, we have

$$y_d = A k \tag{8.16}$$

where y_d is a $P \times 1$ desired output vector,

$$y_d = \begin{bmatrix} y_d(1) \\ y_d(2) \\ \vdots \\ y_d(p) \\ \vdots \\ y_d(P) \end{bmatrix}$$

A is a $P \times n(1+m)$ matrix,

$$A = \begin{bmatrix} \bar{\mu}_1(1) & \bar{\mu}_1(1)x_1(1) & \cdots & \bar{\mu}_1(1)x_m(1) & \cdots & \bar{\mu}_n(1) & \bar{\mu}_n(1)x_1(1) & \cdots & \bar{\mu}_n(1)x_m(1) \\ \bar{\mu}_1(2) & \bar{\mu}_1(2)x_1(2) & \cdots & \bar{\mu}_1(2)x_m(2) & \cdots & \bar{\mu}_n(2) & \bar{\mu}_n(2)x_1(2) & \cdots & \bar{\mu}_n(2)x_m(2) \\ \vdots & \vdots & \cdots & \vdots & \cdots & \vdots & \vdots & \cdots & \vdots \\ \bar{\mu}_1(p) & \bar{\mu}_1(p)x_1(p) & \cdots & \bar{\mu}_1(p)x_m(p) & \cdots & \bar{\mu}_n(p) & \bar{\mu}_n(p)x_1(p) & \cdots & \bar{\mu}_n(p)x_m(p) \\ \vdots & \vdots & \cdots & \vdots & \cdots & \vdots & \vdots & \cdots & \vdots \\ \bar{\mu}_1(P) & \bar{\mu}_1(P)x_1(P) & \cdots & \bar{\mu}_1(P)x_m(P) & \cdots & \bar{\mu}_n(P) & \bar{\mu}_n(P)x_1(P) & \cdots & \bar{\mu}_n(P)x_m(P) \end{bmatrix}$$

and k is an $n(1+m) \times 1$ vector of unknown consequent parameters,

$$k = [k_{10} \, k_{11} \, k_{12} \ldots k_{1m} \, k_{20} \, k_{21} \, k_{22} \ldots k_{2m} \ldots k_{n0} \, k_{n1} \, k_{n2} \ldots k_{nm}]^T$$

Usually the number of input/output patterns P used in training is greater than the number of consequent parameters $n(1+m)$. It means that we are dealing here with an overdetermined problem, and thus an exact solution to Eq. (8.16) may not even exist. Instead, we should find a least-squares estimate of k, k^*, that minimises the squared error $\|Ak - y_d\|^2$. It is done by using the pseudoinverse technique:

$$k^* = (A^T A)^{-1} A^T y_d \tag{8.17}$$

where A^T is the transpose of A, and $(A^T A)^{-1} A^T$ is the pseudoinverse of A if $(A^T A)$ is non-singular.

As soon as the rule consequent parameters are established, we can compute an actual network output vector, y, and determine the error vector, e,

$$e = y_d - y \tag{8.18}$$

In the backward pass, the back-propagation algorithm is applied. The error signals are propagated back, and the antecedent parameters are updated according to the chain rule.

Let us, for instance, consider a correction applied to parameter a of the bell activation function used in neuron $A1$. We may express the chain rule as follows:

$$\Delta a = -\alpha \frac{\partial E}{\partial a} = -\alpha \frac{\partial E}{\partial e} \times \frac{\partial e}{\partial y} \times \frac{\partial y}{\partial (\bar{\mu}_i \, f_i)} \times \frac{\partial (\bar{\mu}_i \, f_i)}{\partial \bar{\mu}_i} \times \frac{\partial \bar{\mu}_i}{\partial \mu_i} \times \frac{\partial \mu_i}{\partial \mu_{A1}} \times \frac{\partial \mu_{A1}}{\partial a} \tag{8.19}$$

where α is the learning rate, and E is the instantaneous value of the squared error for the ANFIS output neuron, that is

$$E = \frac{1}{2} e^2 = \frac{1}{2} (y_d - y)^2 \tag{8.20}$$

Thus, we have

$$\Delta a = -\alpha \, (y_d - y)(-1) f_i \times \frac{\bar{\mu}_i (1 - \bar{\mu}_i)}{\mu_i} \times \frac{\mu_i}{\mu_{A1}} \times \frac{\partial \mu_{A1}}{\partial a} \tag{8.21}$$

or

$$\Delta a = \alpha \, (y_d - y) f_i \, \bar{\mu}_i (1 - \bar{\mu}_i) \times \frac{1}{\mu_{A1}} \times \frac{\partial \mu_{A1}}{\partial a} \tag{8.22}$$

where

$$\frac{\partial \mu_{A1}}{\partial a} = - \frac{1}{\left[1 + \left(\dfrac{x1 - a}{c} \right)^{2b} \right]^2} \times \frac{1}{c^{2b}} \times 2b \times (x1 - a)^{2b-1} \times (-1)$$

$$= \mu_{A1}^2 \times \frac{2b}{c} \times \left(\frac{x1 - a}{c} \right)^{2b-1}$$

Similarly, we can obtain corrections applied to parameters b and c.

In the ANFIS training algorithm suggested by Jang, both antecedent parameters and consequent parameters are optimised. In the forward pass, the consequent parameters are adjusted while the antecedent parameters remain fixed. In the backward pass, the antecedent parameters are tuned while the consequent parameters are kept fixed. However, in some cases, when the input/output data set is relatively small, membership functions can be described by a human expert. In such situations, these membership functions are kept fixed throughout the training process, and only consequent parameters are adjusted (Jang *et al.*, 1997).

Let us now demonstrate an application of an ANFIS for function approximation. In this example, an ANFIS is used to follow a trajectory of the non-linear function defined by the equation

$$y = \frac{\cos(2x1)}{e^{x2}}$$

First, we choose an appropriate architecture for the ANFIS. An ANFIS must have two inputs – $x1$ and $x2$ – and one output – y.

We decide on the number of membership functions to be assigned to each input by choosing the smallest number of membership functions that yields a 'satisfactory' performance. Thus, the experimental study may begin with two membership functions assigned to each input variable.

To build an ANFIS, we choose either a programming language, for example C/C++, or a neuro-fuzzy development tool. We will use one of the most popular tools – the MATLAB Fuzzy Logic Toolbox. It provides a systematic framework for building neuro-fuzzy inference systems and defines rules automatically based on the number of membership functions assigned to each input variable. Thus, in our example, the ANFIS is defined by four rules, and in fact has the structure shown in Figure 8.10.

The ANFIS training data includes 101 training samples. They are represented by a 101×3 matrix $[x1 \ x2 \ y_d]$, where $x1$ and $x2$ are input vectors, and y_d is a desired output vector. The first input vector, $x1$, starts at 0, increments by 0.1 and ends at 10. The second input vector, $x2$, is created by taking the sine of each element of vector $x1$. Finally, each element of the desired output vector, y_d, is determined by the function equation.

An actual trajectory of the function and the ANFIS's output after 1 and 100 epochs of training are depicted in Figure 8.11. Note that Figure 8.11(a) represents results after the least-squares estimator identified the rule consequent para-

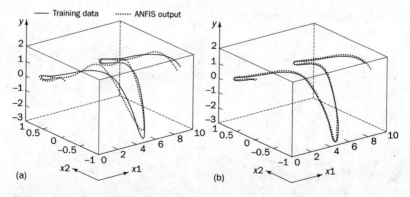

Figure 8.11 Learning in an ANFIS with two membership functions assigned to each input: (a) 1 epoch; (b) 100 epochs

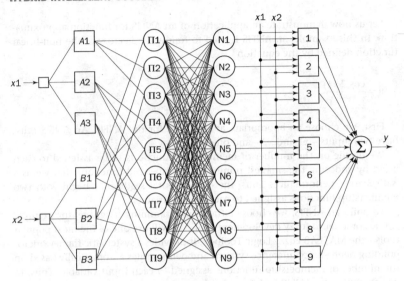

Figure 8.12 An ANFIS model with nine rules

meters for the first time. As we can see, the ANFIS's performance is not always adequate even after 100 epochs of training.

We can achieve some improvement in an ANFIS's performance by increasing the number of epochs, but much better results are obtained when we assign three membership functions to each input variable. In this case, the ANFIS model will have nine rules, as shown in Figure 8.12.

Figure 8.13 shows that the ANFIS's performance improves significantly, and even after one epoch its output quite accurately resembles the desired trajectory. Figure 8.14 illustrates the membership functions before and after training.

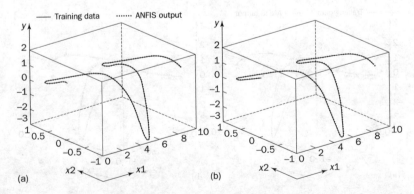

Figure 8.13 Learning in an ANFIS with three membership functions assigned to each input: (a) 1 epoch; (b) 100 epochs

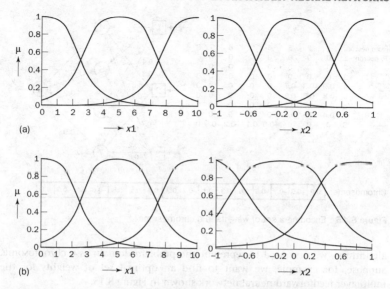

(a) $\longrightarrow x1$ $\longrightarrow x2$

(b) $\longrightarrow x1$ $\longrightarrow x2$

Figure 8.14   Initial and final membership functions of the ANFIS: (a) initial membership functions; (b) membership functions after 100 epochs of training

The ANFIS has a remarkable ability to generalise and converge rapidly. This is particularly important in on-line learning. As a result, Jang's model and its variants are finding numerous applications, especially in adaptive control.

8.5   Evolutionary neural networks

Although neural networks are used for solving a variety of problems, they still have some limitations. One of the most common is associated with neural network training. The back-propagation learning algorithm that is often used because it is flexible and mathematically tractable (given that the transfer functions of neurons can be differentiated) has a serious drawback: it cannot guarantee an optimal solution. In real-world applications, the back-propagation algorithm might converge to a set of sub-optimal weights from which it cannot escape. As a result, the neural network is often unable to find a desirable solution to a problem at hand.

Another difficulty is related to selecting an optimal topology for the neural network. The 'right' network architecture for a particular problem is often chosen by means of heuristics, and designing a neural network topology is still more art than engineering.

Genetic algorithms are an effective optimisation technique that can guide both weight optimisation and topology selection.

Let us first consider the basic concept of an evolutionary weight optimisation technique (Skabar, 2003; Abraham, 2004; Castellano *et al.*, 2007). To use genetic

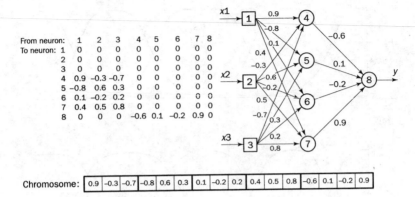

Chromosome: | 0.9 | -0.3 | -0.7 | -0.8 | 0.6 | 0.3 | 0.1 | -0.2 | 0.2 | 0.4 | 0.5 | 0.8 | -0.6 | 0.1 | -0.2 | 0.9 |

Figure 8.15 Encoding a set of weights in a chromosome

algorithms, we first need to represent the problem domain as a chromosome. Suppose, for example, we want to find an optimal set of weights for the multilayer feedforward neural network shown in Figure 8.15.

Initial weights in the network are chosen randomly within some small interval, say $[-1, 1]$. The set of weights can be represented by a square matrix in which a real number corresponds to the weighted link from one neuron to another, and 0 means that there is no connection between two given neurons. In total, there are 16 weighted links between neurons in Figure 8.15. Since a chromosome is a collection of genes, a set of weights can be represented by a 16-gene chromosome, where each gene corresponds to a single weighted link in the network. Thus, if we string the rows of the matrix together, ignoring zeros, we obtain a chromosome.

In addition, each row now represents a group of all the incoming weighted links to a single neuron. This group can be thought of as a functional building block of the network (Montana and Davis, 1989), and therefore should be allowed to stay together passing genetic material from one generation to the next. To achieve this, we should associate each gene not with a single weight but rather with a group of all incoming weights of a given neuron, as shown in Figure 8.15.

The second step is to define a fitness function for evaluating the chromosome's performance. This function must estimate the performance of a given neural network. We can apply here a fairly simple function defined by the reciprocal of the sum of squared errors. To evaluate the fitness of a given chromosome, each weight contained in the chromosome is assigned to the respective link in the network. The training set of examples is then presented to the network, and the sum of squared errors is calculated. The smaller the sum, the fitter the chromosome. In other words, the genetic algorithm attempts to find a set of weights that minimises the sum of squared errors.

The third step is to choose the genetic operators – crossover and mutation. A crossover operator takes two parent chromosomes and creates a single child with

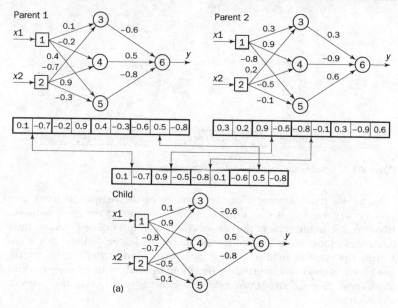

(a)

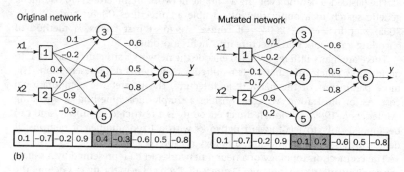

(b)

Figure 8.16   Genetic operations in neural network weight optimisation: (a) crossover; (b) mutation

genetic material from both parents. Each gene in the child's chromosome is represented by the corresponding gene of the randomly selected parent. Figure 8.16(a) shows an application of the crossover operator.

A mutation operator randomly selects a gene in a chromosome and adds a small random value between −1 and 1 to each weight in this gene. Figure 8.16(b) shows an example of mutation.

Now we are ready to apply the genetic algorithm. Of course, we still need to define the population size, that is the number of networks with different weights, the crossover and mutation probabilities and the number of generations.

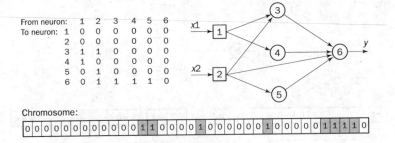

Chromosome:

| 0 | 0 | 0 | 0 | 0 | 0 | 0 | 0 | 0 | 0 | 0 | 0 | 1 | 1 | 0 | 0 | 0 | 0 | 1 | 0 | 0 | 0 | 0 | 0 | 0 | 1 | 0 | 0 | 0 | 0 | 0 | 1 | 1 | 1 | 1 | 0 |

Figure 8.17   Direct encoding of the network topology

So far we have assumed that the structure of the network is fixed, and evolutionary learning is used only to optimise weights in the given network. However, the architecture of the network (i.e. the number of neurons and their interconnections) often determines the success or failure of the application. Usually the network architecture is decided by trial and error; there is a great need for a method of automatically designing the architecture for a particular application. Genetic algorithms may well help us in selecting the network architecture.

The basic idea behind evolving a suitable network architecture is to conduct a genetic search in a population of possible architectures (Melin and Castillo, 2005; Mendivil *et al.*, 2008). Of course, we must first choose a method of encoding a network's architecture into a chromosome.

There are many different ways to encode the network's structure. The key is to decide how much information is required for the network representation. The more parameters of the network architecture, the greater the computational cost. As an illustration, we can consider a simple direct method of encoding (Miller *et al.*, 1989). Although direct encoding is a restricted technique, and can be applied only to feedforward networks with a fixed number of neurons, it demonstrates how a connection topology is evolved.

The connection topology of a neural network can be represented by a square connectivity matrix, as shown in Figure 8.17. Each entry in the matrix defines the type of connection from one neuron (column) to another (row), where 0 means no connection and 1 denotes connection for which the weight can be changed through learning. To transform the connectivity matrix into a chromosome, we need only to string the rows of the matrix together, as shown in Figure 8.17.

Given a set of training examples and a binary string representation for possible network architectures, a basic GA can be described by the following steps:

Step 1: Choose the size of a chromosome population, the crossover and mutation probabilities, and define the number of training epochs.

Step 2: Define a fitness function to measure the performance, or fitness, of an individual chromosome. In general, the network's fitness should be based not only on its accuracy, but also on its learning speed, size and complexity. However, the network's performance is much more important than its size, and therefore the fitness function can still be defined by the reciprocal of the sum of squared errors.

Step 3: Randomly generate an initial population of chromosomes.

Step 4: Decode an individual chromosome into a neural network. Since our networks are restricted to be feedforward, ignore all feedback connections specified in the chromosome. Set initial weights of the network to small random numbers, say in the range $[-1, 1]$. Train the network on a training set of examples for a certain number of epochs using the back-propagation algorithm. Calculate the sum of squared errors and determine the network's fitness.

Step 5: Repeat Step 4 until all the individuals in the population have been considered.

Step 6: Select a pair of chromosomes for mating, with a probability proportionate to their fitness.

Step 7: Create a pair of offspring chromosomes by applying the genetic operators crossover and mutation.

A crossover operator randomly chooses a row index and simply swaps the corresponding rows between two parents, creating two offspring. A mutation operator flips 1 or 2 bits in the chromosome with some low probability, say 0.005.

Step 8: Place the created offspring chromosomes in the new population.

Step 9: Repeat Step 6 until the size of the new chromosome population becomes equal to the size of the initial population, and then replace the initial (parent) chromosome population with the new (offspring) population.

Step 10: Go to Step 4, and repeat the process until a specified number of generations have been considered.

An evolutionary cycle of evolving a neural network topology is presented in Figure 8.18.

In addition to neural network training and topology selection, evolutionary computation can also be used to optimise transfer functions and select suitable input variables. Evolving a set of critical inputs from a large number of possible input variables with complex or unknown functional relationships is an area of current research that has a great potential for evolutionary neural networks. Further topics on new areas of evolutionary computation research in neural systems can be found in Affenzeller *et al.* (2009) and Melin and Castillo (2005).

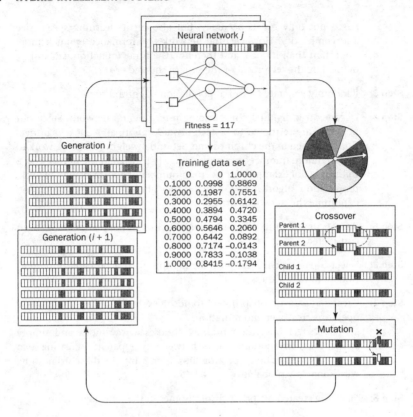

Figure 8.18 The evolutionary cycle of evolving a neural network topology

8.6 Fuzzy evolutionary systems

Evolutionary computation is also used in the design of fuzzy systems, particularly for generating fuzzy rules and adjusting membership functions of fuzzy sets. In this section, we introduce an application of genetic algorithms to select an appropriate set of fuzzy IF-THEN rules for a classification problem (Ishibuchi *et al.*, 1995).

To apply genetic algorithms, we need to have a population of feasible solutions – in our case, a set of fuzzy IF-THEN rules. We need to obtain this set. For a classification problem, a set of fuzzy IF-THEN rules can be generated from numerical data (Ishibuchi *et al.*, 1992). First, we use a **grid-type fuzzy partition** of an input space.

Figure 8.19 shows an example of the fuzzy partition of a two-dimensional input space into 3×3 fuzzy subspaces. Black and white dots here denote the training patterns of Class 1 and Class 2, respectively. The grid-type fuzzy

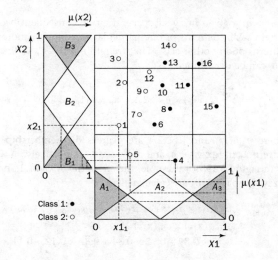

Figure 8.19 Fuzzy partition by a 3 × 3 fuzzy grid

partition can be seen as a rule table. The linguistic values of input $x1$ (A_1, A_2 and A_3) form the horizontal axis, and the linguistic values of input $x2$ (B_1, B_2 and B_3) form the vertical axis. At the intersection of a row and a column lies the rule consequent.

In the rule table, each fuzzy subspace can have only one fuzzy IF-THEN rule, and thus the total number of rules that can be generated in a $K \times K$ grid is equal to $K \times K$. Fuzzy rules that correspond to the $K \times K$ fuzzy partition can be represented in a general form as

Rule R_{ij}:
IF $\quad x1_p$ is A_i $\qquad\qquad\qquad\qquad i = 1, 2, \ldots, K$
AND $\quad x2_p$ is B_j $\qquad\qquad\qquad\qquad j = 1, 2, \ldots, K$
THEN $\quad \mathbf{x}_p \in C_n \left\{ CF_{A_iB_j}^{C_n} \right\} \qquad \mathbf{x}_p = (x1_p, x2_p), p = 1, 2, \ldots, P$

where K is the number of fuzzy intervals in each axis, $\mathbf{x}_p$ is a training pattern on input space $X1 \times X2$, P is the total number of training patterns, C_n is the rule consequent (which, in our example, is either Class 1 or Class 2), and $CF_{A_iB_j}^{C_n}$ is the certainty factor or likelihood that a pattern in fuzzy subspace A_iB_j belongs to class C_n.

To determine the rule consequent and the certainty factor, we use the following procedure:

Step 1: Partition an input space into $K \times K$ fuzzy subspaces, and calculate the **strength** of each class of training patterns in every fuzzy subspace.

Each class in a given fuzzy subspace is represented by its training patterns. The more training patterns, the stronger the class. In other words, in a given fuzzy subspace, the rule consequent becomes more certain when patterns of one particular class appear more often than patterns of any other class. The strength of class C_n in fuzzy subspace A_iB_j can be determined as

$$\beta_{A_iB_j}^{C_n} = \sum_{\substack{p=1 \\ x_p \in C_n}}^{P} \mu_{A_i}(x1_p) \times \mu_{B_j}(x2_p), \quad x_p = (x1_p, x2_p) \tag{8.23}$$

where $\mu_{A_i}(x1_p)$ and $\mu_{B_i}(x2_p)$ are degrees of membership of training pattern x_p in fuzzy set A_i and fuzzy set B_j, respectively.

In Figure 8.19, for example, the strengths of Class 1 and Class 2 in fuzzy subspace A_2B_1 are calculated as

$$\beta_{A_2B_1}^{Class1} = \mu_{A_2}(x_4) \times \mu_{B_1}(x_4) + \mu_{A_2}(x_6) \times \mu_{B_1}(x_6) + \mu_{A_2}(x_8) \times \mu_{B_1}(x_8)$$
$$+ \mu_{A_2}(x_{15}) \times \mu_{B_1}(x_{15})$$
$$= 0.75 \times 0.89 + 0.92 \times 0.34 + 0.87 \times 0.12 + 0.11 \times 0.09 = 1.09$$

$$\beta_{A_2B_1}^{Class2} = \mu_{A_2}(x_1) \times \mu_{B_1}(x_1) + \mu_{A_2}(x_5) \times \mu_{B_1}(x_5) + \mu_{A_2}(x_7) \times \mu_{B_1}(x_7)$$
$$= 0.42 \times 0.38 + 0.54 \times 0.81 + 0.65 \times 0.21 = 0.73$$

Step 2: Determine the rule consequent and the certainty factor in each fuzzy subspace. As the rule consequent is determined by the strongest class, we need to find class C_m such that

$$\beta_{A_iB_j}^{C_m} = max\left[\beta_{A_iB_j}^{C_1}, \beta_{A_iB_j}^{C_2}, \ldots, \beta_{A_iB_j}^{C_N}\right] \tag{8.24}$$

If a particular class takes the maximum value, the rule consequent is determined as C_m. For example, in fuzzy subspace A_2B_1, the rule consequent is Class 1.

Then the certainty factor can be calculated:

$$CF_{A_iB_j}^{C_m} = \frac{\beta_{A_iB_j}^{C_m} - \beta_{A_iB_j}}{\sum_{n=1}^{N} \beta_{A_iB_j}^{C_n}} \tag{8.25}$$

where

$$\beta_{A_iB_j} = \frac{\sum_{\substack{n=1 \\ n \neq m}}^{N} \beta_{A_iB_j}^{C_n}}{N-1} \tag{8.26}$$

For example, the certainty factor of the rule consequent corresponding to fuzzy subspace A_2B_1 can be calculated as

$$CF_{A_2B_1}^{Class2} = \frac{1.09 - 0.73}{1.09 + 0.73} = 0.20$$

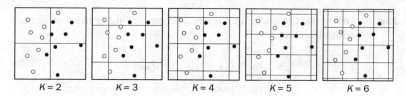

Figure 8.20   Multiple fuzzy rule tables

How do we interpret the certainty factor here?

The certainty factor specified by Eq. (8.25) can be interpreted as follows. If all the training patterns in fuzzy subspace A_iB_j belong to the same class C_m, then the certainty factor is maximum and it is certain that any new pattern in this subspace will belong to class C_m. If, however, training patterns belong to different classes and these classes have similar strengths, then the certainty factor is minimum and it is uncertain that a new pattern will belong to class C_m.

This means that patterns in fuzzy subspace A_2B_1 can be easily misclassified. Moreover, if a fuzzy subspace does not have any training patterns, we cannot determine the rule consequent at all. In fact, if a fuzzy partition is too coarse, many patterns may be misclassified. On the other hand, if a fuzzy partition is too fine, many fuzzy rules cannot be obtained, because of the lack of training patterns in the corresponding fuzzy subspaces. Thus, the choice of the density of a fuzzy grid is very important for the correct classification of an input pattern.

Meanwhile, as can be seen in Figure 8.19, training patterns are not necessarily distributed evenly in the input space. As a result, it is often difficult to choose an appropriate density for the fuzzy grid. To overcome this difficulty, we use multiple fuzzy rule tables (Ishibuchi *et al.*, 1992); an example of these is shown in Figure 8.20. The number of these tables depends on the complexity of the classification problem.

Fuzzy IF-THEN rules are generated for each fuzzy subspace of multiple fuzzy rule tables, and thus a complete set of rules can be specified as

$$S_{ALL} = \sum_{K=2}^{L} S_K, \qquad K = 2, 3, \ldots, L \tag{8.27}$$

where S_K is the rule set corresponding to a fuzzy rule table K.

The set of rules S_{ALL} generated for multiple fuzzy rule tables shown in Figure 8.20 contains $2^2 + 3^2 + 4^2 + 5^2 + 6^2 = 90$ rules.

Once the set of rules S_{ALL} is generated, a new pattern, $\mathbf{x} = (x1, x2)$, can be classified by the following procedure:

Step 1:   In every fuzzy subspace of the multiple fuzzy rule tables, calculate the degree of compatibility of a new pattern with each class:

$$\alpha_{K\{A_iB_j\}}^{C_n} = \mu_{K\{A_i\}}(x1) \times \mu_{K\{B_j\}}(x2) \times CF_{K\{A_iB_j\}}^{C_n} \tag{8.28}$$

$$n = 1, 2, \ldots, N; \quad K = 2, 3, \ldots, L; \quad i = 1, 2, \ldots, K; \quad j = 1, 2, \ldots, K$$

Step 2: Determine the maximum degree of compatibility of the new pattern with each class:

$$\alpha^{C_n} = max\Big[\alpha_{1\{A_1B_1\}}^{C_n}, \alpha_{1\{A_1B_2\}}^{C_n}, \alpha_{1\{A_2B_1\}}^{C_n}, \alpha_{1\{A_2B_2\}}^{C_n},$$ (8.29)

$$\alpha_{2\{A_1B_1\}}^{C_n}, \dots, \alpha_{2\{A_1B_K\}}^{C_n}, \alpha_{2\{A_2B_1\}}^{C_n}, \dots, \alpha_{2\{A_2B_K\}}^{C_n}, \dots, \alpha_{2\{A_KB_1\}}^{C_n}, \dots, \alpha_{2\{A_KB_K\}}^{C_n}, \dots,$$

$$\alpha_{L\{A_1B_1\}}^{C_n}, \dots, \alpha_{L\{A_1B_K\}}^{C_n}, \alpha_{L\{A_2B_1\}}^{C_n}, \dots, \alpha_{L\{A_2B_K\}}^{C_n}, \dots, \alpha_{L\{A_KB_1\}}^{C_n}, \dots, \alpha_{L\{A_KB_K\}}^{C_n}\Big]$$

$$n = 1, 2, \dots, N$$

Step 3: Determine class C_m with which the new pattern has the highest degree of compatibility, that is

$$\alpha^{C_m} = max\big[\alpha^{C_1}, \alpha^{C_2}, \dots, \alpha^{C_N}\big]$$ (8.30)

Assign pattern $\mathbf{x} = (x1, x2)$ to class C_m.

The number of multiple fuzzy rule tables required for an accurate pattern classification may be quite large. Consequently, a complete set of rules S_{ALL} can be enormous. Meanwhile, the rules in S_{ALL} have different classification abilities, and thus by selecting only rules with high potential for accurate classification, we can dramatically reduce the size of the rule set.

The problem of selecting fuzzy IF-THEN rules can be seen as a combinatorial optimisation problem with two objectives. The first, more important, objective is to maximise the number of correctly classified patterns; the second is to minimise the number of rules (Ishibuchi *et al.*, 1995). Genetic algorithms can be applied to this problem.

In genetic algorithms, each feasible solution is treated as an individual, and thus we need to represent a feasible set of fuzzy IF-THEN rules as a chromosome of a fixed length. Each gene in such a chromosome should represent a fuzzy rule in S_{ALL}, and if we define S_{ALL} as

$$S_{ALL} = 2^2 + 3^2 + 4^2 + 5^2 + 6^2$$

the chromosome can be specified by a 90-bit string. Each bit in this string can assume one of three values: 1, −1 or 0.

Our goal is to establish a compact set of fuzzy rules S by selecting appropriate rules from the complete set of rules S_{ALL}. If a particular rule belongs to set S, the corresponding bit in the chromosome assumes value 1, but if it does not belong to S the bit assumes value −1. **Dummy rules** are represented by zeros.

What is a dummy rule?

A dummy rule is generated when the consequent of this rule cannot be determined. This is normally the case when a corresponding fuzzy subspace has no training patterns. Dummy rules do not affect the performance of a classification system, and thus can be excluded from rule set S.

How do we decide which fuzzy rule belongs to rule set S and which does not?

In the initial population, this decision is based on a 50 per cent chance. In other words, each fuzzy rule has a 0.5 probability of receiving value 1 in each chromosome represented in the initial population.

A basic genetic algorithm for selecting fuzzy IF-THEN rules includes the following steps (Ishibuchi *et al.*, 1995):

Step 1: Randomly generate an initial population of chromosomes. The population size may be relatively small, say 10 or 20 chromosomes. Each gene in a chromosome corresponds to a particular fuzzy IF-THEN rule in the rule set defined by S_{ALL}. The genes corresponding to dummy rules receive value 0, and all other genes are randomly assigned either 1 or -1.

Step 2: Calculate the performance, or fitness, of each individual chromosome in the current population.

The problem of selecting fuzzy rules has two objectives: to maximise the accuracy of the pattern classification and to minimise the size of a rule set. The **fitness function** has to accommodate both these objectives. This can be achieved by introducing two respective weights, w_P and w_N, in the fitness function:

$$f(S) = w_P \frac{P_s}{P_{ALL}} - w_N \frac{N_S}{N_{ALL}} \tag{8.31}$$

where P_s is the number of patterns classified successfully, P_{ALL} is the total number of patterns presented to the classification system, N_S and N_{ALL} are the numbers of fuzzy IF-THEN rules in set S and set S_{ALL}, respectively.

The classification accuracy is more important than the size of a rule set. This can be reflected by assigning the weights such that

$$0 < w_N \leqslant w_P$$

Typical values for w_N and w_P are 1 and 10, respectively. Thus, we obtain

$$f(S) = 10 \frac{P_s}{P_{ALL}} - \frac{N_S}{N_{ALL}} \tag{8.32}$$

Step 3: Select a pair of chromosomes for mating. Parent chromosomes are selected with a probability associated with their fitness; a better fit chromosome has a higher probability of being selected.

Step 4: Create a pair of offspring chromosomes by applying a standard cross-over operator. Parent chromosomes are crossed at the randomly selected crossover point.

Step 5: Perform mutation on each gene of the created offspring. The mutation probability is normally kept quite low, say 0.01. The mutation is done by multiplying the gene value by -1.

Step 6: Place the created offspring chromosomes in the new population.

Step 7: Repeat Step 3 until the size of the new population becomes equal to the size of the initial population, and then replace the initial (parent) population with the new (offspring) population.

Step 8: Go to Step 2, and repeat the process until a specified number of generations (typically several hundreds) are considered.

The above algorithm can dramatically reduce the number of fuzzy IF-THEN rules needed for correct classification. In fact, several computer simulations (Ishibuchi *et al.*, 1995) demonstrate that the number of rules can be cut down to less than 2 per cent of the initially generated set of rules. Such a reduction leaves a fuzzy classification system with relatively few significant rules, which can then be carefully examined by human experts. This allows us to use fuzzy evolutionary systems as a knowledge acquisition tool for discovering new knowledge in complex databases.

8.7 Summary

In this chapter, we considered hybrid intelligent systems as a combination of different intelligent technologies. First we introduced a new breed of expert systems, called neural expert systems, which combine neural networks and rule-based expert systems. Then we considered a neuro-fuzzy system that was functionally equivalent to the Mamdani fuzzy inference model, and an adaptive neuro-fuzzy inference system, ANFIS, equivalent to the Sugeno fuzzy inference model. Finally, we discussed evolutionary neural networks and fuzzy evolutionary systems.

The most important lessons learned in this chapter are:

• Hybrid intelligent systems are systems that combine at least two intelligent technologies; for example, a combination of a neural network and a fuzzy system results in a hybrid neuro-fuzzy system.

• Probabilistic reasoning, fuzzy set theory, neural networks and evolutionary computation form the core of soft computing, an emerging approach to building hybrid intelligent systems capable of reasoning and learning in uncertain and imprecise environments.

• Both expert systems and neural networks attempt to emulate human intelligence, but use different means. While expert systems rely on IF-THEN rules and logical inference, neural networks use parallel data processing. An expert system cannot learn, but can explain its reasoning, while a neural network can learn, but acts as a black box. These qualities make them good candidates for building a hybrid intelligent system, called a neural or connectionist expert system.

• Neural expert systems use a trained neural network in place of the knowledge base. Unlike conventional rule-based expert systems, neural expert systems can deal with noisy and incomplete data. Domain knowledge can be utilised in an initial structure of the neural knowledge base. After training, the neural knowledge base can be interpreted as a set of IF-THEN production rules.

- A neuro-fuzzy system corresponding to the Mamdani fuzzy inference model can be represented by a feedforward neural network consisting of five layers: input, fuzzification, fuzzy rule, output membership and defuzzification.

- A neuro-fuzzy system can apply standard learning algorithms developed for neural networks, including the back-propagation algorithm. Expert knowledge in the form of linguistic variables and fuzzy rules can be embodied in the structure of a neuro-fuzzy system. When a representative set of examples is available, a neuro-fuzzy system can automatically transform it into a set of fuzzy IF-THEN rules.

- An adaptive neuro-fuzzy inference system, ANFIS, corresponds to the first-order Sugeno fuzzy model. The ANFIS is represented by a neural network with six layers: input, fuzzification, fuzzy rule, normalisation, defuzzification and summation.

- The ANFIS uses a hybrid learning algorithm that combines the least-squares estimator with the gradient descent method. In the forward pass, a training set of input patterns is presented, neuron outputs are calculated on a layer-by-layer basis, and rule consequent parameters are identified by the least-squares estimator. In the backward pass, the error signals are propagated back and the rule antecedent parameters are updated according to the chain rule.

- Genetic algorithms are effective for optimising weights and selecting the topology of a neural network.

- Evolutionary computation can also be used for selecting an appropriate set of fuzzy rules for solving a complex classification problem. While a complete set of fuzzy IF-THEN rules is generated from numerical data by using multiple fuzzy rule tables, a genetic algorithm is used to select a relatively small number of fuzzy rules with high classification power.

Questions for review

1 What is a hybrid intelligent system? Give an example. What constitutes the core of soft computing? What are the differences between 'hard' and 'soft' computing?

2 Why is a neural expert system capable of approximate reasoning? Draw a neural knowledge base for a three-class classification problem. Suppose that an object to be classified is either an apple, an orange or a lemon.

3 Why are fuzzy systems and neural networks considered to be natural complementary tools for building intelligent systems? Draw a neuro-fuzzy system corresponding to the Sugeno fuzzy inference model for the implementation of the AND operation. Assume that the system has two inputs and one output, and each of them is represented by two linguistic values: small and large.

4   Describe the functions of each layer in a neuro-fuzzy system. How is fuzzification done in this system? How does a fuzzy rule neuron combine its multiple inputs? How is defuzzification done in neuro-fuzzy systems?

5   How does a neuro-fuzzy system learn? What system parameters are learned or tuned during training? How does a neuro-fuzzy system identify false rules given by a human expert? Give an example.

6   Describe the functions of each layer of an ANFIS. What are activation functions used by fuzzification neurons in Jang's model? What is a normalised firing strength of a fuzzy rule?

7   How does an ANFIS learn? Describe a hybrid learning algorithm. What are the advantages of this algorithm?

8   How should we change the ANFIS architecture shown in Figure 8.10 if we want to implement a zero-order Sugeno fuzzy model?

9   What are the differences between a neuro-fuzzy system corresponding to the Mamdani fuzzy inference model and an ANFIS?

10   How is a set of weights of a neural network encoded in a chromosome? Give an example. Describe the genetic operations used to optimise the weights of a neural network.

11   How is a neural network topology encoded in a chromosome? Give an example. Outline the main steps of a basic genetic algorithm for evolving an optimal neural network topology.

12   What is a grid–fuzzy partition? Give an example. Why are multiple fuzzy rule tables needed for a complex pattern classification problem? Describe a genetic algorithm for selecting fuzzy IF-THEN rules.

References

Abraham, A. (2004). Meta learning evolutionary artificial neural networks, *Neurocomputing*, 56, 1–38.

Affenzeller, M., Winkler, S., Wagner, S. and Beham, A. (2009). *Genetic Algorithms and Genetic Programming: Modern Concepts and Practical Applications.* Chapman & Hall/CRC Press, Boca Raton, FL.

Castellano, G., Castiello, C., Fanelli, A.M. and Jain, L. (2007). Evolutionary neuro-fuzzy systems and applications, *Advances in Evolutionary Computing for System Design*, L.C. Jain, V. Palade and D. Srinivasan, eds, Springer-Verlag, Berlin, pp. 11–46.

Fu, L.M. (1993). Knowledge-based connectionism for revising domain theories, *IEEE Transactions on Systems, Man, and Cybernetics*, 23(1), 173–182.

Gallant, S.I. (1988). Connectionist expert systems, *Communications of the ACM*, 31(2), 152–169.

Gallant, S.I. (1993). *Neural Network Learning and Expert Systems.* MIT Press, Cambridge, MA.

Ishibuchi, H., Nozaki, K. and Tanaka, H. (1992). Distributed representation of fuzzy rules and its application to pattern classification, *IEEE Transactions on Fuzzy Systems*, 3(3), 260–270.

Ishibuchi, H., Nozaki, K., Yamamoto, N. and Tanaka, H. (1995). Selecting fuzzy If-Then rules for classification problems using genetic algorithms, *Fuzzy Sets and Systems*, 52, 21–32.

Jang, J.-S.R. (1993). ANFIS: Adaptive Network-based Fuzzy Inference Systems, *IEEE Transactions on Systems, Man, and Cybernetics*, 23(3), 665–685.

Jang, J.-S.R., Sun, C.-T. and Mizutani, E. (1997). *Neuro-Fuzzy and Soft Computing: A Computational Approach to Learning and Machine Intelligence*. Prentice Hall, Englewood Cliffs, NJ.

Kasabov, N. (2007). *Evolving Connectionist Systems: The Knowledge Engineering Approach*. Springer-Verlag, Berlin.

Lin, C.T. and Lee, G. (1996). *Neural Fuzzy Systems: A Neuro-Fuzzy Synergism to Intelligent Systems*. Prentice Hall, Englewood Cliffs, NJ.

Melin, P. and Castillo, O. (2005). *Hybrid Intelligent Systems for Pattern Recognition Using Soft Computing: An Evolutionary Approach for Neural Networks and Fuzzy Systems*. Springer-Verlag, Berlin.

Mendivil, S.G., Castillo, O. and Melin, P. (2008). Optimization of artificial neural network architectures for time series prediction using parallel genetic algorithms, *Soft Computing for Hybrid Intelligent Systems*, O. Castillo, P. Melin J. Kacprzyk and W. Pedrycz, eds, Springer-Verlag, Berlin, pp. 387–400.

Miller, G.F., Todd, P.M. and Hedge, S.U. (1989). Designing neural networks using genetic algorithms, *Proceedings of the Third International Conference on Genetic Algorithms*, J.D. Schaffer, ed., Morgan Kaufmann, San Mateo, CA, pp. 379–384.

Montana, D.J. and Davis, L. (1989). Training feedforward networks using genetic algorithms, *Proceedings of the 11th International Joint Conference on Artificial Intelligence*, Morgan Kaufmann, San Mateo, CA, pp. 762–767.

Nauck, D., Klawonn, F. and Kruse, R. (1997). *Foundations of Neuro-Fuzzy Systems*. John Wiley, Chichester.

Nikolopoulos, C. (1997). *Expert Systems: Introduction to First and Second Generation and Hybrid Knowledge Based Systems*. Marcel Dekker, New York.

Russell, S.J. and Norvig, P. (2009). *Artificial Intelligence: A Modern Approach*, 3rd edn. Prentice Hall, Upper Saddle River, NJ.

Sestito, S. and Dillon, T. (1991). Using single layered neural networks for the extraction of conjunctive rules, *Journal of Applied Intelligence*, 1, 157–173.

Skabar, A. (2003). A GA-based neural network weight optimization technique for semi-supervised classifier learning, *Design and Application of Hybrid Intelligent Systems*, A. Abraham, M. Koppen and K. Franke, eds, IOS Press, Amsterdam, pp. 139–146.

Von Altrock, C. (1997). *Fuzzy Logic and NeuroFuzzy Applications in Business and Finance*. Prentice Hall, Upper Saddle River, NJ.

Zadeh, L. (1996). Computing with words – a paradigm shift, *Proceedings of the First International Conference on Fuzzy Logic and Management of Complexity*, Sydney, Australia, 15–18 January, vol. 1, pp. 3–10.

Knowledge engineering

9

In which we discuss how to pick the right tool for the job and build an intelligent system.

9.1 Introduction, or what is knowledge engineering?

Choosing the right tool for the job is undoubtedly the most critical part of building an intelligent system. Having read this far, you are now familiar with rule- and frame-based expert systems, fuzzy systems, artificial neural networks, genetic algorithms, and hybrid neuro-fuzzy and fuzzy evolutionary systems. Although several of these tools handle many problems well, selecting the one best suited to a particular problem can be difficult. Davis's Law states: 'For every tool there is a task perfectly suited to it' (Davis and King, 1977). However, it would be too optimistic to assume that for every task there is a tool perfectly suited to it. In this chapter, we suggest basic guidelines for selecting an appropriate tool for a given task, consider the main steps in building an intelligent system and discuss how to turn data into knowledge.

The process of building an intelligent system begins with gaining an understanding of the problem domain. We first must assess the problem and determine what data is available and what is needed to solve the problem. Once the problem is understood, we can choose an appropriate tool and develop the system with this tool. The process of building intelligent knowledge-based systems is called **knowledge engineering**. It has six basic phases (Waterman, 1986; Durkin, 1994):

1. Problem assessment.
2. Data and knowledge acquisition.
3. Development of a prototype system.
4. Development of a complete system.
5. Evaluation and revision of the system.
6. Integration and maintenance of the system.

The process of knowledge engineering is illustrated in Figure 9.1. Knowledge engineering, despite its name, is still more art than engineering, and a real

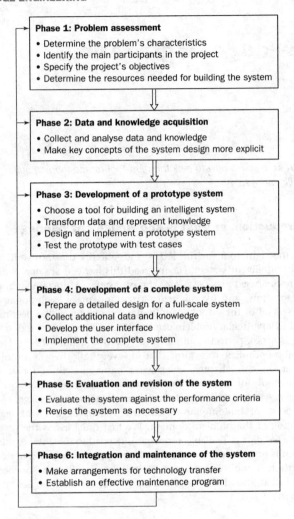

Phase 1: Problem assessment

• Determine the problem's characteristics
• Identify the main participants in the project
• Specify the project's objectives
• Determine the resources needed for building the system

Phase 2: Data and knowledge acquisition

• Collect and analyse data and knowledge
• Make key concepts of the system design more explicit

Phase 3: Development of a prototype system

• Choose a tool for building an intelligent system
• Transform data and represent knowledge
• Design and implement a prototype system
• Test the prototype with test cases

Phase 4: Development of a complete system

• Prepare a detailed design for a full-scale system
• Collect additional data and knowledge
• Develop the user interface
• Implement the complete system

Phase 5: Evaluation and revision of the system

• Evaluate the system against the performance criteria
• Revise the system as necessary

Phase 6: Integration and maintenance of the system

• Make arrangements for technology transfer
• Establish an effective maintenance program

Figure 9.1   The process of knowledge engineering

process of developing an intelligent system is not as neat and clean as Figure 9.1 might suggest. Although the phases are shown in sequence, they usually overlap considerably. The process itself is highly iterative, and at any time we may engage in any development activities. Let us now examine each phase in more detail.

9.1.1 Problem assessment

During this phase we determine the problem's characteristics, identify the project's participants, specify the project's objectives and determine what resources are needed for building the system.

To characterise the problem, we need to determine the problem type, input and output variables and their interactions, and the form and content of the solution.

The first step is to determine the problem type. Typical problems often addressed by intelligent systems are illustrated in Table 9.1. They include **diagnosis, selection, prediction, classification, clustering, optimisation** and **control.**

The problem type influences our choice of the tool for building an intelligent system. Suppose, for example, we develop a system to detect faults in an electric circuit and guide the user through the diagnostic process. This problem clearly belongs to *diagnosis*. Domain knowledge in such problems can often be represented by production rules, and thus a rule-based expert system might be the right candidate for the job.

Of course, the choice of a building tool also depends on the form and content of the solution. For example, systems that are built for diagnostic tasks usually need explanation facilities – the means that enable them to justify their solutions. Such facilities are an essential component of any expert system, but are not available in neural networks. On the other hand, a neural network might be a good choice for *classification* and *clustering* problems where the results are often more important than understanding the system's reasoning process.

The next step in the problem assessment is to identify the participants in the project. Two critical participants in any knowledge engineering project are

Table 9.1 Typical problems addressed by intelligent systems

Problem type	Description
Diagnosis	Inferring malfunctions of an object from its behaviour and recommending solutions.
Selection	Recommending the best option from a list of possible alternatives.
Prediction	Predicting the future behaviour of an object from its behaviour in the past.
Classification	Assigning an object to one of the defined classes.
Clustering	Dividing a heterogeneous group of objects into homogeneous subgroups.
Optimisation	Improving the quality of solutions until an optimal one is found.
Control	Governing the behaviour of an object to meet specified requirements in real time.

the knowledge engineer (a person capable of designing, building and testing an intelligent system) and the domain expert (a knowledgeable person capable of solving problems in a specific area or domain).

Then we specify the project's objectives, such as gaining a competitive edge, improving the quality of decisions, reducing labour costs, and improving the quality of products and services.

Finally, we determine what resources are needed for building the system. They normally include computer facilities, development software, knowledge and data sources (human experts, textbooks, manuals, web sites, databases and examples) and, of course, money.

9.1.2 Data and knowledge acquisition

During this phase we obtain further understanding of the problem domain by collecting and analysing both data and knowledge, and making key concepts of the system's design more explicit.

Data for intelligent systems is often collected from different sources, and thus can be of different types. However, a particular tool for building an intelligent system requires a particular type of data. Some tools deal with continuous variables, while others need to have all variables divided into several ranges, or to be normalised to a single range, say from 0 to 1. Some handle symbolic (textual) data, while others use only numerical data. Some tolerate imprecise and noisy data, while others require only well-defined, clean data. As a result, the data must be transformed, or **massaged**, into the form useful for a particular tool. However, no matter which tool we choose, there are three important issues that must be resolved before massaging the data (Berry and Linoff, 2004).

The first issue is **incompatible** data. Often the data we want to analyse stores text in EBCDIC coding and numbers in packed decimal format, while the tools we want to use for building intelligent systems store text in the ASCII code and numbers as integers with a single- or double-precision floating point. This issue is normally resolved with data transport tools that automatically produce the code for the required data transformation.

The second issue is **inconsistent** data. Often the same facts are represented differently in different databases. If these differences are not spotted and resolved in time, we might find ourselves, for example, analysing consumption patterns of carbonated drinks using data that does not include Coca-Cola just because it was stored in a separate database.

The third issue is **missing** data. Actual data records often contain blank fields. Sometimes we might throw such incomplete records away, but normally we would attempt to infer some useful information from them. In many cases, we can simply fill the blank fields in with the most common or average values. In other cases, the fact that a particular field has not been filled in might itself provide us with very useful information. For example, in a job application form, a blank field for a business phone number might suggest that an applicant is currently unemployed.

Our choice of the system building tool depends on the acquired data. As an example, we can consider a problem of estimating the market value of a property based on its features. This problem can be handled by both expert system and neural network technologies. Therefore, before deciding which tool to apply, we should investigate the available data. If, for instance, we can obtain recent sale prices for houses throughout the region, we might train a neural network by using examples of previous sales rather than develop an expert system using knowledge of an experienced appraiser.

The task of data acquisition is closely related to the task of knowledge acquisition. In fact, we acquire some knowledge about the problem domain while collecting the data.

What are the stages in the knowledge acquisition process?
Usually we start with reviewing documents and reading books, papers and manuals related to the problem domain. Once we become familiar with the problem, we can collect further knowledge through interviewing the domain expert. Then we study and analyse the acquired knowledge, and repeat the entire process again. Knowledge acquisition is an inherently iterative process.

During a number of interviews, the expert is asked to identify four or five typical cases, describe how he or she solves each case and explain, or 'think out loud', the reasoning behind each solution (Russell and Norvig, 2009). However, extracting knowledge from a human expert is a difficult process – it is often called the 'knowledge acquisition bottleneck'. Quite often experts are unaware of what knowledge they have and the problem-solving strategy they use, or are unable to verbalise it. Experts may also provide us with irrelevant, incomplete or inconsistent information.

Understanding the problem domain is critical for building intelligent systems. A classical example is given by Donald Michie (1982). A cheese factory had a very experienced cheese-tester who was approaching retirement age. The factory manager decided to replace him with an 'intelligent machine'. The human tester tested the cheese by sticking his finger into a sample and deciding if it 'felt right'. So it was assumed the machine had to do the same – test for the right surface tension. But the machine was useless. Eventually, it turned out that the human tester subconsciously relied on the cheese's smell rather than on its surface tension and used his finger just to break the crust and let the aroma out.

The data and knowledge acquired during the second phase of knowledge engineering should enable us to describe the problem-solving strategy at the most abstract, conceptual, level and choose a tool for building a prototype. However, we **must not** make a detailed analysis of the problem before evaluating the prototype.

9.1.3 Development of a prototype system

This actually involves creating an intelligent system – or, rather, a small version of it – and testing it with a number of test cases.

What is a prototype?

A prototype system can be defined as a small version of the final system. It is designed to test how well we understand the problem, or in other words to make sure that the problem-solving strategy, the tool selected for building a system, and techniques for representing acquired data and knowledge are adequate to the task. It also provides us with an opportunity to persuade the sceptics and, in many cases, to actively engage the domain expert in the system's development.

After choosing a tool, massaging the data and representing the acquired knowledge in the form suitable for that tool, we design and then implement a prototype version of the system. Once it is built, we examine (usually together with the domain expert) the prototype's performance by testing it with a variety of test cases. The domain expert takes an active part in testing the system, and as a result becomes more involved in the system's development.

What is a test case?

A test case is a problem successfully solved in the past for which input data and an output solution are known. During testing, the system is presented with the same input data and its solution is compared with the original solution.

What should we do if we have made a bad choice of the system building tool?

We should throw the prototype away and start the prototyping phase over again – any attempt to force an ill-chosen tool to suit a problem it was not designed for would only lead to further delays in the system's development. The main goal of the prototyping phase is to obtain a better understanding of the problem, and thus by starting this phase with a new tool, we waste neither time nor money.

9.1.4 Development of a complete system

As soon as the prototype begins functioning satisfactorily, we can assess what is actually involved in developing a full-scale system. We develop a plan, schedule and budget for the complete system, and also clearly define the system's performance criteria.

The main work at this phase is often associated with adding data and knowledge to the system. If, for example, we develop a diagnostic system, we might need to provide it with more rules for handling specific cases. If we develop a prediction system, we might need to collect additional historical examples to make predictions more accurate.

The next task is to develop the user interface – the means of delivering information to a user. The user interface should make it easy for users to obtain any details they need. Some systems may be required to explain their reasoning process and justify their advice, analysis or conclusion, while others need to represent their results in a graphical form.

The development of an intelligent system is, in fact, an evolutionary process. As the project proceeds and new data and knowledge are collected and added to the system, its capability improves and the prototype gradually evolves into a final system.

9.1.5 Evaluation and revision of the system

Intelligent systems, unlike conventional computer programs, are designed to solve problems that quite often do not have clearly defined 'right' and 'wrong' solutions. To evaluate an intelligent system is, in fact, to assure that the system performs the intended task to the user's satisfaction. A formal evaluation of the system is normally accomplished with the test cases selected by the user. The system's performance is compared against the performance criteria that were agreed upon at the end of the prototyping phase.

The evaluation often reveals the system's limitations and weaknesses, so it is revised and relevant development phases are repeated.

9.1.6 Integration and maintenance of the system

This is the final phase in developing the system. It involves integrating the system into the environment where it will operate and establishing an effective maintenance program.

By 'integrating' we mean interfacing a new intelligent system with existing systems within an organisation and arranging for technology transfer. We must make sure that the user knows how to use and maintain the system. Intelligent systems are knowledge-based systems, and because knowledge evolves over time, we need to be able to modify the system.

But who maintains the system?
Once the system is integrated in the working environment, the knowledge engineer withdraws from the project. This leaves the system in the hands of its users. Thus, the organisation that uses the system should have in-house expertise to maintain and modify the system.

Which tool should we use?
As must be clear by now, there is no single tool that is applicable to all tasks. Expert systems, neural networks, fuzzy systems and genetic algorithms all have a place and all find numerous applications. Only two decades ago, in order to apply an intelligent system (or, rather, an expert system), one had first to find a 'good' problem, a problem that had some chance for success. Knowledge engineering projects were expensive, laborious and had high investment risks. The cost of developing a moderate-sized expert system was typically between $250,000 and $500,000 (Simon, 1987). Such 'classic' expert systems as DENDRAL and MYCIN took 20 to 40 person-years to complete. Fortunately, the last few years have seen a dramatic change in the situation. Today, most intelligent systems are built within months rather than years. We use commercially available expert system shells, fuzzy, neural network and evolutionary computation toolboxes, and run our applications on standard PCs. And most

importantly, adopting new intelligent technologies is becoming problem driven, rather than curiosity driven as it often was in the past. Nowadays an organisation addresses its problems with appropriate intelligent tools.

In the following sections, we discuss applications of different tools for solving specific problems.

9.2 Will an expert system work for my problem?

Case study 1: Diagnostic expert systems

I want to develop an intelligent system that can help me to fix malfunctions of my Mac computer. Will an expert system work for this problem?

There is an old but still useful test for prime candidates for expert systems. It is called the *Phone Call Rule* (Firebaugh, 1988): 'Any problem that can be solved by your in-house expert in a 10–30 minute phone call can be developed as an expert system.'

Diagnosis and troubleshooting problems (of course, computer diagnosis is one of them) have always been very attractive candidates for expert system technology. As you may recall, medical diagnosis was one of the first areas to which expert systems were applied. Since then, diagnostic expert systems have found numerous applications, particularly in engineering and manufacturing.

Diagnostic expert systems are relatively easy to develop – most diagnostic problems have a finite list of possible solutions, involve a rather limited amount of well-formalised knowledge, and often take a human expert a short time (say, an hour) to solve.

To develop a computer diagnostic system, we need to acquire knowledge about troubleshooting in computers. We might find and interview a hardware specialist, but for a small expert system there is a better alternative – to use a troubleshooting manual. It provides step-by-step procedures for detecting and fixing a variety of faults. In fact, such a manual contains knowledge in the most concise form that can be directly used in an expert system. There is no need to interview an expert, and thus we can avoid the 'knowledge acquisition bottleneck.'

Computer manuals often include troubleshooting sections, which consider possible problems with the system start-up, computer/peripherals (hard disk, keyboard, monitor, printer), disk drives (floppy disk, CD-ROM), files, and network and file sharing. In our example, we will consider only troubleshooting the Mac system start-up. However, once the prototype expert system is developed, you can easily expand it.

Figure 9.2 illustrates the troubleshooting procedure for the Macintosh computer. As you can see, troubleshooting here is carried out through a series of visual inspections, or tests. We first collect some initial information (the system does not start), infer from it whatever can be inferred, gather additional information (power cords are OK, Powerstrip is OK, etc.) and finally identify

Section 1: System start-up	
Problem	**Action**
1.1. System does not start	• Check power cords (both ends). • Check Powerstrip. • Check screen brightness. • Check phonet connectors. • Check keyboard connectors. • Check pin connectors.
1.2. System starts and then freezes	• Restart the Mac. • Unhook all SCSI devices and restart the Mac. • Restart with the shift key down (turns off extensions). • Remove all extensions and add them back one at a time. Restart the Mac after each addition. If using System 7.5 or higher, use Extensions Manager.
1.3. System starts with a question mark	• Restart the Mac. • Unhook all SCSI devices and restart the Mac. • Restart with the shift key down (turns off extensions). • Zap the PRAM. If this works, turn on virtual memory and the disk cache one at a time (restarting the computer each time). Try making the disk cache smaller, or reduce virtual memory. • Start with Disk Tools and if the hard drive icon shows up, see if there are two system suitcases and/or two finders. If the hard drive icon does not show up, call AV repair. • Run Disk First Aid, MacCheck, or Norton's Disk Doctor. • Do a clean reinstall of the system.
1.4. System starts with a Sad Mac	• Start with Disk Tools and do a clean reinstall of the system. • Run Disk First Aid, MacCheck, or Norton's Disk Doctor. • Start with Disk Tools, and if the hard drive icon does not show up, call AV repair.
1.5. System starts with wrong 'music'	• Check cables.

Figure 9.2 Troubleshooting the system start-up for Macintosh computers

the cause of the system's malfunction. This is essentially data-driven reasoning, which can be best realised with the forward chaining inference technique. The expert system should first ask the user to select a particular task, and once the task is selected, the system should direct troubleshooting by asking the user for additional information until the fault is found.

Let us develop a general rule structure. In each rule, we need to include a clause that identifies the current task. Since our prototype is limited to the

Mac system start-up, the first clause of all rules will identify this task. For example,

```
Rule: 1
if      task is 'system start-up'
then    ask problem

Rule: 2
if      task is 'system start-up'
and     problem is 'system does not start'
then    ask 'test power cords'

Rule: 3
if      task is 'system start-up'
and     problem is 'system does not start'
and     'test power cords' is ok
then    ask 'test Powerstrip'
```

All the other rules will follow this structure. A set of rules to direct troubleshooting when the Mac system does not start (in Leonardo code) is shown in Figure 9.3.

Now we are ready to build a prototype, or in other words to implement the initial set of rules using an expert system development tool.

How do we choose an expert system development tool?

In general, we should match the features of the problem with the capabilities of the tool. These tools range from high-level programming languages such as LISP, PROLOG, OPS, C and Java, to expert system shells. High-level programming languages offer a greater flexibility and can enable us to meet any project requirements, but they do require high-level programming skills. On the other hand, shells, although they do not have the flexibility of programming languages, provide us with the built-in inference engine, explanation facilities and the user interface. We do not need any programming skills to use a shell – we just enter rules in English in the shell's knowledge base. This makes shells particularly useful for rapid prototyping.

So how do we choose a shell?

The appendix provides some details of a few commercial expert system shells currently available on the market. This can help you to choose an appropriate tool; however, the Internet is rapidly becoming the most valuable source of information. Many vendors have web sites, and you can even try and evaluate their products over the Web.

In general, when selecting an expert system shell, you should consider how the shell represents knowledge (rules or frames), what inference mechanism it uses (forward or backward chaining), whether the shell supports inexact reasoning and if so what technique it uses (Bayesian reasoning, certainty factors or fuzzy logic), whether the shell has an 'open' architecture allowing

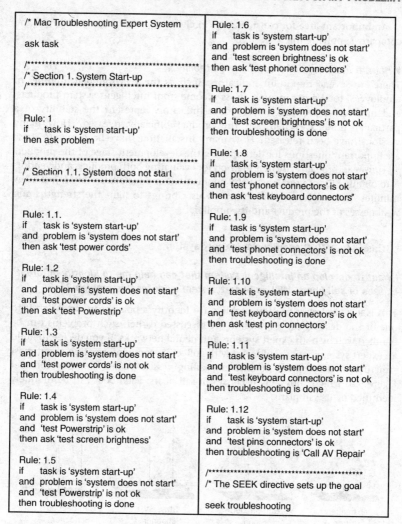

```
/* Mac Troubleshooting Expert System

ask task

/***************************************************
/* Section 1. System Start-up
/***************************************************


Rule: 1
if    task is 'system start-up'
then ask problem

/***************************************************
/* Section 1.1. System does not start
/***************************************************


Rule: 1.1.
if    task is 'system start-up'
and  problem is 'system does not start'
then ask 'test power cords'

Rule: 1.2
if    task is 'system start-up'
and  problem is 'system does not start'
and  'test power cords' is ok
then ask 'test Powerstrip'

Rule: 1.3
if    task is 'system start-up'
and  problem is 'system does not start'
and  'test power cords' is not ok
then troubleshooting is done

Rule: 1.4
if    task is 'system start-up'
and  problem is 'system does not start'
and  'test Powerstrip' is ok
then ask 'test screen brightness'

Rule: 1.5
if    task is 'system start-up'
and  problem is 'system does not start'
and  'test Powerstrip' is not ok
then troubleshooting is done


Rule: 1.6
if    task is 'system start-up'
and  problem is 'system does not start'
and  'test screen brightness' is ok
then ask 'test phonet connectors'

Rule: 1.7
if    task is 'system start-up'
and  problem is 'system does not start'
and  'test screen brightness' is not ok
then troubleshooting is done

Rule: 1.8
if    task is 'system start-up'
and  problem is 'system does not start'
and  test 'phonet connectors' is ok
then ask 'test keyboard connectors'

Rule: 1.9
if    task is 'system start-up'
and  problem is 'system does not start'
and  'test phonet connectors' is not ok
then troubleshooting is done

Rule: 1.10
if    task is 'system start-up'
and  problem is 'system does not start'
and  'test keyboard connectors' is ok
then ask 'test pin connectors'

Rule: 1.11
if    task is 'system start-up'
and  problem is 'system does not start'
and  'test keyboard connectors' is not ok
then troubleshooting is done

Rule: 1.12
if    task is 'system start-up'
and  problem is 'system does not start'
and  'test pins connectors' is ok
then troubleshooting is 'Call AV Repair'

/***************************************************
/* The SEEK directive sets up the goal

seek troubleshooting
```

Figure 9.3 Rules for a prototype of the Mac troubleshooting expert system

access to external data files and programs, and how the user will interact with the expert system (graphical user interface, hypertext).

Today you can buy an expert system shell for less than $50 and run it on your PC or Mac. You can also obtain an expert system shell for free (e.g. CLIPS). However, you should clearly understand your licence obligations, especially whether you need to have a distribution licence allowing the end-user to use your expert system once it is developed.

An important area for consideration in choosing a tool is the stability of the company supplying the tool.

What are indicators of a company's stability?

There are several important indicators, such as the year founded, number of employees, total gross income, gross income from intelligent system products, and number of products sold. Similar indicators represent the stability of a particular product. When was the product officially released? How many versions have been released? How many installations have been made? These are important questions for determining the development stage of the product.

However, probably the best method for evaluating both products and vendors is to obtain a list of users, successful applications and installation sites. Just a few minutes on the phone with the tool's user brings to light the strengths and weaknesses of the product and its supplier.

Case study 2: Classification expert systems

I want to develop an intelligent system that can help me to identify different classes of sail boats. Will an expert system work for this problem?

This is a typical classification problem (to identify a boat means to assign it to one of the defined classes) and, as we discussed earlier, such problems can be handled well by both expert systems and neural networks. If you decide to build an expert system, you should start with collecting some information about mast structures and sail plans of different sailing vessels. As an example, consider Figure 9.4, which shows eight classes of sail boats. Each boat can be uniquely identified by its sail plans.

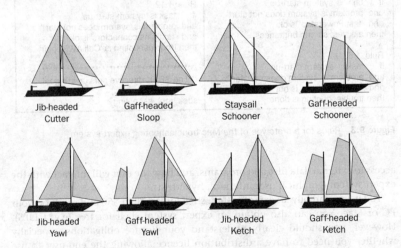

Figure 9.4 Eight classes of sailing vessels

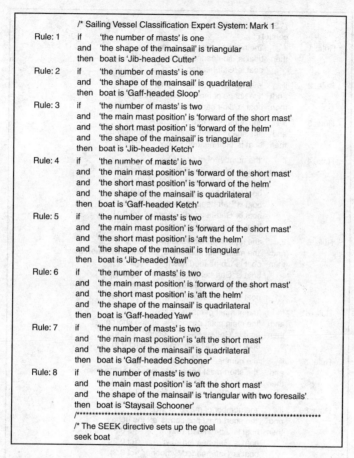

```
                /* Sailing Vessel Classification Expert System: Mark 1
    Rule: 1     if    'the number of masts' is one
                and   'the shape of the mainsail' is triangular
                then  boat is 'Jib-headed Cutter'
    Rule: 2     if    'the number of masts' is one
                and   'the shape of the mainsail' is quadrilateral
                then  boat is 'Gaff-headed Sloop'
    Rule: 3     if    'the number of masts' is two
                and   'the main mast position' is 'forward of the short mast'
                and   'the short mast position' is 'forward of the helm'
                and   'the shape of the mainsail' is triangular
                then  boat is 'Jib-headed Ketch'
    Rule: 4     if    'the number of masts' is two
                and   'the main mast position' is 'forward of the short mast'
                and   'the short mast position' is 'forward of the helm'
                and   'the shape of the mainsail' is quadrilateral
                then  boat is 'Gaff-headed Ketch'
    Rule: 5     if    'the number of masts' is two
                and   'the main mast position' is 'forward of the short mast'
                and   'the short mast position' is 'aft the helm'
                and   'the shape of the mainsail' is triangular
                then  boat is 'Jib-headed Yawl'
    Rule: 6     if    'the number of masts' is two
                and   'the main mast position' is 'forward of the short mast'
                and   'the short mast position' is 'aft the helm'
                and   'the shape of the mainsail' is quadrilateral
                then  boat is 'Gaff-headed Yawl'
    Rule: 7     if    'the number of masts' is two
                and   'the main mast position' is 'aft the short mast'
                and   'the shape of the mainsail' is quadrilateral
                then  boat is 'Gaff-headed Schooner'
    Rule: 8     if    'the number of masts' is two
                and   'the main mast position' is 'aft the short mast'
                and   'the shape of the mainsail' is 'triangular with two foresails'
                then  boat is 'Staysail Schooner'
    /*****************************************************************************
    /* The SEEK directive sets up the goal
    seek boat
```

Figure 9.5   Rules for the boat classification expert system

A set of rules (in Leonardo code) for the sailing vessel classification is shown in Figure 9.5. During a dialogue session with the user, the system obtains the number and position of masts on the unknown vessel as well as the shape of its mainsail, and then uniquely identifies each of the eight boats shown in Figure 9.4.

No doubt when the sky is blue and the sea is calm, this system will help us to identify a sail boat. But this is not always the case. On a rough sea or in foggy conditions, it is difficult, or even impossible, to see clearly the position of masts and the shape of the mainsail. Despite the fact that solving real-world classification problems often involves inexact and incomplete data such as this, we still can use the expert system approach. However, we need to deal with uncertainties. Let us apply the certainty factors theory to our problem. This

```
        /* Sailing Vessel Classification Expert System: Mark 2
        control cf
Rule: 1    if    'the number of masts' is one
           then  boat is 'Jib-headed Cutter'          {cf 0.4};
                 boat is 'Gaff-headed Sloop'          {cf 0.4}

Rule: 2    if    'the number of masts' is one
           and   'the shape of the mainsail' is triangular
           then  boat is 'Jib-headed Cutter'          {cf 1.0}

Rule: 3    if    'the number of masts' is one
           and   'the shape of the mainsail' is quadrilateral
           then  boat is 'Gaff-headed Sloop'          {cf 1.0}

Rule: 4    if    'the number of masts' is two
           then  boat is 'Jib-headed Ketch'           {cf 0.1};
                 boat is 'Gaff-headed Ketch'          {cf 0.1};
                 boat is 'Jib-headed Yawl'            {cf 0.1};
                 boat is 'Gaff-headed Yawl'           {cf 0.1};
                 boat is 'Gaff-headed Schooner'       {cf 0.1};
                 boat is ' Staysail Schooner'         {cf 0.1}

Rule: 5    if    'the number of masts' is two
           and   'the main mast position' is 'forward of the short mast'
           then  boat is 'Jib-headed Ketch'           {cf 0.2};
                 boat is 'Gaff-headed Ketch'          {cf 0.2};
                 boat is 'Jib-headed Yawl'            {cf 0.2};
                 boat is 'Gaff-headed Yawl'           {cf 0.2}

Rule: 6    if    'the number of masts' is two
           and   'the main mast position' is 'aft the short mast'
           then  boat is 'Gaff-headed Schooner'       {cf 0.4};
                 boat is 'Staysail Schooner'          {cf 0.4}

Rule: 7    if    'the number of masts' is two
           and   'the short mast position' is 'forward of the helm'
           then  boat is 'Jib-headed Ketch'           {cf 0.4};
                 boat is 'Gaff-headed Ketch'          {cf 0.4}

Rule: 8    if    'the number of masts' is two
           and   'the short mast position' is 'aft the helm'
           then  boat is 'Jib-headed Yawl'            {cf 0.2};
                 boat is 'Gaff-headed Yawl'           {cf 0.2};
                 boat is 'Gaff-headed Schooner'       {cf 0.2};
                 boat is 'Staysail Schooner'          {cf 0.2}

Rule: 9    if    'the number of masts' is two
           and   'the shape of the mainsail' is triangular
           then  boat is 'Jib-headed Ketch'           {cf 0.4};
                 boat is 'Jib-headed Yawl'            {cf 0.4}

Rule: 10   if    'the number of masts' is two
           and   'the shape of the mainsail' is quadrilateral
           then  boat is 'Gaff-headed Ketch'          {cf 0.3};
                 boat is 'Gaff-headed Yawl'           {cf 0.3};
                 boat is 'Gaff-headed Schooner'       {cf 0.3}

Rule: 11   if    'the number of masts' is two
           and   'the shape of the mainsail' is 'triangular with two foresails'
           then  boat is 'Staysail Schooner'          {cf 1.0}

        seek boat
```

Figure 9.6 Uncertainty management in the boat classification expert system

theory, as you may recall, can manage incrementally acquired evidence, as well as information with different degrees of belief.

Figure 9.6 shows a complete set of rules for solving the sailing vessel classification problem with certainty factors. The expert system is required to classify a boat, or in other words to establish certainty factors for a multi-valued object *boat*. To apply the evidential reasoning technique, the expert system prompts the user to input not only the object value but also the certainty associated with this value. For example, using the Leonardo scale from 0 to 1, we might obtain the following dialogue (the user's answers are indicated by arrows; also note the propagation of certainty factors through the set of rules):

What is the number of masts?
⇒ **two**

To what degree do you believe that the number of masts is two? Enter a numeric certainty between 0 and 1.0 inclusive.
⇒ **0.9**

Rule: 4
if   'the number of masts' is two
then   boat is 'Jib-headed Ketch'   {cf 0.1};
       boat is 'Gaff-headed Ketch'   {cf 0.1};
       boat is 'Jib-headed Yawl'   {cf 0.1};
       boat is 'Gaff-headed Yawl'   {cf 0.1};
       boat is 'Gaff-headed Schooner'   {cf 0.1};
       boat is 'Staysail Schooner'   {cf 0.1}

cf (boat is 'Jib-headed Ketch') = cf ('number of masts' is two) × 0.1 = 0.9 × 0.1 = 0.09
cf (boat is 'Gaff-headed Ketch') = 0.9 × 0.1 = 0.09
cf (boat is 'Jib-headed Yawl') = 0.9 × 0.1 = 0.09
cf (boat is 'Gaff-headed Yawl') = 0.9 × 0.1 = 0.09
cf (boat is 'Gaff-headed Schooner') = 0.9 × 0.1 = 0.09
cf (boat is 'Staysail Schooner') = 0.9 × 0.1 = 0.09

boat is   Jib-headed Ketch   {cf 0.09}
          Gaff-headed Ketch   {cf 0.09}
          Jib-headed Yawl   {cf 0.09}
          Gaff-headed Yawl   {cf 0.09}
          Gaff-headed Schooner   {cf 0.09}
          Staysail Schooner   {cf 0.09}

What is the position of the main mast?
⇒ **aft the short mast**

To what degree do you believe that the main mast position is aft the short mast? Enter a numeric certainty between 0 and 1.0 inclusive.
⇒ **0.7**

Rule: 6
if   'the number of masts' is two
and   'the main mast position' is 'aft the short mast'
then   boat is 'Gaff-headed Schooner'   {cf 0.4};
       boat is 'Staysail Schooner'   {cf 0.4}

$cf_{Rule:6}$ (boat is 'Gaff-headed Schooner') = min [cf ('the number of masts' is two),
cf ('the main mast position' is 'aft the short mast')] × 0.4
= min [0.9, 0.7] × 0.4 = 0.28

$cf_{Rule:6}$ (boat is 'Staysail Schooner') = min [0.9, 0.7] × 0.4 = 0.28

cf (boat is 'Gaff-headed Schooner') = $cf_{Rule:4}$ + $cf_{Rule:6}$ × (1 − $cf_{Rule:4}$)
= 0.09 + 0.28 × (1 − 0.09) = 0.34

cf (boat is 'Staysail Schooner') = 0.09 + 0.28 × (1 − 0.09) = 0.34

boat is	Gaff-headed Schooner	{cf 0.34}
	Staysail Schooner	{cf 0.34}
	Jib-headed Ketch	{cf 0.09}
	Gaff-headed Ketch	{cf 0.09}
	Jib-headed Yawl	{cf 0.09}
	Gaff-headed Yawl	{cf 0.09}

What is the position of the short mast?
⇒ **forward of the helm**

To what degree do you believe that the short mast position is forward of the helm?
Enter a numeric certainty between 0 and 1.0 inclusive.
⇒ **0.6**

Rule: 7
if   'the number of masts' is two
and   'the short mast position' is 'forward of the helm'
then   boat is 'Jib-headed Ketch'   {cf 0.4};
        boat is 'Gaff-headed Ketch'   {cf 0.4}

$cf_{Rule:7}$ (boat is 'Jib-headed Ketch') = min [cf ('the number of masts' is two),
cf ('the short mast position' is 'forward of the helm')] × 0.4
= min [0.9, 0.6] × 0.4 = 0.24

$cf_{Rule:7}$ (boat is 'Gaff-headed Ketch') = min [0.9, 0.6] × 0.4 = 0.24

cf (boat is 'Jib-headed Ketch') = $cf_{Rule:6}$ + $cf_{Rule:7}$ × (1 − $cf_{Rule:6}$)
= 0.09 + 0.24 × (1 − 0.09) = 0.30

cf (boat is 'Gaff-headed Ketch') = 0.09 + 0.24 × (1 − 0.09) = 0.30

boat is	Gaff-headed Schooner	{cf 0.34}
	Staysail Schooner	{cf 0.34}
	Jib-headed Ketch	{cf 0.30}
	Gaff-headed Ketch	{cf 0.30}
	Jib-headed Yawl	{cf 0.09}
	Gaff-headed Yawl	{cf 0.09}

What is the shape of the mainsail?
⇒ **triangular**

To what degree do you believe that the shape of the mainsail is triangular? Enter a
numeric certainty between 0 and 1.0 inclusive.
⇒ **0.8**

Rule: 9
if   'the number of masts' is two
and   'the shape of the mainsail' is triangular
then   boat is 'Jib-headed Ketch'   {cf 0.4};
        boat is 'Jib-headed Yawl'   {cf 0.4}

$cf_{Rule:9}$ (boat is 'Jib-headed Ketch') = min [cf ('the number of masts' is two),
cf ('the shape of the mainsail' is triangular)] $\times$ 0.4
= min [0.9, 0.8] $\times$ 0.4 = 0.32

$cf_{Rule:9}$ (boat is 'Jib-headed Yawl') = min [0.9, 0.8] $\times$ 0.4 = 0.32

cf (boat is 'Jib-headed Ketch') = $cf_{Rule:7}$ + $cf_{Rule:9}$ $\times$ (1 $-$ $cf_{Rule:7}$)
= 0.30 + 0.32 $\times$ (1 $-$ 0.30) = 0.52

cf (boat is 'Jib-headed Yawl') = 0.09 + 0.32 $\times$ (1 $-$ 0.09) = 0.38

boat is   Jib-headed Ketch   {cf 0.52}
          Jib-headed Yawl   {cf 0.38}
          Gaff-headed Schooner   {cf 0.34}
          Staysail Schooner   {cf 0.34}
          Gaff-headed Ketch   {cf 0.30}
          Gaff-headed Yawl   {cf 0.09}

Now we can conclude that the boat is probably a *Jib-headed Ketch* and almost certainly not a *Gaff-headed Ketch* or *Gaff-headed Yawl*.

9.3 Will a fuzzy expert system work for my problem?

We need to decide which problem is a good candidate for fuzzy technology. The basic approach here is simple: if you cannot define a set of exact rules for each possible situation, then use fuzzy logic. While certainty factors and Bayesian probabilities are concerned with the imprecision associated with the outcome of a well-defined event, fuzzy logic concentrates on the imprecision of the event itself. In other words, inherently imprecise properties of the problem make it a good candidate for fuzzy technology.

Fuzzy systems are particularly well suited for modelling human decision making. We often rely on common sense and use vague and ambiguous terms while making important decisions. Doctors, for example, do not have a precise threshold in mind when they decide whether a patient in a post-operative recovery area should be sent to a general hospital floor. Although hypothermia is a significant concern after surgery and the patient's body temperature often plays a vital role in the doctor's decision, such factors as the stability of the patient's blood pressure and his or her perceived comfort at discharge are also taken into account. A doctor makes an accurate assessment not from the precision of a single parameter (say, a body temperature), but rather from evaluating several parameters, some of which are expressed in ambiguous terms (for instance, the patient's willingness to leave the post-operative recovery unit).

Although most fuzzy technology applications are still reported in control and engineering, an even larger potential exists in business and finance (Von Altrock, 1997). Decisions in these areas are often based on human intuition, common sense and experience, rather than on the availability and precision of data. Decision making in business and finance is too complex and too uncertain to lend itself to precise analytical methods. Fuzzy technology provides us with a means of coping with the 'soft criteria' and 'fuzzy data' that are often used in business and finance.

Case study 3: Decision-support fuzzy systems

I want to develop an intelligent system for assessing mortgage applications. Will a fuzzy expert system work for this problem?

Mortgage application assessment is a typical problem to which decision-support fuzzy systems can be successfully applied (Von Altrock, 1997).

To develop a decision-support fuzzy system for this problem, we first represent the basic concept of mortgage application assessment in fuzzy terms, then implement this concept in a prototype system using an appropriate fuzzy tool, and finally test and optimise the system with selected test cases.

Assessment of a mortgage application is normally based on evaluating the market value and location of the house, the applicant's assets and income, and the repayment plan, which is decided by the applicant's income and bank's interest charges.

Where do membership functions and rules for mortgage loan assessment come from?

To define membership functions and construct fuzzy rules, we usually need the help of experienced mortgage advisers and also bank managers, who develop the mortgage granting policies. Figures 9.7 to 9.14 show fuzzy sets for linguistic variables used in our problem. Triangular and trapezoidal membership functions can adequately represent the knowledge of the mortgage expert.

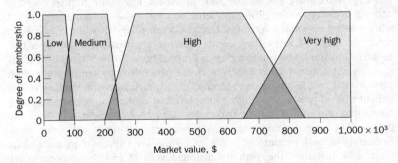

Figure 9.7 Fuzzy sets of the linguistic variable *Market value*

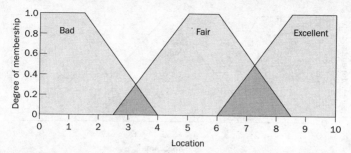

Figure 9.8 Fuzzy sets of the linguistic variable *Location*

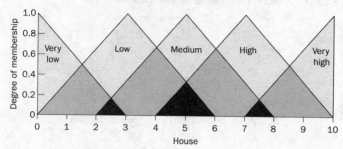

Figure 9.9 Fuzzy sets of the linguistic variable *House*

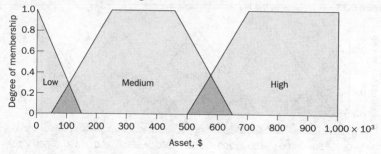

Figure 9.10 Fuzzy sets of the linguistic variable *Asset*

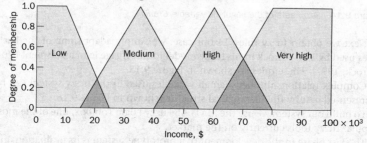

Figure 9.11 Fuzzy sets of the linguistic variable *Income*

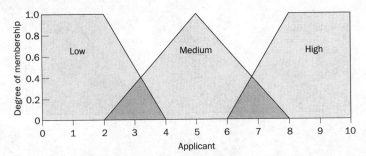

Figure 9.12 Fuzzy sets of the linguistic variable *Applicant*

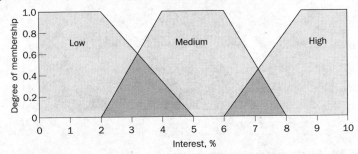

Figure 9.13 Fuzzy sets of the linguistic variable *Interest*

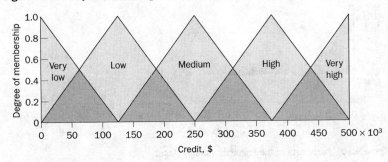

Figure 9.14 Fuzzy sets of the linguistic variable *Credit*

Next we obtain fuzzy rules. In our case, we simply adapt some of the basic rules used by Von Altrock in his fuzzy model for mortgage loan assessment (Von Altrock, 1997). These rules are shown in Figure 9.15.

Complex relationships between all variables used in the fuzzy system can be represented best by the hierarchical structure shown in Figure 9.16.

To build our system we use the MATLAB Fuzzy Logic Toolbox, one of the most popular fuzzy tools currently on the market.

The last phase in the development of a prototype system is its evaluation and testing.

Rule Base 1: Home Evaluation
1. If (Market_value is Low) then (House is Low)
2. If (Location is Bad) then (House is Low)
3. If (Location is Bad) and (Market_value is Low) then (House is Very_low)
4. If (Location is Bad) and (Market_value is Medium) then (House is Low)
5. If (Location is Bad) and (Market_value is High) then (House is Medium)
6. If (Location is Bad) and (Market_value is Very_high) then (House is High)
7. If (Location is Fair) and (Market_value is Low) then (House is Low)
8. If (Location is Fair) and (Market_value is Medium) then (House is Medium)
9. If (Location is Fair) and (Market_value is High) then (House is High)
10. If (Location is Fair) and (Market_value is Very_high) then (House is Very_high)
11. If (Location is Excellent) and (Market_value is Low) then (House is Medium)
12. If (Location is Excellent) and (Market_value is Medium) then (House is High)
13. If (Location is Excellent) and (Market_value is High) then (House is Very_high)
14. If (Location is Excellent) and (Market_value is Very_high) then (House is Very_high)

Rule Base 2: Applicant Evaluation
1. If (Asset is Low) and (Income is Low) then (Applicant is Low)
2. If (Asset is Low) and (Income is Medium) then (Applicant is Low)
3. If (Asset is Low) and (Income is High) then (Applicant is Medium)
4. If (Asset is Low) and (Income is Very_high) then (Applicant is High)
5. If (Asset is Medium) and (Income is Low) then (Applicant is Low)
6. If (Asset is Medium) and (Income is Medium) then (Applicant is Medium)
7. If (Asset is Medium) and (Income is High) then (Applicant is High)
8. If (Asset is Medium) and (Income is Very_high) then (Applicant is High)
9. If (Asset is High) and (Income is Low) then (Applicant is Medium)
10. If (Asset is High) and (Income is Medium) then (Applicant is Medium)
11. If (Asset is High) and (Income is High) then (Applicant is High)
12. If (Asset is High) and (Income is Very_high) then (Applicant is High)

Rule Base 3: Credit Evaluation
1. If (Income is Low) and (Interest is Medium) then (Credit is Very_low)
2. If (Income is Low) and (Interest is High) then (Credit is Very_low)
3. If (Income is Medium) and (Interest is High) then (Credit is Low)
4. If (Applicant is Low) then (Credit is Very_low)
5. If (House is Very_low) then (Credit is Very_low)
6. If (Applicant is Medium) and (House is Very_low) then (Credit is Low)
7. If (Applicant is Medium) and (House is Low) then (Credit is Low)
8. If (Applicant is Medium) and (House is Medium) then (Credit is Medium)
9. If (Applicant is Medium) and (House is High) then (Credit is High)
10. If (Applicant is Medium) and (House is Very_high) then (Credit is High)
11. If (Applicant is High) and (House is Very_low) then (Credit is Low)
12. If (Applicant is High) and (House is Low) then (Credit is Medium)
13. If (Applicant is High) and (House is Medium) then (Credit is High)
14. If (Applicant is High) and (House is High) then (Credit is High)
15. If (Applicant is High) and (House is Very_high) then (Credit is Very_high)

Figure 9.15 Rules for mortgage loan assessment

To evaluate and analyse the performance of a fuzzy system, we can use the output surface viewer provided by the Fuzzy Logic Toolbox. Figures 9.17 and 9.18 represent three-dimensional plots of the fuzzy system for mortgage loan assessment. Finally, the mortgage experts would try the system with several test cases.

Decision-support fuzzy systems may include dozens, and even hundreds, of rules. For example, a fuzzy system for credit-risk evaluation developed by BMW

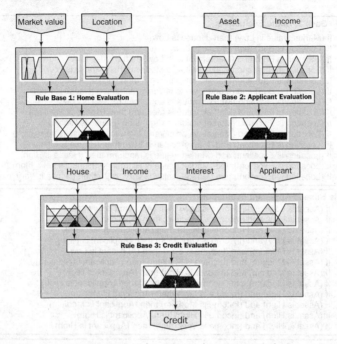

Figure 9.16 Hierarchical fuzzy model for mortgage loan assessment

Bank and Inform Software used 413 fuzzy rules (Güllich, 1996). Large knowledge bases are usually divided into several modules in a manner similar to that shown in Figure 9.16.

In spite of the often large number of rules, decision-support fuzzy systems can be developed, tested and implemented relatively quickly. For instance, it took just two person-years to develop and implement the fuzzy system for credit-risk evaluation. Compare this effort with the 40 person-years it took to develop MYCIN.

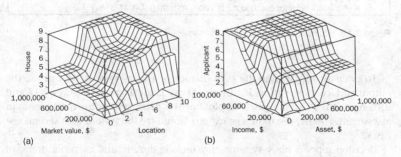

Figure 9.17 Three-dimensional plots: (a) Rule Base 1; (b) Rule Base 2

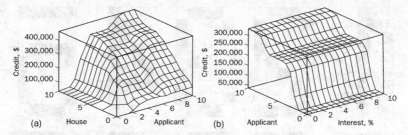

Figure 9.18   Three-dimensional plots for Rule Base 3

9.4   Will a neural network work for my problem?

Neural networks represent a class of very powerful, general-purpose tools that have been successfully applied to prediction, classification and clustering problems. They are used in a variety of areas, from speech and character recognition to detecting fraudulent transactions, from medical diagnosis of heart attacks to process control and robotics, from predicting foreign exchange rates to detecting and identifying radar targets. And the areas of neural network applications continue to expand rapidly.

The popularity of neural networks is based on their remarkable versatility, abilities to handle both binary and continuous data, and to produce good results in complex domains. When the output is continuous, the network can address prediction problems, but when the output is binary, the network works as a classifier.

Case study 4: Character recognition neural networks

I want to develop a character recognition system. Will a neural network work for this problem?

Recognition of both printed and handwritten characters is a typical domain where neural networks have been successfully applied. In fact, **optical character recognition** systems were among the first commercial applications of neural networks.

What is optical character recognition?

It is the ability of a computer to translate character images into a text file, using special software. It allows us to take a printed document and put it into a computer in editable form without the need of retyping the document.

To capture the character images we can use a desktop scanner. It either passes light-sensitive sensors over the illuminated surface of a page or moves a page through the sensors. The scanner processes the image by dividing it into hundreds of pixel-sized boxes per inch and representing each box by either 1 (if the box is filled) or 0 (if the box is empty). The resulting matrix of dots is called a **bit map**. Bit maps can be stored, displayed and printed by a computer,

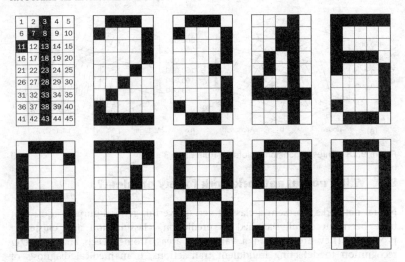

Figure 9.19 Bit maps for digit recognition

but we cannot use a word processor to edit the text – the patterns of dots have to be recognised as characters by the computer. This is the job for a neural network.

Let us demonstrate an application of a multilayer feedforward network for printed character recognition. For simplicity, we can limit our task to the recognition of digits from 0 to 9. In this application, each digit is represented by a 5×9 bit map, as shown in Figure 9.19. In commercial applications, where a better resolution is required, at least 16×16 bit maps are used (Zurada, 1992).

How do we choose the architecture of a neural network for character recognition?

The architecture and size of a neural network depend on the complexity of the problem. For example, handwritten character recognition is performed by rather complex multilayer networks that may include three, or even four, hidden layers and hundreds of neurons (Zurada, 2006; Haykin, 2008). However, for the printed digit recognition problem, a three-layer network with a single hidden layer will give sufficient accuracy.

The number of neurons in the input layer is decided by the number of pixels in the bit map. The bit map in our example consists of 45 pixels, and thus we need 45 input neurons. The output layer has 10 neurons – one neuron for each digit to be recognised.

How do we determine an optimal number of hidden neurons?

Simulation experiments indicate that the number of neurons in the hidden layer affects both the accuracy of character recognition and the speed of training the network. Complex patterns cannot be detected by a small number of hidden neurons; however, too many of them can dramatically increase the computational burden.

Figure 9.20   Neural network for printed digit recognition

Another problem is **overfitting**. The greater the number of hidden neurons, the greater the ability of the network to recognise existing patterns. However, if the number of hidden neurons is too big, the network might simply memorise all training examples. This may prevent it from generalising, or producing correct outputs when presented with data that was not used in training. For instance, the overfitted character recognition network trained with Helvetica-font examples might not be able to recognise the same characters in the Times New Roman font.

The practical approach to preventing overfitting is to choose the smallest number of hidden neurons that yields good generalisation. Thus, at the starting point, an experimental study could begin with as little as two neurons in the hidden layer. In our example, we will examine the system's performance with 2, 5, 10 and 20 hidden neurons and compare results.

The architecture of a neural network (with five neurons in the hidden layer) for the character recognition problem is shown in Figure 9.20. Neurons in the hidden and output layers use a sigmoid activation function. The neural network is trained with the back-propagation algorithm with momentum; the momentum constant is set to 0.95. The input and output training patterns are shown in Table 9.2. The binary input vectors representing the bit maps of the respective digits are fed directly into the network.

The network's performance in our study is measured by the sum of squared errors. Figure 9.21 demonstrates the results; as can be seen from Figure 9.21(a), a neural network with two neurons in the hidden layer cannot converge to a solution, while the networks with 5, 10 and 20 hidden neurons learn relatively fast. In fact, they converge in less than 250 epochs (each epoch represents an entire pass through all training examples). Also note that the network with 20 hidden neurons shows the fastest convergence.

Once the training is complete, we must test the network with a set of test examples to see how well it performs.

Table 9.2 Input and desired output patterns for the digit recognition neural network

Digit	Input patterns Rows in the pixel matrix									Desired output patterns
	1	2	3	4	5	6	7	8	9	
1	00100	01100	10100	00100	00100	00100	00100	00100	00100	1000000000
2	01110	10001	00001	00001	00010	00100	01000	10000	11111	0100000000
3	01110	10001	00001	00001	00010	00001	00001	10001	01110	0010000000
4	00010	00110	00110	01010	01010	10010	11111	00010	00010	0001000000
5	11111	10000	10000	11110	00001	00001	00001	10001	01110	0000100000
6	01110	10001	10000	10000	11110	10001	10001	10001	01110	0000010000
7	11111	00001	00010	00010	00100	00100	01000	01000	01000	0000001000
8	01110	10001	10001	10001	01110	10001	10001	10001	01110	0000000100
9	01110	10001	10001	10001	01111	00001	00001	10001	01110	0000000010
0	01110	10001	10001	10001	10001	10001	10001	10001	01110	0000000001

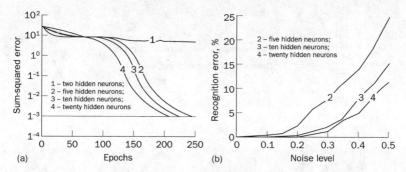

Figure 9.21   Training and performance evaluation of the digit recognition three-layer neural networks: (a) learning curves; (b) performance evaluation

What are the test examples for character recognition? Are they the same as those used for neural network training?

A test set has to be strictly independent from the training examples. Thus, to test the character recognition network, we must present it with examples that include 'noise' – the distortion of the input patterns. This distortion can be created, for instance, by adding some small random values chosen from a normal distribution to the binary input vectors representing bit maps of the 10 digits. We evaluate the performance of the printed digit recognition networks with 1000 test examples (100 for each digit to be recognised). The results are shown in Figure 9.21(b).

Although the average recognition error of the network with 20 hidden neurons is the lowest, the results do not demonstrate significant differences between the networks with 10 and 20 hidden neurons. Both networks can sustain similar levels of noise without sacrificing their recognition performance. On this basis, we may conclude that for the digit recognition problem described here, the use of 10 hidden neurons is adequate.

Can we improve the performance of the character recognition neural network?

A neural network is as good as the examples used to train it. Therefore, we can attempt to improve digit recognition by feeding the network with 'noisy' examples of digits from 0 to 9. The results of such an attempt are shown in Figure 9.22. As we expected, there is some improvement in the performance of the digit recognition network trained with 'noisy' data.

This case study illustrated one of the most common applications of multilayer neural networks trained with the back-propagation algorithm. Modern character recognition systems are capable of processing different fonts in English, French, Spanish, Italian, Dutch and several other languages with great accuracy. Optical character recognition is routinely used by office workers, lawyers, insurance clerks, journalists – in fact anybody who wants to take a printed (or even

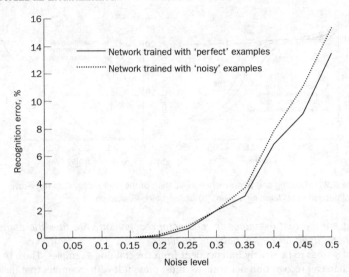

Figure 9.22 Performance evaluation of the digit recognition network trained with 'noisy' examples

handwritten) document and load it into their computer as an editable file. Handwritten digit recognition systems are widely used in processing zip codes on mail envelopes (LeCun *et al.*, 1990).

Case study 5: Prediction neural networks

I want to develop an intelligent system for real-estate appraisal. Will a neural network work for this problem?

Real-estate appraisal is a problem of predicting the market value of a given house based on the knowledge of the sales prices of similar houses. As we mentioned earlier, this problem can be solved with expert systems as well as neural networks. Of course, if we choose to apply a neural network, we will not be able to understand how an appraisal of a particular house is reached – a neural network is essentially a black box to the user and rules cannot be easily extracted from it. On the other hand, an accurate appraisal is often more important than understanding how it was done.

In this problem, the inputs (the house location, living area, number of bedrooms, number of bathrooms, land size, type of heating system, etc.) are well defined, and normally even standardised for sharing the housing market information between different real-estate agencies. The output is also well defined – we know what we are trying to predict. Most importantly, there are many examples we can use for training the neural network. These examples are the features of recently sold houses and their sales prices.

Choosing training examples is critical for an accurate prediction. A training set must cover the full range of values for all inputs. Thus, in the training set for real-estate appraisal, we should include houses that are large and small, expensive and inexpensive, with and without garages, etc. And the training set has to be sufficiently large.

But how do we determine when the size
of a training set is 'sufficiently large'?
A network's ability to generalise is influenced by three main factors: the size of the training set, the architecture of the network and the complexity of the problem. Once the network architecture is decided, the issue of generalisation is resolved by the adequacy of the training set. An appropriate number of training examples can be estimated with **Widrow's rule-of-thumb**, which suggests that, for a good generalisation, we need to satisfy the following condition (Widrow and Stearns, 1985; Haykin, 2008):

$$N = \frac{n_w}{e} \tag{9.1}$$

where N is the number of training examples, n_w is the number of synaptic weights in the network, and e is the network error permitted on test.

Thus, if we allow an error of, say, 10 per cent, the number of training examples should be approximately 10 times bigger than the number of weights in the network.

In solving prediction problems, including real-estate appraisal, we often combine input features of different types. Some features, such as the house's condition and its location, can be arbitrarily rated from 1 (least appealing) to 10 (most appealing). Some features, such as the living area, land size and sales price, are measured in actual physical quantities – square metres, dollars, etc. Some features represent counts (number of bedrooms, number of bathrooms, etc.), and some are categories (type of heating system).

A neural network works best when all its inputs and outputs vary within the range between 0 and 1, and thus all the data must be massaged before we can use it in a neural network model.

How do we massage the data?
Data can be divided into three main types: continuous, discrete and categorical (Berry and Linoff, 2004), and we normally use different techniques to massage different types of data.

Continuous data varies between two pre-set values – minimum and maximum – and can be easily mapped, or massaged, to the range between 0 and 1 as

$$massaged\ value = \frac{actual\ value - minimum\ value}{maximum\ value - minimum\ value} \tag{9.2}$$

For instance, if the living areas of the houses in training examples range between 59 and 231 square metres, we might set the minimum value to 50 and the maximum to 250 square metres. Any value lower than the minimum is mapped to the minimum, and any value higher than the maximum to the maximum. Thus, a living area of, say, 121 square metres would be massaged as

$$massaged\ value_{121} = \frac{121 - 50}{250 - 50} = 0.355$$

This method works well for most applications.

Discrete data, such as the number of bedrooms and the number of bathrooms, also has maximum and minimum values. For example, the number of bedrooms usually ranges from 0 to 4. Massaging discrete data is simple – we assign an equal space to each possible value on the interval from 0 to 1, as shown in Figure 9.23.

A neural network can now handle a feature like the number of bedrooms as a single input. For example, a three-bedroom house would be represented by the input value of 0.75.

This approach is sufficient for most applications with discrete features that have up to a dozen possible values. However, if there are more than a dozen values, a discrete feature should be treated like a continuous one.

Categorical data, such as gender and marital status, can be massaged by using **1 of N coding** (Berry and Linoff, 2004). This method implies that each categorical value is handled as a separate input. For example, marital status, which can be single, divorced, married or widowed, would be represented by four inputs. Each of these inputs can have a value of either 0 or 1. Thus, a married person would be represented by an input vector [0 0 1 0].

Let us now construct a feedforward neural network for real-estate appraisal. Figure 9.24 represents a simplified model that was set up by using training examples with features of the houses recently sold in Hobart.

In this model, the input layer, which includes 10 neurons, passes the massaged input values to the hidden layer. All input features, except *type of heating system*, are treated as single inputs. The type of heating system represents a categorical type of data, which is massaged with 1 of N coding.

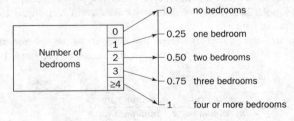

Figure 9.23 Massaging discrete data

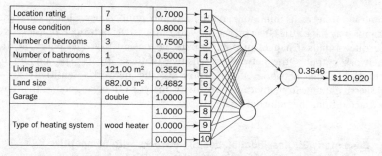

Location rating	7	0.7000	→ 1
House condition	8	0.8000	→ 2
Number of bedrooms	3	0.7500	→ 3
Number of bathrooms	1	0.5000	→ 4
Living area	121.00 m²	0.3550	→ 5
Land size	682.00 m²	0.4682	→ 6
Garage	double	1.0000	→ 7
		1.0000	→ 8
Type of heating system	wood heater	0.0000	→ 9
		0.0000	→ 10

Figure 9.24   Feedforward neural network for real-estate appraisal

The hidden layer includes two neurons, and the output layer is represented by a single neuron. Neurons in the hidden and output layers apply sigmoid activation functions.

The neural network for real-estate appraisal determines the value of a house, and thus the network output can be interpreted in dollars.

But how do we interpret the network output?

In our example, the network output is represented by continuous values in the range between 0 and 1. Thus, to interpret the results, we can simply reverse the procedure we used for massaging continuous data. Suppose, for instance, that in the training set, sales prices range between $52,500 and $225,000, and the output value is set up so that $50,000 maps to 0 and $250,000 maps to 1. Then, if the network output is 0.3546, we can compute that this value corresponds to

$$actual\ value_{0.3546} = 0.3546 \times (\$250,000 - \$50,000) + \$50,000 = \$120,920$$

How do we validate results?

To validate results, we use a set of examples never seen by the network. Before training, all the available data is randomly divided into a training set and a test set. Once the training phase is complete, the network's ability to generalise is tested against examples of the test set.

A neural network is opaque. We cannot see how the network derives its results. But we still need to grasp relationships between the network inputs and the results it produces. Although current research into rule extraction from trained neural networks will eventually bring adequate outcomes, the non-linear characteristics of neurons may prevent the network from producing simple and understandable rules. Fortunately, to understand the importance of a particular input to the network output, we do not need rule extraction. Instead we can use a simple technique called **sensitivity analysis**.

Sensitivity analysis determines how sensitive the output of a model is to a particular input. This technique is used for understanding internal relationships in opaque models, and thus can be applied to neural networks. Sensitivity analysis is performed by measuring the network output when each input is set (one at a time) to its minimum and then its maximum values. Changes in some inputs may have little effect on the network output – the network is not sensitive to these inputs. Changes in other inputs have a much greater effect on the network output – the network is sensitive to these inputs. The amount of change in the network output represents the network's sensitivity to a respective input. In many cases, sensitivity analysis can be as good as the rules extracted from the trained neural network.

Case study 6: Classification neural networks with competitive learning

I want to develop an intelligent system that can divide a group of iris plants into classes and then assign any iris plant to one of these classes. I have a data set with several variables but I have no idea how to separate it into different classes because I cannot find any unique or distinctive features in the data. Will a neural network work for this problem?

Neural networks can discover significant features in input patterns and learn how to separate input data into different classes. A neural network with competitive learning is a suitable tool to accomplish this task.

The competitive learning rule enables a single-layer neural network to combine similar input data into groups or **clusters**. This process is called **clustering**. Each cluster is represented by a single output. In fact, clustering can be defined as the process of dividing an input space into regions, each of which is associated with a particular output (Principe *et al.*, 2000).

For this case study, we will use a data set of 150 elements that contains three classes of iris plants: *Iris setosa, versicolor* and *virginica* (Fisher, 1950). Each plant in the data set is represented by four variables: sepal length, sepal width, petal length and petal width. The sepal length ranges between 4.3 and 7.9 cm, sepal width between 2.0 and 4.4 cm, petal length between 1.0 and 6.9 cm, and petal width between 0.1 and 2.5 cm.

In a competitive neural network, each input neuron corresponds to a single input, and each competitive neuron represents a single cluster. Thus, the network for the iris plant classification problem will have four neurons in the input layer and three neurons in the competitive layer. The network's architecture is shown in Figure 9.25.

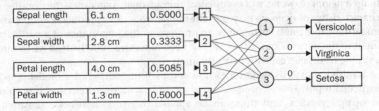

Figure 9.25 Neural network for iris plant classification

However, before the network is trained, the data must be massaged and then divided into training and test sets.

The iris plant data is continuous, varies between some minimum and maximum values, and thus can easily be massaged to the range between 0 and 1 using Eq. (9.2). Massaged values can then be fed to the network as its inputs.

The next step is to generate training and test sets from the available data. The 150-element iris data is randomly divided into a training set of 100 elements and a test set of 50 elements.

Now we can train the competitive neural network to divide input vectors into three classes. Figure 9.26 illustrates the learning process with the learning rate of 0.01. Black dots here represent the input patterns and three spheres denote the weight vectors of the competitive neurons. The location of each sphere is determined by the neuron's weights in the four-dimensional input space.

Initially all weights of the competitive neurons are assigned the same value of 0.5, and thus only one sphere appears in the centre of the input space, as shown in Figure 9.26(a). After training, the weight vectors correspond to the positions of the cluster centres, so that each competitive neuron can now respond to input data in a particular region.

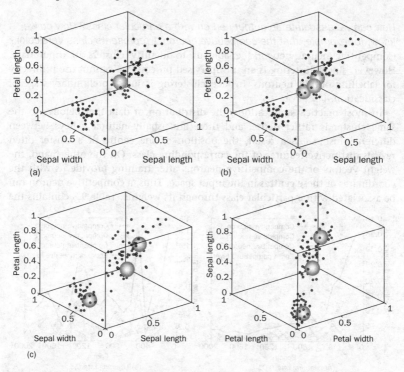

Figure 9.26 Competitive learning in the neural network for iris plant classification: (a) initial weights; (b) weight after 100 iterations; (c) weight after 2000 iterations

How do we know when the learning process is complete?

In a competitive neural network, unlike a multilayer perceptron trained with the back-propagation algorithm, there is no obvious way of knowing whether the learning process is complete or not. We do not know what the desired outputs are, and thus cannot compute the sum of squared errors – a criterion used by the back-propagation algorithm. Therefore, we should use the **Euclidean distance** criterion instead. When no noticeable changes occur in the weight vectors of competitive neurons, a network can be considered to have converged. In other words, if the motion of competitive neurons in the input space remains sufficiently constrained for several subsequent epochs, then we can assume that the learning process is complete.

Figure 9.27 shows the dynamics of the learning process for competitive neurons of the iris classification neural network. The network was trained with two different learning rates. As can be seen in Figure 9.27(b), if the learning rate is too high, the behaviour of competitive neurons may become erratic, and the network may never converge. However, in order to accelerate learning, we can still use large initial values of the learning rate, but as training progresses the learning rate must gradually decrease.

How can we associate an output neuron with a particular class? How do we know, for example, that the competitive neuron 1 represents class Versicolor?

Competitive neural networks enable us to identify clusters in input data. However, since clustering is an unsupervised process, we cannot use it directly for labelling output neurons. In fact, clustering is just a preliminary stage of classification.

In most practical applications, the distribution of data that belongs to the same cluster is rather dense, and there are usually natural valleys between different clusters. As a result, the position of the centre of a cluster often reveals distinctive features of the corresponding class. On the other hand, the weight vectors of the competitive neurons after training provide us with the coordinates of these centres in the input space. Thus, a competitive neuron can be associated with a particular class through its weights. Table 9.3 contains the

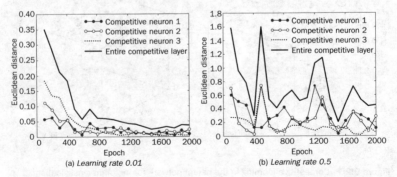

(a) *Learning rate 0.01*   (b) *Learning rate 0.5*

Figure 9.27 Learning curves for competitive neurons of the iris classification neural network

Table 9.3 Labelling the competitive neurons

Neuron	Weights		Dimensions of the iris plant, cm		Class of the iris plant
1	W_{11}	0.4355	Sepal length	5.9	Versicolor
	W_{21}	0.3022	Sepal width	2.7	
	W_{31}	0.5658	Petal length	4.4	
	W_{41}	0.5300	Petal width	1.4	
2	W_{12}	0.6514	Sepal length	6.7	Virginica
	W_{22}	0.4348	Sepal width	3.0	
	W_{32}	0.7620	Petal length	5.5	
	W_{42}	0.7882	Petal width	2.0	
3	W_{13}	0.2060	Sepal length	5.0	Setosa
	W_{23}	0.6056	Sepal width	3.5	
	W_{33}	0.0940	Petal length	1.6	
	W_{43}	0.0799	Petal width	0.3	

final weights of the competitive neurons, decoded values of these weights and the corresponding classes of the iris plant.

How do we decode weights into iris dimensions?
To decode the weights of the competitive neurons into dimensions of the iris plant we simply reverse the procedure used for massaging the Iris data. For example,

$$\textit{Sepal length } W_{11} = 0.4355 \times (7.9 - 4.3) + 4.3 = 5.9 \text{ cm}$$

Once the weights are decoded, we can ask an iris plant expert to label the output neurons.

Can we label the competitive neurons automatically without having to ask the expert?
We can use a test data set for labelling competitive neurons automatically. Once training of a neural network is complete, a set of input samples representing the same class, say class *Versicolor*, is fed to the network, and the output neuron that wins the competition most of the time receives a label of the corresponding class.

Although a competitive network has only one layer of competitive neurons, it can classify input patterns that are not linearly separable. In classification tasks, competitive networks learn much faster than multilayer perceptrons trained with the back-propagation algorithm, but they usually provide less accurate results.

> ## Case study 7: Clustering with a self-organising neural network

I want to develop an intelligent system that can identify potentially failing banks. Will a neural network work for this problem?

In 2008, a series of bank failures triggered a financial crisis. By any historical standard, this crisis was the worst since the Great Depression of the 1930s. The immediate cause of the crisis was the bursting of the US housing bubble. This, in turn, caused the values of securities tied to real-estate pricing to nose-dive, damaging financial institutions world-wide. Bank insolvencies and lack of credits reduced investor confidence and, as a result, the stock market plummeted. In 2009, the global economy contracted by 1.1 per cent, while in developed countries, the contraction reached 3.4 per cent. After intervention by central banks and governments on an unprecedented scale, the global economy began to recover. However, the global financial system remains at risk.

The danger of cascading failures of major banks would be reduced significantly if we could identify banks with potential problems before they face solvency and liquidity crises. There are many reasons for bank failures. These include high risk taking, interest rate volatility, poor management practices, inadequate accounting standards and increased competition from non-depository institutions. Since the crisis, bank regulators have been increasingly concerned with reducing the size of deposit insurance liabilities. It has even been suggested that the best regulatory policy is to close banks before they become undercapitalised. Therefore, identifying potentially failing banks as early as possible is essential for avoiding another major financial crisis.

Over the last 30 years many tools have been developed to identify problem banks. While early models mostly relied on statistical techniques (Abrams and Huang, 1987; Booth *et al.*, 1989; Espahbodi, 1991), most recent developments are based on fuzzy logic and neural networks (Zhang *et al.*, 1999; Alam *et al.*, 2000; Ozkan-Gunay and Ozkan, 2007). Most of these models use a dichotomous classification – bankruptcy versus non-bankruptcy. In the real world, however, banks are ranked in terms of their *likelihood* of bankruptcy. What regulators really need is an early warning system that can 'flag' potentially failing banks. Once such banks are identified, different preventive programmes tailored to each bank's specific needs can be put in place, thereby avoiding a major banking failure.

In this case study, we 'flag' potentially failing banks using cluster analysis.

What is cluster analysis?

Cluster analysis is an exploratory data analysis technique that divides different objects into groups, called *clusters*, in such a way that the degree of association between two objects is maximised if they belong to the same cluster and minimised otherwise.

The term 'cluster analysis' was first introduced over 70 years ago by Robert Tryon (1939). Since then, cluster analysis has been successfully applied in many fields including medicine, archaeology, astronomy, etc. In clustering, there are no predefined classes – objects are grouped together only on the basis of their similarity. For this reason, clustering is often referred to as unsupervised classification. There is no distinction between independent and dependent variables, and when clusters are found the user needs to interpret their meaning.

What methods are used in cluster analysis?

We can identify three major methods used in cluster analysis. These are based on statistics, fuzzy logic and neural networks. In this case study, we will apply a self-organising neural network.

Our goal is to cluster banks using their financial data. The data can be obtained from annual reports of the Federal Deposit Insurance Corporation (FDIC). The FDIC is an independent agency created by the US Congress. It insures deposits, examines and supervises financial institutions, and manages receiverships. To assess the overall financial state of a bank, regulators use the CAMELS (Capital adequacy, Asset, Management, Earnings, Liquidity and Sensitivity to market risk) rating system. The CAMELS ratings have been applied to 8500 banks in the USA. The system was also used by the US government in selecting banks for the capitalisation programme of 2008.

For our case study, we select 100 banks and obtain their financial data from the FDIC annual report for the last year. We adapt the following five ratings based on the CAMELS system:

1. NITA – Net Income divided by Total Assets. NITA represents return on assets. Failing banks have very low or even negative values of NITA.

2. NLLAA – Net Loan Losses divided by Adjusted Assets. Adjusted assets are calculated by subtracting the total loans from the total assets. Failing banks usually have higher NLLAA values than healthy banks.

3. NPLTA – Non-Performing Loans divided by Total Assets. Non-performing loans consist of loans that have passed their due dates by 90 days and non-accrual loans. Failing banks usually have higher values of NPLTA than healthy banks.

4. NLLTL – Net Loan Losses divided by Total Loans. Failing banks have higher loan losses as they often make loans to high-risk borrowers. Thus, failing banks usually have higher values of NLLTL than healthy banks.

5. NLLPLLNI – Sum of Net Loan Losses and Provision for Loan Losses divided by Net Income. The higher the NLLPLLNI value, the poorer the bank performance.

Preliminary investigations of the statistical data can reveal that a number of banks may experience some financial difficulties. Clustering should help us to identify groups of banks with similar problems.

Figure 9.28 shows a self-organising map (SOM) with a 5 × 5 array of 25 neurons in the Kohonen layer. Note that neurons in the Kohonen layer are arranged in a hexagonal pattern.

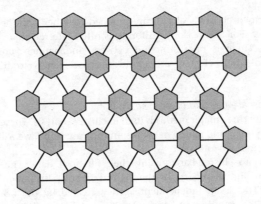

Figure 9.28   The SOM structure

The input data is normalised to be between 0 and 1. The network is trained for 10,000 iterations with a learning rate of 0.1. After training is complete, the SOM forms a semantic map where similar input vectors are mapped close together while dissimilar ones are apart. In other words, similar input vectors tend to excite either the same neuron or neurons closely located to each other in the Kohonen layer. This SOM property can be visualised using the weight distance matrix, also known as the *U-matrix*. Figure 9.29 shows the U-matrix and the SOM sample hit plot for the bank financial data. In the U-matrix, the hexagons represent the neurons in the Kohonen layer. The tints in the regions between neighbouring neurons indicate the distances between them – the darker the tint, the greater the distance. The SOM sample hit plot reveals how many input vectors are attracted by each neuron of the Kohonen layer.

Typically, an SOM identifies fewer clusters than the number of neurons in the Kohonen layer, and thus several input vectors attracted by close neighbouring neurons may, in fact, represent the same cluster. For instance, in Figure 9.29(a), we

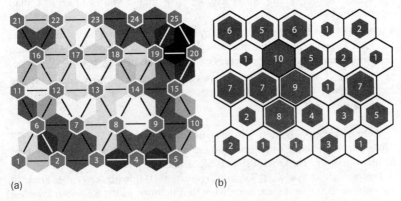

(a)   (b)

Figure 9.29   The 5 × 5 SOM after training: (a) the U-matrix; (b) the sample hit plot

can observe that distances between neurons 3 and 8, 7 and 8, 7 and 12, 7 and 13, 8 and 9, 8 and 13, 8 and 14, 9 and 14, 11 and 12, 12 and 13, 12 and 16, 12 and 17, 13 and 14, 13 and 17, 13 and 18, 14 and 19, 16 and 17, 17 and 18, 17 and 22, 17 and 23, 18 and 19, 18 and 23, 21 and 22 and 22 and 23 are relatively short (the tints in the regions between neighbouring neurons are lighter, so the distances are shorter). Thus, we can reasonably assume that neurons 3, 7, 8, 9, 11, 12, 13, 14, 16, 17, 18, 19, 21, 22 and 23 form a single cluster. At the same time, we should also notice that the distance between neurons 3 and 7 is much greater than the distances between neurons 3 and 8 and neurons 7 and 8. Therefore, it might be useful to examine what makes the input vectors associated with neuron 3 so different from those attracted by neuron 7. Table 9.4 shows results of clustering.

What do these clusters actually mean?

Interpreting the meaning of each cluster is often a difficult task. Unlike classification where the number of classes is decided beforehand, in SOM-based clustering the number of clusters is unknown, and assigning a label or interpretation to each cluster requires some prior knowledge and domain expertise.

For a start, we need a way to compare different clusters. As we discussed in Case Study 6, the centre of a cluster often reveals features that separate one cluster from another. Therefore, determining the average member of a cluster should enable us to interpret the meaning of the entire cluster. Table 9.4 contains the mean, median and standard deviation (SD) values of the CAMELS ratings utilised in this study. Using these values an expert can identify groups of banks that exhibit similar patterns of behaviour or experience similar problems.

Let us begin our analysis by identifying problem banks with negative returns on their assets. As can be seen in Table 9.4, three clusters, E, F and G, have negative values of NITA. For example, banks included in Cluster E have mean net losses of 0.06 per cent of their total assets. On the other hand, healthy banks usually report a positive return on their assets. Thus, banks included in Cluster A, which has the highest value of NITA, could be considered healthy.

Regarding the NLLAA rating, Cluster D has the highest mean value, followed by Cluster E. Note that although banks in Cluster E are problem banks, their NLLAA values are at least 12 times lower than those of Cluster D (a 3.63 per cent mean against 44.48 per cent). This could be a clear indication that the three banks associated with Cluster D experience severe difficulties with their loans (even though they still have a positive return on their assets). Banks in Clusters A, B and C show negative NLLAA values, which is normal for healthy banks.

The value of NPLTA is highest for Cluster B, followed by the problem banks in Clusters E, F and G. This may indicate that the bank in Cluster B (Cluster B is a solitary cluster) experiences difficulties in recovering its loans. In fact, the situation with this particular bank could be even worse than with the problem banks associated with Clusters E, F and G.

Finally, the values of NLLTL and NLLPLLNI are highest for the two banks in Cluster H, followed by the problem banks. Because higher values of NLLTL indicate higher loan losses, we may find that banks in Cluster H are involved in

Table 9.4 Clustering results of the 5 × 5 SOM

Cluster	Size	Neuron number	Financial profile of the cluster														
			NITA			NLLAA			NPLTA			NLLTL			NLLPLLNI		
			Mean	Median	SD	Mean	Median	SD	Mean	Median	SD	Mean	Median	SD	Mean	Median	SD
A	4	1,6	0.0369	0.0369	0.0043	-0.1793	-0.1340	0.2516	0.0125	0.0100	0.0055	0.0050	0.0057	0.0036	0.2839	0.2839	0.0164
B	1	2	0.0121	0.0121	0	-0.4954	-0.4954	0	0.0323	0.0323	0	0.0006	0.0006	0	1.1522	1.1522	0
C	75	3,7,8,9, 11,12,13, 14,16,17, 18,19,21, 22,23	0.0101	0.0094	0.0097	-0.0699	-0.0701	0.1646	0.0153	0.0144	0.0102	0.0143	0.0121	0.0093	0.8399	0.6973	0.7252
D	3	4	0.0066	0.0041	0.0064	0.4448	0.4528	0.0672	0.0190	0.0185	0.0058	0.0133	0.0145	0.0068	0.1894	0.1676	0.1617
E	13	5,10,15	-0.0006	-0.0010	0.0044	0.0363	0.0357	0.0257	0.0205	0.0166	0.0144	0.0388	0.0376	0.0108	8.0965	7.1786	3.9200
F	1	20	-0.0092	-0.0092	0	0.0089	0.0089	0	0.0215	0.0215	0	0.0055	0.0055	0	9.4091	9.4091	0
G	1	24	-0.0060	-0.0060	0	0.0199	0.0199	0	0.0198	0.0198	0	0.0662	0.0662	0	0.3612	0.3612	0
H	2	25	0.0014	0.0015	0.0019	0.0225	0.0225	0.0048	0.0164	0.0164	0.0029	0.0740	0.0740	0.0052	10.9785	10.9785	1.2720

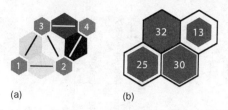

(a)   (b)

Figure 9.30   The 2 × 2 SOM after training: (a) the U-matrix; (b) the sample hit plot

providing loans to high-risk borrowers. High risk taking also contributed to the poor performance of these banks, reflected by the high NLLPLLNI values.

An important part of cluster analysis is to identify outliers, objects that do not naturally fall into any larger cluster. As can be seen in Table 9.4, there are three banks that are viewed as solitary clusters – Cluster B, Cluster F and Cluster G. These banks are outliers, and each of them has a unique financial profile. While conventional clustering algorithms, such as K-means clustering, do not handle outliers well, an SOM can easily identify them.

How many clusters are required?

It is difficult to determine the number of clusters in a multidimensional data set. In fact, when a clustering algorithm attempts to create larger clusters, outliers are often forced into these clusters. This may result not only in poorer clustering, but, even worse, in failing to distinguish unique objects.

As an example, let us cluster the same set of banks using a 2 × 2 SOM. The SOM is trained for 1000 iterations. Figure 9.30 shows the U-matrix and the SOM sample hit plot. Obviously, now we have only four clusters. Further investigation reveals that, based on their average values, banks associated with neurons 1, 2 and 3 can be classified as healthy, while 13 banks attracted by neuron 4 are failing. Two failing banks and two banks with unusually high values of NLLPLLNI, previously identified by the 5 × 5 SOM, are now absorbed by the 'healthy' cluster.

How can we test the SOM performance?

In order to test a neural network, including an SOM, we need a test set. From the FDIC annual report we can obtain a list of failed banks, and collect appropriate financial statement data. Several studies of bank failures suggest that failed banks could be detected between 6 and 12 months before the call date, and in some cases as early as four years before a bank fails (Alam *et al.*, 2000; Eichengreen, 2002). Although solvency and liquidity are the most important predictors of a failure close to the call date, asset quality, earnings and management practices become increasingly significant as the time before failure increases. To test the SOM performance, we select 10 banks that failed last year, and collect their one-year-prior financial statement data. Table 9.5 contains the mean, median and standard deviation (SD) values of their CAMELS ratings. Now we can apply 10 input vectors to see the SOM response.

Table 9.5 Financial profile of the failing banks

NITA		NLLAA			NPLTA			NLLTL			NLLPLLNI		
Mean	Median	SD	Mean	Median	SD	Mean	Median	SD	Mean	Median	SD	Mean	Median	SD
−0.0625	−0.0616	0.0085	0.0642	0.0610	0.0234	0.0261	0.0273	0.0065	0.0341	0.0339	0.0092	7.3467	6.9641	3.8461

As expected, in the 2×2 SOM, all 10 input vectors are attracted by neuron 4. In the 5×5 SOM, the situation is more complicated. Six input vectors are attracted by neuron 5, two by neuron 10, one by neuron 20 and two by neuron 24. Thus, in both cases, failing banks are clustered correctly.

Finally, a word of caution. Although an SOM is a powerful clustering tool, the exact meaning of each cluster is not always clear, and a domain expert is usually needed to interpret the results. Also an SOM is a neural network, and any neural network is only as good as the data that goes into it. In this case study, we have used only five financial variables. However, to identify problem banks well in advance of their failure, we might need many more variables that hold additional information about bank performance (researchers in the industry use up to 29 financial variables based on the CAMELS rating system).

A good example of challenges associated with clustering is given in Berry and Linoff (2004). A large bank decided to increase its market share in home equity loans. It gathered data on 5000 customers who had home equity loans and 5000 customers who did not have them. The data included appraised value of a house, amount of credit available, amount of credit granted, customer age, marital status, number of children and household income. The data was then used to train an SOM. It identified five clusters. One of the clusters was particularly interesting. It contained customers who took home equity loans. These customers were in their forties, married with children in their late teens. The bank assumed that they were taking loans to pay college tuition fees for their children. Thus, the bank organised a marketing campaign to offer home equity loans as a means to pay for college education. However, the results of the campaign were disappointing.

Further investigation revealed that the problem was in the interpretation of the clusters identified by the SOM. Consequently, the bank decided to include more information about its customers such as type of account, deposit system, credit card system, etc. After retraining the SOM, it was discovered that customers who took home equity loans in addition to being in their forties with college-age children often also had business accounts. So, the bank concluded that when children left home to go to college, parents took out home equity loans to start new businesses. The bank organised a new marketing campaign targeting this group of potential customers, and this time the campaign was successful.

9.5 Will genetic algorithms work for my problem?

Genetic algorithms are applicable to many optimisation problems (Haupt and Haupt, 2004). Optimisation is essentially the process of finding a better solution to a problem. This implies that the problem has more than one solution and the solutions are not of equal quality. A genetic algorithm generates a population of competing candidate solutions and then causes them to evolve through the process of natural selection – poor solutions tend to die out, while better solutions survive and reproduce. By repeating this process over and over again, the genetic algorithm breeds an optimal solution.

Case study 8: The travelling salesman problem

I want to develop an intelligent system that can produce an optimal itinerary. I am going to travel by car and I want to visit all major cities in Western and Central Europe and then return home. Will a genetic algorithm work for this problem?

This problem is well known as the **travelling salesman problem** (TSP). Given a finite number of cities, *N*, and the cost of travel (or the distance) between each pair of cities, we need to find the cheapest way (or the shortest route) for visiting each city exactly once and returning to the starting point.

Although the TSP became known as early as the eighteenth century, only in the late 1940s and early 1950s was the problem studied seriously and then publicised as a typical NP-hard problem (Dantzig *et al.*, 1954; Flood, 1955). Such problems are hard to solve by combinatorial search techniques. The search space for the TSP includes all possible combinations of *N* cities, and thus the size of the search space equals *N*! (the factorial of the number of cities). Because the number of cities can be quite large, examining the alternative routes one by one is not feasible.

The TSP is naturally represented in numerous transportation and logistics applications such as arranging routes for school buses to pick up children in a school district, delivering meals to home-bound people, scheduling stacker cranes in a warehouse, planning truck routes to pick up parcel post, and many others. A classic example of the TSP is the scheduling of a machine to drill holes in a circuit board. In this case, the holes are the cities, and the cost of travel is the time it takes to move the drill head from one hole to the next.

Over the years the size of the TSP has grown dramatically, moving from the solution of a 49-city problem (Dantzig *et al.*, 1954) up to the fairly recent solution of a 15,112-city problem (Applegate *et al.*, 2001).

Researchers apply different techniques to solve this problem. These techniques include simulated annealing (Laarhoven and Aarts, 2009), discrete linear programming (Lawler *et al.*, 1985), neural networks (Hopfield and Tank, 1985), branch-and-bound algorithms (Tschoke *et al.*, 1995), Markov chains (Martin *et al.*, 1991) and genetic algorithms (Potvin, 1996). Genetic algorithms are particularly suitable for the TSP because they can rapidly direct the search to promising areas of the search space.

How does a genetic algorithm solve the TSP?

First, we need to decide how to represent a route of the salesman. The most natural way of representing a route is path representation (Michalewicz, 1996). Each city is given an alphabetic or numerical name, the route through the cities is represented as a chromosome, and appropriate genetic operators are used to create new routes.

Suppose we have nine cities numbered from 1 to 9. In a chromosome, the order of the integers represents the order in which the cities will be visited by the salesman. For example, a chromosome

| 1 | 6 | 5 | 3 | 2 | 8 | 4 | 9 | 7 |

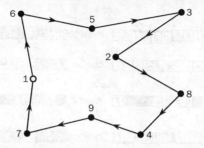

Figure 9.31 An example of the salesman's route

represents the route shown in Figure 9.31. The salesman starts at *City* 1, visits all the other cities once and returns to the starting point.

How does the crossover operator work in the TSP?

The crossover operator in its classical form cannot be directly applied to the TSP. A simple exchange of parts between two parents would produce illegal routes containing duplicates and omissions – some cities would be visited twice while others would not be visited at all. For example, exchanging parts of the two parent chromosomes

Parent 1: | 1 | 6 | 5 | 3 | 2 | 8 | 4 | 9 | 7 | Parent 2: | 3 | 7 | 6 | 1 | 9 | 4 | 8 | 2 | 5 |

would produce one route with *City* 5 visited twice and *City* 7 omitted, and the other with *City* 7 visited twice and *City* 5 omitted

Child 1: | 1 | 6 | 5 | 3 | 9 | 4 | 8 | 2 | 5 | Child 2: | 3 | 7 | 6 | 1 | 2 | 8 | 4 | 9 | 7 |

Clearly, the classical crossover with a single crossover point does not work in the TSP. To overcome this problem, a number of two-point crossover operators were proposed (Goldberg, 1989). For example, Goldberg and Lingle (1985) suggested the *partially mapped crossover*, and Davis (1985) introduced the *ordered crossover*. However, most operators are based on creating an offspring by choosing a part of a route from one parent and preserving the order of cities from the other parent. Figure 9.32 demonstrates how the crossover operator works.

First, two crossover points (marked by the | character) are chosen uniformly at random along the strings of two parent chromosomes. Chromosome material between crossover points defines swap sections. Two offspring chromosomes are created by interchanging the swap sections between the parents; in Figure 9.32 asterisks represent yet undecided cities. Next, the original cities from each parent are placed in their original order, omitting cities present in the other parent's swap section. For example, Cities 1, 9, 4 and 8, which appear in the swap section from the second parent, are removed from the first parent. The remaining cities are then placed in the offspring, preserving their original order. As a result, an offspring represents a route partly determined by each of its parents.

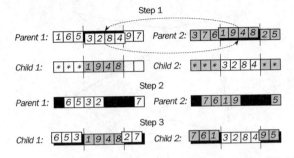

Figure 9.32 Crossover operators for the TSP

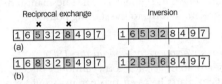

Figure 9.33 Mutation operators for the TSP: (a) original chromosomes; (b) mutated chromosomes

How does the mutation operator work in the TSP?

There are two types of mutation operators: reciprocal exchange and inversion (Michalewicz, 1996). Figures 9.33(a) and (b) show how they work. The reciprocal exchange operator simply swaps two randomly selected cities in the chromosome. The inversion operator selects two random points along the chromosome string and reverses the order of the cities between these points.

How do we define a fitness function in the TSP?

While creating genetic operators for the TSP is not trivial, the design of a fitness function is straightforward – all we need to do is to evaluate the total length of the route. The fitness of each individual chromosome is determined as the reciprocal of the route length. In other words, the shorter the route, the fitter the chromosome.

Once the fitness function is defined and genetic operators are constructed, we can implement and run the GA.

As an example, let us consider the TSP for 20 cities placed in a 1×1 square. First, we choose the size of a chromosome population and the number of generations to run. We might start with a relatively small population and after a few generations examine the solutions obtained. Figure 9.34 shows the best route created by 20 chromosomes after 100 generations. As we can see, this route is not optimal and obviously can be improved. Let us increase the size of the chromosome population and run the GA again. Figure 9.35(a) demonstrates the results. The total length of the route decreases by 20 per cent – a very significant improvement.

But how do we know that the GA has actually found the optimal route?

The fact is, we don't. Only further trial runs on different sizes of chromosome populations with different rates of crossover and mutation can provide the answer.

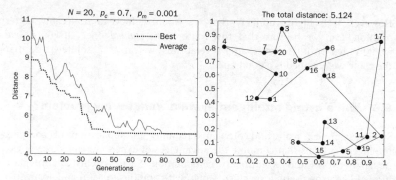

Figure 9.34 Performance graph and the best salesman's routes created in a population of 20 chromosomes after 100 generations

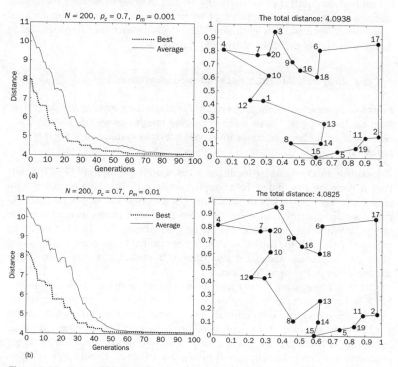

Figure 9.35 Performance graphs and the best routes created in a population of 200 chromosomes: (a) mutation rate is 0.001; (b) mutation rate is 0.01

Let us, for example, increase the mutation rate up to 0.01. Figure 9.35(b) shows the results. Although the total distance decreased slightly, the salesman's route is still similar to the one shown in Figure 9.35(a). Perhaps we might now attempt to increase the size of the chromosome population and rerun the GA.

However, it is highly unlikely that we would achieve a noticeably better solution. Can we be sure that this route is *the optimal* one? Of course, we wouldn't bet on it! However, after several runs, we can be absolutely sure that the route we obtained is a good one.

9.6   Will a hybrid intelligent system work for my problem?

Solving complex real-world problems requires an application of complex intelligent systems that combine the advantages of expert systems, fuzzy logic, neural networks and evolutionary computation. Such systems can integrate human-like expertise in a specific domain with abilities to learn and adapt to a rapidly changing environment.

Although the field of hybrid intelligent systems is still evolving, and most hybrid tools are not yet particularly effective, neuro-fuzzy systems have already matured as an advanced technology with numerous successful applications. While neural networks can learn from data, the key benefit of fuzzy logic lies in its ability to model decision-making of humans.

Case study 9: Neuro-fuzzy decision-support systems

I want to develop an intelligent system for diagnosing myocardial perfusion from cardiac images. I have a set of cardiac images as well as the clinical notes and physician's interpretation. Will a hybrid system work for this problem?

Diagnosis in modern cardiac medicine is based on the analysis of SPECT (Single Proton Emission Computed Tomography) images. By injecting a patient with radioactive tracer, two sets of SPECT images are obtained: one is taken 10–15 minutes after the injection when the stress is greatest (stress images), and the other is taken 2–5 hours after the injection (rest images). The distribution of the radioactive tracer in the cardiac muscle is proportional to the muscle's perfusion. Thus by comparing stress and rest images, a cardiologist can often detect abnormalities in the heart function.

The SPECT images are usually represented by high-resolution two-dimensional black-and-white pictures with up to 256 shades of grey. Brighter patches on the image correspond to well-perfused areas of the myocardium, while darker patches may indicate the presence of an ischemia. Unfortunately a visual inspection of the SPECT images is highly subjective; physicians' interpretations are therefore often inconsistent and susceptible to errors. Clearly an intelligent system that can help a cardiologist to diagnose cardiac SPECT images would be of great value.

For this study, we use 267 cardiac diagnostic cases. Each case is accompanied by two SPECT images (the stress image and the rest image), and each image is divided into 22 regions. The region's brightness, which in turn reflects perfusion inside this region, is expressed by an integer number between 0 and 100 (Kurgan *et al.*,

2001). Thus, each cardiac diagnostic case is represented by 44 continuous features and one binary feature that assigns an overall diagnosis – normal or abnormal.

The entire SPECT data set consists of 55 cases classified as normal (positive examples) and 212 cases classified as abnormal (negative examples). This set is divided into training and test sets. The training set has 40 positive and 40 negative examples. The test set is represented by 15 positive and 172 negative examples.

Can we train a back-propagation neural network to classify the SPECT images into normal and abnormal?

A back-propagation neural network can indeed address the SPECT image classification problem – the size of the training set appears to be sufficiently large, and the network can work here as a classifier. The number of neurons in the input layer is determined by the total number of regions in the stress and rest images. In this example, each image is divided into 22 regions, so we need 44 input neurons. Since SPECT images are to be classified as either normal or abnormal, we should use two output neurons. Experimental trials show that a good generalisation can be obtained with as little as 5 to 7 neurons in the hidden layer. The back-propagation network learns relatively fast and converges to a solution.

However, when we test the network on the test set, we find that the network's performance is rather poor – about 25 per cent of normal cardiac diagnostic cases are misclassified as abnormal and over 35 per cent of abnormal cases are misclassified as normal; the overall diagnostic error exceeds 33 per cent. This indicates that the training set may lack some important examples (a neural network is only as good as the examples used to train it). Despite this, we still can significantly improve the accuracy of the diagnosis.

First, we need to redefine the problem. To train the network, we use the same number of positive and negative examples. Although in real clinical trials the ratio between normal and abnormal SPECT images is very different, the misclassification of an abnormal cardiac case could lead to infinitely more serious consequences than the misclassification of a normal case. Therefore, in order to achieve a small classification error for abnormal SPECT images, we might agree to have a relatively large error for normal images.

The neural network produces two outputs. The first output corresponds to the possibility that the SPECT image belongs to the class *normal*, and the second to the possibility that the image belongs to the class *abnormal*. If, for example, the first (*normal*) output is 0.92 and the second (*abnormal*) is 0.16, the SPECT image is classified as normal, and we can conclude that the risk of a heart attack for this case is low. On the other hand, if the *normal* output is low, say 0.17, and the *abnormal* output is much higher, say 0.51, the SPECT image is classified as abnormal, and we can infer that the risk of a heart attack in this case is rather high. However, if the two outputs are close – say the *normal* output is 0.51 and the *abnormal* 0.49 – we cannot confidently classify the image.

Can we use fuzzy logic for decision making in medical diagnosis?

Doctors do not keep precise thresholds in mind when they classify SPECT images. A cardiologist examines perfusion across all regions in the diagnosed image and also compares the brightness of the corresponding myocardium regions on the stress and rest images. In fact, doctors often rely on their experience and intuition in detecting abnormalities of the myocardium. Fuzzy logic provides us with a means of modelling how the cardiologist assesses the risk of a heart attack.

To build a fuzzy system, we first need to determine input and output variables, define fuzzy sets and construct fuzzy rules. For our problem, there are two inputs (*NN output 1* and *NN output 2*) and one output (the *risk* of a heart attack). The inputs are normalised to be within the range of [0, 1], and the output can vary between 0 and 100 per cent. Figures 9.36, 9.37 and 9.38 demonstrate fuzzy sets of the linguistic variables used in the fuzzy system. Fuzzy rules are shown in Figure 9.39.

Figure 9.40 represents a complete structure of the neuro-fuzzy decision-support system for assessing the risk of a cardiac decease. To build this system,

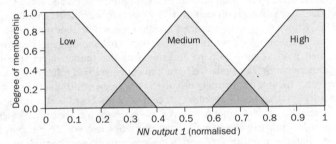

Figure 9.36 Fuzzy sets of the neural network output *normal*

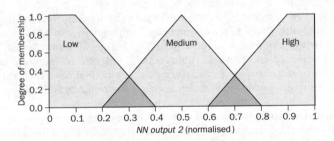

Figure 9.37 Fuzzy sets of the neural network output *abnormal*

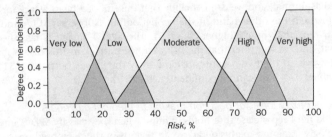

Figure 9.38 Fuzzy sets of the linguistic variable *Risk*

1. If (NN_output1 is Low) and (NN_output2 is Low) then (Risk is Moderate)
2. If (NN_output1 is Low) and (NN_output2 is Medium) then (Risk is High)
3. If (NN_output1 is Low) and (NN_output2 is High) then (Risk is Very_high)
4. If (NN_output1 is Medium) and (NN_output2 is Low) then (Risk is Low)
5. If (NN_output1 is Medium) and (NN_output2 is Medium) then (Risk is Moderate)
6. If (NN_output1 is Medium) and (NN_output2 is High) then (Risk is High)
7. If (NN_output1 is High) and (NN_output2 is Low) then (Risk is Very_low)
8. If (NN_output1 is High) and (NN_output2 is Medium) then (Risk is Low)
9. If (NN_output1 is High) and (NN_output2 is High) then (Risk is Moderate)

Figure 9.39   Fuzzy rules for assessing the risk of a heart decease

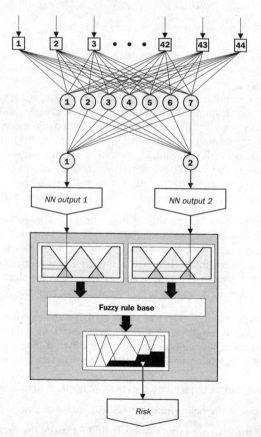

Figure 9.40   Hierarchical structure of the neuro-fuzzy system for risk assessment of the cardiac decease

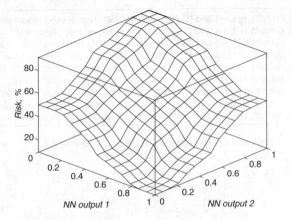

Figure 9.41 Three-dimensional plot for the fuzzy rule base

we can use the MATLAB Neural Network and MATLAB Fuzzy Logic Toolboxes. Once the system is developed, we can study and analyse its behaviour on the three-dimensional plot shown in Figure 9.41.

The system's output is a crisp number that represents a patient's risk of a heart attack. Based on this number, a cardiologist can now classify cardiac cases with greater certainty – when the risk is quantified, a decision-maker has a much better chance of making the right decision. For instance, if the risk is low, say smaller than 30 per cent, the cardiac case can be classified as *normal*, but if the risk is high, say greater than 50 per cent, the case is classified as *abnormal*.

However, cardiac cases with the risk between 30 and 50 per cent cannot be classified as either *normal* or *abnormal* – rather, such cases are *uncertain*.

Can we still classify at least some of these uncertain cases using the knowledge of an experienced cardiologist?
An experienced cardiologist knows that, in normal heart muscle, perfusion at maximum stress is usually higher than perfusion at rest for the same region of the muscle. Thus we can expect to make an uncertain case more certain when we apply the following heuristics to all corresponding regions:

1. If perfusion inside region *i* at stress is higher than perfusion inside the same region at rest, then the risk of a heart attack should be decreased.
2. If perfusion inside region *i* at stress is not higher than perfusion inside the same region at rest, then the risk of a heart attack should be increased.

These heuristics can be implemented in the diagnostic system as follows:

Step 1: Present the neuro-fuzzy system with a cardiac case.

Step 2: If the system's output is less than 30, classify the presented case as *normal* and then stop. If the output is greater than 50, classify the case as *abnormal* and stop. Otherwise, go to Step 3.

Step 3: For region 1, subtract perfusion at rest from perfusion at stress. If the result is positive, decrease the current risk by multiplying its value by 0.99. Otherwise, increase the risk by multiplying its value by 1.01. Repeat this procedure for all 22 regions and then go to Step 4.

Step 4: If the new risk value is less than 30, classify the case as *normal*; if the risk is greater than 50, classify the case as *abnormal*; otherwise, classify the case as *uncertain*.

When we now apply the test set to the neuro-fuzzy system, we find that the accuracy of diagnosis has dramatically improved – the overall diagnostic error does not exceed 5 per cent, while only 3 per cent of abnormal cardiac cases are misclassified as normal. Although we have not improved the system's performance on normal cases (over 30 per cent of normal cases are still misclassified as abnormal), and up to 20 per cent of the total number of cases are classified as uncertain, the neuro-fuzzy system can actually achieve even better results in classifying SPECT images than a cardiologist can. Most importantly, the abnormal SPECT images can now be recognised with much greater accuracy.

In this example, the neuro-fuzzy system has a heterogeneous structure – the neural network and fuzzy system work as independent components (although they cooperate in solving the problem). When a new case is presented to the diagnostic system, the trained neural network determines inputs to the fuzzy system. Then the fuzzy system, using predefined fuzzy sets and fuzzy rules, maps the given inputs to an output, and thereby obtains the risk of a heart attack.

Are there any successful neuro-fuzzy systems with a homogeneous structure?

A typical example of a neuro-fuzzy system with a homogeneous structure is an Adaptive Neuro-Fuzzy Inference System (ANFIS). It cannot be divided into two independent and distinct parts. In fact, an ANFIS is a multilayer neural network that performs fuzzy inferencing.

Case study 10: Time-series prediction

I want to develop a tool to predict an aircraft's trajectory during its landing aboard an aircraft carrier. I have a database of landing trajectories of various aircraft flown by different pilots, and I also can use RADAR numerical data, which provides real-time trajectories of landing aircraft. My goal is to predict an aircraft's trajectory at least 2 seconds in advance, based on the aircraft's current position. Will a neuro-fuzzy system work for this problem?

The landing of an aircraft, particularly aboard aircraft carriers, is an extremely complex process. It is affected by such variables as the flight deck's space constraints and its motions (both pitch and roll), the aircraft's ordinance and fuel load, continuous mechanical preparations, and – the most critical of all –

time constraints. The ship may be heaving 10 feet up and 10 feet down, making a 20-foot displacement from a level deck. In addition, it is difficult to see approaching aircraft at night or during stormy conditions.

Responsibility for the aircraft's final approach and landing lies with the Landing Signal Officer (LSO). In fact, the LSO, not the pilot, makes the most important decision to wave off (i.e. abort landing). When an aircraft is within 1 nautical mile of the landing deck, which roughly corresponds to 60 seconds in real time, the aircraft's flight is carefully observed and guided. During this critical time, the LSO needs to predict the aircraft's position at least 2 seconds ahead. Such problems are known in mathematics as **time-series prediction** problems.

What is a time series?

A time series can be defined as a set of observations, each one being recorded at a specific time. For instance, a time series can be obtained by recording the aircraft's positions over a time interval of, say, 60 seconds before landing. Real-world time-series problems are non-linear and often exhibit chaotic behaviour, which makes them hard to model.

Prediction of the aircraft's landing trajectory is mainly based on the experience of the LSO (all LSOs are trained pilots). An automatic prediction system can use aircraft-position data given by the ship's RADAR, and also data records of previous landings executed by pilots flying different types of aircraft (Richards, 2002). The system is trained off-line with the past data. Then it is presented on-line with the current motion profile, and required to predict the aircraft's motion in the next few seconds. A time-series prediction of an aircraft trajectory is shown in Figure 9.42.

To predict an aircraft's position on-line we will use an ANFIS. It will learn from time-series data of given landing trajectories in order to determine the membership function parameters that best allow the system to track these trajectories.

What do we use as ANFIS inputs?

To predict a future value for a time series, we use values that are already known. For example, if we want to predict an aircraft's position 2 seconds ahead, we may use its current position data as well as data recorded, say, 2, 4 and 6 seconds

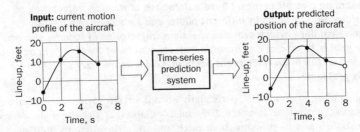

Figure 9.42 On-line time-series predication of an aircraft trajectory

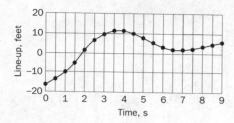

	Inputs			Desired
x_1	x_2	x_3	x_4	output
−17.4	2.1	11.0	3.9	4.2
−12.9	7.5	10.1	2.1	4.9
−10.0	9.8	8.2	2.0	5.3

Figure 9.43   An aircraft trajectory and a data set built to train the ANFIS

before the current position. These four known values represent an input pattern – a four-dimensional vector of the following form:

$$\mathbf{x} = [x(t - 6) \quad x(t - 4) \quad x(t - 2) \quad x(t)]$$

where $x(t)$ is the aircraft's position recorded at the point in time t.

The ANFIS output corresponds to the trajectory prediction: the aircraft's position 2 seconds ahead, $x(t + 2)$.

For this case study, we will use 10 landing trajectories – five for training and five for testing. Each trajectory is a time series of the aircraft's position data points recorded every half a second over a time interval of 60 seconds before landing. Thus, a data set for each trajectory contains 121 values.

How do we build a data set to train the ANFIS?
Let us consider Figure 9.43; it shows an aircraft trajectory and a 3×5 training data set created from the trajectory data points sampled every 2 seconds. Input variables x_1, x_2, x_3 and x_4 correspond to the aircraft's flight positions at $(t - 6)$, $(t - 4)$, $(t - 2)$ and t, respectively. The desired output corresponds to the 2-second-ahead prediction, $x(t + 2)$. The training data set shown in Figure 9.43 is built with t equal to 6.0 s (the first row), 6.5 s (the second row) and 7.0 s (the third row).

By applying the same procedure to a landing trajectory recorded over a time interval of 60 seconds, we obtain 105 training samples represented by a 105×5 matrix. Thus, the entire data set, which we use for training the ANFIS, is represented by a 525×5 matrix.

How many membership functions should we assign to each input variable?
A practical approach is to choose the smallest number of membership functions. Thus, we may begin with two membership functions assigned to each input variable.

Figure 9.44 shows an actual aircraft trajectory and the ANFIS's output after 1 and 100 epochs of training. As can be seen, even after 100 epochs, the ANFIS's performance is still unsatisfactory. We can also see that we have not achieved any significant improvement by increasing the number of epochs.

How can we improve the ANFIS's performance?
The ANFIS's performance can be significantly improved by assigning three membership functions to each input variable. Figure 9.45 demonstrates the

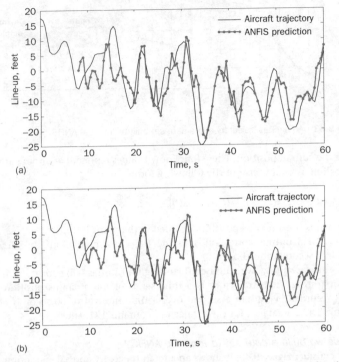

Figure 9.44 Performance of the ANFIS with four inputs and two membership functions assigned to each input: (a) 1 epoch; (b) 100 epochs

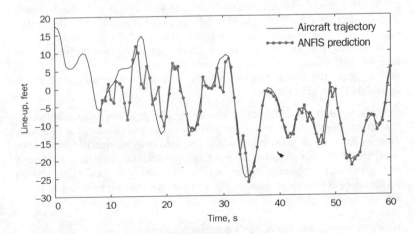

Figure 9.45 Performance of the ANFIS with four inputs and three membership functions assigned to each input after 1 epoch of training

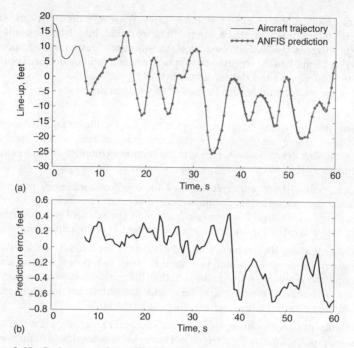

Figure 9.46   Performance of the ANFIS with six inputs and two membership functions assigned to each input: (a) prediction after 1 epoch; (b) prediction errors

results: after only 1 epoch of training the ANFIS predicts the aircraft trajectory more accurately than it did in the previous study after 100 epochs.

Another way of improving time-series prediction is to increase the number of input variables. Let us, for example, examine an ANFIS with six inputs that correspond to the aircraft's flight positions at $(t-5)$, $(t-4)$, $(t-3)$, $(t-2)$, $(t-1)$ and t, respectively. The ANFIS output is still the 2-second-ahead prediction. The training data set is now represented by a 535×7 matrix.

Once we assign the smallest number of membership functions to each input variable, we can train the ANFIS for 1 epoch and observe its performance on a test trajectory. Figure 9.46 shows the results. As we can see, the six-input ANFIS outperforms the ANFIS with four inputs, and provides satisfactory predictions after just one epoch of training.

9.7 Summary

In this chapter, we considered knowledge engineering. First, we discussed what kinds of problems can be addressed with intelligent systems, and introduced the six main phases of the knowledge engineering process. Next we examined typical applications of expert systems, fuzzy systems, neural networks and genetic algorithms. We demonstrated how to build intelligent systems for solving diagnosis, selection, prediction, classification, clustering and optimisation problems. Finally, we discussed applications of hybrid neuro-fuzzy systems for decision support and time-series prediction.

The most important lessons learned in this chapter are:

- Knowledge engineering is the process of building intelligent knowledge-based systems. There are six main steps: assess the problem; acquire data and knowledge; develop a prototype system; develop a complete system; evaluate and revise the system; and integrate and maintain the system.

- Intelligent systems are typically used for diagnosis, selection, prediction, classification, clustering, optimisation and control. The choice of a tool for building an intelligent system is influenced by the problem type, availability of data and expertise, and the form and content of the required solution.

- Understanding the problem's domain is critical for building an intelligent system. Developing a prototype system helps us to test how well we understand the problem and to make sure that the problem-solving strategy, the tool selected for building a system, and the techniques for representing acquired data and knowledge are adequate to the task.

- Intelligent systems, unlike conventional computer programs, are designed to solve problems that quite often do not have clearly defined 'right' and 'wrong' solutions. Therefore, the system is normally evaluated with test cases selected by the user.

- Diagnostic and troubleshooting problems are very attractive candidates for expert systems. Diagnostic expert systems are easy to develop because most diagnostic problems have a finite list of possible solutions, involve a limited amount of well-formalised knowledge, and usually take a human expert a short time to solve.

- Solving real-world classification problems often involves inexact and incomplete data. Expert systems are capable of dealing with such data by managing incrementally acquired evidence as well as information with different degrees of belief.

- Fuzzy systems are well suited for modelling human decision making. Important decisions are often based on human intuition, common sense and experience, rather than on the availability and precision of data. Fuzzy technology provides us with a means of coping with the 'soft criteria' and 'fuzzy data'. Although decision-support fuzzy systems may include dozens, even hundreds, of rules, they can be developed, tested and implemented relatively quickly.

- Neural networks represent a class of general-purpose tools that are successfully applied to prediction, classification and clustering problems. They are used in such areas as speech and character recognition, medical diagnosis, process control and robotics, identifying radar targets, predicting foreign exchange rates and detecting fraudulent transactions. The areas of neural network applications are expanding very rapidly.

- Multilayer back-propagation neural networks are particularly good at solving prediction and classification problems. However, choosing training examples is critical – a training set must cover the full range of values for all inputs. A neural network is only as good as the data that goes into it.

- Neural networks with competitive learning are suitable for solving clustering and classification problems. In a competitive neural network, each competitive neuron is associated with a single cluster. However, since clustering is an unsupervised process, we cannot use it directly for labelling competitive neurons. In most practical applications, a domain expert is required to interpret the meaning of each cluster.

- Genetic algorithms are applicable to complex optimisation problems. A genetic algorithm generates a population of possible solutions and causes them to evolve through the process of natural selection. To ensure that an optimal solution is found, we need to run the genetic algorithm on various sizes of chromosome populations, with different rates of crossover and mutation.

- Solving complex real-world problems often requires an application of complex intelligent systems capable of integrating human-like expertise in a specific domain with the ability to learn. Although the field of hybrid intelligent systems is still evolving, neuro-fuzzy systems have already found numerous applications in the area of decision support.

Questions for review

1 What is knowledge engineering? Describe the main steps in knowledge engineering. Why is choosing the right tool for the job the most critical part of building an intelligent system?

2 What are the stages in the knowledge acquisition process? Why is knowledge acquisition often called a bottleneck of the process of knowledge engineering? How can the acquired data affect our choice of the system building tool?

3 What is a prototype? What is a test case? How do we test an intelligent system? What should we do if we have made a bad choice of system building tool?

4 Why is adopting new intelligent technologies becoming problem driven, rather than curiosity driven, as it often was in the past?

5 What makes diagnosis and troubleshooting problems so attractive for expert system technology? What is a phone call rule?

6 How do we choose a tool to develop an expert system? What are the advantages of expert system shells? How do we choose an expert system shell for building an intelligent system?

7 Develop a rule-based expert system for diagnosing an air conditioning system. An air conditioning system is a complex device with many areas and parts which are not accessible to an untrained person. Despite this, several things can be checked before calling for service. This expert system should diagnose simple problems which you may be able to repair yourself, and thus avoid an unnecessary call to the service company.

An air conditioning system may have the following problems: unit freezing, leaking water, not cooling, and not running. See a troubleshooting manual for details. You can also find some useful information on the following website: http://www.accheckup.com/trouble.htm

8   A set of rules shown below uses Bayesian accumulation of evidence for assessing chest pain complaints made by a patient. Evaluate the system and provide a full trace of the reasoning process. Determine the probability of heart disease if the patient suffers from chest pain and his or her electrocardiogram is positive.

control bayes

Rule: 1
if   chest_pain is true {LS 0.2 LN 0.01}
then heart_disease is true {prior 0.1}

Rule: 2
if   chest_pain is true
and electrocardiogram is positive {LS 95 LN 5}
then heart_disease is true

/*The SEEK directive sets up the goal of the rule set
seek heart_disease

9   A set of rules shown below uses certainty factors for assessing chest pain complaints. Determine the certainty of heart disease if the patient suffers from chest pain and his or her electrocardiogram is positive. Provide a full trace of the reasoning process.

control cf

Rule: 1
if   chest_pain is true
then heart_disease is true {cf 0.1}

Rule: 2
if   electrocardiogram is positive
then heart_disease is true {cf 0.7}

Rule: 3
if   electrocardiogram is negative
then heart_disease is true {cf 0.05}

/*The SEEK directive sets up the goal of the rule set
seek heart_disease

10 Why are fuzzy systems particularly well suited for modelling human decision making? Why does fuzzy technology have great potential in areas such as business and finance?

11 Develop a fuzzy system for direct marketing. Assume that the target group is defined as 'fathers in their prime working years with income above average'. The 'prime working years' group is defined as between 40 and 55 years old, and the average income is $45,000. Make sure that your fuzzy system is capable of targeting men in their late thirties with at least two children and a high income.

12 Develop a fuzzy expert system for detecting fraudulent claims for home insurance. Assume the following seven input variables: the number of claims filed by a claimant in the last 12 months, amount of the current claim, how long a claimant was with the current insurer, average balance on all accounts over the last 12 months, the number of overdrafts over the last 12 months, annual income of a claimant, and whether a fundamental change occurred in the claimant's life in the last four months (for instance, he or she got married or divorced, lost a job, or became a parent). Assume that the output of a fuzzy system is the likelihood of a fraud (a number between zero and one, with zero meaning that the insurance claim is non-fraudulent, and one that the likelihood of a fraud is very high).

Use a hierarchical fuzzy modelling approach. First, evaluate *insurance history* (use the first three input variables), *banking history* (use the fourth and fifth input variables), and *claimant status* (use the last two input variables). Then, evaluate *fraud likelihood* using *insurance history*, *banking history* and *claimant status* as inputs.

13 What is the basis for the popularity of neural networks? In what areas have neural networks been applied most successfully? Explain why and give examples.

14 Why do we need to massage data before using it in a neural network model? How do we massage the data? Give examples of massaging continuous and discrete data. What is 1 of *N* coding?

15 Develop a back-propagation neural network to classify rock crabs into males and females using five anatomic measurements (in mm): frontal lobe size, rear width, carapace length, carapace width and body depth. The data set contains 100 specimens, 50 males and 50 females. The data set is located on the book's website: http://www.booksites.net/negnevitsky

16 Develop a back-propagation neural network for diagnosing breast cancer based on features computed from a digitised image of a fine needle aspirate (FNA) of a breast mass. The data set contains 150 cases. Each case is diagnosed as malignant or benign based on 10 real-valued features: radius, texture, perimeter, area, smoothness, compactness, concavity, concave points, symmetry and fractal dimension. The data set is located on the book's website: http://www.booksites.net/negnevitsky. Explain the difficulties and limitations of your diagnostic neural network.

17 Develop a neuro-fuzzy system with a heterogeneous structure for the problem described in Question 16. Note that first you need to redefine the problem so that the system output becomes the estimated risk of breast cancer.

18 Use a self-organising neural network for cluster analysis of waste-water treatment plant data. The data set contains 527 instances. Each instance has 38 attributes. The data set is located at the UCI Machine Learning Repository website: http://archive.ics.uci.edu/ml/datasets/Water+Treatment+Plant

19 Develop a genetic algorithm for optimising the location of an emergency response unit in order to minimise the response time to a medical emergency in a city. The city is mapped into a 7 km × 7 km grid, shown in Figure 9.47. A number in each sector of the grid represents an average number of emergencies per year in a given sector.

A fitness function can be defined as a reciprocal of the sum of distances weighted by emergency rates:

$$f(x,y) = \sum_{n=1}^{49} \lambda_n \sqrt{(x_n - x_{eru})^2 + (y_n - y_{eru})^2}$$

where λ_n is the emergency rate in sector n; (x_n, y_n) are the coordinates of the centre of sector n; and (x_{eru}, y_{eru}) are the location coordinates of the emergency response

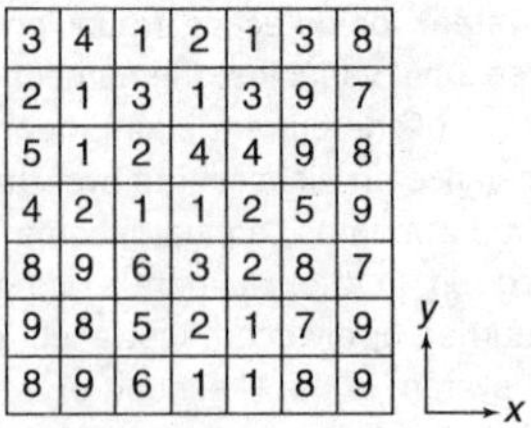

3	4	1	2	1	3	8
2	1	3	1	3	9	7
5	1	2	4	4	9	8
4	2	1	1	2	5	9
8	9	6	3	2	8	7
9	8	5	2	1	7	9
8	9	6	1	1	8	9

y
$\rightarrow x$

Figure 9.47 A grid map of a 7 km × 7 km city

3	4	1	2	1	3	8
2	1	3	1	3	9	7
5	1	2	4	4	9	8
4	2	1	1	2	5	9
8	9	6	3	2	8	7
9	8	5	2	1	7	9
8	9	6	1	1	8	9

y
$\rightarrow x$

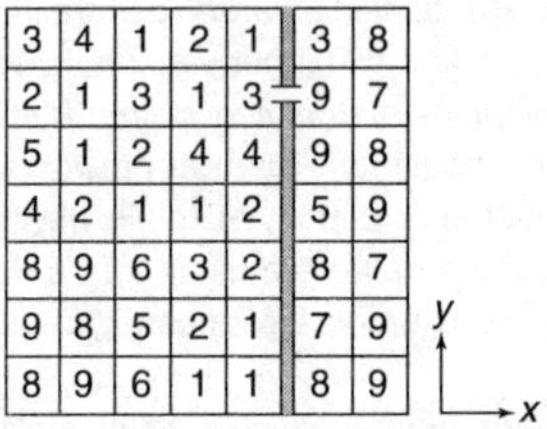

Figure 9.48 A grid map of a 7 km × 7 km city divided by a river

unit. It can be assumed that the emergency response unit can be located only in the centre of a sector.

20 Develop a genetic algorithm for the problem described in Question 19 assuming that there is a river that divides the city into two parts, West and East, at $x = 5$ km. West and East are connected by a bridge located at $x = 5$ km and $y = 5.5$ km, as shown in Figure 9.48.

   Find the optimal location of the emergency response unit and compare it with the one obtained in Question 19.

References

Abrams, B.A. and Huang, C.J. (1987). Predicting bank failures: the role of structure in affecting recent failure experiences in the USA, *Applied Economics*, 19, 1291–1302.

Alam, P., Booth, D., Lee, K. and Thordarson, T. (2000). The use of fuzzy clustering algorithm and self-organizing neural networks for identifying potentially failing banks: an experimental study, *Expert Systems with Applications*, 18(3), 185–199.

Applegate, D., Bixby, R., Chvátal, V. and Cook, W. (2001). TSP cuts which do not conform to the template paradigm, *Computational Combinatorial Optimization*, M. Junger and D. Naddef, eds, Springer-Verlag, Berlin, pp. 261–304.

Berry, M. and Linoff, G. (2004). *Data Mining Techniques for Marketing, Sales, and Customer Relationship Management*, 2nd edn. John Wiley, New York.

Booth, D.E., Alam, P., Ahkam, S.N. and Osyk, B. (1989). A robust multivariate procedure for the identification of problem savings and loan institutions, *Decision Sciences*, 20, 320–333.

Dantzig, G., Fulkerson, R. and Johnson, S. (1954). Solution of a large-scale traveling salesman problem, *Operations Research*, 2, 393–410.

Davis, L. (1985). Applying adaptive algorithms to epistatic domains, *Proceedings of the 9th International Joint Conference on Artificial Intelligence*, A. Joshi, ed., Morgan Kaufmann, Los Angeles, pp. 162–164.

Davis, R. and King, J. (1977). An overview of production systems, *Machine Intelligence*, 8, 300–322.

Durkin, J. (1994). *Expert Systems: Design and Development*. Prentice Hall, Englewood Cliffs, NJ.

Eichengreen, B. (2002). *Financial Crises and What to Do About Them*, Oxford University Press, Oxford.

Espahbodi, P. (1991). Identification of problem banks and binary choice models, *Journal of Banking and Finance*, 15(1), 53–71.

Firebaugh, M. (1988). *Artificial Intelligence: A Knowledge-Based Approach*. Boyd & Fraser, Boston, MA.

Fisher, R.A. (1950). *Contributions to Mathematical Statistics*. John Wiley, New York.

Flood, M.M. (1955). The traveling salesman problem, *Operations Research*, 4, 61–75.

Goldberg, D.E. (1989). *Genetic Algorithms in Search Optimization and Machine Learning*. Addison-Wesley, Reading, MA.

Goldberg, D.E. and Lingle, R. (1985). Alleles, loci and the traveling salesman problem, *Proceedings of the 1st International Conference on Genetic Algorithms*, J.J. Grefenstette, ed., Lawrence Erlbaum Associates, Pittsburgh, PA, pp. 154–159.

Güllich, H.-P. (1996). Fuzzy logic decision support system for credit risk evaluation, *EUFIT Fourth European Congress on Intelligent Techniques and Soft Computing*, Aachen, pp. 2219–2223.

Haupt, R.L. and Haupt, S.E. (2004). *Practical Genetic Algorithms*, 2nd edn. John Wiley, New York.

Haykin, S. (2008). *Neural Networks and Learning Machines*, 3rd edn. Prentice Hall, Englewood Cliffs, NJ.

Hopfield, J.J. and Tank, D.W. (1985). Neural computation of decisions in optimization problems, *Biological Cybernetics*, 52, 141–152.

Kurgan, L.A., Cios, K.J., Tadeusiewicz, R., Ogiela, M. and Goodenday, L. (2001). Knowledge discovery approach to automated cardiac SPECT diagnosis, *Artificial Intelligence in Medicine*, 23(2), 149–169.

Laarhoven, P.J.M. and Aarts, E.H.L. (2009). *Simulated Annealing: Theory and Applications*. Springer Netherlands, Dordrecht.

Lawler, E.L., Lenstra, J.K., Rinnooy Kan, A.H.G. and Shmoys, D.B. (1985). *The Traveling Salesman Problem: A Guided Tour of Combinatorial Optimization*. John Wiley, Chichester.

LeCun, Y., Boser, B., Denker, J.S., Henderson, D., Howard, R.E., Hubbard, W. and Jackel, L.D. (1990). Handwritten digit recognition with a back-propagation network, *Advances in Neural Information Processing Systems*, D.S. Touretzky, ed., Morgan Kaufmann, San Mateo, CA, vol. 2, pp. 396–404.

Martin, O., Otto, S.W. and Felten, E.W. (1991). Large-step Markov chains for the traveling salesman problem, *Complex Systems*, 5(3), 299–326.

Michalewicz, Z. (1996). *Genetic Algorithms + Data Structures = Evolutionary Programs*, 3rd edn. Springer-Verlag, New York.

Michie, D. (1982). The state of the art in machine learning, *Introductory Readings in Expert Systems*, Gordon and Breach, New York, pp. 209–229.

Ozkan-Gunay, E.N. and Ozkan, M. (2007). Prediction of bank failures in emerging financial markets: an ANN approach, *Journal of Risk Finance*, 8(5), 465–480.

Potvin, J.V. (1996). Genetic algorithms for the traveling salesman problem, *Annals of Operations Research*, 63, 339–370.

Principe, J.C., Euliano, N.R. and Lefebvre, W.C. (2000). *Neural and Adaptive Systems: Fundamentals Through Simulations*. John Wiley, New York.

Richards, R. (2002). Application of multiple artificial intelligence techniques for an aircraft carrier landing decision support tool, *Proceedings of the IEEE International Conference on Fuzzy Systems, FUZZ-IEEE'02*, Honolulu, Hawaii.

Russell, S.J. and Norvig, P. (2009). *Artificial Intelligence: A Modern Approach*, 3rd edn. Prentice Hall, Upper Saddle River, NJ.

Simon, R. (1987). The morning after, *Forbes*, October 19, pp. 164–168.

Tryon, R.C. (1939). *Cluster Analysis*, McGraw-Hill, New York.

Tschoke, S., Lubling, R. and Monien, B. (1995). Solving the traveling salesman problem with a distributed branch-and-bound algorithm on a 1024 processor network, *Proceedings of the 9th IEEE International Parallel Processing Symposium*, Santa Barbara, CA, pp. 182–189.

Von Altrock, C. (1997). *Fuzzy Logic and NeuroFuzzy Applications in Business and Finance*. Prentice Hall, Upper Saddle River, NJ.

Waterman, D.A. (1986). *A Guide to Expert Systems*. Addison-Wesley, Reading, MA.

Widrow, B. and Stearns, S.D. (1985). *Adaptive Signal Processing*. Prentice Hall, Englewood Cliffs, NJ.

Zhang, G., Hu, M.Y., Patuwo, B.E. and Indro, D.C. (1999). Artificial neural networks in bankruptcy prediction: general framework and cross-validation analysis, *European Journal of Operation Research*, 116, 16–32.

Zurada, J.M. (2006). *Introduction to Artificial Neural Systems*, 2nd edn. Jaico, Mumbai.

Data mining and knowledge discovery

10

In which we introduce data mining as an integral part of knowledge discovery in large databases and consider the main techniques and tools for turning data into knowledge.

10.1 Introduction, or what is data mining?

If you feel you are experiencing information overload, you are right! You and everyone around you are overloaded with information. The amount of new data stored on computer hard disks is doubling every year, and is now measured in terabytes, petabytes (1000 terabytes, or 10^{15} bytes) and even exabytes (1,000,000 terabytes, or 10^{18} bytes). A terabyte is equivalent to about 2 million books. The 19 million books in the US Library of Congress contain about 10 terabytes of information. According to the IDC White Paper 'As the economy contracts, the digital universe expands', in 2008, the digital universe (the information that is created, captured or replicated in digital form) was 487 exabytes (Gantz and Reinsel, 2009). By 2012, the amount of digital information is expected to reach 2500 exabytes. If converted to pages and assembled into books, the digital universe would stretch to Pluto and back 50 times. And this staggering stack of books is almost doubling every year! At the current rate of growth, it is rising 20 times faster than a rocket. It took the Atlas V 13 months to reach Pluto, but it would take the growing stack of books just three weeks.

We truly live in a rapidly expanding universe of information, but there are often enormous difficulties in extracting the information we need from huge amounts of data. NASA, for example, has more data than it can analyse. Human Genome Project researchers have to store and process thousands of bytes for each of the 3 billion DNA bases that make up the human genome. Every day exabytes of data are circulated via the Internet, and we need methods that can help us extract meaningful information and knowledge from them.

Modern society is based on information. Yet most of the information stored on our computers appears in its raw form as facts, observations and measurements. These facts, observations and measurements constitute data. Data is what we collect and store. As the cost of computing power continues to fall, the amount of accumulated data is increasing at an exponential rate. The problem is what to do with all these valuable resources. After all, what we need is knowledge. Knowledge is what helps us make informed decisions.

While traditional databases are good at storing and providing access to data, they are not so good at carrying out meaningful analysis of it. This is where **data mining**, or **knowledge discovery in databases** (KDD) as it is also known, can be useful.

The term 'data mining' is normally associated with the extraction of knowledge from data. Data mining can also be defined as the exploration and analysis of *large* quantities of data in order to discover meaningful patterns and rules (Berry and Linoff, 2004). The ultimate goal of data mining is to discover knowledge.

Data mining can be viewed as a natural evolution of computerised databases. While traditional database management tools help the user to extract specific data from a database, data mining facilitates the finding of hidden patterns (correlations, trends, anomalies and clusters) within the data stored in a database and the making of predictions about new data. Traditional tools usually expect the user to form a hypothesis about relationships present in the database. This hypothesis is then either proved or disproved through a series of queries against the data. Let us consider an example. Suppose we obtained data from a study on high blood pressure. Such data normally includes information on each person's age, gender, weight and height, sporting activities, smoking and drinking habits. With a query tool, a user can select a specific variable, say smoking, that might affect the outcome, in our case blood pressure. The user's aim here is to compare the number of smokers and non-smokers among people with high blood pressure. However, by selecting this variable, the user *makes an assumption* that there is a strong correlation between high blood pressure and smoking.

With a data mining tool, instead of assuming certain relationships between different variables in a data set (and studying these relationships one at a time), we can determine the most significant factors that influence the outcome. Thus, instead of assuming a correlation between blood pressure and smoking, we can automatically identify the most significant risk factors. We can also examine different groups, or clusters, of people with high blood pressure. Data mining does not need any hypotheses – it discovers hidden relationships and patterns automatically.

Data mining is often compared to gold mining. Large quantities of ore must be processed before the gold can be extracted. Data mining can help us find the 'hidden gold' of knowledge in raw data.

Data mining usually starts with raw data and finishes with extracted knowledge. An overall process of turning raw data into knowledge is shown in Figure 10.1. This process includes five steps of data transformation.

The first step is **data selection** when the data relevant to the analysis is decided on and multiple data sources are identified. Because the data we might need can be stored in a variety of different formats such as text files, relational tables and spreadsheets, and often distributed across many databases, this step is perhaps the most time consuming in the entire process of data mining.

The second step includes **data fusing** and **data cleaning** (also known as **data cleansing**). At this stage all the relevant data is retrieved from the target

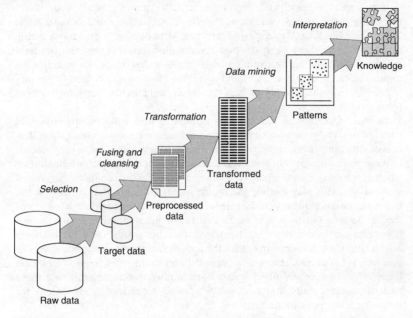

Figure 10.1 The process of data mining and knowledge discovery

databases and integrated in a common source. Redundant and inconsistent data is removed from the collection.

The third step is **data transformation**, also known as **data consolidation**. It is a stage when the cleansed data is transformed into forms suitable for data mining.

These three steps of the data mining process are often grouped together and identified as **preprocessing**. The purpose of preprocessing is simply to transform the raw data into a format appropriate for subsequent data mining.

The fourth step is **data mining** itself, the crucial stage when a variety of data mining techniques is applied to extract information potentially useful to the user.

The fifth and final step is **interpretation** of the results, the stage when the discovered knowledge is presented to the user in the form he or she can easily understand and use. This final stage is often associated with the process of integrating data mining into decision-support systems.

How is data mining applied in practice?

Although data mining is still largely a new, evolving field, it has already found numerous applications in banking, finance, marketing and telecommunications. Many companies use data mining today, but refuse to talk about it.

A few areas in which data mining is used for strategic benefits are direct marketing, trend analysis and fraud detection (Abramowicz and Zurada, 2001; Witten and Frank, 2005). In direct marketing, data mining is used for targeting people who are most likely to buy certain products and services. In trend analysis, it is used to determine trends in the marketplace, for example by modelling the stock market. In fraud detection, data mining is used to identify insurance claims, mobile phone calls and credit card purchases that are the most likely to be fraudulent.

In most applications, data mining is used to find and describe structural patterns in data, generalise, and make accurate predictions. A classical application of data mining is credit analysis for small business loans. Banks keep records of their loans, both current and historical. Apart from the loan details, including whether the loan was repaid on time, a loan record contains secondary information. This may include the recent profits and outstanding debts of the business, the credit history of the owner, and so on. In order to reduce the risk of 'bad' or defaulted loans, a bank manager may attempt to mine the bank's records hoping to find some meaningful patterns. In other words, the bank manager attempts to learn decision criteria for the appraisal of new loan applications. The goal here is to establish the patterns that distinguish the cases of 'good' or repaid loans from 'bad' or defaulted loans. Data mining techniques can find these patterns automatically and thus make a more accurate risk assessment for incoming loan applications.

What are data mining techniques?

Data mining is a practical subject, and as such tends to use any technique that helps to extract more knowledge from available data. In fact, data mining is often regarded as an 'anything goes' affair – it uses anything from statistical methods and query tools to sophisticated machine learning techniques. Most of the intelligent techniques used in data mining have already been discussed in this book. Data mining is not so much a single method but a heterogeneous group of different tools and techniques. This group includes the following:

- Statistical methods and data visualisation tools.
- Query tools.
- On-line analytical processing (OLAP).
- Decision trees and association rules.
- Neural networks and neuro-fuzzy systems.

Success of data mining often depends on the choice of the data mining tool. A preliminary investigation of the data can help us understand its specific characteristics, and thus select an appropriate data analysis technique. This preliminary process is known as **data exploration**. Data exploration includes summary statistics, visualisation, principal component analysis, query tools and OLAP (Witten and Frank, 2005; Tan *et al.*, 2006).

10.2 Statistical methods and data visualisation

Visualisation is a very useful data exploration technique for discovering patterns in data sets. **Data visualisation** can be defined as the representation of information in a graphical or tabular form (Tan *et al.*, 2006). Once the information is visualised, we can interpret and understand it. In everyday life, we often use data visualisation tools such as graphs, histograms and diagrams to present election results or changes in the stock market. People absorb visual information quickly and easily because the brain has very powerful pattern processing abilities, evolved over millions of years. Visualisation is particularly important in the initial stages of data exploration.

Visualisation is a data-driven technique of data mining. We visualise data in order to reveal patterns, relationships and trends hidden within our data. It is the patterns found in the data that give rise to a hypothesis.

What software packages are available for visualising information about data?

Several software packages are available for both personal computers and mainframe machines. Among the most popular packages are Statistical Analysis System (SAS), Statgraphics, Minitab and MATLAB Statistics Toolbox. These packages have a wide range of basic and advanced statistical analysis and visualisation capabilities.

Many graphical data exploration techniques rely on **summary statistics**. Summary statistics can be defined as a set of values that represents various characteristics of data, such as **mean**, **median**, **mode**, **range** and **standard deviation** (Montgomery *et al.*, 2001). We should note, however, that although summary statistics provide useful information about the data, their limitations must be well understood. A classical example is the **average income**. The average (or mean) income of a population may lead us to believe that it represents the income of *most* people. In fact, however, the average is much higher than most people's income because of the high-income earners, the outliers, such as Bill Gates. To assist in identifying such outliers, it is often necessary to use data visualisation techniques.

Graphical data representation methods include dot diagrams, stemplots, histograms and box plots (Hand *et al.*, 2001). However, the most popular visualisation technique used in statistical analysis is a scatter plot. A **scatter plot** (also known as a scattergram) is a two-dimensional graph for representing the degree of correlation between two variables. The data is represented as a collection of points. The position of each point on the horizontal axis is determined by one variable and on the vertical axis by the other variable (Utts, 2004). For example, to display a correlation between a man's height (the first variable) and his weight (the second variable), we first select a group of men (a sample set), measure their heights and weights and then plot the data related to each man in a two-dimensional coordinate system assigning 'height' to the x-axis and 'weight' to the y-axis.

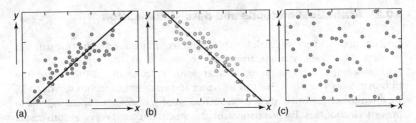

Figure 10.2 Scatter plots: (a) positive correlation; (b) negative correlation; (c) null correlation

A scatter plot can indicate different types of correlations. If the dots are scattered from lower left to upper right, there is a **positive** correlation, but if they are scattered from upper left to lower right, there is a **negative** correlation. A line of best fit can be drawn to study such correlations. A scatter plot can, however, also demonstrate that there is no correlation (or a **null** correlation) between two variables being studied. Figure 10.2 shows examples of scatter plots.

Scatter plots are particularly useful when we deal with a large number of data points. In a preliminary investigation of data, scatter plots often help us to reveal complex relationships between variables and to discover patterns and outliers.

Let us now inspect the plots shown in Figures 10.2(a) and (b) more thoroughly. Both plots show that a great majority of points are scattered randomly around straight lines. These lines can be represented by linear equations of the form

$$y = \beta_0 + \beta_1 x \tag{10.1}$$

where x is the **independent** variable (also called input variable or **regressor**) – it is the variable being manipulated; y is the **dependent** variable (also called output variable or **regressand**) – it is the observed result of the independent variable manipulation; and β_0 and β_1 are obtained through a process called **regression**, and are called the **regression coefficients**.

The term 'regression' was introduced in the 19th century by Sir Francis Galton, a Victorian anthropologist and eugenicist. He was the first to apply statistical methods to study anthropological differences between human communities. In his study, Galton demonstrated that the heights of offspring of tall ancestors tend to regress down towards an average (Galton, 1877). Later his work was extended into a more general statistical context.

In data mining, regression can be defined as a statistical technique for finding a mathematical equation that best fits the data. The simplest form of regression is linear regression – it uses a straight line to fit the data. Thus, Eq. (10.1) determines appropriate values for β_0 and β_1 to predict the value of y based on a given value of x. Advanced regression models, such as multiple regression, can use several input variables and allow the fitting of non-linear equations, including exponential, logarithmic, quadratic and gaussian functions (Seber and Wild, 1989).

Equation (10.1) presents the dependent variable y as a linear function of the regressor x. However, as we can see from Figures 10.2(a) and (b), the actual values of the variable y do not fall precisely on a straight line; this is just our assumption that the linear function can fit all the data. In fact, each actual value of the dependent variable y is determined by Eq. (10.1) plus a random error, ε. Thus, for n pairs of observations $(x_1, y_1), (x_2, y_2), \ldots, (x_n, y_n)$, we have

$$y_i = \beta_0 + \beta_1 x_i + \varepsilon_i, \qquad i = 1, 2, \ldots, n \tag{10.2}$$

where β_0 and β_1 are unknown regression coefficients, and ε_i is a random error with mean zero and variance σ^2.

How do we determine regression coefficients?

For a linear regression model, the right regression coefficients should result in a straight line that represents the 'best fit' to the data. The criterion for estimating the 'best fit' is based on the method of least squares. The least-squares estimates of the intercept, $\hat{\beta}_0$, and the slope $\hat{\beta}_1$ of the line are determined as

$$\hat{\beta}_1 = \frac{\sum_{i=1}^{n} y_i x_i - \left[\left(\sum_{i=1}^{n} y_i \right) \left(\sum_{i=1}^{n} x_i \right) \Big/ n \right]}{\sum_{i=1}^{n} x_i^2 - \left[\left(\sum_{i=1}^{n} x_i \right)^2 \Big/ n \right]} \tag{10.3}$$

and

$$\hat{\beta}_0 = \bar{y} - \hat{\beta}_1 \bar{x} \tag{10.4}$$

where

$$\bar{y} = \frac{\sum_{i=1}^{n} y_i}{n} \quad \text{and} \quad \bar{x} = \frac{\sum_{i=1}^{n} x_i}{n}$$

Therefore, the fitted regression line is defined as

$$\hat{y} = \hat{\beta}_0 + \hat{\beta}_1 x \tag{10.5}$$

Now, we can rewrite Eq. (10.2) in the following form:

$$y_i = \hat{\beta}_0 + \hat{\beta}_1 x_i + e_i, \quad i = 1, 2, \ldots, n \tag{10.6}$$

where $e_i = y_i - \hat{y}_i$ is called the **residual**. Residuals represent the error in the fit of the model to the actual data, and, thus, provide a good indication of the model's accuracy.

How do outliers affect a linear regression model?

Outliers, especially those located far away from most of the data, can dramatically change the position of the regression line (the least-squares estimates are dragged towards the outliers). As an illustration, we consider the data set given in Table 10.1 (Daniel and Wood, 1999). Measurements are taken at a chemical plant, and the set contains 20 samples. The independent variable, x, is the acid number of a chemical determined by titration, and the dependent variable, y, is its organic acid content determined by extraction and weighing. The aim here is to determine how well values obtained by the relatively inexpensive titration method can serve to estimate those obtained by the more expensive extraction and weighing technique.

The scatter plot shown in Figure 10.3(a) suggests a strong statistical correlation between the acid number determined by titration and the organic acid content determined by extraction and weighing. Thus, we can reasonably assume a linear model, calculate the least-squares estimates, $\hat{\beta}_0$ and $\hat{\beta}_1$, and then substitute the obtained values into Eq. (10.5) of the fitted regression line:

$$\hat{y} = 35.4583 + 0.3216x$$

Table 10.1 Pilot-plant data (Daniel and Wood, 1999)

Observation	Independent variable: acid number	Dependent variable: organic acid content
1	123	76
2	109	70
3	62	55
4	104	71
5	57	55
6	37	48
7	44	50
8	100	66
9	16	41
10	28	43
11	138	82
12	105	68
13	159	88
14	75	58
15	88	64
16	164	88
17	169	89
18	167	88
19	149	84
20	167	88

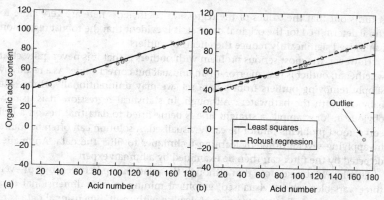

Figure 10.3 Effect of outliers on the regression line: (a) original data and the least-squares regression line; (b) influence of the outlier

Using this regression model, we can predict the organic acid content based on the acid number. For example, if the acid number is $x = 150$, then the estimated value of the organic acid content is

$$\hat{y} = 35.4583 + 0.3216 \cdot 150 = 83.6983$$

Although this estimate is, of course, subject to error, the method of least squares does provide us with a reasonable prediction model.

Suppose now that one of the observations was recorded incorrectly. For instance, the y value of the 17th observation was written down as -8 instead of 89. This error significantly affects the position of the regression line, as can be seen in Figure 10.3(b). The least-squares regression line is now defined by the following equation:

$$\hat{y} = 44.0528 + 0.1911x$$

How can we address the problem of outliers?

Outliers are often caused by noisy data, so statisticians usually attempt to check the data and remove the detected outliers. In simple linear regression models, a visual detection of outliers is also possible.

Although outliers dramatically affect the regression, we can still reduce their influence by applying so-called **robust** regression. Robust regression uses the least median of squares instead of the least squares (Rousseeuw and Leroy, 2003). The regression line defined by the method of least median of squares is shown in Figure 10.3(b). The fitted regression model is represented by the following equation:

$$\hat{y} = 35.3950 + 0.3226x$$

It turns out that the values of the regression coefficients here are very close to those determined for the original data set. It is evident that the robust regression can indeed significantly reduce the effects of outliers.

However, the most serious problem with outliers is that it is never quite clear whether an outlier is just an error, or an unusual but correct value. As a result, by simply removing outliers from a data set, we may unintentionally 'throw the baby out with the bathwater'. Although, in statistical regression, it is usually obvious if, for example, a straight line is being fitted to data that lies on a bell curve, most problems cannot be easily visualised. A solution can often be found by applying several different learning techniques to filter the data. Anomalies detected by the filter can then be examined by a human expert.

Finally, we should note that although the relationship between two or even three variables can be visualised, graphical mining in high-dimensional data presents a real challenge. One way of dealing with multidimensional data is to reduce the number of dimensions.

How can we reduce the dimensionality of data without losing important information?

In multidimensional data, it is not uncommon to discover that some variables are highly correlated with each other. In other words, there could be a significant redundancy in the information provided by the variables. In the extreme case of two perfectly correlated variables, say x and y, one of them is redundant since if we know the value of x, the value of y can easily be determined. A mathematical procedure that transforms a large number of correlated variables into a smaller number of uncorrelated variables is called **principal component analysis** (PCA). PCA can reduce the dimensionality of data without significant loss of information. PCA is applied in such areas as face recognition and image compression. It is also a common technique used in data mining for finding patterns in large multidimensional data sets.

10.3   Principal component analysis

PCA is a common method used in statistics for maximising the information content in high-dimensional data (Jolliffe, 2002). It was first introduced by Karl Pearson over a century ago (Pearson, 1901). In mathematical terms, PCA finds a set of m orthogonal vectors in the data space that represents the largest variance, and then projects the data from its original n-dimensional space into the m-dimensional subspace, where $m \ll n$, thereby reducing the data dimensionality. In other words, a large number of correlated variables are transformed into a smaller number of uncorrelated variables called **principal components**. In data mining, PCA is often used as a data preprocessing technique.

As an illustration, let us consider the two-dimensional (bivariate) data set shown in Figure 10.4. Figure 10.4(a) represents the set within the horizontal $X1$ and the vertical $Y1$ axes. By projecting the data points onto each of the two axes, we obtain density plots. Figure 10.4(b) shows the same data set within the

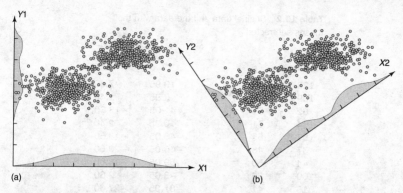

Figure 10.4 An application of PCA: (a) projecting data onto the axes $X1$ and $Y1$; (b) projecting data onto the axes $X2$ and $Y2$

rotated axes $X2$ and $Y2$ resulted from the application of PCA to this set. We see that by projecting the data points onto the axis $X2$, we capture the fact that the data set is *bimodal* (with two peaks). By contrast, the bimodal nature of this data set is completely obscured when it is projected onto the axis $Y2$. Clusters are more likely to be distinguished by projecting data in the high-variance direction (axis $X2$) than in the low-variance one (axis $Y2$). By projecting data in a high-variance direction, we can retain most of the information, and thus can reduce the data dimensionality.

In this example, the cluster structure of the data set was evident from the beginning. However, in the case of high-dimensional data sets, the intrinsic nature of the data is usually concealed and to reveal it we must perform PCA.

How does PCA work?

First, we calculate a **covariance matrix** of our data represented within the original coordinates. Then, we determine the eigenvalues and eigenvectors of the covariance matrix. Eigenvectors represent the axes of the transformed space, sorted in order of eigenvalues. Each eigenvalue shows the variance along its axis – the greater the variance, the more information is preserved along this axis. Finally, we project the original data onto the transformed space formed by the eigenvectors with the largest eigenvalues.

Let us demonstrate how PCA works on a simple example. We will use a two-dimensional data set and show what PCA is doing at each step.

Step 1:   *Obtain data and subtract the mean*
               In this example, we will use the data set given in Table 10.1. For PCA, we need to subtract the mean of the data dimension from each data value in this dimension. In our case, $\bar{x} = 103.05$ and $\bar{y} = 68.60$. Table 10.2 presents the normalised data set with the means subtracted.

Table 10.2 Original data and the data with the means subtracted

x	y	x − x̄	y − ȳ
123	76	19.95	7.40
109	70	5.95	1.40
62	55	−41.05	−13.60
104	71	0.95	2.40
57	55	−46.05	−13.60
37	48	−66.05	−20.60
44	50	−59.05	−18.60
100	66	−3.05	−2.60
16	41	−87.05	−27.60
28	43	−75.05	−25.60
138	82	34.95	13.40
105	68	1.95	−0.60
159	88	55.95	19.40
75	58	−28.05	−10.60
88	64	−15.05	−4.60
164	88	60.95	19.40
169	89	65.95	20.40
167	88	63.95	19.40
149	84	45.95	15.40
167	88	63.95	19.40

Step 2: **Calculate the covariance matrix**

Covariance is a measure of the linear relationship between two variables. While variance operates on a single variable only, covariance is measured between two variables. For example, for a three-dimensional data set, we can measure covariance between the x and y dimensions, the x and z dimensions and the y and z dimensions.

Variance and covariance are closely related. The equation for variance can be expressed as

$$\text{var}(x) = \frac{\sum_{i=1}^{n}(x_i - \bar{x})^2}{n} = \frac{\sum_{i=1}^{n}(x_i - \bar{x})(x_i - \bar{x})}{n} \quad (10.7)$$

We can then replace the second set of parentheses with the term $(y_i - \bar{y})$, and obtain the equation for covariance:

$$\text{cov}(x, y) = \frac{\sum_{i=1}^{n}(x_i - \bar{x})(y_i - \bar{y})}{n} \quad (10.8)$$

Note that the covariance of any variable with itself is that variable's variance:

$$\text{cov}(x,x) = \frac{\sum_{i=1}^{n}(x_i - \bar{x})(x_i - \bar{x})}{n} = \frac{\sum_{i=1}^{n}(x_i - \bar{x})^2}{n} = \text{var}(x) \qquad (10.9)$$

A positive value of covariance indicates that two variables are correlated positively. Likewise, a negative value implies that two variables are correlated negatively. Zero covariance means that two variables are independent from each other, or uncorrelated. The absolute value of covariance serves also as a measure of data redundancy.

It is common to represent the covariance between all possible pairs of a given multidimensional data set as a square matrix called a **covariance matrix**. The covariance matrix is symmetric with respect to the main diagonal. The diagonal elements are the variances within particular dimensions and the off-diagonal elements are the covariances between dimensions. Since the data used in our example is two dimensional, the covariance matrix is a 2×2 matrix:

$$\mathbf{C} = \begin{bmatrix} \text{cov}(x,x) & \text{cov}(x,y) \\ \text{cov}(y,x) & \text{cov}(y,y) \end{bmatrix} = \begin{bmatrix} \text{var}(x) & \text{cov}(x,y) \\ \text{cov}(y,x) & \text{var}(y) \end{bmatrix}$$

$$= \begin{bmatrix} 2580.7 & 830.0 \\ 830.0 & 268.4 \end{bmatrix}$$

The non-diagonal elements in this matrix are positive, which indicates that both variables, x and y, follow the same trend.

Step 3: *Calculate eigenvalues and eigenvectors of the covariance matrix*
Eigenvalues and **eigenvectors** are properties of a square matrix. Let A be a positive-definite symmetric square matrix. Then A can be diagonalised by a matrix of its orthonormal eigenvectors as

$$\mathbf{A} = \mathbf{E}\mathbf{\Lambda}\mathbf{E}^T \qquad (10.10)$$

where E is an $n \times n$ orthonormal matrix, T denotes matrix transposition, and Λ is an $n \times n$ diagonal matrix defined by the eigenvalues

$$\mathbf{\Lambda} = \begin{bmatrix} \lambda_1 & 0 & \cdots & 0 \\ 0 & \lambda_2 & \cdots & 0 \\ \vdots & \vdots & \ddots & \vdots \\ 0 & 0 & \cdots & \lambda_n \end{bmatrix} \qquad (10.11)$$

The associated eigenvectors form the columns of the matrix E:

$$\mathbf{E} = [e_1 \; e_2 \; \cdots \; e_n] \qquad (10.12)$$

From Eq. (10.10), it follows that

$$AE = E\Lambda \tag{10.13}$$

or, equivalently,

$$Ae_i = \lambda_i e_i, \quad i = 1, 2, \ldots, n \tag{10.14}$$

where e_i is the ith eigenvector associated with the ith eigenvalue λ_i.
If we arrange the eigenvalues in decreasing order such that

$$\lambda_1 > \lambda_2 > \ldots > \lambda_i > \ldots > \lambda_n$$

the associated eigenvectors will reveal directions of the principal components in order of their significance. Thus, the vector e_1 will represent the axis along which multidimensional data has the highest variance.

How can we find eigenvalues?

If a square matrix A is small (no bigger than 4×4), we can find the determinant

$$\det(A - \lambda I) = 0 \tag{10.15}$$

and then expand it into a characteristic polynomial. By finding roots of this characteristic polynomial, we can find the eigenvalues of the matrix A. We cannot, however, solve a polynomial of order greater than 4 by a finite sequence of arithmetic operations, and, hence, iterative methods are normally used (Wilkinson, 1988).

Let us now calculate the eigenvalues and eigenvectors for the covariance matrix C determined earlier (in our calculations, we use MATLAB). The eigenvalues and associated eigenvectors are arranged in decreasing order

$$\text{eigenvalues} = \begin{bmatrix} 2847.7 \\ 1.3 \end{bmatrix}; \quad \text{eigenvectors} = \begin{bmatrix} -0.9519 & 0.3063 \\ -0.3063 & -0.9519 \end{bmatrix}$$

Thus,

$$\lambda_1 = 2847.7 \text{ and } e_1 = \begin{bmatrix} -0.9519 \\ -0.3063 \end{bmatrix}; \quad \lambda_2 = 1.3 \text{ and } e_2 = \begin{bmatrix} 0.3063 \\ -0.9519 \end{bmatrix}$$

Figure 10.5 represents a plot of the normalised pilot-plant data (means subtracted) within the axes formed by the eigenvectors e_1 and e_2. We can see that one of the eigenvectors, e_1, represents a line of best fit. This eigenvector reveals the most important pattern in the data. The second eigenvector, e_2, shows the other, less important, pattern – all points are located slightly off the line of best fit.

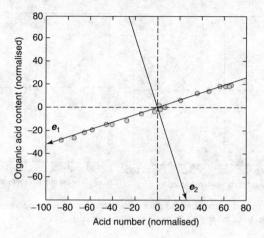

Figure 10.5 A plot of the normalised pilot-plant data within the axes formed by the eigenvectors e_1 and e_2

Eigenvectors of the covariance matrix provide us with the axes of the transformed space. Now we need to represent our data in terms of these eigenvectors.

Step 4: *Choose components and derive a new data set*

Once a set of eigenvalues is determined and arranged in decreasing order, we can ignore the eigenvalues of lesser significance, and thereby reduce the dimensionality of the original data set. For example, if the original data set was n dimensional, and so we obtained n eigenvalues, we could decide to keep only m largest eigenvalues. The m associated eigenvectors would form the columns of a matrix called a **feature vector**. Then, we could project the original data onto the **feature space** formed by the feature vector, and thus transform the original n-dimensional data set into the m-dimensional one. To project a data set onto a feature space, we simply multiply the normalised original data set by the feature vector. This method of data transformation is known as **subspace decomposition** (Oja, 1983).

If we compare the eigenvalues obtained in our example, we can see that they are very different. Because $\lambda_1 \gg \lambda_2$, the second eigenvalue may be discarded, and thus our data set can become one dimensional.

Let us now evaluate two possible cases of the data transformation – when we keep both eigenvalues and when only the largest eigenvalue is used. In the first case, we obtain the plot shown in Figure 10.6(a). Because no information has been lost in this transformation, the plot represents the normalised original data

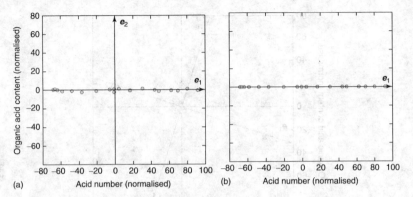

Figure 10.6 Plots of the normalised data projected onto the feature space formed by: (a) both eigenvectors, e_1 and e_2; (b) a single eigenvector, e_1

within rotated axes e_1 and e_2. In fact, we find the same plot as was shown in Figure 10.5. In the second case, when we keep only the first largest eigenvalue, we obtain the plot shown in Figure 10.6(b). We can see that this is effectively a one-dimensional plot – all data variances caused by the second eigenvector have been removed.

How can we get the original data back?

We need to remember that by removing principal components of lesser significance, we lose some information. So, unless we keep *all* the eigenvectors in our transformation, we cannot retrieve the original data unchanged – some information will be lost.

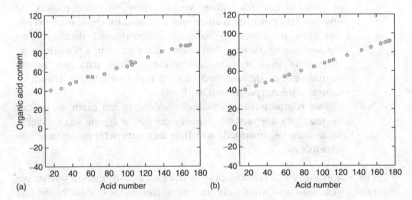

Figure 10.7 Plots of the reconstructed pilot-plant data derived using: (a) both eigenvectors e_1 and e_2; (b) a single eigenvector e_1

In general, the original n-dimensional data set is reconstructed by multiplying the transformed m-dimensional data by the transpose of the m-dimensional feature vector and adding the mean of the data dimension to each data value in this dimension. Figure 10.7(a) shows a plot created with the data reconstructed by the complete feature vector. As expected, we obtained the same plot as in Figure 10.3(a). Figure 10.7(b) demonstrates the effect of the *reduced* feature vector. We notice that while the data variation along the principal eigenvector e_1 is retained, the variation along the eigenvector e_2 has gone.

Case study 11: Dimensionality reduction

I want to develop an intelligent tool for determining cholesterol levels directly from measurements of the spectral content of a blood serum sample without the need for separating cholesterol fractions. I have a set of wavelength measurements as well as reference measurements of cholesterol in lipoprotein fractions. What data mining technique should I use to solve this problem?

Current practice of cholesterol measurements is based on separating cholesterol into high-density (HDL), low-density (LDL) and very low-density (VLDL) lipoprotein fractions using ultracentrifugation methods. Cholesterol concentration in each fraction is then calculated by analytical methods and the total cholesterol level is determined. Unfortunately, ultracentrifugation methods are expensive and time consuming.

It was suggested, however, that cholesterol levels could be measured directly by employing a derivatisation reaction that would produce a mixture of products coloured differently for each lipoprotein component (Purdie *et al.*, 1992). Then the mixture could be analysed for HDL, LDL and VLDL fractions directly using absorption spectrophotometry techniques. As a result, the separation of cholesterol into fractions would become unnecessary, thus eliminating the need for expensive ultracentrifugation methods.

In this case study, we have measurements of 21 wavelengths of the spectrum for 264 patients. For the same patients, we also have reference measurements of cholesterol in HDL, LDL and VLDL fractions obtained by the standard fraction separation method. It appears that a back-propagation neural network can be trained to predict cholesterol levels in HDL, LDL and VLDL fractions given the measurements of 21 wavelengths.

The entire data set (264 cases) is randomly divided into training (60 per cent), validation (20 per cent) and test (20 per cent) sets. A validation set can be used to stop training early – the network is trained on the training data until its performance on the validation data fails to improve for a number of consecutive epochs. This indicates that generalisation has reached its peak and training has to be stopped to avoid overfitting. The test data provides a completely independent test of the network performance.

For this case study, we create a three-layer network with a sigmoid activation function in the hidden layer and a linear activation function in the output layer.

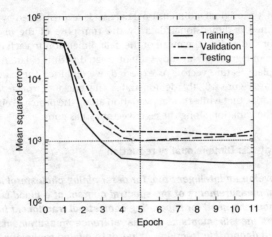

Figure 10.8 The ANN learning curve of the cholesterol-level prediction

The number of neurons in the input layer is determined by the number of wavelengths of the spectrum, so we need 21 input neurons. We want to predict three values (HDL, LDL and VLDL), and thus we should have three neurons in the output layer. A number of trials demonstrate that a good generalisation can be reached with just seven neurons in the hidden layer. Figure 10.8 represents the learning curve. It can be seen that the validation error reached its minimum at epoch 5, and as it did not improve over a specified number of subsequent epochs, the training was terminated. The learning curve demonstrates that the network has been trained successfully and overfitting has been avoided.

Let us now examine the network performance by presenting it with the test data and then performing regression analysis between the desired outputs and the actual outputs of the network. Figure 10.9 shows the results.

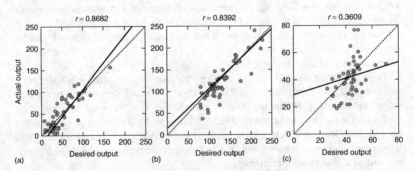

Figure 10.9 Scatter plots of the ANN outputs relative to targets: (a) HDL; (b) LDL; (c) VLDL

The r value, which appears on the top of each scatter plot, is the Pearson's correlation coefficient (the Pearson's r) – a measure of the correlation between two variables – X (desired output) and Y (actual output). The correlation coefficient can range from $+1$ (perfect positive correlation) to -1 (perfect negative correlation). The larger the r value, the stronger the association between the two variables and the more accurately we can predict the values of HDL, LDL and VLDL. As we can see, the first two outputs (HDL and LDL) are reasonably close to the desired outputs (the r values exceed 0.9), but the third output (VLDL) does not track the desired outputs well.

Of course, we could go on and try to improve the ANN accuracy by modifying its architecture or increasing the number of training epochs, but we would find that despite all our efforts the r value for VLDL could not improve significantly.

Can we use an ANFIS to improve the accuracy of the cholesterol-level prediction?

An ANFIS benefits from a sophisticated hybrid learning algorithm and can indeed demonstrate better performance than a classical back-propagation technique. However, it entails a large number of parameters, which are optimised during training. As a result, MATLAB can easily run out of memory trying to tune parameters of the Sugeno-type fuzzy inference system even when the number of inputs is relatively small. We should also keep in mind that an ANFIS can achieve good generalisation only if the size of training data is several times larger than the number of parameters being optimised. Therefore, before we can apply an ANFIS model to predict cholesterol levels, we need to reduce the number of inputs. This task can be accomplished by PCA.

We normalise the input data, calculate the covariance matrix, and obtain eigenvalues and eigenvectors. Table 10.3 contains eigenvalues (principal components) presented in decreasing order. Only the first seven principal components are shown as values of the consequent components become negligible. Now we need to decide how many principal components we should keep to capture most of the variability in the input data.

A simple solution is to visualise the relative importance of the principal components. A line segment plot that shows the fraction of total variance in the data as explained by each principal component is called a **scree plot**. Figure 10.10 shows such a plot. As you can see, the plot looks like the side of a mountain, where 'scree' refers to a slope of loose rocks accumulated at the base of the mountain. We can ignore principal components at the base because a

Table 10.3 Total variance explained by the principal components

Component number	1	2	3	4	5	6	7
Eigenvalue	0.225947	0.010530	0.000356	0.000175	0.000046	0.000031	0.000021
Fraction of the total variance, %	95.2883	4.4406	0.1500	0.0737	0.0193	0.0131	0.0088

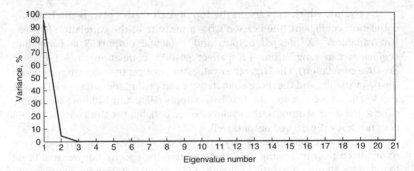

Figure 10.10 Scree plot for the 21-dimensional spectrum data set

sharp drop in the plot indicates that the subsequent components contribute little to the overall data variance. In Figure 10.10, the first principal component accounts for almost 95.29 per cent of the total variance in the 21 variables, the second for 4.44 per cent and the third for 0.15 per cent, while the remaining 18 components account for only 0.12 per cent of the total variance. This plot strongly suggests that only the first two eigenvalues represent meaningful variance in the input data – they account for more than 99 per cent of variability. Therefore, the dimensionality of the input vectors can be reduced from 21 to 2.

Now we can transform the original 21-dimensional data set into a two-dimensional one, train an ANFIS, and compare its performance with the ANN. Because the input vectors become two dimensional, we use an ANFIS with two neurons in the input layer. We should choose the smallest number of membership functions, and thus we assign two fuzzification neurons with a bell activation function to each input variable. Consequently the ANFIS will contain four fuzzy rules. As the ANFIS architecture permits only one output, we will use three identical models, each predicting cholesterol in a single lipoprotein fraction.

The total number of input and output parameters in each ANFIS model is 24, with 12 input parameters (two inputs; each input has two bell activation functions and each function has three parameters) and 12 output parameters (four rules; each rule is specified by three parameters).

For this study, we randomly split the transformed data into two sets: training (80 per cent) and test (20 per cent). Thus, the ratio between the number of parameters and the number of training cases presented to each ANFIS is about 1 to 8, which guarantees good generalisation.

Figure 10.11 shows the scatter plots of the ANFIS outputs relative to targets. All three ANFIS models were trained for 10 epochs with the same training data set, and then tested on the same test set. As we can see, the ANFIS models perform better than the ANN even though the former were trained on the reduced two-dimensional data set.

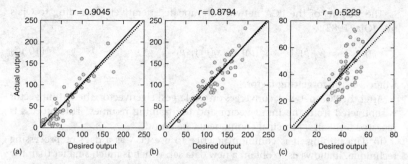

Figure 10.11 Scatter plots of the ANFIS outputs relative to targets: (a) HDL; (b) LDL; (c) VLDL

Can we implement PCA in a neural network?

Many specialised neural networks and learning algorithms have been applied to perform PCA. We can, for example, use a two-layer feedforward linear network where the input layer with n neurons represents n-dimensional space and the output layer with m neurons extracts m principal components. Such a network is called a PCA network and is shown in Figure 10.12.

Training a PCA neural network produces a weight vector w that is equal to the largest eigenvector e_1, so that the following condition is satisfied:

$$Ae_1 = \lambda_1 e_1 \tag{10.16}$$

where A is the input autocorrelation matrix.

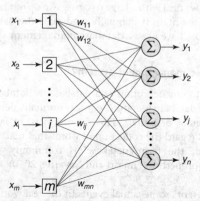

Figure 10.12 A PCA neural network

The weights of the PCA network are updated iteratively according to Oja's rule (Oja, 1982):

$$w_{ij}(p+1) = w_{ij}(p)\left[1 - \phi y_j^2(p)\right] + \phi x_i(p)\, y_j(p) \tag{10.17}$$

where ϕ is the forgetting factor.

After the PCA network converges on the largest eigenvector, the output vector is subtracted from the input vector and the training resumes. This process is repeated until all n principal components are found.

In data mining, it is common practice to use PCA as a data preprocessing technique. It allows us to obtain a new data set, which is much smaller than the original one, and yet produces the same (or almost the same) analytical results.

While statistical methods including PCA are often used as a first step in data exploration, database queries and OLAP represent more sophisticated tools developed specifically to deal with large quantities of data accumulated in modern organisations.

10.4 Relational databases and database queries

Many organisations collect and store massive amounts of data, and they need rapid access to that data in order to respond quickly to any change in the market.

How do modern organisations maintain large databases?

A database can be maintained manually but it can also be computerised. For example, we often maintain manually an indexed address book with names and contact details of our friends – we simply add new names and rewrite existing addresses and phone numbers when they change. Of course, we can use a personal organiser as an alternative to the 'old technology', and thus computerise our personal database.

However, when we deal with a large database, we do not have any alternative – we simply cannot maintain it manually, and need the database to be computerised. In other words, we need a **database management system**.

What is a database management system?

Let us first return to our definition of a database. A **database** is a collection of related data (in the database literature, context normally determines whether the word 'data' is singular or plural). This definition is, in fact, quite broad. For example, we could regard the collection of words that make up this chapter as a database. However, the term 'database' is commonly associated with the following implicit properties (Elmasri and Navathe, 2010):

- a database represents some actual events in the real world;
- a database is a logical collection of data with some specific meaning;

- a database is built for some intended applications and thus has an intended group of users.

A database must be organised and managed so that a user can update data in the database as well as search for and retrieve desired subsets of data. A set of programs that enables a user to create and maintain a database is called a **database management system** (DBMS). The DBMS makes creating, populating, manipulating and sharing the database among various users and applications possible. **Creating** a database involves defining the database structure, and specifying types and constraints of the data to be stored. **Populating** a database means entering data into the database and storing it on some storage medium. **Manipulating** a database usually includes such functions as updating the database, querying for some specific data, and generating reports. **Sharing** a database implies providing multiple users with concurrent access to the database.

For making informed decisions, database users need rapid access to a large volume of data. In organisations, data is often stored in a collection of tables and spreadsheets. A set of formally described tables from which data can be accessed or reassembled without having to reorganise the tables themselves is called a **relational database**. The relational database model was first introduced by Ted Codd of IBM in 1970 in his paper 'A relational model of data for large shared data banks' (Codd, 1970). Since the early 1980s, the model has been implemented in many commercial DBMSs such as Oracle and Rdb (from Oracle), Informix Dynamic Server (from IBM) and SQL Server and Access (from Microsoft).

In a relational database, each table (called a **relation**) is assigned a unique name. All tables are divided into columns and rows. Columns (or fields) specify **attributes** of a table, and rows (called **tuples**) store values of these attributes. When a table is created, the user needs to describe formally the data type associated with each column. Typical data types are: **character** (holds a string of letters, numbers and special characters of a fixed or variable length, such as 'DC086421'), **integer** (holds an integer such as 14), **decimal** (holds a decimal number such as 5.65), **date** (holds a date such as '2010-10-22') and **time** (holds a time such as '11:52:12').

It is relatively easy to create and access a relational database, but even more importantly, it is easy to extend it. After the original database is created, a new data attribute can be added without the need to modify any existing application.

Consider a simple example. Figure 10.13 shows fragments of relations *Item*, *Customer*, *Employee* and *Transaction* of the relational database *Department_store*. The table *Item* has columns *Item_ID*, *Category*, *Brand*, *Model*, *Description*, *Price* and *Stock*. Here the data type of the attribute *Item_ID* is declared as char(8), so the column *Item_ID* would hold strings of a fixed length, eight characters each. The data type of *Category* is varchar(15), so it would contain strings of a *variable* size with a maximum length of 15 characters. The data type of *Price* is decimal (6,2), so it would hold decimal numbers, each with a maximum of six digits and two digits to the right of the decimal point. The data type of *Stock* is int(4), so it would hold *int*egers with a maximum of four digits. Similarly, we declare

Item

Item_ID	Category	Brand	Model	Description	Price	Stock
DC086421	Digital Camera	Canon	Rebel Xsi	12.2 MP/18-55 mm	899.84	121
DC086532	Digital Camera	Nikon	D80	10.2 MP/18-135 mm	1074.84	64
...	...	...	...	...	...	...

Customer

Customer_ID	Name	Age	ZIP_code	State	Address	Income
016745	Smith, Alex	56	4851	NY	106 1st Ave, New York	95000
016749	Green, Jane	19	1419	NY	7 Lake Ave, Rochester	32000
...	...	...	...	...	...	...

Employee

Employee_ID	Name	Age	Department	Job_category	Salary	Commission
032E	Jones, Mary	26	Electronics	Sales	37500	3
037H	Brown, Mark	21	Hardware	Sales	29500	2
...	...	...	...	...	...	...

Transaction

Trans_ID	Item_ID	Payment	Date	Time	Customer_ID	Employee_ID
045728	DC086421	Visa	2008-10-22	11:52:12	016745	032E
...	...	...	...	...	...	...

Figure 10.13 Fragments of relations of the relational database *Department_store*

the data types of all other attributes in the tables *Customer*, *Employee* and *Transaction*.

In a relational database, tables are 'related' to each other. This ensures that data can be joined together across the tables without repeating all the data in every table. In our example, the table *Transaction* includes attributes *Item_ID*, *Customer_ID* and *Employee_ID*, which are also the attributes of the tables *Item*, *Customer* and *Employee*, respectively.

However, for effective data management it is not sufficient to describe the data structure of a relational database and populate its relations with data. We also need to be able to specify, access and retrieve any subset of data from the database for further analysis.

How can we retrieve data from a relational database?

Data in a relational database can be accessed using database **queries**. These queries are written in Structured Query Language (SQL). SQL is formed by a command language that allows the retrieval, insertion, updating, and deletion of data. SQL is both an ANSI (American National Standards Institute) and ISO (International Organization for Standardization) standard computer language for accessing and manipulating database systems.

SELECT * FROM Item
WHERE Category = 'Digital Camera' AND Brand = 'Nikon'

Item_ID	Category	Brand	Model	Description	Price	Stock
DC086527	Digital Camera	Nikon	L18	8.0 MP/3 × Zoom	139.84	186
DC086532	Digital Camera	Nikon	D80	10.2 MP/18-135 mm	1074.84	64
...	...	...	...	...	...	...

Figure 10.14   An example of the SQL query carried out on a single table

The first version of SQL, called SEQUEL, was developed by Donald Chamberlin and Raymond Boyce of IBM in the early 1970s (Chamberlin and Boyce, 1974). It was designed for IBM System R, the first prototype relational database system. Later SQL was formally standardised by the ANSI and since then has become an essential part of most commercial DBMSs. Although there are many different versions of SQL now, they all support the same major keywords (such as SELECT, FROM, WHERE, UPDATE, DELETE, INSERT, AND, OR and NOT).

In the examples below, we will use the MySQL Database System (Forta, 2005; DuBois, 2008). The MySQL software is available either as an open source product (the most popular open source database system) or can be purchased as a standard commercial licence. The program runs as a server providing multi-user access to a number of databases.

With SQL, we can query relational databases and retrieve specified subsets of data. Suppose that a store manager wants to check current stocks of Nikon digital cameras. The manager can access the database using a simple query shown in Figure 10.14, and thereby obtain the desired subset of data. In this query, we immediately see two keywords SELECT and FROM. In fact, the most basic SQL query looks as follows:

SELECT column_name FROM table_name

The query selects the content of the column named *column_name* from the table called *table_name*. Note that multiple column names can be used, as well as multiple table names. The result is stored in a result table (called the *result-set*).

In the query shown in Figure 10.14, instead of the column name, we use the symbol * to select all columns of the table *Item*. However, the store manager wants to retrieve stocks of only Nikon digital cameras. To do this, a WHERE clause is added to the SELECT statement. The query returns a list of all records of the table *Item* where the value of the attribute *Category* is 'Digital Camera' and the value of the attribute *Brand* is 'Nikon'. Note that selection conditions listed in the WHERE clause can be separated by the keywords AND, OR and NOT. This example demonstrates that a relational query operates as a filter and allows the user to retrieve a subset of data by specifying constraints for the selected attributes.

In most cases, however, we have to retrieve data from two or more tables. Suppose the store manager needs to see results of a recent promotion of VistaQuest compact digital cameras. This information can be retrieved from

```
SELECT Item.Brand, Item.Model, Item.Price, Transaction.Date
FROM Item, Transaction
WHERE Transaction.Item_ID=Item.Item_ID
AND Item.Brand='VistaQuest'
AND Transaction.Date between '2010-10-23' and curdate()
```

Brand	Model	Price	Date
VistaQuest	VQ-7024	69.84	2010-10-23
VistaQuest	VQ-5115 Pink	54.84	2010-10-23
VistaQuest	VQ-5015 Silver	54.84	2010-10-23
VistaQuest	VQ-7024	69.84	2010-10-23
VistaQuest	VQ-5115 Blue	54.84	2010-10-24
VistaQuest	VQ-7024	69.84	2010-10-24
...	...	...	...

Figure 10.15 An example of the SQL query carried out on multiple tables

two tables, *Item* and *Transaction*. As we can see from Figure 10.13, these two tables have a common attribute, *Item_ID*, and thus we can extract data from both tables by matching their *Item_ID* columns. Figure 10.15 shows the SQL query and obtained result-set. In this query, the FROM clause is used to join the tables. Because the same column names may occur in different tables, we must specify which table we mean when referring to the column. This is done by using the table name as a prefix followed by the dot and the name of the column, as seen in the SELECT clause of the query. The WHERE clause states that the two tables have to be matched by their respective *Item_ID* attributes. The BETWEEN ... AND operator is used to select a range of data between two dates, 2010-10-23 and the *current date*.

The query returns a list of VistaQuest cameras sold since the beginning of the promotion campaign. The result table, in fact, can include hundreds or even thousands of rows. Unfortunately, such a table may not be very useful – what the manager actually needs is the summary table, which includes the total number of cameras sold. This can be achieved by using the SQL built-in aggregate functions for counting and calculations such as AVG (returns the average value of a column), COUNT (returns the number of rows of a column), MAX (returns the highest value of a column), MIN (returns the lowest value of a column) and SUM (returns the total sum of a column). Figure 10.16 shows the SQL query that uses COUNT and SUM functions. The GROUP BY clause is added to specify that the SUM function has to be executed for each unique *Model* value. Using the result-set, the store manager can now examine the outcomes of the promotion campaign by comparing current sales of VistaQuest cameras with sales before the promotion started.

What is the difference between database queries and data mining?

A database query can be considered as data mining in its basic form. Queries do provide the user with the opportunity to question relational databases and retrieve subsets of data according to specified conditions. For example, using

```
SELECT Item.Brand, Item.Model, COUNT(Item.Model), SUM(Item.Price)
FROM Item, Transaction
WHERE Transaction.Item_ID=Item.Item_ID
AND Item.brand='VistaQuest'
AND Transaction.Date between '2010-10-23' and curdate()
GROUP BY Model
```

Brand	Model	COUNT(Item.Model)	SUM(Item.Price)
VistaQuest	VQ-5015 Silver	34	1864.56
VistaQuest	VQ-5115 Blue	42	2303.28
VistaQuest	VQ-5115 Pink	39	2138.76
VistaQuest	VQ-7024	93	6495.12
...	...	...	...

Figure 10.16   An example of the SQL query with aggregate functions

relational queries, we can extract such information as a list of all items sold last month; total sales grouped by category, brand or model; a list of customers who spent in excess of $1000 over the past 12 months; or a list of employees whose sales were over $10,000 in the last month. In fact, we can go even further.

Suppose we want to conduct a targeted campaign to promote a new product. For a promotion to be successful, we need to know the main characteristics of potential customers such as age, income, marital status, suburb, home ownership, debts, etc. Surely, we can use our databases and pull out a list of customers who bought similar products in the past. Using the SQL aggregate functions, we can determine the average age, average income and average debt of a potential customer. If the result-set is not very big, we might also identify some common characteristics among our potential customers, for example home ownership. However, all this information may not reveal actual clusters of people we want to find – young people with high incomes and large debts might be interested in the same product as older people with low incomes and small debts. Data mining can discover these hidden clusters automatically.

Database queries are *assumption based* – a user must ask the *right* question. In contrast to a query, data mining constructs a model of the data automatically; it discovers data patterns, searches for trends, generalises and makes predictions. Data mining often uses relational databases because they represent the most commonly available and rich data repositories.

10.5 The data warehouse and multidimensional data analysis

Relational databases matured in the 1980s. This led to the widespread application of data management systems and automation of the operational aspects of a business.

However, a new challenge emerged – how to achieve a broader view across the entire organisation or business. This challenge was answered in the late 1980s and early 1990s when the first enterprise **data warehouses** were built. Data was brought together from many operational databases in order to provide a manager of the organisation with a corporate-wide view.

What is the data warehouse?

The term 'data warehouse' was first introduced by Bill Inmon, 'The Father of Data Warehousing', in the early 1990s. He defined a data warehouse as 'a subject-oriented, integrated, time-variant and non-volatile collection of data in support of management's decision making process' (Inmon, 1992). A data warehouse is a large integrated database designed and built mainly for decision-support applications.

What are the main characteristics of a data warehouse?

The main characteristic of a data warehouse is its size. A data warehouse is really big – it includes millions, even billions, of data records. However, that is not all. In his definition, Bill Inmon specified four major features of a data warehouse: subject orientation, integration, time variance and non-volatility.

Subject orientation represents the fundamental difference between operational databases and a data warehouse. While operational databases are built to support specific day-to-day business operations, a data warehouse is developed to analyse particular subjects. In banking, for example, operational databases contain independent records of customer savings, loans and other transactions; a data warehouse pulls that data together to provide specific financial information, such as fees, profits and losses. Data that is not relevant for decision making is excluded from the data warehouse.

Integration means that the data is gathered into a data warehouse from a variety of different databases, including on-line operational databases, relational databases and flat files. Data is cleaned and merged into a consistent database.

Time variance reflects the fact that the data in a data warehouse is identified with a particular period of time. The user can generate reports over a specified interval, and thus observe changes in the data over time.

Non-volatility implies that the data in a data warehouse is stable and long-standing. A data warehouse often includes several years' worth of data (in contrast, a typical operational database has a 60- to 90-day time horizon). In fact, a data warehouse usually does not require the latest operational data – the data in a data warehouse is non-real time.

To make business decisions, a manager is often required to take a broader view of the business, ignoring specific details of the day-to-day activities. A data warehouse allows the user to examine how a particular value is changing over time, and thus discover trends in the data. Queries are usually executed interactively such that the result of one query leads to the next.

A data warehouse can be viewed as a separate relational database system that contains copies of data from operational database systems.

Why do we need to copy data from one system to another? Why do we need to have a separate data warehouse?

Operational DBMSs are designed and built to automate the operational aspects of a business. For example, when a sale is made in a department store, a new data record is automatically inserted into the *Transaction* table, and all relevant records (such as stock, employee and customer) are updated accordingly. Operational database systems are concerned with the day-to-day operations – there is no need to keep historical data. On the other hand, if we wanted to use an operational database system in business decision making, we would need to retain data for a long period of time, often up to 10 years. If we then attempted to run decision-support queries, the system performance would deteriorate, slowing to a crawl or even collapsing every time we ran a query.

To make matters even worse, different operational database systems often run on different hardware platforms and use different operating systems. Some applications can also be developed in-house. As a result, distributed database systems that are run on different machines in different geographical locations may be incompatible.

This is why data needs to be copied from the operational systems and stored in some common format in a separate database called a data warehouse.

How do we design a data warehouse?

A data warehouse is a *different* type of database, and it has to be designed differently. A data warehouse contains a much larger volume of data and it has to support complex business-type queries. However, the bigger the database, the harder it is to query it.

Relational databases are based on a relational data model. The model represents interactions between numerous relational tables. While this model is well suited for SQL queries, it can provide only a flat two-dimensional view of the business, which is not adequate for decision making.

An alternative approach is to use a **multidimensional data model**. Instead of examining individual relations, such as *Item*, *Customer* or *Transaction*, and the relationships between them, a multidimensional model views data in terms of a **data cube**.

What is a data cube?

A data cube provides a way to view data from a number of different perspectives. For example, a manager of a large corporation like Wal-Mart, which operates a chain of department stores, can find out if his or her stores in the state of New York are outperforming those in California. He or she can also ask if certain stores are doing better this quarter than the last. Are video games selling better than cell phones? A data cube also allows the manager to discover new trends.

A data cube can be defined as the means for representing multidimensional aggregated data. A data cube, or a multidimensional data model, describes data using **dimensions** and **facts** (Gray *et al.*, 1996; 1998).

Dimensions represent entities with respect to which we keep our records and generate data warehouse queries. For example, a retailer creates a data warehouse to keep records of the store's sales with respect to *Time* (when the transaction occurred), *Item* (what was sold), *Employee* (who made the sale) and *Customer* (who bought the item). If a data warehouse is created for a corporation, which operates a chain of stores, we will need to add the *Store* dimension as well (where the transaction took place). A **dimension** can be defined as a collection of logically related attributes. For instance, the *Time* dimension typically includes *date, week, month, quarter* and *year*, while the *Item* dimension may have such attributes as *item_ID, model, brand, category,* and *department*. Each dimension has a table associated with it. This table is called a **dimension table**.

A data cube is organised around a central theme, for example a retail data warehouse usually has *Sales* as its central theme. This theme is represented by **facts**, specific data stored in a warehouse. Facts are represented by measures, such as the amount of sales in dollars and the number of items sold. Facts are stored in the **fact table**. The fact table is the largest table in the data warehouse – it holds numerical details of all sales made in our store. Consequently, if we want to keep sales records for a historically significant period (years rather than days), the fact table may become very large indeed, with hundreds of millions of rows. Fortunately, the data contained in the fact table does not necessarily have to have the finest level of detail – rather it should maintain summaries, such as total daily sales of each item. For decision making we do not need the specific details of each transaction.

While the fact table contains numerical data and is updated regularly (usually append-only), dimension tables contain attributes used for grouping data when queries are performed. These attributes are rarely updated, although they do change over time. For example, an employee or customer may change their address, or a new item category has to be added. This phenomenon is referred to as **slowly changing dimensions** (Kimball and Ross, 2002).

Although in geometry a cube has three dimensions, in data warehousing a cube, or rather a data cube, is multidimensional. A data cube can be viewed as a multipointed star, as shown in Figure 10.17. The centre of the star corresponds to the fact table and the points represent dimensions. Each dimension has a hierarchical structure, which may include several levels of abstraction. For example, the *Time* dimension has five hierarchical levels: *date, week, month, quarter* and *year*. The whole star structure is called a **starnet model** (Han and Kamber, 2006).

A starnet model uses traditional parent–child hierarchical relationships. For instance, *week* is a child of *month*, *month* is a child of *quarter*, and so on. A parent holds aggregated sums, or *rollups*, of the data contained in its child. A starnet model allows a user to browse through the data across any number of dimensions. The user can roll up (e.g. from *month* to *quarter* and from *quarter* to *year* along the *Time* dimension) or drill down (from *state* to *city* and from *city* to

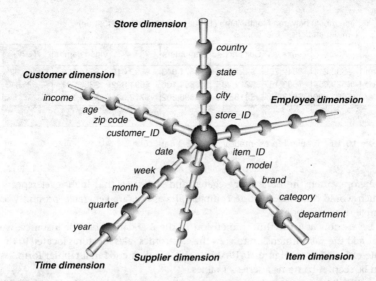

Figure 10.17   Data cube representation as a starnet model

store_ID along the *Store* dimension). Thus, we might query for total sales of a particular item (say, a new Nintendo video game) or a category of items (cameras, cell phones, computers, TVs or video games) purchased in a particular city (say, Trenton) or a state (New Jersey) over the last week (month or quarter). We might also compare these figures with sales in the previous year over the same period of time. After all, a sales increase is a good indicator of a growing business. All such queries would take data from different hierarchical levels in three different dimensions: *Item*, *Store* and *Time*.

The data cube model is similar to a Rubik's cube – the user can easily turn one combination of dimensions into another. When we create a cube, we take facts from the fact table (numerical data) and add them up by store, quarter, store and quarter, and any other possible combination of dimensions and their hierarchical levels.

How does a data cube work?

To understand how a data cube works, we can start with a simple two-dimensional cube. The 2-D cube can, in fact, be represented by a single table, as shown in Figure 10.18. This table contains sales data of the electronics department. Data is shown in respect to the *Time* and *Item* dimensions. Note that the table includes a column and a row that show summarisation over rows and columns, respectively. These totals are often referred to as 'marginals', as they appear on the 'margins' of a table. The marginals can be derived, and therefore may not necessarily be included in the database. However, for large data sets, it is not efficient to compute the marginals upon every query.

Time.month between MonthName (1, true) and MonthName (3, true)
Item.department = 'Electronics'

	Audio	Cameras	Cell phones	Computers	TVs	Video games	Total
Jan	$532,211	$612,765	$227,482	$871,043	$692,015	$314,806	$3,250,322
Feb	$529,654	$603,187	$211,285	$854,106	$691,892	$306,021	$3,196,145
Mar	$561,290	$618,951	$218,572	$896,202	$712,020	$369,142	$3,376,177
Total	$1,623,155	$1,834,903	$657,339	$2,621,351	$2,095,927	$989,969	$9,822,644

Figure 10.18 Tabular representation of the 2-D data cube

Therefore, often the data is aggregated and stored so that high-level reports, which would otherwise require complex processing, are generated promptly as simple select procedures.

Let us now add the third dimension to the 2-D data cube. For instance, we may add the *Store* dimension to view the electronics sales for stores located in the state of New Jersey. Figure 10.19 shows the 3-D data cube in a tabular form. As can be seen, it contains a series of tables.

A 3-D data cube can also be represented as the cube shown in Figure 10.20. The three dimensions *Time*, *Item* and *Store* form the cube's axes. Facts are contained in the cube's cells. Each cell appears at the intersection defined by taking single members in each dimension. For example, members *Jan*, *Audio* and *Trenton* specify the cell that contains the value of audio sales in Trenton, NJ for

Time.month between MonthName (1, true) and MonthName (3, true)
Item.department = 'Electronics'
Store.state = 'NJ'

Trenton, NJ							
	Audio	Cameras	Cell phones	Computers	TVs	Video games	Total
Jan	$204,518	$213,107	$80,522	$318,582	$214,328	$86,232	$1,117,289
Feb	$201,386	$208,425	$76,341	$317,374	$212,230	$82,349	$1,098,105
Mar	$206,651	$214,931	$83,711	$323,485	$215,234	$87,027	$1,131,039
Total	$612,555	$636,463	$240,574	$959,441	$641,792	$255,608	$3,346,433

... ...

Saddle Brook, NJ							
	Audio	Cameras	Cell phones	Computers	TVs	Video games	Total
Jan	$164,460	$142,097	$64,292	$213,487	$132,348	$63,927	$780,611
Feb	$161,507	$136,374	$56,348	$243,970	$134,082	$61,402	$793,683
Mar	$167,934	$143,983	$61,323	$245,092	$134,961	$64,920	$818,213
Total	$493,901	$422,454	$181,963	$702,549	$401,391	$190,249	$2,392,507

... ...

Figure 10.19 Tabular representation of the 3-D data cube

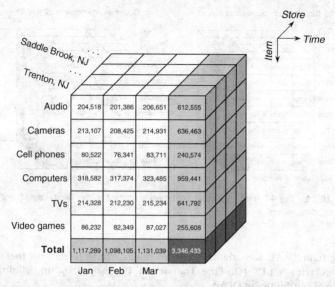

Figure 10.20   The 3-D data cube representation according to the *Time*, *Item* and *Store* dimensions

the month of January ($204,518). Aggregated data is found in the cells located on the sides, edges and corners of the cube.

Although it is difficult to view things in more than three dimensions, we still can display any *n*-D data cube as a series of (*n* − 1)-D cubes. Thus, if we add the fourth dimension to our data cube, for example the *Customer* dimension, we can obtain a series of 3-D cubes shown in Figure 10.21. We should, however, remember that the term 'data cube' is just a metaphor – it is used only to convey the concept of a multidimensional data model. In reality, data cubes are presented in 'normal' formats including spreadsheets, charts and graphs.

Because the data cube contains data in an aggregated form, it seems to know the answer even before we ask a question. For example, if we asked for total sales by year and city, these numbers would already be on hand. If we asked for total sales by quarter, category and supplier, these numbers would already be available too. This is what makes a data cube so remarkable. You can ask any question and promptly receive the answer, usually in less than a second.

How can we build and run our own data cubes?

Software technology that supports a multidimensional view and quick access to large amounts of data is called **on-line analytical processing** (OLAP). The requirements for OLAP were first formulated in the white paper by Codd and Associates (Codd *et al.*, 1993). OLAP allows us to efficiently analyse data in a warehouse by building and running our own data cubes.

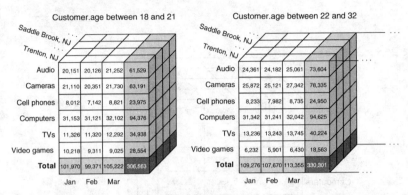

Figure 10.21 The 4-D data cube representation according to the *Time, Item, Store* and *Customer* dimensions

The term 'OLAP' was originally created to distinguish it from the traditional database term 'OLTP' (On-Line Transaction Processing) by underlining the analytical capabilities of OLAP.

OLTP systems can operate with a large number of relational tables incorporating multiple and complex relationships. They update and delete large groups of records at lightning speed. However, the very design that allows OLTP systems to perform transaction operations quickly and accurately does make it hard to use them for data analysis. Although OLTP can run simple queries using SQL, these queries utilise only relatively small sets of data. For analytical processing (e.g. finding total sales grouped by category, state and quarter), we would be required to extract much larger volumes of data, and thus run so-called 'stored procedures' – groups of SQL statements compiled into a single execution plan. These procedures can take hours to run. Moreover, they can significantly slow down and even stall the OLTP system itself.

While OLTP systems are developed for managing operational databases, OLAP systems are designed for analytical processing of data stored in a data warehouse. Creating a data warehouse separates OLAP databases from OLTP databases. Copying data from operational databases into a data warehouse lets the OLTP system continue to operate efficiently and, at the same time, ensures that the OLAP system can support complex queries that are necessary for making business decisions. OLAP runs a data cube such that a user can view data from different perspectives.

How does OLAP facilitate data viewing from different perspectives? What operations can OLAP do?

Multidimensional querying is essentially an exploratory process performed by navigating along dimensions, increasing or decreasing the level of detail, thus discovering 'interesting' trends and relationships. Several OLAP operations facilitate this process. OLAP can 'slice and dice', 'drill down' and 'roll up' data in a data cube. Let us consider the main OLAP operations:

- **Roll up.** The roll-up operation aggregates the data in a data cube by climbing up hierarchical levels of a selected dimension. For example, by ascending the *Store* dimension of the data cube shown in Figure 10.17 from the level of *city* to the level of *state* and then *country*, we aggregate the data by state and country, respectively.

  The roll-up operation can also be performed by dimensionality reduction when one or more dimensions are removed from a given cube. For example, if we have a 3-D cube with *Time*, *Item* and *Store* dimensions (as in Figure 10.20), the roll-up operation can be accomplished by removing, say, the *Item* dimension. The resulting 2-D cube will represent the total sales by *Store* and *Time*.

- **Drill down.** The drill-down operation is simply a reverse of the roll-up operation. It is achieved either by descending through hierarchical levels of a selected dimension or by adding new dimensions to a given data cube. The drill-down operation provides us with more detailed data.

- **Slice.** The slice operation forms a sub-cube by selecting a single member of a hierarchical level on a chosen dimension of the cube. For example, if we select member *Trenton* from the hierarchical level *city* on the dimension *Store* of the 3-D cube shown in Figure 10.20, we obtain a 2-D sub-cube. In fact, 'slices' of a data cube represent cross-tabular reports similar to those shown in Figure 10.19.

- **Dice.** The dice operation works similar to the slice operation, but the selection is made using two or more members. This operation defines a sub-cube by constraining all dimensions of the given cube. For example, by constraining two dimensions of the 3-D cube of Figure 10.20 as

  Time.month between MonthName (1, true) and MonthName (2, true)
  AND (Item.category = 'Audio' or Item.category = 'Cameras')

  we obtain the sub-cube (still 3-D) shown in Figure 10.22.

- **Pivot.** The pivot (also called rotate) operation changes the axis orientation of a report or a page. For example, we can swap the rows and columns of the report shown in Figure 10.18. The initial report represents members of the *Item* dimension as columns and members of the *Time* dimension as rows; the pivot operation provides a report that has months as columns and items as rows.

A data cube can be built (or rather defined) using the SQL-based query language (Bulos and Forsman, 2006; Celko, 2006). To facilitate OLAP queries the SQL has been extended. For example, the Oracle Database 10*g* offers functions such as ranking, moving-window aggregates, period-over-period comparisons, statistical functions, histograms, and hypothetical rank and distribution (Hobbs *et al.*, 2005).

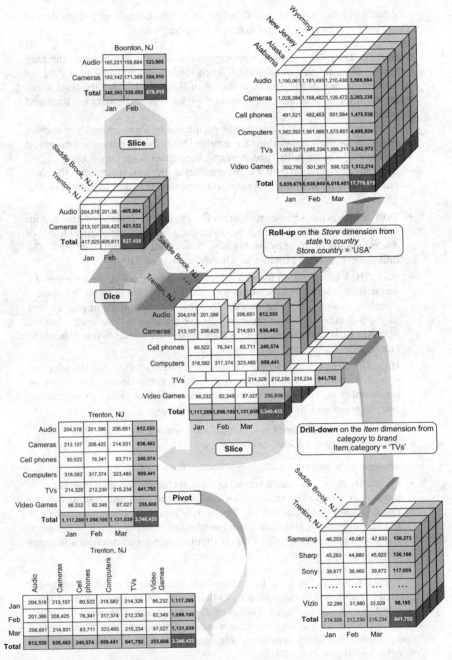

Figure 10.22 Main OLAP operations on a data cube

Is OLAP data mining?

OLAP is a powerful analytical tool. It supports a multidimensional view of the data in a data warehouse. OLAP allows an interactive user-directed data analysis by means of 'slice and dice', 'drill-down' and 'roll-up' operations. These operations are, in fact, data mining operations (although limited) – they do allow us to discover new knowledge in data. However, data mining represents a much broader view of data analysis. It not only can perform data summarisation and comparison tasks, but also addresses sophisticated machine learning problems including classification, prediction, clustering, association and time-series analysis.

While OLAP is a *user-directed* data analysis tool, which requires active participation by the user, data mining is normally associated with an *automated* extraction of knowledge from data – it facilitates finding hidden patterns within the data stored in a database and making predictions about new data automatically. Using OLAP tools, we usually start our analysis with a hypothesis and then query the data warehouse in order either to prove or disprove it. With data mining tools, the burden of asking the right questions is shifted to the computer.

It is interesting to note, however, that data mining functions such as classification, prediction and association have already been integrated into modern OLAP systems. For example, Microsoft SQL Server and Oracle Database 10g not only enable users to access data cubes but also allow them to use data mining tools (Hobbs *et al.*, 2005; Han and Kamber, 2006).

Although data mining often relies on intelligent technologies such as neural networks and neuro-fuzzy systems, the most popular tools are decision trees and market basket analysis.

10.6 Decision trees

A **decision tree** can be defined as a map of the reasoning process. It describes a data set by a tree-like structure. Decision trees are particularly good at solving classification problems.

Figure 10.23 shows a decision tree for identifying households that are likely to respond to the promotion of a new consumer product, such as a new banking service. Typically, this task is performed by determining the demographic characteristics of the households that responded to the promotion of a similar product in the past. Households are described by their ownership, income, type of bank account, etc. One field in the database (named *Household*) shows whether a household responded to the previous promotion campaign.

A decision tree consists of **nodes**, **branches** and **leaves**. In Figure 10.23, each box represents a node. The top node is called the **root node**. The tree always starts from the root node and grows down by splitting the data at each level into new nodes. The root node contains the entire data set (all data records), and child nodes hold respective subsets of that set. All nodes are connected by branches. Nodes that are at the end of branches are called **terminal nodes**, or leaves.

Each node contains information about the total number of data records at that node, and the distribution of values of the dependent variable.

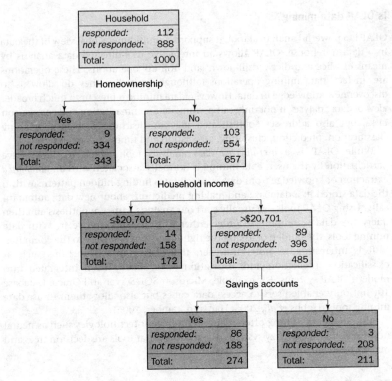

Figure 10.23 An example of a decision tree

What is the dependent variable?

The dependent variable determines the goal of the study; it is chosen by the user. In our example, *Household* is set up as the dependent variable, and it can have a value of either *responded* or *not responded*.

Below the root node we find the next level of the tree. Here, the tree selects variable *Homeownership* as a **predictor** for the dependent variable, and separates all households according to the predictor's values. The separation of data is called a **split**. In fact, *Homeownership* is just one of the fields in the database.

How does the decision tree select a particular split?

A split in a decision tree corresponds to the predictor with the maximum separating power. In other words, the best split does the best job in creating nodes where a single class dominates.

In our example, *Homeownership* best splits households that responded to the previous promotion campaign from those that did not. In Figure 10.23, we can

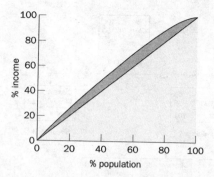

Figure 10.24 Computation of the Gini coefficient of inequality

see that, while only 11.2 per cent of all households responded, a great majority of them were *not* home owners.

There are several methods of calculating the predictor's power to separate data. One of the best known methods is based on the Gini coefficient of inequality.

What is the Gini coefficient?

The Gini coefficient is, essentially, a measure of how well the predictor separates the classes contained in the parent node.

Corrado Gini, an Italian economist, introduced a rough measure of the amount of inequality in the income distribution in a country. Computation of the Gini coefficient is illustrated in Figure 10.24. The diagonal corresponds to an absolutely equal distribution of wealth, and the curve above it represents a real economy, where there is always some inequality in the income distribution. The curve's data is ordered from the richest to the poorest members of the society. The Gini coefficient is calculated as the area between the curve and the diagonal divided by the area below the diagonal. For a perfectly equal wealth distribution, the Gini coefficient is equal to zero. For complete inequality when only one person has all the income, the Gini coefficient becomes unity.

CART (Classification and Regression Trees) uses the Gini measure of inequality for selecting splits (Breiman *et al.*, 1984). Let us compare two alternative trees shown in Figure 10.25. Suppose, at the root node, we have two classes, *Class A* and *Class B*. A decision tree strives to isolate the largest class; that is, to pull out the data records of *Class A* into a single node. This ideal, however, can rarely be achieved; in most cases, a database field that clearly separates one class from the others does not exist. Therefore, we need to choose among several alternative splits.

A tree shown in Figure 10.25(a) is grown automatically with splits being selected by the Gini measure of inequality. In Figure 10.25(b), we select the splits using our own judgement or informed guesswork. The resulting trees are

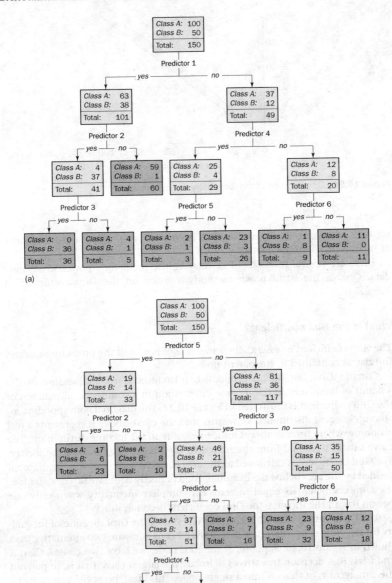

Figure 10.25 Selecting an optimal decision tree: (a) splits selected by Gini; (b) splits selected by guesswork

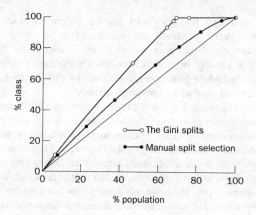

Figure 10.26 Gain charts of *Class A*

compared on a **gain chart** (also called a **lift chart**) shown in Figure 10.26. The chart maps the cumulative percentage of instances of *Class A* at a terminal node to the cumulative percentage of the total population at the same node. The diagonal line here represents the outcome if each terminal node contained a random sample of the population. The results clearly demonstrate the advantages of the tree constructed with the Gini splits.

Can we extract rules from a decision tree?

The path from the root node to the bottom leaf reveals a decision rule. For example, a rule associated with the bottom right leaf in Figure 10.25(a) can be represented as follows:

if	(Predictor 1 = *no*)
and	(Predictor 4 = *no*)
and	(Predictor 6 = *no*)
then	class = *Class A*

Case study 12: Decision trees for data mining

I have the results of a community health survey, and I want to understand which people are at greater risk of having high blood pressure. Will decision trees work for this problem?

A typical task for decision trees is to determine conditions that may lead to certain outcomes. This makes decision trees a good choice for profiling people with high blood pressure, and community health surveys can provide us with the necessary data.

High blood pressure, also called hypertension, occurs when the body's smaller blood vessels narrow. This causes the heart to work harder to maintain the pressure, and although the body can tolerate increased blood pressure for months and even years, eventually the heart may fail.

Blood pressure can be categorised as optimal, normal or high. Optimal pressure is below 120/80, normal is between 120/80 and 130/85, and hypertension is diagnosed when blood pressure is over 140/90. Figure 10.27 shows an example of a data set used in a hypertension study.

Decision trees are as good as the data they represent. Unlike neural networks and fuzzy systems, decision trees do not tolerate noisy and polluted data. Therefore, the data must be cleaned before we can start data mining.

Almost all databases are polluted to some degree. In a hypertension study, we might find that such fields as *Alcohol Consumption* or *Smoking* have been left blank or contain incorrect information. We must also check our data for possible inconsistencies and typos. However, no matter how hard we try, we can rarely remove all the pollution in advance – some abnormalities in the data can only be discovered during the data mining process itself.

We might also attempt to enrich the data. We have, for example, such variables as *weight* and *height*, from which we can easily derive a new variable, *obesity*. This variable is calculated with a body-mass index (BMI): that is, the weight in kilograms divided by the square of the height in metres. Men with BMIs of 27.8 or higher and women with BMIs of 27.3 or higher are classified as obese.

Once data for the hypertension study is prepared, we can choose a decision tree tool. In our study, we use KnowledgeSEEKER by Angoss – a comprehensive tool for building classification trees.

KnowledgeSEEKER starts a decision tree with the root node for the dependent variable *Blood pressure* and divides all respondents into three categories: *optimal*, *normal* and *high*. In this study, 319 people (32 per cent) have optimal, 528 people (53 per cent) normal and 153 people (15 per cent) high blood pressure.

Then KnowledgeSEEKER determines the influence of each variable on blood pressure, and makes a ranked list of the most important variables. In our study, *age* emerges at the top of the list, and KnowledgeSEEKER creates the next level of the tree by splitting respondents by their age, as shown in Figure 10.28. As we can see, the risk of high blood pressure increases as one ages. Hypertension is significantly more prevalent after age 50.

We grow the tree by creating new splits. Let us, for example, make the second-level node for age group 51–64. KnowledgeSEEKER splits this group by *Obesity*. This is because, in our example, *Obesity* is found to be a key indicator of whether someone of age 51 to 64 has high blood pressure. In Figure 10.28, we can see that 48 per cent of obese individuals in this group suffer from hypertension. In fact, the increase in blood pressure in an ageing population may be due primarily to weight gain.

As we continue growing the tree node by node, we might find that African Americans have a much higher risk of hypertension than any other group, and smoking and heavy drinking increase this risk even further.

Community Health Survey: Hypertension Study (California, USA)	
Gender	☑ Male ☐ Female
Age	☐ 18–34 years ☐ 35–50 years ☑ 51–64 years ☐ 65 or more years
Race	☑ Caucasian ☐ African American ☐ Hispanic ☐ Asian or Pacific Islander
Marital status	☐ Married ☐ Separated ☑ Divorced ☐ Widowed ☐ Never married
Household income	☐ Less than $20,700 ☐ $20,701–$45,000 ☑ $45,001–$75,000 ☐ $75,001 and over
Alcohol consumption	☐ Abstain from alcohol ☐ Occasional (a few drinks per month) ☑ Regular (one or two drinks per day) ☐ Heavy (three or more drinks per day)
Smoking	☐ Nonsmoker ☐ 1–10 cigarettes per day ☑ 11–20 cigarettes per day ☐ More than one pack per day
Caffeine intake	☐ Abstain from coffee ☑ One or two cups per day ☐ Three or more cups per day
Salt intake	☐ Low-salt diet ☑ Moderate-salt diet ☐ High-salt diet
Physical activities	☐ None ☑ One or two times per week ☐ Three or more times per week
Height **Weight**	178 cm 93 kg
Blood pressure	☐ Optimal ☐ Normal ☑ High

Obesity	☑ Obese ☐ Not obese

Figure 10.27 A data set for a hypertension study

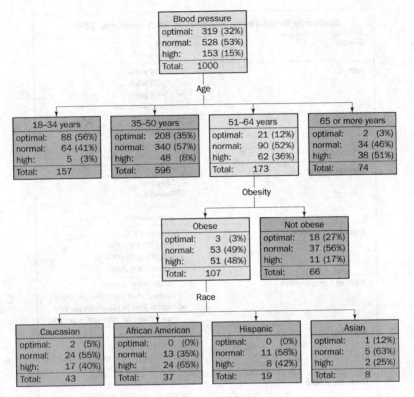

Figure 10.28 Hypertension study: growing a decision tree

Can we look at a specific split?

Decision tree tools, including KnowledgeSEEKER, allow us to look at any split. Figure 10.29 shows splits by *Gender* created for age groups 35–50 and 51–64. As you can see, the results reveal that a higher percentage of men than women have hypertension before age 51, but after that the ratio reverses, and women are more likely to have high blood pressure than are men.

The main advantage of the decision tree approach to data mining is that it visualises the solution; it is easy to follow any path through the tree. Relationships discovered by a decision tree can be expressed as a set of rules, which can then be used in developing an expert system.

Decision trees, however, have several drawbacks. Continuous data, such as age or income, has to be grouped into ranges, which can unwittingly hide important patterns.

Another common problem is the handling of missing and inconsistent data – decision trees can produce reliable outcomes only when they deal with 'clean' data.

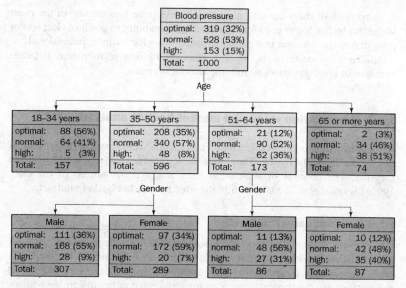

Figure 10.29 Hypertension study: forcing a split

However, the most significant limitation of decision trees comes from their inability to examine more than one variable at a time. This confines trees to only the problems that can be solved by dividing the solution space into several successive rectangles. Figure 10.30 illustrates this point. The solution space of the hypertension study is first divided into four rectangles by *age*, then age group 51–64 is further divided into those who are overweight and those who are not. And finally, the group of obese people is divided by *race*. Such a 'rectangular' classification may not correspond well with the actual distribution of data. This leads to data fragmentation, when the tree is so large and the amount of data passing from the root node to the bottom leaves is so small that discovering meaningful patterns and rules becomes difficult. To minimise fragmentation, we often need to trim back some of the lower nodes and leaves.

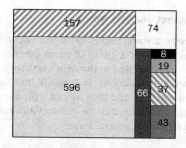

Figure 10.30 Solution space of the hypertension study

In spite of all these limitations, decision trees have become one of the most successful technologies used for data mining. The ability to produce clear sets of rules makes the decision tree particularly attractive for business professionals.

Similar to decision trees, we can uncover hidden relationships between variables in large databases by mining association rules.

10.7 Association rules and market basket analysis

Association rules express concurrent relationships, called **associations**, between objects in large databases. They state how different objects tend to group together. The concept of association rules was first introduced in the early 1990s (Agrawal *et al.*, 1993) and initially used for **market basket analysis**.

What is market basket analysis?

Suppose we observe a customer in a supermarket. The customer has a basket filled with various items such as apples, bananas, orange juice, detergent, milk, etc. One basket tells us about one customer – it cannot reveal any useful associations among items. However, many baskets (or rather information about items purchased by many customers) can indeed tell us which items are frequently purchased together. For example, a manager of a grocery store may find that spaghetti is often purchased together with pasta sauce. This information represents an association rule that relates co-occurring events. Market basket analysis answers such questions as *'If a customer purchases item A, what is the chance that he or she will also buy item B?'* and *'If a customer buys items A and B, what other items is he or she more likely to buy?'*

Market basket analysis can be used by the manager of a grocery store in floor placement, inventory control, marketing and advertising campaigns. Most likely, you are already familiar with market basket analysis and association rules if you use amazon.com. When you buy a book, say, *Artificial Intelligence: A Guide to Intelligent Systems* by Michael Negnevitsky, amazon.com will also suggest to you *items frequently bought together*. This suggestion is based on a simple association rule: *'Customers who buy book A are also likely to buy book B.'*

How does market basket analysis work?

Market basket analysis always begins with transactions. Each transaction contains either a single item or a group of items purchased at one time. Note that we are normally not interested in the item's quantity or its cost. Table 10.4 represents a set of seven transactions. It suggests that *Sauce* and *Spaghetti* are likely to be purchased together, and thus we can write the following association rule: *'If a customer purchases Sauce, then the customer also purchases Spaghetti.'* This rule can be rewritten in a more general form:

$$\{Sauce\} \rightarrow \{Spaghetti\}[support = 57\%, \ confidence = 80\%]$$

Table 10.4   Grocery transactions

Transactions	Items
1	Beef, Milk, Sauce, Spaghetti
2	Sauce, Spaghetti
3	Bread, Sauce, Spaghetti
4	Cheese, Detergent, Sauce
5	Bread, Detergent, Milk
6	Beef, Cheese, Chicken, Milk
7	Milk, Sauce, Spaghetti

The rule states that 57 per cent of customers buy *Sauce* and *Spaghetti* together and those who buy sauce also buy *Spaghetti* 80 per cent of the time. Support and confidence are used for selecting valid association rules.

How do we define support and confidence of an association rule?

Let us first define the problem of mining association rules in mathematical terms. Let $I = \{I_1, I_2, \ldots, I_m\}$ be a set of items, and $T = \{T_1, T_2, \ldots, T_n\}$ be a set of transactions, where each transaction $T_i \subseteq I$. Then an association rule can be written as

$$X \rightarrow Y$$

where X and Y are sets of items, called itemsets, $X \subset I$, $Y \subset I$ and $X \cap Y = \emptyset$.

Transaction T_i is said to contain an itemset X if X is a subset of T_i, that is $X \subset T_i$. For example, transaction {*Bread, Sauce, Spaghetti*} contains seven itemsets: {*Bread*}, {*Sauce*}, {*Spaghetti*}, {*Bread, Sauce*}, {*Bread, Spaghetti*}, {*Sauce, Spaghetti*} and {*Bread, Sauce, Spaghetti*} itself.

Support of the association rule, $X \rightarrow Y$, is defined as a probability of the union of the two itemsets, X and Y, occurring in the transaction set T:

$$support(X \rightarrow Y) = p_{X \cup Y} = \frac{n_{X \cup Y}}{n} \tag{10.18}$$

where $n_{X \cup Y}$ is the number of transactions in the transaction set T that contains the union of the two itemsets, X and Y; and n is the total number of transactions in the set T.

If support is too low, the rule may just occur accidentally. In our example, *Sauce* and *Spaghetti* are bought together four times out of seven, so the rule support is 57 per cent.

Confidence of the association rule, $X \rightarrow Y$, is defined as the conditional probability of itemset Y occurring in a transaction given that itemset X has already occurred in the same transaction:

$$confidence\ (X \rightarrow Y) = p(Y|X) = \frac{n_{X \cup Y}}{n_X} \tag{10.19}$$

where n_X is the number of transactions in the transaction set **T** that contains itemset X.

Confidence is a measure of the rule accuracy. In our example, four out of five customers who bought *Sauce* also bought *Spaghetti*. Thus, the rule confidence is 80 per cent. Typically, we select association rules with higher confidence and lower support.

The goal of mining association rules is to discover all association rules in the transaction set **T** that have support and confidence greater than or equal to the user-specified values of *minimum support* and *minimum confidence*, respectively. If we specify, for example, *minimum support* = 25% and *minimum confidence* = 75%, we will obtain the following valid rules:

> *Rule 1:* {*Sauce*} → {*Spaghetti*} [*support* = 57%, *confidence* = 80%]
> *Rule 2:* {*Spaghetti*} → {*Sauce*} [*support* = 57%, *confidence* = 100%]
> *Rule 3:* {*Beef*} → {*Milk*} [*support* = 29%, *confidence* = 100%]

Clearly, we can generate many more association rules. In general, the number of rules grows exponentially with the number of items. Given the number of items, m, we can calculate the total number of possible association rules, R (Tan *et al.*, 2006):

$$R = 3^m - 2^{m+1} + 1 \tag{10.20}$$

Thus, for just eight items used in our example we can generate 6050 rules. Taking into account that a typical supermarket has about 20,000 different items in stock, the problem of mining association rules becomes huge. Without a doubt, it would be impossible to generate all combinations of association rules. In fact, however, we do not need to produce a complete set of rules as most of them would have very low support and confidence. What we need is a robust algorithm capable of reducing the number of association rules to a manageable level. The **Apriori algorithm** is a good example of such an algorithm (Berry and Linoff, 2004; Tan *et al.*, 2006). It is used in most commercial products for mining association rules.

What is the Apriori algorithm?

The Apriori algorithm is one of the first algorithms developed to address the problem of exponential growth of the number of association rules. However, before discussing the Apriori algorithm, we need to consider the concept of a *frequent* (also called *large*) itemset.

A data set of m items can generate $2^m - 1$ itemsets. In most practical applications, m is very large indeed, and therefore the search space of itemsets can become unmanageable. So, we need a strategy for trimming the search space. This strategy is based on the concept of a frequent itemset. An itemset is said to be frequent if the number of its occurrences in the transaction data set exceeds a specified value of minimum support. If an itemset is frequent, then all of its subsets must also be frequent. This is known as the **Apriori principle**. Conversely, if an itemset is *infrequent*, then all of its super sets must also be infrequent.

To illustrate the concept of a frequent itemset, we consider the itemset lattice shown in Figure 10.31. Here, the four-level hierarchical lattice (the null itemset can be excluded) is constructed from the itemset $\{A, B, C, D\}$. One-item sets are located at the top level of the lattice and the largest, four-item set at the bottom. The lines represent set–subset relationships. If an itemset is frequent, then any subset along a path above it is also frequent. For example, if the itemset $\{A, B, C\}$ is frequent, then all its subsets $\{A, B\}$, $\{A, C\}$, $\{B, C\}$, $\{A\}$, $\{B\}$ and $\{C\}$ must be frequent too. This is known as the **monotone** (or **upward closed**) **property of support**.

If, however, an itemset is infrequent, then any super set in a path below it is also infrequent. This is known as the **anti-monotone** (or **downward closed**) **property of support**. As can be seen in Figure 10.31, the entire sub-graph can be pruned once an itemset is found to be infrequent. This is called **support-based pruning**. The Apriori algorithm uses support-based pruning to control the growth of the search space of itemsets.

Mining of association rules is carried out in two stages. In the first stage, the Apriori algorithm finds all frequent itemsets, and in the second it generates high-confidence rules from the frequent itemsets found in the first stage.

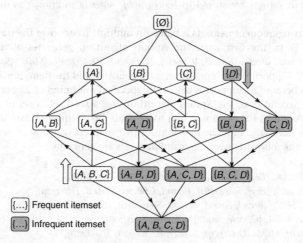

Figure 10.31 Itemset lattice for $\{A, B, C, D\}$

Table 10.5 Support for all non-empty itemsets contained in Table 10.4

Itemsets	Support	Itemsets	Support
{Beef}	29%	{Chicken, Milk}	14%
{Bread}	29%	{Detergent, Milk}	14%
{Cheese}	29%	{Detergent, Sauce}	14%
{Chicken}	14%	{Milk, Sauce}	29%
{Detergent}	29%	{Milk, Spaghetti}	29%
{Milk}	57%	{Sauce, Spaghetti}	57%
{Sauce}	71%		
{Spaghetti}	57%	{Beef, Cheese, Chicken}	14%
		{Beef, Cheese, Milk}	14%
{Beef, Cheese}	14%	{Beef, Chicken, Milk}	14%
{Beef, Chicken}	14%	{Beef, Milk, Sauce}	14%
{Beef, Milk}	29%	{Beef, Milk, Spaghetti}	14%
{Beef, Sauce}	14%	{Beef, Sauce, Spaghetti}	14%
{Beef, Spaghetti}	14%	{Bread, Detergent, Milk}	14%
{Bread, Detergent}	14%	{Bread, Sauce, Spaghetti}	14%
{Bread, Milk}	14%	{Cheese, Chicken, Milk}	14%
{Bread, Sauce}	14%	{Cheese, Detergent, Sauce}	14%
{Bread, Spaghetti}	14%	{Milk, Sauce, Spaghetti}	29%
{Cheese, Chicken}	14%		
{Cheese, Detergent}	14%	{Beef, Cheese, Chicken, Milk}	14%
{Cheese, Milk}	14%	{Beef, Milk, Sauce, Spaghetti}	14%
{Cheese, Sauce}	14%		

To demonstrate how the Apriori algorithm works, we refer to Table 10.4 and calculate support for all non-empty itemsets. Results are presented in Table 10.5. All items in subsets are stored in *lexicographic order* (also known as dictionary order).

Generating frequent itemsets is based on multiple passes over the transaction data set **T**. In the first pass, the Apriori algorithm generates all one-item candidate sets: {Beef}, {Bread}, {Cheese}, {Chicken}, {Detergent}, {Milk}, {Sauce} and {Spaghetti}. Support for each one-item set is counted, and the itemset {Chicken} is discarded because its support is below the specified minimum of 25 per cent.

In the second pass, the Apriori algorithm uses a **seed set** (a set of frequent itemsets found in the previous pass) to generate two-item candidate sets. Each candidate itemset is produced by joining two itemsets of the seed set. In our example, the following two-item candidate sets are generated:

{Beef, Bread}, {Beef, Cheese}, {Beef, Detergent}, {Beef, Milk},
{Beef, Sauce}, {Beef, Spaghetti}, {Bread, Cheese}, {Bread, Detergent},
{Bread, Milk}, {Bread, Sauce}, {Bread, Spaghetti}, {Cheese, Detergent},
{Cheese, Milk}, {Cheese, Sauce}, {Cheese, Spaghetti},
{Detergent, Milk}, {Detergent, Sauce}, {Detergent, Spaghetti},
{Milk, Sauce}, {Milk, Spaghetti}, {Sauce, Spaghetti}

We obtain 21 candidate sets in total; however, only four of them are frequent:

{*Beef, Milk*}, {*Milk, Sauce*}, {*Milk, Spaghetti*}, {*Sauce, Spaghetti*}

In the third and all subsequent passes, the Apriori algorithm joins two itemsets if they both have exactly the same items except one. For example, {*Beef, Milk*} is joined with other two-item sets that have either *Beef* or *Milk*. As a result, we obtain the following three-item candidate sets:

{*Beef, Milk, Sauce*}, {*Beef, Milk, Spaghetti*}, {*Milk, Sauce, Spaghetti*}

Not all candidates from this set are frequent. In fact, a candidate set is frequent only if all of its subsets are in the seed set formed in the previous pass. Because subset {*Beef, Sauce*} of the first candidate and subset {*Beef, Spaghetti*} of the second candidate are not in the seed set, these candidates are discarded. So, after the third pass, there is only one frequent three-item set:

{*Milk, Sauce, Spaghetti*}

Note that the number of passes over the transaction data is equal to the size of the largest itemset. In practice, we often limit its size to just a few items because long association rules are hard to understand and use.

How does the Apriori algorithm generate association rules?

Once all frequent itemsets are found, generating association rules becomes straightforward.

Any frequent itemset Y which contains at least two items can be partitioned into two non-empty subsets, X and $(Y - X)$. The rule $X \rightarrow (Y - X)$ is generated if the ratio of the support of set Y to the support of subset X ($X \subset Y$) is greater than or equal to the user-specified value of minimum confidence:

$$\text{IF } \frac{support(Y)}{support(X)} \geq minimum\ confidence,\ \text{THEN } X \rightarrow (Y - X) \qquad (10.21)$$

Note that since the values of support of both itemsets, Y and X, have already been found during the frequent itemset generation stage, there is no need to scan the transaction data set again.

To illustrate how association rules are generated, we consider a frequent two-item set, $Y = \{Beef, Milk\}$, assuming that the minimum confidence is 75 per cent. The frequent itemset Y includes two non-empty subsets: $X1 = \{Beef\}$ and $X2 = \{Milk\}$. For subset $X1$ we obtain

$$\frac{support\ (Y)}{support\ (X1)} = \frac{support\ (\{Beef, Milk\})}{support\ (\{Milk\})} = \frac{29}{29} = 1$$

This means that the confidence of the association rule

$$X1 \;\rightarrow\; (Y - X1) \text{ or } \{Beef\} \rightarrow \{Milk\}$$

is 100 per cent, just as we calculated using Eq. (10.19). Similarly, for the second subset, $X2$, we have

$$\frac{support\,(Y)}{support\,(X2)} = \frac{support\,(\{Beef, Milk\})}{support\,(\{Milk\})} = \frac{29}{57} = 0.5$$

This means that the confidence of the association rule

$$X2 \;\rightarrow\; (Y - X2) \text{ or } \{Milk\} \rightarrow \{Beef\}$$

is only 50 per cent, and, thus, this is not a valid (high-confidence) rule and has to be discarded.

A complete set of the association rules is presented in Table 10.6. Let us examine these rules. We find that, unlike support, confidence does not have the monotone property; that is, the confidence of the rule $X \rightarrow Y$ can be larger, equal to, or smaller than the confidence of another rule $x \rightarrow y$, where $x \subseteq X$ and $y \subseteq Y$. For example, $\{Milk, Sauce\} \rightarrow \{Spaghetti\}$ is a high-confidence rule, but the rule $\{Milk\} \rightarrow \{Spaghetti\}$ has a low confidence; $\{Sauce\} \rightarrow \{Milk, Spaghetti\}$ is a low-confidence rule, but the rule $\{Sauce\} \rightarrow \{Spaghetti\}$ has a high confidence.

On the other hand, rules generated from the same frequent itemset do have the anti-monotone property of confidence; that is, if the rule $X \rightarrow (Y - X)$ does

Table 10.6 Association rules generated from the grocery transactions

Large itemsets	Association rules	Confidence
{Beef, Milk}	{Beef} → {Milk}	100%
	{Milk} → {Beef}	50%
{Milk, Sauce}	{Milk} → {Sauce}	50%
	{Sauce} → {Milk}	40%
{Milk, Spaghetti}	{Milk} → {Spaghetti}	50%
	{Spaghetti} → {Milk}	50%
{Sauce, Spaghetti}	{Sauce} → {Spaghetti}	80%
	{Spaghetti} → {Sauce}	100%
{Milk, Sauce, Spaghetti}	{Milk, Sauce} → {Spaghetti}	100%
	{Milk, Spaghetti} → {Sauce}	100%
	{Sauce, Spaghetti} → {Milk}	50%
	{Milk} → {Sauce, Spaghetti}	50%
	{Sauce} → {Milk, Spaghetti}	40%
	{Spaghetti} → {Milk, Sauce}	50%

not satisfy the confidence requirement, then any rule $x \rightarrow (Y - x)$, where x is a subset of X, does not satisfy this requirement either. For example, if the rule {*Sauce, Spaghetti*} $\rightarrow$ {*Milk*} is a low-confidence rule, then the rules {*Sauce*} $\rightarrow$ {*Milk*} and {*Spaghetti*} $\rightarrow$ {*Milk*} have low confidence too. In fact, this is a common law for any set of association rules generated from the same frequent itemset. We can easily prove it (Tan *et al.*, 2006). Let us express the rule confidence as

$$confidence\,(X \rightarrow \{Y - X\}) = \frac{support\,(Y)}{support\,(X)}$$

and

$$confidence\,(x \rightarrow \{Y - x\}) = \frac{support\,(Y)}{support\,(x)}$$

Since x is a subset of X, *support* $(x) \geq$ support (X), and therefore

$$confidence\,(x \rightarrow \{Y - x\}) \leq\ confidence\,(X \rightarrow \{Y - X\})$$

In general, each large k-item set can produce $2^k - 2$ association rules. For example, a four-item set, {A, B, C, D}, generates 14 association rules. These rules can be presented as the lattice shown in Figure 10.32. As can be seen, the lattice has five $(k + 1)$ levels. Level 0 has a single rule with four (k) items in the antecedent and an empty consequent. Level 1 consists of rules with one item in their consequents, Level 2 rules with two items, and Level 3 rules with three

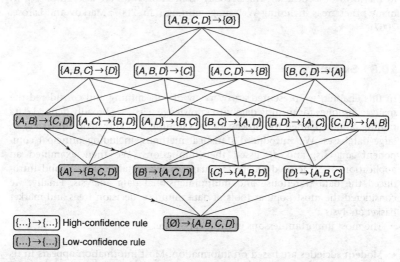

Figure 10.32 Association rule lattice generated from the itemset {*A, B, C, D*}

items. The last level, Level 4, has a single rule with an empty antecedent and four (k) items in the consequent.

According to the anti-monotone property of confidence, if any rule in the lattice has a low confidence, we can remove the entire sub-graph spanned by this rule. For example, if we find that the rule $\{A, B\} \rightarrow \{C, D\}$ has a low confidence, all rules containing the itemset $\{C, D\}$ in their consequents also have low confidence and can be discarded, as shown in Figure 10.32.

The Apriori algorithm starts by generating all candidate rules that have one item in the rule consequent. The confidence of each rule is calculated, and rules that have low confidence are removed. High-confidence rules are used to generate new candidate rules. This generate-and-test procedure is straightforward and efficient.

Finally, a word of caution. A major difficulty in market basket analysis is that we can find many trivial rules that have very low real value. Therefore, choosing the right set of items is paramount.

All items in a supermarket fall into taxonomies, hierarchical categories formed according to the product codes. Taxonomies always start with the most general products and move towards increasing levels of details. As a result, the number of frequent itemsets can be dramatically reduced simply by using higher levels of taxonomies, for example 'frozen vegetables' instead of 'frozen peas', 'frozen carrots', etc. Also, generalised itemsets usually have sufficient support as they occur regularly in many transactions. So, what is the *right* level of generalisation? It always depends on the item's importance for producing actionable results. A common approach is to generalise everything except items of interest.

Market basket analysis is a useful technique for undirected data mining, particularly in the retail industry. Its appeal comes from the clarity of the results in the form of association rules. Today association rules are also employed in many other areas including Web usage mining (Liu, 2007; Markov and Larose, 2007).

10.8 Summary

In this chapter, we presented an overview of data mining and considered the main techniques for turning data into knowledge. First, we broadly defined data mining, and explained the process of data mining and knowledge discovery in large databases. We introduced statistical methods, including principal component analysis, and discussed their limitations. We then examined an application of Structured Query Language in relational databases, and introduced the data warehouse and multidimensional data analysis. Finally, we considered the most popular tools of data mining – decision trees and market basket analysis.

The most important lessons of this chapter are:

- Modern societies are based on information. Most information appears in its raw form as facts, observations and measurements. These constitute data, which is what we collect and store. As the cost of computing power continues to fall, the amount of accumulated data is increasing exponentially. Yet traditional databases are not designed for carrying out meaningful analysis of the data – this is where data mining comes into play.

- Data mining is the extraction of knowledge from raw data. It can also be defined as the exploration and analysis of *large* quantities of data in order to discover meaningful patterns and rules. The ultimate goal of data mining is to discover knowledge.

- Data mining is a practical subject, and is regarded as an 'anything goes' affair – it includes diverse techniques ranging from statistical methods and query tools to sophisticated machine learning techniques. Data mining is not so much a single method but a heterogeneous group of different tools and techniques including statistical methods and data visualisation tools, query tools, on-line analytical processing, decision trees, association rules, neural networks and neuro-fuzzy systems.

- Although data mining is still largely a new and evolving field, it has already found numerous applications. In direct marketing, data mining is used for targeting people who are most likely to buy certain products and services. In trend analysis, it is used to identify trends in the marketplace, for example by modelling the stock market. In fraud detection, data mining is used to identify insurance claims, cellular phone calls and credit card purchases that are the most likely to be fraudulent.

- The success of data mining often depends on the choice of the data mining tool. Preliminary investigation can help us understand specific characteristics of the data, and thus select an appropriate data analysis technique. This preliminary process is known as data exploration and includes summary statistics, visualisation, principal component analysis, query tools and OLAP.

- Data visualisation is defined as the representation of information in a graphical or tabular form. Once the information is visualised, we can interpret and understand it. Visualisation is particularly important in the initial stages of data exploration. Graphical data representation methods include dot diagrams, stemplots, histograms, box plots and scatter plots.

- Despite the apparent appeal of data visualisation, graphical mining in high-dimensional data cannot be easily accomplished. One way of dealing with multidimensional data is to reduce the number of dimensions.

- Principal component analysis can reduce the data dimensionality without significant loss of information. PCA is a mathematical procedure that trans-forms a large number of correlated variables into a smaller number of uncorrelated variables. In data mining, PCA is often used as a data preproces-sing technique. It allows us to obtain a new data set which is much smaller than the original one, yet produces the same (or almost the same) analytical results.

- While statistical methods including PCA are often used as a first step in data exploration, database queries and OLAP represent more sophisticated tools developed specifically to deal with large quantities of data accumulated in modern organisations.

- Database queries can be considered as data mining in its basic form. Queries provide the user with the opportunity to question databases and retrieve subsets of data according to specified conditions. However, database queries are assumption based – a user must ask the *right* questions.

- OLAP allows us to analyse data stored in a data warehouse. OLAP systems support complex multidimensional queries by running a data cube such that a user can increase or decrease the level of detail and view data from a number of different perspectives. OLAP is a user-directed analytical tool – it requires the active participation of the user.

- One of the most popular tools used in data mining is a decision tree, a tool that describes a data set by a tree-like structure. Decision trees are particularly good at solving classification problems – it is easy to follow any path through the tree. The ability to produce clear sets of rules makes the decision tree particularly attractive for business professionals.

- Another popular tool of data mining is market basket analysis. It answers such questions as '*If a customer purchases item A, what is the chance that he or she will also buy item B?*' and '*If a customer buys items A and B, what other items is he or she more likely to buy?*' The appeal of market basket analysis comes from the clarity of the association rules it generates. Market basket analysis is often used for undirected data mining, particularly in the retail industry.

Questions for review

1 What is data mining? Describe the overall process of data mining and knowledge discovery. How is data mining applied in practice? Give examples. What are data mining tools?

2 What is data exploration? Define data visualisation. Give examples of graphical data representation methods and their applications in everyday life.

3 What is a scatter plot? How do we define a linear regression model and determine regression coefficients? Explain how outliers can affect a linear regression model. What is robust regression?

4 What is principal component analysis? How does PCA work? Give an example. How do we decide how many principal components we should keep to capture most of the information contained in a given data set?

5 What is a database management system? What is a relational database? Define tables of the relational database *Travel_agency*.

6 What is a query? Give examples of basic SQL queries. What is the difference between database querying and data mining?

7 What is a data warehouse? What are its main characteristics? Why do we need to copy data from operational database management systems into a data warehouse?

Table 10.7 An example of market basket transactions

Transactions	Items
1	Bread, Cheese, Orange Juice, Sugar
2	Bread, Milk
3	Beef, Cheese, Milk, Orange Juice
4	Bread, Cheese, Milk, Orange Juice
5	Beef, Bread, Cheese, Milk

8 What are a data cube and a starnet model? Give an example of a 3-D data cube and represent the cube in tabular form.

9 What is on-line analytical processing? How does OLAP facilitate data viewing from different perspectives? What operations can OLAP carry out?

10 What is a decision tree? What are dependent variables and predictors? What is the Gini coefficient? How does a decision tree select predictors?

11 What are the advantages and limitations of the decision tree approach to data mining? Why are decision trees particularly attractive to business professionals?

12 What is market basket analysis? What is an association rule? Give examples of association rules. Define support and confidence.

13 What is a frequent itemset? Construct an itemset lattice for the itemset {A, B, C, D, E} and explain the concept of the monotone and anti-monotone properties of support.

14 Consider the set of five transactions shown in Table 10.7. Using the Apriori algorithm, find the frequent itemset and generate association rules. Assume that the minimum support is 60 per cent and the minimum confidence is 80 per cent.

References

Abramowicz, W. and Zurada, J. (2001). *Knowledge Discovery for Business Information Systems*. Kluwer Academic Publishers, Norwell, MA.

Agrawal, R., Imielinski, T. and Swami, A. (1993). Mining association rules between sets of items in large databases, *Proceedings of the 1993 International Conference on Management of Data (SIGMOD 93)*, pp. 207–216.

Berry, M. and Linoff, G. (2004). *Data Mining Techniques for Marketing, Sales, and Customer Relationship Management*, 2nd edn. John Wiley, New York.

Breiman, L., Friedman, J.H., Olshen, R.A. and Stone, C.J. (1984). *Classification and Regression Trees*, Wadsworth, Belmont, CA.

Bulos, D. and Forsman, S. (2006). *Olap Database Design: Delivering on the Promise of the Data Warehouse*, Elsevier, Amsterdam.

Celko, J. (2006). *Joe Celko's Analytics and OLAP in SQL*, The Morgan Kaufmann Series in Data Management Systems, Elsevier, San Francisco.

Chamberlin, D.D. and Boyce, R.F. (1974). SEQUEL: A Structured English Query Language, *Proceedings of the 1974 ACM SIGFIDET Workshop on Data Description, Access and Control*, Ann Arbor, MI, pp. 249–264.

Codd, E.F. (1970). A relational model of data for large shared data banks, Communications of the ACM, 13(6), 377–387.

Codd, E.F., Codd, S.B. and Salley, C.T. (1993). Providing OLAP (on-line analytical processing) to user-analysts: An IT mandate. Technical Report, E.F. Codd and Associates.

Daniel, C. and Wood, F.S. (1999). *Fitting Equations to Data: Computer Analysis of Multifactor Data*, 2nd edn. John Wiley, New York.

DuBois, P. (2008). *MySQL: Developer's Library*, 4th edn. Addison-Wesley Professional, Reading, MA.

Elmasri, R. and Navathe, S.B. (2010). *Fundamentals of Database Systems*, 6th edn. Pearson Education, Boston, MA.

Forta, B. (2005). *MySQL: Crash Course*. Sams Publishing, Indianapolis.

Galton, F. (1877). Typical laws of heredity, *Nature*, 15.

Gantz, J. and Reinsel, D. (2009). As the economy contracts, the digital universe expands, *An IDC White Paper* – sponsored by EMC Corporation, IDC, May.

Gray, J., Bosworth, A., Layman, A. and Pirahesh, H. (1996). Data cube: a relational aggregation operator generalizing group-by, cross-tab, and sub-total, *Proceedings of the 12th International Conference on Data Engineering (ICDE)*, New Orleans, pp. 152–159.

Gray, J., Chaudhuri, S., Bosworth, A., Layman, A., Reichart, D., Venkatrao, M., Pellow, F. and Pirahesh, H. (1998). Data cube: a relational aggregation operator generalizing group-by, cross-tab, and sub-totals, *Readings in Database Systems*, 3rd edn. Morgan Kaufmann, San Francisco, pp. 555–567.

Han, J. and Kamber, M. (2006). *Data Mining: Concepts and Techniques*, 2nd edn. Elsevier, Amsterdam.

Hand, D., Mannila, H. and Smyth, P. (2001). *Principles of Data Mining*. MIT Press, Cambridge, MA.

Hobbs, L., Hillson, S., Lawande, S. and Smith, P. (2005). *Oracle Database 10g Data Warehousing*. Elsevier, Amsterdam.

Inmon, W.H. (1992). *Building the Data Warehouse*. John Wiley, New York.

Jolliffe, I.T. (2002). *Principal Component Analysis*, 2nd edn. Springer-Verlag, New York.

Kimball, R. and Ross, M. (2002). *The Data Warehouse Toolkit: The Complete Guide to Dimensional Modeling*, 2nd edn. John Wiley, New York.

Liu, B. (2007). *Web Data Mining: Exploring Hyperlinks, Contents, and Usage Data*. Springer-Verlag, Berlin.

Markov, Z. and Larose, D.T. (2007). *Data Mining the Web: Uncovering Patterns in Web Content, Structure, and Usage*. John Wiley, Hoboken, NJ.

Montgomery, D.C., Runger, G.C. and Hubele, N.F. (2001). *Engineering Statistics*, 2nd edn. John Wiley, New York.

Oja, E. (1982). A simplified neural model as a principal component analyzer, *Journal of Mathematical Biology*, 15, 239–245.

Oja, E. (1983). *Subspace Methods of Pattern Recognition*. Research Studies Press, Letchworth, Herts.

Pearson, K. (1901). On lines and planes of closest fit to systems of points in space, *Philosophical Magazine*, 2, 559–572.

Purdie, N., Lucas, E.A. and Talley, M. (1992). Direct measure of total cholesterol and its distribution among major serum lipoproteins, *Clinical Chemistry*, 38(9),1645–1646.

Rousseeuw, R.J. and Leroy, A.M. (2003). *Robust Regression and Outlier Detection*. John Wiley, Hoboken, NJ.

Seber, G.A.F. and Wild, C.J. (1989). *Nonlinear Regression*. John Wiley, New York.

Tan, P.N., Steinbach, M. and Kumar, V. (2006). *Introduction to Data Mining*. Addison-Wesley, Boston, MA.

Utts, J.M. (2004). *Seeing Through Statistics*, 3rd edn. Duxbury Press, Pacific Grove, CA.

Wilkinson, J.H. (1988). *The Algebraic Eigenvalue Problem*. Oxford University Press, New York.

Witten, I.H. and Frank, E. (2005). *Data Mining: Practical Machine Learning Tools and Techniques*, 2nd edn. Elsevier, Amsterdam.

Glossary

The glossary entries are coded using the following abbreviations:

es = expert systems
fl = fuzzy logic
nn = neural networks
ec = evolutionary computation
dm = data mining
ke = knowledge engineering

Action potential

An output signal (also called *nerve impulse*) of a biological neuron that does not lose strength over long distances. When an action potential occurs, the neuron is said to 'fire an impulse'. [nn]

Activation function

A mathematical function that maps the net input of a **neuron** to its output. Commonly used activation functions are: **step**, **sign**, **linear** and **sigmoid**. Also referred to as **Transfer function**. [nn]

Adaptive learning rate

A **learning rate** adjusted according to the change of **error** during **training**. If the error at the current **epoch** exceeds the previous value by more than a predefined ratio, the learning rate is decreased. However, if the error is less than the previous one, the learning rate is increased. The use of an adaptive learning rate accelerates **learning** in a **multilayer perceptron**. [nn]

Aggregate set

A **fuzzy set** obtained through **aggregation**. [fl]

Aggregation

The third step in **fuzzy inference**; the process of combining **clipped** or **scaled** consequent **membership functions** of all **fuzzy rules** into a single **fuzzy set** for each output variable. [fl]

Algorithm

A set of step-by-step instructions for solving a problem.

AND

A logical operator; when used in a **production rule**, it implies that all antecedents joined with AND must be true for the rule **consequent** to be true. [es]

Antecedent

A conditional statement in the IF part of a **rule**. Also referred to as **Premise**. [es]

a-part-of
An **arc** (also known as **'part-whole'**) that associates subclasses representing components with a superclass representing the whole. For example, an engine is *a-part-of* a car. [es]

Approximate reasoning
Reasoning that does not require a precise matching between the IF part of a **production rule** with the **data** in the **database**. [es]

Apriori algorithm
An algorithm for learning **association rules**. It operates on large **databases** containing transactions (e.g. collections of items bought by customers). [dm]

Arc
A directed labelled link between nodes in a **semantic network** that indicates the nature of the connection between adjacent nodes. The most common arcs are **is-a** and **a-part-of**. [es]

Architecture
see **Topology**. [nn]

Artificial intelligence (AI)
The field of computer science concerned with developing machines that behave in a way that would be considered intelligent if observed in humans.

Artificial neural network (ANN)
An information-processing paradigm inspired by the structure and functions of the human brain. An ANN consists of a number of simple and highly interconnected processors, called **neurons**, which are analogous to the biological neurons in the brain. The neurons are connected by weighted links that pass signals from one neuron to another. While in a biological neural network, learning involves adjustments to the **synapses**, ANNs learn through repeated adjustments of the **weights**. These weights store the knowledge needed to solve specific problems. [nn]

Assertion
A **fact** derived during **reasoning**. [es]

Association rule
A **rule** that expresses concurrent relationships, called associations, between items in large **databases**. It states how different items tend to group together. Association rules are used in **market basket analysis**. [dm]

Associative memory
The type of memory that allows us to associate one thing with another. For example, we can recall a complete sensory experience, including sounds and scenes, when we hear only a few bars of music. We can also recognise a familiar face even in an unfamiliar environment. An associative ANN recalls the closest 'stored' training pattern when presented with a similar input pattern. The **Hopfield network** is an example of the associative ANN. [nn]

Attribute
A property of an **object**. For example, the object 'computer' might have such attributes as 'model', 'processor', 'memory' and 'cost'. [es]

---

es = expert systems   fl = fuzzy logic   nn = neural networks   ec = evolutionary computation

Axon

A single long branch of a biological **neuron** that carries the output signal (**action potential**) from the cell. An axon may be as long as a metre. In an **ANN**, an axon is modelled by the neuron's output. [nn]

Back-propagation

see **Back-propagation algorithm**. [nn]

Back-propagation algorithm

The most popular method of **supervised learning**. The algorithm has two phases. First, a training input pattern is presented to the **input layer**. The network propagates the input pattern from layer to layer until the output pattern is generated by the **output layer**. If this pattern is different from the desired output, an **error** is calculated and then propagated backwards through the network from the output layer to the input layer. The **weights** are modified as the error is propagated. Also referred to as **Back-propagation**. [nn]

Backward chaining

An **inference technique** that starts with a hypothetical solution (a goal) and works backward, matching **rules** from the **rule base** with **facts** from the **database** until the **goal** is either verified or proven wrong. Also referred to as **Goal-driven reasoning**. [es]

Bayesian reasoning

A statistical approach to uncertainty management in **expert systems** that propagates uncertainties throughout the system based on a **Bayesian rule** of evidence. [es]

Bayesian rule

A statistical method for updating the probabilities attached to certain **facts** in the light of new evidence. [es]

Bidirectional associative memory (BAM)

A class of **neural networks** that emulates characteristics of **associative memory**; proposed by Bart Kosko in the 1980s. The BAM associates patterns from one set to patterns from another set, and vice versa. Its basic architecture consists of two fully connected **layers** – an **input layer** and an **output layer**. [nn]

Bit

A binary digit. The smallest unit of information. **Data** stored in a computer is composed of bits. [ke]

Bit map

A representation of an image by rows and columns of dots. Bit maps can be stored, displayed and printed by a computer. Optical scanners are used to transform text or pictures on paper into bit maps. The scanner processes the image by dividing it into hundreds of **pixels** per inch and representing each pixel by either 1 or 0. [ke]

Black box

A model that is opaque to its user; although the model can produce correct results, its internal relationships are not known. An example of a black box is a **neural network**. To understand the relationships between outputs and inputs of a black box, **sensitivity analysis** can be used. [ke]

---

dm = data mining   ke = knowledge engineering

Boolean logic
A system of logic based on Boolean algebra, named after George Boole. It deals with two truth values: 'true' and 'false'. The Boolean conditions of true and false are often represented by 0 for 'false' and 1 for 'true'.

Branch
A connection between **nodes** in a **decision tree**. [dm]

Building block
A group of **genes** that gives a **chromosome** a high **fitness**. According to the building block hypothesis, an optimal solution can be found by joining several building blocks together in a single chromosome. [ec]

Byte
A set of 8 **bits** that represents the smallest addressable item of information in a modern computer. The information in a byte is equivalent to a letter in a word. One gigabyte is about 1,000,000,000 (2^{30} or 1,073,741,824) bytes, approximately equal to 1000 novels. [ke]

C
A general-purpose programming language, originally developed at Bell Labs along with the Unix operating system.

C++
An object-oriented extension of C.

CART (Classification and Regression Trees)
A tool for **data mining** that uses **decision trees**. CART provides a set of **rules** that can be applied to a new data set for predicting outcomes. CART segments **data records** by creating binary splits. [dm]

Categorical data
The **data** that fits into a small number of discrete categories. For example, gender (male or female) or marital status (single, divorced, married or widowed). [ke]

Centroid technique
A **defuzzification** method that finds the point, called the *centroid* or *centre of gravity*, where a vertical line would slice the **aggregate set** into two equal masses. [fl]

Certainty factor
A number assigned to a **fact** or a **rule** to indicate the certainty or confidence one has that this fact or rule is valid. Also referred to as **Confidence factor**. [es]

Certainty theory
A theory for managing uncertainties in **expert systems** based on inexact **reasoning**. It uses certainty factors to represent the level of belief in a hypothesis given that a particular event has been observed. [es]

Child
see **Offspring**. [ec]

---

es = expert systems   fl = fuzzy logic   nn = neural networks   ec = evolutionary computation

Child
In a **decision tree**, a child is a **node** produced by splitting the **data** of a node located at the preceding hierarchical level of the tree. A child node holds a subset of the data contained in its **parent**. [dm]

Chromosome
A string of **genes** that represent an individual. [ec]

Class
A group of **objects** with common **attributes**. *Animal, person, car* and *computer* are all classes. [es]

Class-frame
A frame that represents a **class**. [es]

Clipping
A common method of correlating the **consequent** of a **fuzzy rule** with the truth value of the rule **antecedent**. The method is based on cutting the consequent **membership function** at the level of the antecedent truth. Since the top of the membership function is sliced, the clipped **fuzzy set** loses some information. [fl]

Cloning
Creating an **offspring** that is an exact copy of a **parent**. [ec]

Clustering
The process of dividing a heterogeneous group of objects into homogeneous subgroups. Clustering **algorithms** find groups of items that are similar in some respect. For example, clustering can be used by an insurance company to group customers according to age, assets, income and prior claims. [ke]

Coding
The process of transforming information from one scheme of representation to another. [ec]

Cognitive science
The interdisciplinary study of how **knowledge** is acquired and used. Its contributing disciplines include **artificial intelligence**, psychology, linguistics, philosophy, neuroscience and education. Also, the study of **intelligence** and intelligent systems, with reference to intelligent behaviour as computation.

Common sense
A general **knowledge** of how to solve real-world problems, usually obtained through practical experience. [ke]

Competitive learning
Unsupervised learning in which **neurons** compete among themselves such that only one neuron will respond to a particular input pattern. The neuron that wins the 'competition' is called the winner-takes-all neuron. **Kohonen self-organising feature maps** are an example of an ANN with competitive learning. [nn]

Complement
In classical **set theory**, the complement of set *A* is the set of elements that are not members of *A*. In the **fuzzy set theory**, the complement of a set is an opposite of this set. [fl]

---

dm = data mining   ke = knowledge engineering

Confidence factor
see **Certainty factor**. [es]

Conflict
A state in which two or more **production rules** match the **data** in the **database**, but only one rule can actually be fired in a given cycle. [es]

Conflict resolution
A method for choosing which **production rule** to fire when more than one rule can be fired in a given cycle. [es]

Conjunction
The logical operator AND that joins together two **antecedents** in a **production rule**. [es]

Connection
A link from one **neuron** to another to transfer signals. Also referred to as **synapse**, which is often associated with the **weight** that determines the strength of the transferred signal. [nn]

Consequent
A conclusion or action in the IF part of a **rule**. [es]

Continuous data
The **data** that takes an infinite number of possible values on some interval. Examples of continuous data include height, weight, household income, the living area of a house. Continuous variables are usually measurements, and do not have to be integers. [ke]

Convergence
An ANN is said to have converged when the **error** has reached a pre-set threshold indicating that the network has learned the task. [nn]

Convergence
A tendency of individuals in the population to be the same. A **genetic algorithm** is said to have converged when a solution has been reached. [ec]

Crossover
A **reproduction** operator that creates a new **chromosome** by exchanging parts of two existing chromosomes. [ec]

Crossover probability
A number between zero and one that indicates the probability of two **chromosomes** crossing over. [ec]

Darwinism
Charles Darwin's theory that states that **evolution** occurs through natural **selection**, coupled with random changes of inheritable characteristics. [ec]

Data
Facts, measurements or observations. Also, a symbolic representation of facts, measurements or observations. Data is what we collect and store.

---

es = expert systems   fl = fuzzy logic   nn = neural networks   ec = evolutionary computation

Data cleaning
The process of detecting and correcting obvious errors and replacing missing **data** in a database. Also referred to as **Data cleansing**. [dm]

Data cleansing
see **Data cleaning**. [dm]

Data cube
The means for representing multidimensional aggregated **data**. It provides a way to view data from a number of different perspectives. The data cube model is similar to a Rubik's cube – the user can easily turn one combination of dimensions into another. [dm]

Data-driven reasoning
see **Forward chaining**. [es]

Data mining
The extraction of **knowledge** from **data**. Also, the exploration and analysis of large amounts of data in order to discover meaningful patterns and **rules**. The ultimate goal of data mining is to discover knowledge. [dm]

Data record
A set of values corresponding to the **attributes** of a single **object**. A data record is a row in a **database**. Also referred to as **Record**. [dm]

Data visualisation
The graphical representation of **data** that helps the **user** in understanding the structure and meaning of the information contained in the data. Also referred to as **Visualisation**. [dm]

Data warehouse
A large database that includes millions, even billions, of **data records** designed to support decision making in organisations. It is structured for rapid on-line queries and managerial summaries. [dm]

Database
A collection of structured **data**. Database is the basic component of an **expert system**. [es]

Database management system (DBMS)
A set of programs that enables a user to create and maintain a **database**. [dm]

Decision-support system
An interactive computer-based system designed to help a person or a group of people to make decisions in a specific **domain**. [es]

Decision tree
A graphical representation of a data set that describes the **data** by tree-like structures. A decision tree consists of **nodes**, **branches** and **leaves**. The tree always starts from the **root node** and grows down by splitting the data at each level into new nodes. Decision trees are particularly good at solving classification problems. Their main advantage is **data visualisation**. [dm]

Deductive reasoning
Reasoning from the general to the specific. [es]

dm = data mining   ke = knowledge engineering

Defuzzification
The last step in **fuzzy inference**; the process of converting a combined output of **fuzzy rules** into a crisp (numerical) value. The input for the defuzzification process is the **aggregate set** and the output is a single number. [fl]

Degree of membership
A numerical value between 0 and 1 that represents the degree to which an element belongs to a particular **set**. Also referred to as **Membership value**. [fl]

Delta rule
A procedure for updating **weights** in a **perceptron** during **training**. The delta rule determines the weight correction by multiplying the neuron's input with the **error** and the **learning rate**. [nn]

Demon
A **procedure** that is attached to a **slot** and executed if the slot value is changed or needed. A demon usually has an IF-THEN structure. Demon and **method** are often used as synonyms. [es]

DENDRAL
A **rule-based expert system** developed at Stanford University in the late 1960s for analysing chemicals, based on the mass spectral **data** provided by a mass spectrometer. DENDRAL marked a major 'paradigm shift' in **AI**: a shift from general-purpose, knowledge-sparse methods to domain-specific, knowledge-intensive techniques. [es]

Dendrite
A branch of a biological **neuron** that transfers information from one part of a cell to another. Dendrites typically serve an input function for the cell, although many dendrites also have output functions. In an **ANN**, dendrites are modelled by inputs to a neuron. [nn]

Deterministic model
A mathematical model that postulates exact relationships between **objects** (no random variables are recognised). Given a set of input **data**, the deterministic model determines its output with complete certainty. [es]

Discrete data
Data that can only take a finite number of values. Discrete data can be represented by whole numbers or fractional values, that is, distinct values. Examples of discrete data include the number of children in a family, the number of bedrooms in a house, the number of masts of a sailing vessel. [ke]

Disjunction
The logical operator **OR** that joins together two **antecedents** in a **production rule**. [es]

Domain
A relatively narrow problem area. For example, diagnosing blood diseases within the medical diagnostics field. **Expert systems** work in well-focused specialised domains. [es]

Domain expert
see **Expert**. [es]

---

es = expert systems   fl = fuzzy logic   nn = neural networks   ec = evolutionary computation

EMYCIN
Empty **MYCIN**, an **expert system shell** developed at Stanford University in the late 1970s. It has all the features of the MYCIN system except the **knowledge** of infectious blood diseases. EMYCIN is used to develop diagnostic **expert systems**. [es]

End-user
see **User**. [es]

Epoch
The presentation of the entire **training set** to an **ANN** during **training**. [nn]

Error
The difference between the actual and desired outputs in an **ANN** with **supervised learning**. [nn]

Euclidean distance
The shortest distance between two points in space. In Cartesian coordinates, the Euclidean distance between two points, (x_1, y_1) and (x_2, y_2), is determined by the Pythagorean theorem $\sqrt{(x_1 - x_2)^2 + (y_1 - y_2)^2}$.

Evolution
A series of genetic changes by which a living organism acquires characteristics that distinguish it from other organisms. [ec]

Evolution strategy
A numerical optimisation procedure similar to a focused Monte Carlo search. Unlike **genetic algorithms**, evolution strategies use only a **mutation** operator, and do not require a problem to be represented in a coded form. Evolution strategies are used for solving technical optimisation problems when no analytical objective function is available, and no conventional optimisation method exists. [ec]

Evolutionary computation
Computational models used for simulating **evolution** on a computer. The field of evolutionary computation includes **genetic algorithms**, **evolution strategies** and **genetic programming**. [ec]

Exhaustive search
A problem-solving technique in which every possible solution is examined until an acceptable one is found. [es]

Expert
A person who has deep **knowledge** in the form of **facts** and **rules** and strong practical experience in a particular **domain**. Also referred to as **Domain expert**. [es]

Expert system
A computer program capable of performing at the level of a human **expert** in a narrow **domain**. Expert systems have five basic components: the **knowledge base**, the **database**, the **inference engine**, the **explanation facilities** and the **user interface**. [es]

Expert system shell
A skeleton **expert system** with the **knowledge** removed. Also referred to as **Shell**. [es]

---

dm = data mining   ke = knowledge engineering

Explanation facility
A basic component of an **expert system** that enables the **user** to query the expert system about how it reached a particular conclusion and why it needs a specific **fact** to do so. [es]

Facet
A means of providing extended **knowledge** about an **attribute** of a frame. Facets are used to establish the attribute value, control the **user** queries, and tell the **inference engine** how to process the attribute. [es]

Fact
A statement that has the property of being either true or false. [es]

Feedback neural network
A **topology** of an ANN in which **neurons** have feedback loops from their outputs to their inputs. An example of a feedback network is the **Hopfield network**. Also referred to as **Recurrent network**. [nn]

Feedforward neural network
A **topology** of an ANN in which **neurons** in one **layer** are connected to the neurons in the next layer. The input signals are propagated in a forward direction on a layer-by-layer basis. An example of a feedforward network is a multilayer **perceptron**. [nn]

Field
A space allocated in a **database** for a particular **attribute**. (In a spreadsheet, fields are called cells.) A tax form, for example, contains a number of fields: your name and address, tax file number, taxable income, etc. Every field in a database has a name, called the field name. [dm]

Firing a rule
The process of executing a **production rule** or, more precisely, executing the THEN part of a rule when its IF part is true. [es]

Fitness
The ability of a living organism to survive and reproduce in a specific environment. Also, a value associated with a **chromosome** that assigns a relative merit to that chromosome. [ec]

Fitness function
A mathematical function used for calculating the **fitness** of a **chromosome**. [ec]

Forward chaining
An **inference technique** that starts from the known **data** and works forward, matching the facts from the **database** with **production rules** from the **rule base** until no further rules can be fired. Also referred to as **Data-driven reasoning**. [es]

Frame
A **data** structure with typical **knowledge** about a particular **object**. Frames are used to represent knowledge in a **frame-based expert system**. [es]

Frame-based expert system
An **expert system** in which **frames** represent a major source of **knowledge**, and both **methods** and **demons** are used to add actions to the frames. In frame-based systems, **production rules** play an auxiliary role. [es]

---

es = expert systems   fl = fuzzy logic   nn = neural networks   ec = evolutionary computation

Fuzzification
The first step in **fuzzy inference**; the process of mapping crisp (numerical) inputs into degrees to which these inputs belong to the respective **fuzzy sets**. [fl]

Fuzzy expert system
An **expert system** that uses **fuzzy logic** instead of **Boolean logic**. A fuzzy expert system is a collection of **fuzzy rules** and **membership functions** that are used to reason about **data**. Unlike conventional **expert systems**, which use **symbolic reasoning**, fuzzy expert systems are oriented towards numerical processing. [fl]

Fuzzy inference
The process of reasoning based on **fuzzy logic**. Fuzzy inference includes four steps: **fuzzification** of the input variables, **rule evaluation**, **aggregation** of the rule outputs and **defuzzification**. [fl]

Fuzzy logic
A system of logic developed for representing conditions that cannot be easily described by the binary terms 'true' and 'false'. The concept was introduced by Lotfi Zadeh in 1965. Unlike **Boolean logic**, fuzzy logic is multi-valued and handles the concept of partial truth (truth values between 'completely true' and 'completely false'). Also referred to as **Fuzzy set theory**. [fl]

Fuzzy rule
A conditional statement in the form IF x is A THEN y is B, where x and y are **linguistic variables**, and A and B are **linguistic values** determined by **fuzzy sets**. [fl]

Fuzzy set
A **set** with fuzzy boundaries, such as 'short', 'average' or 'tall' for men's height. To represent a fuzzy set in a computer, we express it as a function and then map the elements of the set to their **degree of membership**. [fl]

Fuzzy set theory
see Fuzzy logic. [fl]

Fuzzy singleton
A **fuzzy set** with a **membership function** equal to unity at a single point on the **universe of discourse** and zero everywhere else. Also referred to as **Singleton**. [fl]

Fuzzy variable
A quantity that can take on **linguistic values**. For example, the fuzzy variable 'temperature' might have values such as 'hot', 'medium' and 'cold'. [fl]

Gene
A basic unit of a **chromosome** that controls the development of a particular feature of a living organism. In Holland's chromosome, a gene is represented by either 0 or 1. [ec]

General Problem Solver (GPS)
An early **AI** system that attempted to simulate human methods of problem solving. The GPS was the first attempt to separate the problem-solving technique from the **data**. However, the program was based on the general-purpose **search** mechanism. This approach, now referred to as a weak method, applied weak information about the problem

dm = data mining   ke = knowledge engineering

domain, and resulted in weak performance of the program in solving real-world problems. [es]

Generalisation
The ability of an ANN to produce correct results from **data** on which it has not been trained. [nn]

Generation
One iteration of a **genetic algorithm**. [ec]

Genetic algorithm
A type of **evolutionary computation** inspired by Darwin's theory of **evolution**. A genetic algorithm generates a population of possible solutions encoded as **chromosomes**, evaluates their **fitness**, and creates a new population by applying genetic operators – **crossover** and **mutation**. By repeating this process over many **generations**, the genetic algorithm breeds an optimal solution to the problem. [ec]

Genetic operator
An operator in **genetic algorithms** or **genetic programming**, which acts upon the **chromosome** in order to produce a new individual. Genetic operators include **crossover** and **mutation**. [ec]

Genetic programming
An application of **genetic algorithms** to computer programs. Genetic programming is most easily implemented where the programming language permits a program to be manipulated as data and the newly created data to be executed as a program. This is one of the reasons why **LISP** is used as the main language for genetic programming. [ec]

Global minimum
The lowest value of a function over the entire range of its input parameters. During **training**, the **weights** of an ANN are adjusted to find the global minimum of the **error** function. [nn]

Global optimisation
Finding the true optimum in the entire **search space**. [ec]

Goal
A hypothesis that an **expert system** attempts to prove. [es]

Goal-driven reasoning
see **Backward chaining**. [es]

Hard-limit activation function
An **activation function** represented by the **step** and **sign functions**. Also referred to as Hard limiter. [nn]

Hard limiter
see **Hard-limit activation function**. [nn]

Hebb's Law
The **learning law** introduced by Donald Hebb in the late 1940s; it states that if **neuron** i is near enough to excite neuron j and repeatedly participates in its activation, the synaptic **connection** between these two neurons is strengthened and neuron j becomes more

es = expert systems   fl = fuzzy logic   nn = neural networks   ec = evolutionary computation

sensitive to stimuli from neuron *i*. This law provides the basis for **unsupervised learning**. [nn]

Hebbian learning
Unsupervised learning that relates a change in the **weight** of the synaptic **connection** between a pair of **neurons** to a product of the incoming and outgoing signals. [nn]

Hedge
A qualifier of a **fuzzy set** used to modify its shape. Hedges include adverbs such as 'very', 'somewhat', 'quite', 'more or less' and 'slightly'. They perform mathematical operations of concentration by reducing the **degree of membership** of fuzzy elements (e.g. very tall men), dilation by increasing the degree of membership (e.g. more or less tall men) and intensification by increasing the degree of membership above 0.5 and decreasing those below 0.5 (e.g. indeed tall men). [fl]

Heuristic
A strategy that can be applied to complex problems; it usually – but not always – yields a correct solution. Heuristics, which are developed from years of experience, are often used to reduce complex problem solving to more simple operations based on judgement. Heuristics are often expressed as **rules-of-thumb**. [es]

Heuristic search
A search technique that applies **heuristics** to guide the **reasoning**, and thus reduce the **search space** for a solution. [es]

Hidden layer
A **layer** of **neurons** between the **input** and **output layers**; called 'hidden' because neurons in this layer cannot be observed through the input/output behaviour of the **neural network**. There is no obvious way to know what the desired output of the hidden layer should be. [nn]

Hidden neuron
A **neuron** in the **hidden layer**. [nn]

Hopfield network
A single-layer **feedback neural network**. In the Hopfield network, the output of each neuron is fed back to the inputs of all other neurons (there is no self-feedback). The Hopfield network usually uses **McCulloch and Pitts neurons** with the **sign activation function**. The Hopfield network attempts to emulate characteristics of the **associative memory**. [nn]

Hybrid system
A system that combines at least two intelligent technologies. For example, combining a **neural network** with a fuzzy system results in a hybrid neuro-fuzzy system. [ke]

Hypothesis
A statement that is subject to proof. Also, a **goal** in **expert systems** that use **backward chaining**. [es]

Individual
A single member of a **population**. [ec]

---

dm = data mining   ke = knowledge engineering

Inductive reasoning
Reasoning from the specific to the general. [es]

Inference chain
The sequence of steps that indicates how an **expert system** applies **rules** from the **rule base** to reach a conclusion. [es]

Inference engine
A basic component of an **expert system** that carries out **reasoning** whereby the expert system reaches a solution. It matches the **rules** provided in the **rule base** with the **facts** contained in the **database**. Also referred to as **Interpreter**. [es]

Inference technique
The technique used by the **inference engine** to direct **search** and **reasoning** in an **expert system**. There are two principal techniques: **forward chaining** and **backward chaining**. [es]

Inheritance
The process by which all characteristics of a **class-frame** are assumed by the **instance-frame**. Inheritance is an essential feature of **frame-based systems**. A common use of inheritance is to impose default features on all instance-frames. [es]

Initialisation
The first step of the **training** algorithm that sets **weights** and **thresholds** to their initial values. [nn]

Input layer
The first **layer** of **neurons** in an **ANN**. The input layer accepts input signals from the outside world and redistributes them to neurons in the next layer. The input layer rarely includes computing neurons and does not process input patterns. [nn]

Input neuron
A **neuron** in the **input layer**. [nn]

Instance
A specific **object** from a **class**. For example, class 'computer' may have instances *IBM Aptiva S35* and *IBM Aptiva S9C*. In **frame-based expert systems**, all characteristics of a class are inherited by its instances. [es]

Instance
A member of the **schema**. For example, chromosomes $\boxed{1\ 1\ 1\ 0}$ and $\boxed{1\ 0\ 1\ 0}$ are the instances of the schema $\boxed{1\ *\ *\ 0}$. [ec]

Instance-frame
A **frame** that represents an **instance**. [es]

Instantiation
The process of assigning a specific value to a variable. For example, 'August' is an instantiation of the object 'month'. [es]

Intelligence
The ability to learn and understand, to solve problems and to make decisions. A machine is thought to be intelligent if it can achieve human-level performance in some cognitive task.

---

es = expert systems   fl = fuzzy logic   nn = neural networks   ec = evolutionary computation

Interpreter
see **Inference engine**. [es]

Intersection
In classical **set theory**, an intersection between two **sets** contains elements shared by these sets. For example, the intersection of *tall men* and *fat men* contains all men who are tall *and* fat. In **fuzzy set theory**, an element may partly belong to both sets, and the intersection is the lowest **membership value** of the element in both sets. [fl]

is-a
An **arc** (also known as 'a-kind-of') that associates a superclass with its subclasses in a **frame-based expert system**. For example, if *car is-a vehicle*, then *car* represents a subclass of more general superclass vehicle. Each subclass inherits all features of the superclass. [es]

Knowledge
A theoretical or practical understanding of a subject. Knowledge is what helps us to make informed decisions.

Knowledge acquisition
The process of acquiring, studying and organising **knowledge**, so that it can be used in a **knowledge-based system**. [ke]

Knowledge base
A basic component of an expert system that contains knowledge about a specific **domain**. [es]

Knowledge-based system
A system that uses stored **knowledge** for solving problems in a specific **domain**. A knowledge-based system is usually evaluated by comparing its performance with the performance of a human **expert**. [es]

Knowledge engineer
A person who designs, builds and tests a **knowledge-based system**. The knowledge engineer captures the **knowledge** from the **domain expert**, establishes reasoning methods and chooses the development software. [ke]

Knowledge engineering
The process of building a **knowledge-based system**. There are six main steps: assess the problem; acquire **data** and **knowledge**; develop a prototype system; develop a complete system; evaluate and revise the system; integrate and maintain the system. [ke]

Knowledge representation
The process of structuring **knowledge** to be stored in a **knowledge-based system**. In **AI**, **production rules** are the most common type of knowledge representation. [ke]

Kohonen self-organising feature maps
A special class of ANNs with **competitive learning** introduced by Teuvo Kohonen in the late 1980s. The Kohonen map consists of a single **layer** of computation **neurons** with two types of **connections**: forward connections from the neurons in the input layer to the neurons in the output layer, and lateral connections between neurons in the output layer. The lateral connections are used to create a competition between neurons. A neuron learns

---

dm = data mining   ke = knowledge engineering

by shifting its **weights** from inactive connections to active ones. Only the winning neuron and its neighbourhood are allowed to learn. [nn]

Layer
A group of **neurons** that have a specific function and are processed as a whole. For example, a **multilayer perceptron** has at least three layers: an **input layer**, an **output layer** and one or more **hidden layers**. [nn]

Leaf
A bottom-most **node** of a **decision tree**; a node without **children**. Also referred to as a **Terminal node**. [dm]

Learning
The process by which **weights** in an **ANN** are adjusted to achieve some desired behaviour of the network. Also referred to as **Training**. [nn]

Learning rate
A positive number less than unity that controls the amount of changes to the **weights** in the **ANN** from one iteration to the next. The learning rate directly affects the speed of network training. [nn]

Learning rule
A procedure for modifying **weights** during **training** in an **ANN**. [nn]

Linear activation function
An **activation function** that produces an output equal to the net input of a **neuron**. Neurons with the linear activation function are often used for linear approximation. [nn]

Linguistic value
A language element that can be assumed by a **fuzzy variable**. For example, the fuzzy variable 'income' might assume such linguistic values as 'very low', 'low', 'medium', 'high' and 'very high'. Linguistic values are defined by **membership functions**. [fl]

Linguistic variable
A variable that can have values that are language elements, such as words and phrases. In **fuzzy logic**, terms linguistic variable and **fuzzy variable** are synonyms. [fl]

LISP (LISt Processor)
One of the oldest high-level programming languages. LISP, which was developed by John McCarthy in the late 1950s, has become a standard language for **artificial intelligence**.

Local minimum
The minimum value of a function over a limited range of its input parameters. If a local minimum is encountered during **training**, the desired behaviour of an **ANN** may never be achieved. The usual method of getting out of a local minimum is to randomise the **weights** and continue training. [nn]

Machine learning
An adaptive mechanism that enable computers to learn from experience, learn by example and learn by analogy. Learning capabilities improve the performance of an intelligent

---

es = expert systems   fl = fuzzy logic   nn = neural networks   ec = evolutionary computation

system over time. Machine learning is the basis of adaptive systems. The most popular approaches to machine learning are **artificial neural networks** and **genetic algorithms**.

Market basket analysis
A **data mining** technique that discovers non-obvious statistical relationships between items by looking at how often two or more items appear in the same context. Market basket analysis answers such questions as '*If a customer purchases item A, what is the chance that he or she will also buy item B?*' and '*If a customer buys items A and B, what other items is he or she more likely to buy?*' [dm]

Massaging data
The process of modifying the **data** before it is applied to the **input layer** of an ANN. [nn]

McCulloch and Pitts neuron model
A **neuron** model proposed by Warren McCulloch and Walter Pitts in 1943, which is still the basis for most **artificial neural networks**. The model consists of a linear combiner followed by a **hard limiter**. The net input is applied to the hard limiter, which produces an output equal to $+1$ if its input is positive and -1 if it is negative. [nn]

Membership function
A mathematical function that defines a **fuzzy set** on the **universe of discourse**. Typical membership functions used in **fuzzy expert systems** are triangles and trapezoids. [fl]

Membership value
see **Degree of membership**. [fl]

Metaknowledge
Knowledge about knowledge; knowledge about the use and control of **domain** knowledge in **expert systems**. [es]

Metarule
A **rule** that represents **metaknowledge**. A metarule determines a strategy for the use of task-specific rules in the **expert system**. [es]

Method
A **procedure** associated with an **attribute** of a **frame**. A method can determine the attribute's value or execute a series of actions when the attribute's value changes. Most **frame-based expert systems** use two types of methods: WHEN CHANGED and WHEN NEEDED. Method and **demon** are often used as synonyms. [es]

Momentum constant
A positive constant less than unity included in the **delta rule**. The use of momentum accelerates **learning** in a **multilayer perceptron** and helps to prevent it from getting caught in a **local minimum**. [nn]

Multilayer perceptron
The most common **topology** of an ANN in which **perceptrons** are connected together to form **layers**. A multilayer perceptron has the **input layer**, at least one **hidden layer** and the **output layer**. The most popular method of training a multilayer perceptron is **back-propagation**. [nn]

Multiple inheritance
The ability of an **object** or a **frame** to inherit information from multiple superclasses. [es]

---

dm = data mining   ke = knowledge engineering

Mutation
A genetic operator that randomly changes the gene value in a chromosome. [ec]

Mutation probability
A number between zero and one that indicates the probability of mutation occurring in a single gene. [ec]

MYCIN
A classic rule-based expert system developed in the 1970s for the diagnosis of infectious blood diseases. The system used certainty factors for managing uncertainties associated with knowledge in medical diagnosis. [es]

Natural selection
The process by which the fittest individuals have a better chance to mate and reproduce, and thereby to pass on their genetic material to the next generation. [ec]

Neural computing
A computational approach to modelling the human brain that relies on connecting a large number of simple processors to produce complex behaviour. Neural computing can be implemented on specialised hardware or with software, called artificial neural networks, that simulates the structure and functions of the human brain on a conventional computer. [nn]

Neural network
A system of processing elements, called neurons, connected together to form a network. The fundamental and essential characteristic of a biological neural network is the ability to learn. Artificial neural networks also have this ability; they are not programmed, but learn from examples through repeated adjustments of their weights. [nn]

Neuron
A cell that is capable of processing information. A typical neuron has many inputs (dendrites) and one output (axon). The human brain contains roughly 10^{12} neurons. Also, a basic processing element of an ANN that computes the weighted sum of the input signals and passes the result through its activation function to generate an output. [nn]

Node
A decision point of a decision tree. [dm]

Noise
A random external disturbance that affects a transmitted signal. Noisy data contains errors associated with the way the data was collected, measured and interpreted. [dm]

NOT
A logical operator used for representing the negation of a statement. [es]

Object
A concept, abstraction or thing that can be individually selected and manipulated, and that has some meaning for the problem at hand. All objects have identity and are clearly distinguishable. *Michael Black, Audi 5000 Turbo, IBM Aptiva S35* are examples of objects. In

es = expert systems   fl = fuzzy logic   nn = neural networks   ec = evolutionary computation

object-oriented programming, an object is a self-contained entity that consists of both **data** and **procedures** to manipulate the data. [es]

Object-oriented programming
A programming method that uses **objects** as a basis for analysis, design and implementation. [es]

Offspring
An individual that was produced through **reproduction**. Also referred to as a **child**. [ec]

On-line analytical processing (OLAP)
Software technology that supports a multidimensional view and quick access to large amounts of **data**. OLAP can 'slice and dice', 'drill down' and 'roll up' data in a **data cube**. [dm]

Operational database
A **database** used for the daily operation of an organisation. **Data** in operational databases is regularly updated. [dm]

OPS
A high-level programming language derived from **LISP** for developing **rule-based expert systems**. [es]

Optimisation
An iterative process of improving the solution to a problem with respect to a specified objective function. [ec]

OR
A logical operator; when used in a **production rule**, it implies that if any of the **antecedents** joined with OR is true, then the rule **consequent** must also be true. [es]

Outlier
A value that is numerically distinct from the rest of the **data**. [dm]

Output layer
The last **layer** of **neurons** in an ANN. The output layer produces the output pattern of the entire network. [nn]

Output neuron
A **neuron** in the **output layer**. [nn]

Overfitting
A state in which an ANN has memorised all the training examples, but cannot generalise. Overfitting may occur if the number of **hidden neurons** is too big. A practical approach to preventing overfitting is to choose the smallest number of hidden neurons that yields good **generalisation**. Also referred to as **Over-training**. [nn]

Over-training
see **Overfitting**. [nn]

Parallel processing
A computational technique that carries out multiple tasks simultaneously. A human brain is an example of a parallel information-processing system: it stores and processes

---

dm = data mining   ke = knowledge engineering

information simultaneously throughout the whole biological **neural network**, rather than at specific locations. [nn]

Parent
An individual that produces one or more other individuals, known as **offspring** or **child**. [ec]

Parent
In a **decision tree**, a parent node is a **node** that splits its **data** between nodes at the next hierarchical level of the tree. The parent node contains a complete data set, while **child** nodes hold subsets of that set. [dm]

Pattern recognition
Identification of visual or audio patterns by computers. Pattern recognition involves converting patterns into digital signals and comparing them with patterns already stored in the memory. **Artificial neural networks** are successfully applied to pattern recognition, particularly in such areas as voice and character recognition, radar target identification and robotics. [nn]

Perceptron
The simplest form of a **neural network**, suggested by Frank Rosenblatt. The operation of the perceptron is based on the **McCulloch and Pitts neuron model**. It consists of a single **neuron** with adjustable **synaptic weights** and a **hard limiter**. The perceptron learns a task by making small adjustments in the weights to reduce the difference between the actual and desired outputs. The initial weights are randomly assigned and then updated to obtain an output consistent with the training examples. [nn]

Performance
A statistical evaluation of **fitness**. [ec]

Performance graph
A graph that shows the average **performance** of the entire **population** and the performance of the best individual in the population over the chosen number of **generations**. [ec]

Pixel
*Pic*ture *el*ement; a single point in a graphical image. Computer monitors display pictures by dividing the screen into thousands (or millions) of pixels arranged into rows and columns. The pixels are so close together that they appear as one image. [ke]

Population
A group of individuals that breed together. [ec]

Premise
see **Antecedent**. [es]

Principal component analysis (PCA)
A mathematical procedure that transforms a large number of correlated variables into a smaller number of uncorrelated variables. [dm]

Probability
A quantitative description of the likely occurrence of a particular event. Probability is expressed mathematically as a number with a range between zero (an absolute impossibility) to unity (an absolute certainty). [es]

---

es = expert systems   fl = fuzzy logic   nn = neural networks   ec = evolutionary computation

Procedure
A self-contained arbitrary piece of computer code. [es]

Production
A term often used by cognitive psychologists to describe a **rule**. [es]

Production rule
A statement expressed in the IF (antecedent) THEN (consequent) form. If the **antecedent** is true, then the **consequent** is also true. Also referred to as **Rule**. [es]

PROLOG
A high-level programming language developed at the University of Marseilles in the 1970s as a practical tool for programming in logic; a popular language for **artificial intelligence**.

PROSPECTOR
An **expert system** for mineral exploration developed by the Stanford Research Institute in the late 1970s. To represent **knowledge**, PROSPECTOR used a combined structure that incorporated **production rules** and a **semantic network**. [es]

Query tool
Software that allows a **user** to create and direct specific questions to a **database**. A query tool provides the means for extracting the desired information from a database. [dm]

Reasoning
The process of drawing conclusions or inferences from observations, **facts** or assumptions. [es]

Record
see **Data record**. [dm]

Recurrent network
see **Feedback neural network**. [nn]

Regression analysis
A statistical technique for finding a mathematical equation that best fits the **data**. [dm]

Relational database
A **set** of formally described tables from which **data** can be accessed or reassembled without having to reorganise the tables themselves. [dm]

Reproduction
The process of creating **offspring** from **parents**. [ec]

Root
see **Root node**. [dm]

Root node
The top most **node** of a **decision tree**. The tree always starts from the root node and grows down by splitting the **data** at each level into new nodes. The root node contains the entire data set (all **data records**), and **child** nodes hold subsets of that set. Also referred to as **Root**. [dm]

---

dm = data mining   ke = knowledge engineering

Roulette wheel selection

A method of selecting a particular individual in the **population** to be a **parent** with a probability equal to its **fitness** divided by the total fitness of the population. [ec]

Rule

see **Production rule**. [es]

Rule base

The **knowledge base** that contains a set of **production rules**. [es]

Rule-based expert system

An **expert system** whose **knowledge base** contains a set of **production rules**. [es]

Rule evaluation

The second step in **fuzzy inference**; the process of applying the fuzzy inputs to the **antecedents** of **fuzzy rules**, and determining the **truth value** for the antecedent of each rule. If a given rule has multiple antecedents, the fuzzy operation of **intersection** or **union** is carried out to obtain a single number that represents the result of evaluating the antecedent. [fl]

Rule-of-thumb

A **rule** that expresses a **heuristic**. [es]

Scaling

A method of correlating the **consequent** of a **fuzzy rule** with the **truth value** of the rule **antecedent**. It is based on adjusting the original **membership function** of the rule consequent by multiplying it by the truth value of the rule antecedent. Scaling helps to preserve the original shape of the **fuzzy set**. [fl]

Scatter plot

A two-dimensional graph for representing the degree of correlation between two variables. The **data** is represented as a collection of points. The position of each point on the horizontal axis is determined by one variable and on the vertical axis by the other variable. [dm]

Schema

A bit string of ones, zeros and asterisks, where each asterisk can assume either value 1 or 0. For example, the schema $\boxed{1 * * 0}$ stands for a set of four 4-bit strings with each string beginning with 1 and ending with 0. [ec]

Schema theorem

A theorem that relates the expected number of **instances** of a given **schema** in the consequent **generation** with the **fitness** of this schema and the average fitness of **chromosomes** in the current generation. The theorem states that a schema with above-average fitness tends to occur more frequently in the next generation. [ec]

Search

The process of examining a set of possible solutions to a problem in order to find an acceptable solution. [es]

Search space

The set of all possible solutions to a given problem. [es]

---

es = expert systems   fl = fuzzy logic   nn = neural networks   ec = evolutionary computation

Selection
The process of choosing **parents** for **reproduction** based on their **fitness**. [ec]

Self-organised learning
see **Unsupervised learning**. [nn]

Semantic network
A method of **knowledge representation** by a graph made up of labelled **nodes** and **arcs**, where the nodes represent **objects** and the arcs describe relationships between these objects. [es]

Sensitivity analysis
A technique of determining how sensitive the output of a model is to a particular input. Sensitivity analysis is used for understanding relationships in opaque models, and can be applied to **neural networks**. Sensitivity analysis is performed by measuring the network output when each input is set (one at a time) to its minimum and then its maximum values. [ke]

Set
A collection of elements (also called members).

Set theory
The study of **sets** or **classes** of **objects**. The set is the basic unit in mathematics. Classical set theory does not acknowledge the **fuzzy set**, whose elements can belong to a number of sets to some degree. Classical set theory is bivalent: the element either does or does not belong to a particular set. That is, classical set theory gives each member of the set the value of 1, and all members that are not within the set a value of 0.

Shell
see **Expert system shell**. [es]

Sigmoid activation function
An **activation function** that transforms the input, which can have any value between plus and minus infinity, into a reasonable value in the range between 0 and 1. **Neurons** with this function are used in a **multilayer perceptron**. [nn]

Sign activation function
A **hard-limit activation function** that produces an output equal to +1 if its input is positive and −1 if it is negative. [nn]

Singleton
see **Fuzzy singleton**. [fl]

Slot
A component of a **frame** in a **frame-based system** that describes a particular **attribute** of the frame. For example, the frame 'computer' might have a slot for the attribute 'model'. [es]

Soma
The body of a biological **neuron**. [nn]

Step activation function
A **hard-limit activation function** that produces an output equal to +1 if its input is positive and 0 if it is negative. [nn]

---

dm = data mining   ke = knowledge engineering

Structured Query Language (SQL)

A command language that allows the retrieval, insertion, updating and deletion of **data**. The first version of SQL, called *SEQUEL*, was developed by Donald Chamberlin and Raymond Boyce of IBM in the early 1970s. [dm]

Summary statistics

A set of values that represent various characteristics of **data**, such as mean, median, mode, range and standard deviation. [dm]

Supervised learning

A type of **learning** that requires an external teacher, who presents a sequence of training examples to the ANN. Each example contains the input pattern and the desired output pattern to be generated by the network. The network determines its actual output and compares it with the desired output from the training example. If the output from the network differs from the desired output specified in the training example, the network **weights** are modified. The most popular method of supervised learning is **back-propagation**. [nn]

Survival of the fittest

The law according to which only individuals with the highest **fitness** can survive to pass on their genes to the next generation. [ec]

Symbol

A character or a string of characters that represents some **object**. [es]

Symbolic reasoning

Reasoning with **symbols**. [es]

Synapse

A chemically mediated **connection** between two **neurons** in a biological **neural network**, so that the state of the one cell affects the state of the other. Synapses typically occur between an **axon** and a **dendrite**, though there are many other arrangements. See also **Connection**. [nn]

Synaptic weight

see **Weight**. [nn]

Terminal node

see **Leaf**. [dm]

Test set

A data set used for testing the ability of an **ANN** to generalise. The test data set is strictly independent of the **training set**, and contains examples that the network has not previously seen. Once **training** is complete, the network is validated with the test set. [nn]

Threshold

A specific value that must be exceeded before the output of a **neuron** is generated. For example, in the **McCulloch and Pitts neuron model**, if the net input is less than the threshold, the neuron output is −1. But if the net input is greater than or equal to the threshold, the neuron becomes activated and its output attains a value +1. Also referred to as **Threshold value**. [nn]

---

es = expert systems   fl = fuzzy logic   nn = neural networks   ec = evolutionary computation

Threshold value
see **Threshold**. [nn]

Topology
A structure of a **neural network** that refers to the number of **layers** in the neural network, the number of **neurons** in each layer and **connections** between neurons. Also referred to as **Architecture**. [nn]

Toy problem
An artificial problem, such as a game. Also, an unrealistic adaptation of a complex problem. [es]

Training
see **Learning**. [nn]

Training set
A data set used for **training** an ANN. [nn]

Transfer function
see **Activation function**. [nn]

Truth value
In general, the terms truth value and **membership value** are used as synonyms. The truth value reflects the truth of a fuzzy statement. For example, the fuzzy proposition x is A (0.7) suggests that element x is a member of **fuzzy set** A to the degree 0.7. This number represents the truth of the proposition. [fl]

Turing test
A test designed to determine whether a machine can pass a behaviour test for **intelligence**. Turing defined the intelligent behaviour of a computer as the ability to achieve human-level performance in cognitive tasks. During the test a human interrogates someone or something by questioning it via a neutral medium such as a remote terminal. The computer passes the test if the interrogator cannot distinguish the machine from a human.

Union
In classical **set theory**, the union of two **sets** consists of every element that falls into either set. For example, the union of *tall men* and *fat men* contains all men who are either tall *or* fat. In **fuzzy set theory**, the union is the reverse of the **intersection**; that is, the union is the **largest membership** value of the element in either set. [fl]

Universe of discourse
The range of all possible values that are applicable to a given variable. [fl]

Unsupervised learning
A type of **learning** that does not require an external teacher. During learning an ANN receives a number of different input patterns, discovers significant features in these patterns and learns how to classify input data into appropriate categories. Also referred to as **Self-organised learning**. [nn]

User
A person who uses a **knowledge-based system** when it is developed. For example, the user might be an analytical chemist determining molecular structures, a junior doctor

---

dm = data mining   ke = knowledge engineering

diagnosing an infectious blood disease, an exploration geologist trying to discover a new mineral deposit, or a power system operator seeking advice in an emergency. Also referred to as **End-user**. [es]

User interface
A means of communication between a **user** and a machine. [es]

Visualisation
see **Data visualisation**. [dm]

Weight
The value associated with a **connection** between two **neurons** in an **ANN**. This value determines the strength of the connection and indicates how much of the output of one neuron is fed to the input of another. Also referred to as **Synaptic weight**. [nn]

WHEN CHANGED method
A **procedure** attached to a **slot** of a **frame** in a **frame-based expert system**. The WHEN CHANGED method is executed when new information is placed in the slot. [es]

WHEN NEEDED method
A **procedure** attached to a **slot** of a **frame** in a **frame-based expert system**. The WHEN NEEDED method is executed when information is needed for problem solving, but the slot value is unspecified. [es]

Appendix:
AI tools and vendors

Expert system shells

ACQUIRE

A knowledge acquisition and expert system development tool. Knowledge is represented by production rules and pattern-based action tables. ACQUIRE does not require special training in building expert systems. A domain expert can create a knowledge base and develop applications without help from the knowledge engineer.

Acquired Intelligence Inc.
205 - 1095 McKenzie Avenue
Victoria, BC, Canada, V8P 2L5
Phone: +1 (250) 479-8646
Fax: +1 (250) 479-0764

http://www.aiinc.ca/acquire/acquire.shtml

Exsys Corvid

A general-purpose Java-based tool for building expert systems. Decision-making steps are described by building logic diagrams and rules. Exsys Corvid can be delivered over the Web using the Corvid Servlet Runtime, which dynamically builds HTML pages for the user interface, or via the Java Applet Runtime displaying them on the client machine. Systems can communicate with databases through standard ODBC/JDBC interfaces and SQL commands. Exsys Corvid can also be run as a stand-alone application allowing it to be integrated into other information architectures.

EXSYS
6301 Indian School Rd. NE, Suite 700
Albuquerque, NM 87110, USA
Phone: +1 (505) 888-9494
Fax: +1 (505) 888-9509

http://www.exsys.com/

FICO Blaze Advisor

A sophisticated tool for developing rule-based object-oriented expert systems. Multiple methods can be used to create and manage rules. These methods include decision trees, scorecards, decision tables, formula builder, graphical decision flows and customised templates. Blaze Advisor monitors the business performance captured through user-defined events. The system has an open architecture, which enables ease of integration with any computing environment and accepts inputs from multiple databases, XML documents, Java objects, .NET/COM objects and COBOL copybooks.

Fair Isaac Corporation
901 Marquette Avenue, Suite 3200
Minneapolis, MN 55402, USA
Phone: +1 (612) 758-5200
Phone: +1 (415) 472-2211
Fax: +1 (612) 758 5201

http://www.fico.com/en/Products/Pages/default.aspx

Flex

A frame-based expert system toolkit. Supports frame-based reasoning with inheritance, rule-based programming and data-driven procedures. Flex has its own English-like knowledge specification language (KSL). The main structures in Flex are frames and instances with slots for organising objects, default and current values for storing data, demons and constraints for adding functionality to slot values, rules and relations for expressing knowledge and expertise, functions and actions for defining imperative processes, and questions and answers for end-user interaction. The KSL supports mathematical, Boolean and conditional expressions.

Logic Programming Associates Ltd
Studio 30, Royal Victoria Patriotic Building
Trinity Road, London SW18 3SX, UK
Phone: +44 (0)20 8871-2016
Fax: +44 (0)20 8874-0449

http://www.lpa.co.uk/flx.htm

G2 Rule Engine Platform

An interactive object-oriented, graphical environment for the development and on-line deployment of intelligent systems. Objects are organised in hierarchical classes with multiple inheritance. Developers can model an application by representing and connecting objects graphically. Expert knowledge is expressed by rules. G2 works efficiently in real time and events are time-stamped. G2 runs on Microsoft Windows, Red Hat Linux and Linux Enterprise, Sun Solaris SPARC, IBM AIX, HP-UX and Compaq Tru64 UNIX.

Gensym Corporation
6011 West Courtyard Drive, Suite 300
Austin, TX 78730, USA
Phone: +1 (512) 377-9700
e-mail: info@gensym.com

http://www.gensym.com

Intellix

A comprehensive tool developed by combining neural network and expert system technologies. The tool provides a user-friendly environment where no programming skills are required. Domain knowledge is represented by production rules and examples. The system uses a combined technique of pattern matching (neural networks) and rule interpretation, and is capable of learning in real time.

Intellix Denmark
Nikolaj Plads 32, 2
DK-1067 Copenhagen K, Denmark
Phone: +45 3314-8100
Fax: +45 3314-8130
e-mail: info@intellix.com

http://www.intellix.com/products/designer/designer.html

JESS

The Java Expert System Shell (JESS) is available as a free download (including its complete Java source code) from Sandia National Laboratories. JESS was originally inspired by CLIPS (C Language Integrated Production System), but has grown into a complete tool of its own. The JESS language is still compatible with CLIPS – JESS scripts are valid CLIPS scripts and vice versa. JESS adds many features to CLIPS, including backward chaining and the ability to manipulate and directly reason about Java objects. Despite being implemented in Java, JESS runs faster than CLIPS.

Sandia National Laboratories, California
PO Box 969
Livermore, CA 94551-0969, USA
e-mail: ejfried@sandia.gov

http://herzberg.ca.sandia.gov/jess

Vanguard Knowledge Automation System

A comprehensive tool developed for Web-based integrated applications. It includes Vanguard Studio, Vanguard Server, Web Development Add-in and Content Management System (CMS). CMS is a Web-based expert system development tool for non-programmers. It uses visual editors and a visual logic display to help business workers automate their expertise and collaborate using only their Web browsers. Vanguard Studio uses the Web Development Add-in, which allows the user to control how models look and behave in the Web environment.

Vanguard Software Corporation
1100 Crescent Green
Cary, NC 27518, USA
Phone: +1 (919) 859-4101
Fax: +1 (919) 851-9457
e-mail: info@vanguardsw.com

http://www.vanguardsw.com/products/knowledge-automation-system/

VisiRule

A rule-based graphical tool for developing and delivering business rule systems and components by drawing the decision logic. The business logic is identified and represented as a sequence of graphical icons and links. The underlying logic-based inference engines ensure a high degree of compliance and accuracy. VisiRule is ideal for building regulatory compliance systems, financial decision-making systems and validation systems. It supports multiple, linked charts. VisiRule charts can be delivered within the Windows environment or embedded within Java, VB, Delphi, C/C++, .NET and C# using the LPA Intelligence Server toolkit. Charts can also be published on the Web.

Logic Programming Associates Ltd
Studio 30, Royal Victoria Patriotic Building
Trinity Road, London SW18 3SX, UK
Phone: +44 (0)20 8871-2016
Fax: +44 (0)20 8874-0449

http://www.lpa.co.uk/

Visual Rules

Visual Rules is based on a graphical modelling approach. It supplements the Unified Modeling Language (UML) used in IT with business logic that is suitable for business people. Code generation is automated and standardised.

Innovations
Software Technology Corp.
161 N. Clark Street
Chicago, Illinois 60601, USA
Phone: +1 (312) 523-2176
Fax: +1 (312) 268-6286
e-mail: info@innovations-software.com

http://www.innovations-software.com

XMaster

The system consists of two basic packages: XMaster Developer and XMaster User. With XMaster Developer the user creates a knowledge base simply by building up a list of possible *hypotheses* and a list of *items of evidence*. The items of evidence are then associated with the relevant hypotheses. XMaster also enables the user to incorporate uncertain or approximate relationships into the knowledge base. It uses Bayesian reasoning for managing uncertainties.

Chris Naylor Research Limited
14 Castle Gardens
Scarborough, North Yorkshire
YO11 1QU, UK
Phone: +44 (1)723 354590
e-mail: ChrisNaylor@ChrisNaylor.co.uk

http://www.chrisnaylor.co.uk/

XpertRule

A tool for developing rule-based expert systems. Domain knowledge is represented by decision trees, examples, truth tables and exception trees. Decision trees are the main knowledge representation method. Examples relate outcomes to attributes. A truth table is an extension to examples – it represents a set of examples covering every possible combination of cases. From examples, truth tables and exception trees, XpertRule automatically generates a decision tree. XpertRule also uses fuzzy reasoning, which can be integrated with crisp reasoning and with GA optimisation.

XpertRule Software
Innovation Forum, Innovation Park
51 Frederick Road
Salford M6 6FP, UK
Phone: +44 (0)870 60-60-870
Fax: +44 (0)870 60-40-156
e-mail: info@xpertrule.com

http://www.xpertrule.com/

Fuzzy logic tools

FLINT

The Fuzzy Logic INferencing Toolkit (FLINT) is a versatile fuzzy logic inference system that
makes fuzzy rules available within a sophisticated programming environment. FLINT
supports the concepts of fuzzy variables, fuzzy qualifiers and fuzzy modifiers (linguistic
hedges). Fuzzy rules are expressed in a simple, uncluttered syntax. Furthermore, they can
be grouped into matrices, commonly known as fuzzy associative memory (FAM). FLINT
provides a comprehensive set of facilities for programmers to construct fuzzy expert
systems and decision-support applications on all LPA-supported hardware and software
platforms.

Logic Programming Associates Ltd
Studio 30, Royal Victoria Patriotic Building
Trinity Road, London SW18 3SX, UK
Phone: +44 (0)20 8871-2016
Fax: +44 (0)20 8874-0449
e-mail: tech_team@lpa.co.uk

http://www.lpa.co.uk/fln.htm

Fuzzy Control Manager

The Fuzzy Control Manager (FCM) provides a graphical user interface (GUI) that allows the
user to display any relevant data while developing, debugging, and optimising a fuzzy
system. Offers the point-and-click rule editor and graphical editor of membership
functions. The FCM enables the user to generate a source code in C assembler or binary
codes.

TransferTech GmbH
Eichendorffstr. 1
D-38110 Braunschweig, Germany
Phone: +49 5307-490-9160
Fax: +49 5307-490-9161
e-mail: info@transfertech.de

http://www.transfertech.de/wwwe/fcm/fcme_gen.htm

Fuzzy Query

An application based on Win32. It allows the user to query a database using the power and
semantic flexibility of the Structured Query Language. Fuzzy Query provides information
beyond the strict restrictions of Boolean logic. The user sees not only the candidates that

best meet some specified criteria, but also the candidates that just barely miss the cut. Each record returned by Fuzzy Query shows data ranked by the degree to which it meets the specified criteria.

Fuzzy Systems Solutions
Sonalysts Inc.
215 Parkway North
Waterford, CT 06385, USA
Phone: +1 (860) 526-8091
Fax: +1 (860) 447-8883
e-mail: FuzzyQuery@Sonalysts.com

http://fuzzy.sonalysts.com/

FuzzyJ Toolkit

A set of Java classes that provide the capability for handling fuzzy reasoning. It is useful for exploring fuzzy logic in a Java setting. The work is based on earlier experience building the FuzzyCLIPS extension to the CLIPS Expert System Shell. The toolkit can be used as stand-alone to create fuzzy rules and do reasoning. It can also be used with JESS, the Expert System Shell from the Sandia National Laboratories. FuzzyJ is available as a free download.

Integrated Reasoning Group
NRC Institute for Information Technology
1200 Montreal Road, Building M-50
Ottawa, ON, Canada, K1A 0R6
Phone: +1 (613) 993-9101
Fax: +1 (613) 952-9907
e-mail: info@nrc-cnrc.gc.ca

http://www.nrc-cnrc.gc.ca/eng/ibp/iit/past-projects/fuzzyj-toolkit.html

fuzzyTECH

fuzzyTECH is the world's leading family of software development tools for fuzzy logic and neuro-fuzzy solutions. It provides two basic products: *Editions* for technical applications and *Business* for applications in finance and business. The tree view enables structured access to all components of a fuzzy logic system under design in the same way that Windows Explorer lets users browse the structure of their PCs. The Editor and Analyser windows allow each component of a fuzzy system to be designed graphically.

Inform Software Corporation
525 West Monroe Street, Suite 2360
Chicago, IL 60661, USA
Phone: +1 (312) 575-0578
Fax: +1 (312) 575-0581
e-mail: office@informusa.com

INFORM GmbH
Pascalstrasse 23
D-52076 Aachen, Germany
Phone: +49 2408-9456-5000
Fax: +49 2408-9456-5001
e-mail: hotline@inform-ac.com

http://www.fuzzytech.com/

jFuzzyLogic

A fuzzy logic tool written in Java. It implements the Fuzzy Control Language (FCL) specification (IEC 1131p7). Parametric optimisation algorithms include Derivate, Gradient Descent and Jump. Membership functions can be implemented as continuous (GenBell, Sigmoidal, Trapezoidal, Gaussian, PieceWiseLinear, Triangular, Cosing and Dsigm), discrete (Singleton, GenericSingleton) and customer defined. jFuzzyLogic is available as a free download.

Pablo Cingolani
e-mail: pcingola@users.sourceforge.net

http://jfuzzylogic.sourceforge.net/html/index.html

Mathematica Fuzzy Logic Package

The package represents built-in functions that facilitate defining inputs and outputs, creating fuzzy sets, manipulating and combining fuzzy sets and relations, applying fuzzy inference functions, and incorporating defuzzification routines. Experienced fuzzy logic designers find it easy to use the package to research, model, test and visualise highly complex systems. *Fuzzy Logic* requires *Mathematica* 5.0–5.2 and is available for Windows, Mac OS, Linux x86, and san Solaris platforms.

Wolfram Research, Inc.
100 Trade Center Drive
Champaign, IL 61820-7237, USA
Phone: +1 (217) 398-0700
Fax: +1 (217) 398-0747

http://www.wolfram.com/products/applications/fuzzylogic/

MATLAB Fuzzy Logic Toolbox

Features a simple point-and-click interface that guides the user through the steps of fuzzy design, from set-up to diagnosis. It provides built-in support for the latest fuzzy logic methods, such as fuzzy clustering and adaptive neuro-fuzzy learning. The toolbox's interactive graphics let the user visualise and fine-tune system behaviour.

The MathWorks, Inc.
3 Apple Hill Drive
Natick, MA 01760-2098, USA
Phone: +1 (508) 647-7000
Fax: +1 (508) 647-7001

http://www.mathworks.com/products/fuzzylogic/

rFLASH

rFLASH (Rigel's Fuzzy Logic Applications Software Helper) is a code generator that creates a set of subroutines and tables in the MCS-51 assembly language to implement Fuzzy Logic Control (FLC) applications. The code generated runs on the 8051 family of microcontrollers. rFLASH software includes a code generator and a simulator. As a code generator, rFLASH creates the FLC code directly from a high-level Control Task Description File (CTDF). As a simulator, rFLASH generates the outputs from given inputs on the PC. The simulator can test several inputs and fine-tune the terms or rules accordingly.

Rigel Corporation
PO Box 90040
Gainesville, FL 32607, USA
Phone: +1 (352) 384-3766
e-mail: techsupport@rigelcorp.com

http://www.rigelcorp.com/flash.htm

Right Rule

An independent library for implementing a fuzzy logic inference engine. The library is available in the form of a C++ class library for embedded systems and C# module for desktop/server applications. The fuzzy logic inference engine is designed for the Microsoft .NET Micro Framework, and aimed at embedded control systems with a short development cycle and flexible characteristics.

BLUEdev Ltd
Ap. Melaxrinou 24
Patras 26442, Greece
Phone: +30 2610-4546-00
Fax: +30 2610-4546-01
e-mail: support@bluedev.eu

http://www.bluedev.eu/t2c/

Neural network tools

BrainMaker

The neural network software for business and marketing forecasting; stock, bond, commodity and futures prediction; pattern recognition; medical diagnosis – almost any activity where the user needs special insight. The user does not need any special programming or computer skills. BrainMaker uses the Back Propagation algorithm. It runs on a Mac or PC.

California Scientific
4011 Seaport
West Sacramento, CA 95691, USA
Phone: +1 (916) 372-6800
USA toll free: 1-800-284-8112
e-mail: sales@calsci.com

http://www.calsci.com/BrainIndex.html

EasyNN-plus

A neural network software system for Microsoft Windows. It can generate multilayer neural networks from imported files. Numerical data, text or images can be used to create the neural networks. The neural networks can then be trained, validated and queried. All diagrams, graphs and input/output data produced or used by the neural networks can be displayed. The graphs, grid and network diagrams are updated dynamically, so the user can see how everything is working. Neural networks can then be used for data analysis, prediction, forecasting, classification and time-series projection.

Neural Planner Software Ltd
18 Seymour Road
Cheadle Hulme
Cheshire, SK8 6LR, UK
Phone: +44 7817-680-689
Fax: +44 8700-518-079
e-mail: support@easynn.com

http://www.easynn.com

G2 NeurOn-Line

Built on Gensym's G2 real-time rule engine platform, G2 NeurOn-Line combines neural network and rule-based technology for managing variability in real time. Its neural network models act as soft sensors to analyse on-line operational data and estimate and predict important process variables that would otherwise be impractical to measure in real time. The neural networks can use both historical and real-time data. G2 NeurOn-Line's predictions take into account variability to drive decisions that result in efficient settings for processes.

Gensym Corporation
6011 West Courtyard Drive, Suite 300
Austin, TX 78730, USA
Phone: +1 (512) 377-9700
e-mail: info@gensym.com

http://www.gensym.com

MATLAB Neural Network Toolbox

A complete neural network engineering environment within MATLAB. It has a modular, open and extensible design that provides comprehensive support for many proven network paradigms such as multilayer perceptrons with back-propagation learning, recurrent networks, competitive layers and self-organising maps. The toolbox has a graphical user interface for designing and managing the networks.

The MathWorks, Inc.
3 Apple Hill Drive
Natick, MA 01760-2098, USA
Phone: +1 (508) 647-7000
Fax: +1 (508) 647-7001

http://www.mathworks.com/products/neuralnet/

NeuNet Pro

A general-purpose software tool for pattern recognition, data mining, modelling and prediction using neural networks. It is a powerful, easy-to-use, point-and-click, graphical development environment. NeuNet Pro can access data directly from MDB database files; data may contain up to 255 fields. It provides comprehensive graphical reporting of prediction accuracy including confusion matrix, scatter graph and time-series graph.

CorMac Technologies Inc.
28 North Cumberland Street
Thunder Bay, ON, Canada, P7A 4K9
Phone: +1 (807) 345-7114
Fax: +1 (613) 822-5625
e-mail: douglas@cormactech.com

http://www.cormactech.com/

NeuralWorks Predict

An integrated, state-of-the-art tool for creating and deploying prediction and classification applications. Predict combines neural network technology with genetic algorithms, statistics and fuzzy logic automatically to find optimal or near-optimal solutions for a wide range of problems. Predict requires no prior knowledge of neural networks. For advanced users, Predict also offers direct access to all key training and network parameters. In the Microsoft Windows environment it can be run either as an add-in for Microsoft Excel to take advantage of Excel's data-handling capabilities, or as a command line program. In the Unix and Linux environments, NeuralWorks Predict runs as a command line program.

NeuralWare
230 East Main Street, Suite 200
Carnegie, PA 15106-2700, USA
Phone: +1 (412) 278-6280
Fax: +1 (412) 278-6289
e-mail: info@neuralware.com

http://www.neuralware.com/products.jsp

NeuroCoM

The Neuro Control Manager (NeuroCoM) is a high-performance tool for developing and testing neural networks. The NeuroCoM has a window-oriented graphical user interface that facilitates both neural network training and its analysis. This interface also helps to visualise the neural network architecture, transfer functions and the learning process. The NeuroCoM can generate a source code in C.

TransferTech GmbH
Eichendorffstr 1
D-38110 Braunschweig, Germany
Phone: +49 (05307) 490-91-60
Fax: +49 (05307) 490-91-61
Phone: +49 (531) 890-255
Fax: +49 (531) 890-355
e-mail: info@transfertech.de

http://www.transfertech.de/wwwe/ncm/ncme_scr.htm

NeuroModel

Creates models specially adapted to the needs of the process industry. Models are created from the process data records, and are then used to analyse the process itself. NeuroModel can map up to 255 consecutive variables, so that even complex processes with hundreds of variables can be visualised and modelled.

atlan-tec Systems GmbH
CEO: Dipl.-Ing. Thomas Froese
Hanns-Martin-Schleyer-Str. 18 a
Haus 3/ 1. Obergeschoss
47877 Willich-Münchheide II, Germany
Phone: +49 2154-9248-0
Fax: +49 2154-9248-100
e-mail: info@atlan-tec.com

http://www.atlan-tec.com/neuromodel_en.html

NeuroShell 2

Combines powerful neural network architectures, a user interface driven by Microsoft Windows icons, sophisticated utilities and popular options to give users the ultimate neural network experimental environment. It is recommended for academic users, or for users who are concerned with classic neural network paradigms like back-propagation. Users interested in solving real problems should consider AI Trilogy: the NeuroShell Predictor, NeuroShell Classifier and GeneHunter.

Ward Systems Group, Inc.
Executive Park West
5 Hillcrest Drive
Frederick, MD 21703, USA
Phone: +1 (301) 662-7950
Fax: +1 (301) 663-9920
e-mail: sales@wardsystems.com

http://www.wardsystems.com/neuroshell2.asp

NeuroSolutions

This software combines a modular, icon-based, network-design interface with an implementation of learning procedures, such as recurrent back-propagation and back-propagation through time. Other features include graphical user interface and C++ source code generation. There are three levels of NeuroSolutions: the Educator, the entry level intended for those who want to learn about neural networks; the Users level, which extends the Educator with a variety of neural models for static pattern-recognition applications; and the Consultants level that offers enhanced models for dynamic pattern recognition, time-series prediction and process control.

NeuroDimension, Inc.
3701 NW 40th Terrace, Suite 1
Gainesville, FL 32606, USA
Phone: +1 (352) 377-5144
USA toll free: 1-800-634-3327
Fax: +1 (352) 377-9009
e-mail: info@nd.com

http://www.neurosolutions.com/products/ns

STATISTICA Automated Neural Networks

STATISTICA Automated Neural Networks (SANN) is one of the most advanced and best performing neural network applications on the market. It guides the user through the process of creating neural networks and offers integrated pre- and post processing, including data selection, nominal-value encoding, scaling, normalisation and missing value substitution. SANN can combine different networks and network architectures to form ensembles. It automatically performs neural network analyses in Microsoft Excel spreadsheets, or incorporates neural network procedures in custom applications developed in C, C++, C#, Java, etc.

StatSoft, Inc.
2300 East 14th Street
Tulsa, OK 74104, USA
Phone: +1 (918) 749-1119
Fax: +1 (918) 749-2217
e-mail: info@statsoft.com

http://www.statsoft.com/products/statistica-automated-neural-networks

Trajan 6.0 Professional

A sophisticated neural network simulation package that can be used for data mining, inference, modelling and prediction. One of Trajan's major features is the Intelligent Problem Solver, which streamlines the entire neural design process. Intelligent Problem Solver handles exploratory selection of model type and complexity, selection of variables and training procedures. Trajan supports Multilayer Perceptrons, Kohonen Networks, Radial Basis Functions, Linear Models, Probabilistic and Generalised Regression Neural Networks. Training algorithms include the Back Propagation, Levenburg–Marquardt and Conjugate Gradient Descent algorithms. Error plotting, automatic cross-verification and a variety of stopping conditions are also included.

> Trajan Software Ltd
> The Old Rectory, Low Toynton,
> Horncastle, Lincs, LN9 6JU, UK
> Phone: +44 1507 524-077
> Fax: +44 8700 515-931
> e-mail: sales@trajan-software.demon.co.uk
>
> http://www.trajan-software.demon.co.uk/

Evolutionary computation tools

Evolutionary Optimizer

The Evolutionary Optimizer (EVO) is a generic tool for optimising system properties determined by numerical parameters. The system provides a user-friendly graphical interface and requires no knowledge of programming.

> TransferTech GmbH
> Eichendorffstr. 1
> D-38110 Braunschweig, Germany
> Phone: +49 5307-490-9160
> Fax: +49 5307-490-9161
> e-mail: info@transfertech.de
>
> http://www.transfertech.de/wwwe/evo/evoe_gen.htm

Evolver

A genetic algorithm optimisation add-in for Microsoft Excel. It uses innovative genetic algorithms to solve optimization problems quickly in finance, distribution, scheduling, resource allocation, manufacturing, budgeting, engineering, and more. Virtually any type of problem that can be modelled in Excel can be solved by Evolver. Its genetic algorithms arrive at the best overall 'global' solution to a problem. It requires no knowledge of programming or GA theory and ships with a fully illustrated manual, several examples, and free, unlimited technical support.

> Palisade Corporation
> 798 Cascadilla Street
> Ithaca, NY 14850, USA
> Phone: +1 (607) 277-8000
> USA/Canada toll free: 1-800-432-7475

Fax: +1 (607) 277-8001
e-mail: sales@palisade.com

http://www.palisade.com/evolver/

GEATbx

The Genetic and Evolutionary Algorithm Toolbox (GEATbx) for use with MATLAB is the most comprehensive implementation of evolutionary algorithms in MATLAB. A broad range of operators is fully integrated into the environment, which constitutes a powerful optimisation tool applicable to a wide range of problems.

Hartmut Pohlheim
Charlottenstr. 23, 13156 Berlin, Germany
Phone: +49 700 7645-4346
Fax: +49 700 7645-4346
e-mail: support@geatbx.com

http://www.geatbx.com/

GeneHunter

A powerful solution for optimisation problems. GeneHunter includes an Excel add-in which allows the user to run an optimisation problem from Excel, as well as a dynamic link library of genetic algorithm functions that may be called from programming languages such as Microsoft Visual Basic or C.

Ward Systems Group, Inc.
Executive Park West
5 Hillcrest Drive
Frederick, MD 21703, USA
Phone: +1 (301) 662-7950
Fax: +1 (301) 663-9920
e-mail: sales@wardsystems.com

http://www.wardsystems.com/genehunter.asp

GenSheet

Implements genetic algorithms as fast C-coded dynamic link libraries. GenSheet supports genetic operations for binary, integer, real and permutation representations, and includes special commands for constrained non-linear optimisation, genetic classifiers, job-shop scheduling and computing minimum variance portfolio. GenSheet requires Microsoft Excel. All GenSheet commands are configured in an easy-to-use Excel menubar. GenSheet provides interactive help and a tutorial.

Inductive Solutions, Inc.
380 Rector Place, Suite 4A
New York, NY 10280, USA
Phone: +1 (212) 945-0630
Fax: +1 (212) 945-0367
e-mail: roy@inductive.com

http://www.inductive.com/softgen.htm

MATLAB Global Optimization Toolbox

Global Optimization Toolbox provides methods that search for global solutions to problems that contain multiple maxima or minima. Customised genetic algorithms can be created by modifying initial population and fitness scaling options or by defining parent selection, crossover and mutation functions. Pattern search is customised by defining polling, searching and other functions. The toolbox has a graphical user interface for designing and managing genetic algorithms.

The MathWorks, Inc.
3 Apple Hill Drive
Natick, MA 01760-2098, USA
Phone: +1 (508) 647-7000
Fax: +1 (508) 647-7001

http://www.mathworks.com/products/global-optimization/

OptiGen Library

The OptiGen Library is an object-oriented programming interface. It combines the power of single- and multi-objective genetic algorithms, advanced attribute selection algorithms and other optimisation strategies such as simulated annealing into a common object-oriented interface. The OptiGen Library supports all .NET languages, Visual Studio C++ and ActiveX (COM)-capable languages, including VBA in Microsoft Office products.

NeuroDimension, Inc.
3701 NW 40th Terrace, Suite 1
Gainesville, FL 32606, USA
Phone: +1 (352) 377-5144
USA toll free: 1-800-634-3327
Fax: +1 (352) 377-9009
e-mail: info@nd.com

http://www.nd.com/genetic/

xl bit

A genetic algorithm add-in for Microsoft Excel. It requires no knowledge of programming. The system allows 500 chromosomes maximum, multiple fitness functions, four types of variables (binary, integer, non-integer and permutation), three options for crossover methods, and provides a user-friendly graphical interface.

XLPert Enterprise
e-mail: sales@xlpert.com

http://www.xlpert.com/

Data mining

Angoss KnowledgeSEEKER

A powerful data mining solution which offers data profiling, advanced data visualisation and decision tree capabilities. It is widely used in marketing, sales and risk functions. KnowledgeSEEKER can import data from virtually any data source - statistical files, file servers and databases through native drivers for SAS, SPSS, as well as using text and ODBC.

It also allows calculations to be performed in the data warehouse, avoiding data movement to and from the software that slows response time.

Angoss Software Corporation
111 George Street, Suite 200
Toronto, ON, Canada, M5A 2N4
Phone: +1 (416) 593-1122
Fax: +1 (416) 593-5077

http://www.angoss.com/

BLIASoft Knowledge Discovery

BLIASoft Knowledge Discovery is a decision-support tool. It extracts models from data. Training data can be qualitative or quantitative. BLIASoft Knowledge Discovery can use incomplete, uncertain and even contradictory data. It is easy to use and does not require any specific skills in data processing.

BLIA Solutions
1, rue du Pont Guilhemery
31 000 Toulouse, France
e-mail: support@bliasolutions.com

http://www.bliasoft.com

FICO Model Builder for Decision Trees

A graphical development tool which combines data-driven analysis with human expertise rapidly to create easy-to-view, editable decision trees. The software examines and splits strategy segments to produce branches that isolate similar target groups. A user can then select variables that represent the most effective splits based on performance measures. It can instantly compare strategies without the need to write code.

Fair Isaac Corporation
901 Marquette Avenue, Suite 3200
Minneapolis, MN 55402, USA
Phone: +1 (612) 758 5200
Fax: +1 (612) 758 5201

http://www.fico.com/en/Products/Pages/default.aspx

IBM DB2 Data Warehouse Edition

DB2 Data Warehouse Edition (DWE) is a suite of products that provides a comprehensive business intelligence platform. A user can build a complete data warehousing solution that includes a highly scalable relational database, data access capabilities, business intelligence analytics and front-end analysis tools. DB2 Data Warehouse Standard Edition includes the following products: DB2 Universal Database Workgroup Server, DB2 Cube Views, DB2 Intelligent Miner and DB2 Office Connect.

IBM Corporation
1 New Orchard Road
Armonk, NY 10504-1722, USA
Phone: +1 877-426-6006
Fax: +1 800-314-1092

http://www-01.ibm.com/software/data/iminer/

Investigator II
Investigator II provides easy-to-use tools for analysing, forecasting and monitoring business performance. It transforms data into reports and charts that support decisions. It allows a user to monitor, report and compare any grouping of facts concerning products and markets and their performance indicators, in a single view, covering the past, present and future. Investigator II supports Bayesian classifier, case-based reasoning, decision tree, C means clustering, data fusion, K means, Kohonen clustering, neural nets and principal component analysis.

Solutions4Planning Ltd
Garrick House
138 London Road
Gloucester GL1 3PL, UK
Phone: +44 1276-485-711

http://www.solutions4planning.com/investigator-2.html

KXEN Analytic Framework
Provides solutions for classification, regression, attribute importance, clustering (also known as segmentation), forecasting and market basket analysis. It discovers natural groupings or common behaviours in a set of individuals and provides the corresponding description of each of the segments, generates rules that identify patterns in transactional data describing which events are most likely to occur together, and predicts meaningful patterns and trends in data over time using chronologically ordered data to forecast the results of the next periods of time. Unlike traditional data mining tools, KXEN Analytic Framework can handle a very high number of input attributes (over 10,000).

KXEN, Inc.
201 Mission Street, Suite 1950
San Francisco, CA 94105-1831, USA
Phone: +1 (415) 904-4160
Fax: +1 (415) 904-9041
e-mail: sales-us@kxen.com

http://www.kxen.com/

Oracle Data Mining
Oracle Data Mining (ODM) is a priced option to Oracle Database 11g Enterprise Edition. It enables a user to build and deploy applications that deliver predictive analytics. Applications can be built using SQL and Java APIs that automatically mine Oracle data and deploy results in real time. Because the data, models and results remain in the Oracle Database, data movement is eliminated, security is maximised and information latency is minimised. ODM models can be included in SQL queries and embedded in applications. ODM can perform classification, regression analysis, anomaly detection, clustering, market basket analysis and feature extraction.

Oracle Corporation
500 Oracle Parkway
Redwood Shores, CA 94065, USA
Phone: +1 (650) 506-7000 or +1 800-392-2999
e-mail: oraclesales_us@oracle.com

http://www.oracle.com/technology/products/bi/odm/index.html

Partek Discovery Suite

Partek Discovery Suite integrates methods of data analysis and visualisation with classical statistics enabling researchers to find solutions quickly to a wide variety of pattern analysis and recognition problems. It does not have any restrictions on the number of rows or columns, so analysing, editing and processing large data sets can be easily achieved. Also useful for mapping high-dimensional data to a lower dimension for visualisation, analysis or modelling.

> Partek Incorporated
> 12747 Olive Blvd., Suite 205
> St. Louis, MO 63141, USA
> Phone: +1 (314) 878-2329
> Fax: +1 (314) 275-8453
> e-mail: inquire@partek.com

> http://www.partek.com/partekds

Portrait Customer Analytics

A powerful, easy-to-use, predictive analytics solution which extends existing marketing and analytic environments by adding powerful 3-D data visualisation. An easy-to-use interface converts data into visual information. Portrait Customer Analytics provides rapid modelling automation for churn/attrition, campaign response, cross-sell/up-sell, risk/default, customer lifetime value and profitability. Pre-loaded modelling techniques include decision trees, regression, additive scorecards and clustering.

> Portrait Software
> The Smith Centre
> The Fairmile
> Henley-on-Thames
> RG9 6AB, UK
> Phone: +44 1491-416-600
> Fax: +44 1491-416-601

> http://www.portraitsoftware.com/

SAS Enterprise Miner

SAS uses a range of techniques for the collection, classification, analysis and interpretation of data to reveal patterns, anomalies, key variables and relationships. SAS Enterprise Miner provides the most comprehensive set of advanced predictive and descriptive modelling algorithms, including market basket analysis, decision trees, gradient boosting, least angular regression splines, neural networks, linear and logistic regression, partial least-squares regression and many more.

> SAS Institute Inc.
> 100 SAS Campus Drive
> Cary, NC 27513-2414, USA
> Phone: +1 (919) 677-8000
> Fax: +1 (919) 677-4444

> http://www.sas.com/technologies/analytics/datamining/miner/

TIBCO Spotfire Miner

A product for data mining and visual programming that enables organisations to discern the patterns, trends and relationships hidden in their collected data. It has an easy-to-use interface designed for statisticians and business analysts. Spotfire Miner's visual workflow diagrams document each step of an application, making it easy to replicate results. Spotfire Miner provides data processing nodes to support every step of the data mining process, including data access (file and database), exploration and transformation; data cleaning; model building; logistic and linear regression, classification and regression trees, neural networks, naive Bayes, K-means clustering, principal component analysis, association rules and Cox regression; model assessment; and data export.

TIBCO Spotfire Main Office
212 Elm Street
Somerville, MA 02144, USA
Phone: +1 (617) 702-1600
Fax: +1 (617) 702-1700
e-mail: mds@tibco.com

http://spotfire.tibco.com/products/data-mining-applications.aspx

Vanguard Decision Tree

The Vanguard Decision Tree Suite is an integrated application, which includes Vanguard Studio and Decision Tree Analysis add-in components. This gives a user the ability to perform classic decision tree analysis and Markov simulations.

Vanguard Software Corporation
1100 Crescent Green
Cary, NC 27518, USA
Phone: +1 (919) 859-4101
Fax: +1 (919) 851-9457
e-mail: info@vanguardsw.com

http://www.vanguardsw.com/products/decision-tree-suite/

Viscovery SOMine

Viscovery SOMine is a desktop application for explorative data mining, visual cluster analysis, statistical profiling, segmentation and classification based on self-organising maps and classical statistics in an intuitive workflow environment. Since its first release in 1996, Viscovery SOMine has become a standard for commercial data mining based on SOMs. It provides modelling tools for explorative data mining, cluster definition, profiling and segmentation, as well as convenient statistical functions, such as Ward clustering, group profiles and descriptive statistics. Viscovery SOMine uses standardised software, requiring no special customisation, installation, hardware infrastructure or system maintenance.

Viscovery Software GmbH
Kupelwiesergasse 27
A-1130 Vienna, Austria
Phone: +43 1 532-05-70
Fax: +43 1 532-05-70-33
e-mail: inquire@partek.com

http://www.eudaptics.co.at/

VisiRex

Visual Rule Extraction (VisiRex) is a general-purpose software tool for performing data mining, data prediction and knowledge discovery using inductive rule extraction. It discovers interesting and useful patterns and rules within a database, generates comprehensive statistical reports, builds colour-coded decision trees with adjustable tree pruning and segments the data into clusters. VisiRex also allows the user to build predictive models using a portion of the data and then test the models using another portion.

CorMac Technologies Inc.
28 North Cumberland Street
Thunder Bay, ON, Canada, P7A 4K9
Phone: +1 (807) 345-7114
Fax: +1 (613) 822-5625
e-mail: douglas@cormactech.com

http://cormactech.com/visirex/

Index

A

accelerated learning 185–8
accidental property 140
action, *see* rule, consequent
action potential 166
activation function 169
    bell 278
    hard limit 169
    hyperbolic tangent 185
    linear 169–70
    saturated linear 189
    sigmoid 169–70, 177
    sign 169, 189
    step 169
activation level 168
activity balance point 202
activity product rule 201
    generalised 202
adaptive learning rate 186–8
adaptive neuro-fuzzy inference
        system 277, 353–4, 383–4
    architecture 277–9
        defuzzificztion layer 279
        fuzzification layer 278
        input layer 278
        normalisation layer 279
        rule layer 278–9
        summation neuron 279
    learning 280–2
adaptive topology 220
Advice Taker 6
Affenzeller, M. 289
aggregate fuzzy set 110–11
aggregation 110, 137
AI, *see* artificial intelligence
AI 'winter' 12
algebraic sum, *see* probabilistic OR

algorithm 34
a-kind-of, *see* is-a
AND 172
AND product 109
Anderson C. 13
ANFIS, *see* adaptive neuro-fuzzy
        inference system
ANN, *see* artificial neural network
antecedent, *see* rule, antecedent
a-part-of 137–8
approximate reasoning 262–3
Apriori algorithm 412–18
Apriori principle 413
artificial intelligence 2, 6, 260
    foundations 5–6
    history 5–17, 19–20
    paradigm shift 9
artificial neural network 12–13, 165, 167
ASCII code 304
association 137–8, 410
association rule 410–18
    confidence 411–12
    support 411–12
associative memory 187
associativity 100–1
attribute 131
Automatic Computing Engine 2
axon 166

B

back-propagation, *see* back-propagation
        algorithm
back-propagation algorithm 13,
        179–80
backward chaining 38–40
BAM, *see* bidirectional associative memory
Barto, A. 13

BASIC 30, 32
Bayes, T. 60
Bayesian reasoning 61–5, 65–72
Bayesian rule 60–1, 73
bell activation function 278
belongs-to 137–8
Berkeley Initiative in Soft Computing 20, 259
bidirectional associative memory 196–200
   architecture 196–7
   convergence 200
   stability 199
   storage capacity 200
   training algorithm 197–9
binary logic 89
bit map 323
Black, M. 88, 125
book-keeping facilities 33
Boole, G. 428
Boolean logic 87–8
Boyce, R. 389, 448
brain 2, 4, 166, 187
branch 401
break package 33
Broomhead, D. 13
Bryson, A. 13
Buchanan, B. 9, 19, 83

C

C 30, 32, 121, 253, 283, 310
C++ 121, 253, 283
Cantor, G. 97
Castillo, O 289
CART 403
categorical data 330
Central Limit Theorem 2
centre of gravity 111–12
centroid technique 111
cerebral cortex 205
certainty factor 10, 74–5, 77–8, 291–3
certainty factors theory 74–80
Chamberlin, D. 389, 448
character recognition 323–8
characteristic function 91
child chromosome 222–3
child node 401
chromosome 221, 232, 237
   decoding 228
   encoding 221, 236–7, 344–5
   evaluation 221, 237–8, 346–7
   offspring 222–3

parent 222–3
population 224
   average fitness 224
   size 224, 239
class-frame 134–5
classification 303, 312–17, 332–5
clipped membership function 110
clipping 109, 110
CLIPS 311
cloning 226
cluster 332, 336
   analysis 336–7
clustering 303, 332, 336–43
Codd, T. 387, 397
COG, *see* centre of gravity
Colmerauer, A. 19
common sense 87
commutativity 100
competitive learning 209–12, 332–5
competitive learning rule 207, 209
competitive neural network 205,
   332–5
complement 98
concentration 95–6
conclusion, *see* rule, consequent
condition, *see* rule, antecedent
conditional probability 59
conflict resolution 47–9
conflict set 47
conjunction 26, 77, 109
connectionist expert system, *see* neural expert
   system
consequent, *see* rule, consequent
containment 98–9
continuous data 329–30
control 303
convergence 183, 195, 200, 229
Cook, S. 19
correlation minimum, *see* clipping
correlation product, *see* scaling
cortex, *see* cerebral cortex
covariance matrix 375–7
Cox, E. 20
crisp set 89–91
crossover 221, 226, 248–50, 345–6
   probability 224

D

Dartmouth College workshop 6, 19
Darwin, C. 219, 220, 430, 436

data 304–5, 365–7
  categorical 330
  continuous 329–30
  discrete 330
  incompatible 304
  incomplete 304
data acquisition 304
database 31, 386–7
  operational 350
  relational 387–8
database management system 386–7
data cleaning 304, 366–7
data consolidation, *see* data transformation
data cube 393–8
  dimension 394–5
  fact 394–5
  starnet model 394–5
data-driven reasoning, *see* forward chaining
data exploration 368
data fusing 366–7
data mining 365–8
data selection 366
data transformation 367
data visualisation 369
data warehouse 391–3
Davis, L. 345
Davis's law 301
dBASE III 150, 152
DBMS, *see* database management system
De Morgan's Laws 102–3
debugging aids 33
decision support system 318–23, 348–53
decision tree 401–3
  branch 401
  child node 401
  dependent variable 401–2
  leaf 401
  parent node 401
  root node 401
  split 402, 403–5
Deep Blue 165
defuzzification 111–12, 273
  centroid technique 111
  sum-product composition 273
defuzzification layer 273, 279
degree of confidence, *see* certainty factor
degree of membership 92
delta rule 172
  generalised 185
demon 133, 142

DENDRAL 9–10, 12, 19, 40, 307
dendrite 166
dependent variable 401–2
developer interface 32–3
  debugging aids 33
  input/output facilities 33
  knowledge base editor 32–3
diagnosis 303, 308–12, 348–53
dilation 95–6
discrete data 330
disjunction 26, 77, 107
distributivity 101
domain expert, *see* expert
dummy rule 294

E

EBCDIC code 304
Edmonds, D. 5
eigenvalue 375, 377–80
eigenvector 375, 377–80
Electronic Numerical Integrator and
  Calculator 5, 19
EMYCIN 10, 19
end-user, *see* user
Enigma 2
epoch 172, 183
error gradient 178
essential property 140
Euclidean distance 207–8, 334
evidential reasoning 74–80, 315–17
evolution 219–21
evolution strategy 14, 242–4
  $(1 + 1)$-evolution strategy 242–4
evolutionary computation 14, 219
evolutionary fitness 220
evolutionary neural network 285–7
exclusive-OR 172, 180–1, 184–5,
  275–6
exhaustive search 51
expert 25, 29, 56, 67, 73, 87
expert system 8–12, 28, 33–5
  frame-based 149–61
  fuzzy 113–24, 317–23
  neural 262–8
  rule-based 30–3, 41–7, 50–1, 308–17
expert system shell 28, 310–12
explanation facilities 32, 263
  how 32
  why 32
external interface 32

F

facet 133–4
  inference facet 134
  prompt facet 134
  search order facet 149
  value facet 133
fact 31
FAM, *see* fuzzy associative memory
feature space 379
feature vector 379
feedback neural network 188–9
feedforward neural network 175
Feigenbaum E. 9, 10, 19
Feller, W. 57
Fine, T. 57
firing a rule 31, 36, 146
first-order Sugeno fuzzy model 277
fit-vector 94
fitness 221
fitness function 222, 237–8, 346
Fogel, D. 20
forgetting factor 201–2, 386
FORTRAN 6, 30, 32, 245, 253
forward chaining 37–8, 309
frame 131–2, 133–8, 140
  class 134–5
  instance 134–5
frame-based expert system 134–7, 137–8,
    138–42, 146, 149–61
fully connected neural network 176
fundamental memory 192–3
fuzzification 107
fuzzification layer 269, 278
fuzzy associative memory 118
fuzzy evolutionary system 290–6
fuzzy expert system 113–24, 317–22
fuzzy grid 290–3
fuzzy inference 106–13
  Mamdani 106–12, 113
  Sugeno 112–13, 114
Fuzzy Knowledge Builder 121
fuzzy logic 15–17, 87–9
fuzzy reasoning 104–5
fuzzy rule 15, 103–6, 112
fuzzy rule layer 271–2, 278–9
fuzzy rule table 119, 291
  multiple 293
fuzzy set 89–94
  clipping 110
  scaling 110

fuzzy set theory, *see* fuzzy logic
fuzzy singleton 112
fuzzy thinking 87–9
fuzzy variable 94–5

G

gain chart 405
Galton, F. 370
gene 221, 237
General Problem Solver 6, 19
generalisation 137, 325, 329, 381–4
generalised activity product rule 202
generalised delta rule 185
generation 222
genetic algorithm 14, 222–3, 295–6, 343–8
  convergence 229
  performance 229–31, 346–7
genetic operator 221, 226, 345–6
  cloning 226
  crossover 221, 226, 248–50, 345–6
  mutation 221, 226, 250–1, 346
genetic programming 14, 245–53
genetics 220
Gini, C. 403
Gini coefficient 403
global optimum 229–30
goal 38, 146
goal-driven reasoning, *see* backward chaining
Goldberg, D. 345
GPS, *see* General Problem Solver
Gray coding 229
grid-type fuzzy partition 290–1
Grossberg, S. 13

H

Hakel, M. 56
hard limiter 169
Haykin, S. 19
Hebb, D. 200, 214, 436
Hebb's Law 200–1
Hebbian learning 200–4
hedge 95–7
  a little 97
  extremely 96, 97
  indeed 96, 97
  more or less 96, 97
  slightly 97
  somewhat 97
  very 96, 97
  very very 96, 97

heuristic 28, 33
hidden layer 175–6
Ho, Y.-C. 13
Holland, J. 14, 20, 221, 226, 232, 254, 435
Hopfield, J. 13, 19, 189, 213
Hopfield network 188–96
  architecture 189
  convergence 195
  fundamental memory 192–3, 196
  storage capacity 195–6
  training algorithm 193–4
Human Genome Project 365
human expert, *see* expert
hybrid intelligent system 259–60, 348–57
hyperbolic tangent 185

I

idempotency 101–2
identity 102
IF-THEN rule, *see* production rule
Inmon, W.H. 392
inference chain 36–7
inference engine 31, 146–7, 262
inheritance 134, 138–42
  multiple 140–1
  one-parent 139–40
input layer 175, 269, 278
input/output facilities 33
instance-frame 134–5
intelligence 1–2, 219
intelligent behaviour test, *see* Turing test
intelligent machine 4, 18, 165
  character recognition 323–8
  classification 303, 312–17, 332–5
  clustering 303, 332, 336–43
  control 303
  decision support 318–23, 348–53
  diagnosis 303, 308–12, 348–53
  optimisation 303, 344–8
  prediction 303, 328–32, 353–7
  selection 303
  troubleshooting 308–12
intensification 96
intersection 99, 109
inversion 346
involution 102
is-a 136, 137–8
iteration 172, 183, 222

J

Jacobs, R. 185
Jang, R. 277, 282
Java 310
joint probability 59

K

Karp, R. 19
Kasparov, G. 165
knowledge 25, 365–6
knowledge acquisition 9, 305
knowledge acquisition bottleneck 9, 305
knowledge base 31, 41–3, 69, 80–1, 262, 263
knowledge base editor 32–3
knowledge discovery 366
knowledge engineer 29
knowledge engineering 10, 301–2
  complete system development 306–7
  data and knowledge acquisition 304–5
  evaluation and revision 307
  integration and maintenance 307
  problem assessment 303–4
  prototype development 306
knowledge representation 26, 50, 103–4,
    131–2, 133–8
KnowledgeSEEKER 406, 408
Kohonen, T. 13, 19, 205, 215, 439
Kohonen layer 206, 337–8
Kohonen network 206
  architecture 206, 338
  training algorithm 209–11
Kosko, B. 20, 196, 214, 427
Kowalski, R. 19
Koza, J. 14, 20, 245, 255

L

law of the excluded middle 55
leaf 401
learning 165
  accelerated 185–8
  competitive 209–12, 332–5
  Hebbian 200–4
  supervised 171–2, 179–80
  unsupervised 200–3, 209–12
learning rate 171
  adaptive 186–8
LeCun, Y. 13
Lederberg, J. 9, 19

Leonardo, *see* Leonardo expert system shell
Leonardo expert system shell   41, 69, 310, 313, 315
Level5 Object   141, 149, 152, 155
lift chart, *see* gain chart
Lighthill, J.   8, 19
Lighthill report   8, 19
likelihood of necessity   67
likelihood of sufficiency   66
linear activation function   169–70
linear fit function   94
linearly separable function   170, 173–4
Lingle, R.   345
linguistic value   94–5
linguistic variable   94–5
LISP   6, 11, 14, 19, 30, 245–6, 310
   atom   245–6
   list   245–6
   S-expression   246, 253
List Processor, *see* LISP
local optimum   229–30
logical operation   172
   AND   172
   exclusive-OR   172, 180–1, 184–5, 275–6
   NOT   61
   OR   172
Lowe, D.   13
Lukasiewicz, J.   88, 125

M

machine learning   165, 219
Malevich, K.   140
Mamdani, E.   20, 106
Mamdani fuzzy inference   106–12, 113
Manhattan Project   5
market basket analysis   410
massaging data   329–30
Mathematica   253
MATLAB Fuzzy Logic Toolbox   20, 109, 121–2, 283, 320, 352
MATLAB Neural Network Toolbox   19, 352
MATLAB Statistics Toolbox   369
McCarthy, J.   5, 6, 19, 245, 440
McClelland, J.   13, 19
McCulloch, W.   5, 6, 13, 19, 169, 213, 441
McCulloch and Pitts neuron model   5, 169
means-ends analysis   6–7
measure of belief   75
measure of disbelief   75
Melin, P.   289

membership function   92
   trapezoid   116–17
   triangle   116–17, 271
membership value, *see* degree of membership
Mendel, G.   220
metaknowledge   49
metarule   50
method   142
   WHEN CHANGED   133, 142
   WHEN NEEDED   133, 142, 146
Mexican hat function   206–7
Michalewicz, Z.   220
Michie, D.   305
Microsoft Excel   150
Minitab   369
Minsky, M.   5, 6, 13, 19, 131, 132, 134, 174
momentum constant   185–6
Monte Carlo search   14, 245
multidimensional data model, *see* data cube
multilayer perceptron   175
   architecture   175–6
     hidden layer   175–6
     input layer   175
     output layer   175
   convergence   183
   learning   179–80
     accelerated learning   185–8
multiple antecedents   26, 77, 105
multiple consequents   27, 105
multiple evidences   62
multiple fuzzy rule tables   293
multiple hypotheses   62
multiple inheritance   140–1
multi-valued logic   89
mutation   221, 226, 250–1, 346
   probability   226
MYCIN   10, 12, 15, 19, 40, 74, 76, 83, 84, 307
MySQL   389

N

NASA   9, 365
Naylor, C.   72
Negoita, C.   20
neo-Darwinism   220
net certainty   76–7
neural computing   5, 6, 12, 167–70
neural expert system   262–8
neural knowledge base   262–3

neural network 12–13, 166–8
  artificial 12–13, 167
  biological 166
  competitive 205, 332–5
  evolutionary 285–7
  feedback 188–9
  feedforward 175
  fully connected 176
  recurrent 188–9
  self-organising 200–1, 205
neuro-fuzzy system 268–76
  architecture 269–73
    defuzzification layer 273
    fuzzification layer 269
    fuzzy rule layer 271–2
    input layer 269
    output membership layer 272–3
  learning 273–6
neuron 166–8
  artificial 168
  binary model 169
  biological 166
Newell, A. 6, 7, 19, 30
NOT 61
NP-complete problem 8, 235
NP-hard problem 336
normalisation layer 279
normalised firing strength 279
numerical object 27

O

object 27, 132
  numerical 27
  symbolic 27
object-oriented programming 132
odds 67–8
  posterior 68
  prior 67
offspring chromosome, *see* child
  chromosome
Oja's rule 386
OLAP, *see* on-line analytical processing
OLTP, *see* on-line transaction processing
one-parent inheritence 138–40
on-line analytical processing 397–401
on-line transaction processing 398
operational database 350
operations of fuzzy sets 98–100
  complement 98
  containment 98–9

  intersection 99, 109
  union 100, 107
OPS 11, 30, 310
optical character recognition 323–4
optimisation 303, 344–8
OR 172
ordered crossover 345
outlier 341, 372–4
output layer 175
output membership layer 272–3
overfitting 325, 381–2

P

Papert, S. 13, 174
paradox of logic 89–90
  Pythagorean School 89
  Russell's Paradox 89
parent chromosome 222–3
parent node 401
Parker, D. 13
partially mapped crossover 345
part-whole, *see* a-part-of
Pascal 30, 32, 121, 253
PCA, *see* principal component analysis
PCA neural network 385–6
Pearson, K. 374
Pearson's correlation coefficient 383
perceptron 6, 170–2
  convergence theorem 6
  learning rule 171–2
Phone Call Rule 308
Pitts, W. 5, 6, 13, 19, 169, 213, 441
plasticity 166
possibility theory 88
posterior odds 68
posterior probability 62
prediction 303, 328–32, 353–7
premise, *see* rule, antecedent
principal component analysis 374–85
principle of dichotomy 89
principle of topographic map formation
  205
prior odds 67
prior probability 62
probabilistic OR 109, 273
probability 57–61
  conditional 59
  joint 59
  posterior 62
  prior 62

probability theory 57–61
procedure 133
production model 30–1
production rule 26–8
programmer 29–30
PROLOG 11, 19, 30, 310
PROSPECTOR 10–11, 12, 15, 19, 56, 65, 74, 82, 84
prototype 306
Pythagorean School 89
Pythagorean Theorem 247, 253

Q
query tool 388, 390–1

R
reasoning 31
    approximate 262–3
    Bayesian 61–5, 65–72
    data-driven 37–8, 309
    evidential 74–80, 315–17
    fuzzy 104–5
    goal-driven 38–40
    symbolic 34
Rechenberg, I. 14, 20, 242, 255
reciprocal exchange 346
recurrent neural network 188–9
reference super set, *see* universe of discourse
regression 370
    linear 370–3
    robust 373–4
regression coefficient 370–1
reinforcement learning 13
relation 387
reproduction 221
    probability 225–6
root node 401
Rosenblatt, F. 6, 170, 171, 213, 444
roulette wheel selection 225
Roussel, P. 19
rule 26–8
    antecedent 26
    consequent 26
rule-based expert system 30–3, 41–7, 50–1, 308–17
rule evaluation 107–10
rule extraction 263–8
rule-of-thumb 10, 33
rule table, *see* fuzzy rule table

Rumelhart, D. 13, 19
run 222
run-time knowledge acquisition 33
Russell's Paradox 89

S
sample hit plot 338, 341
saturated linear function 189
scaled membership function 110
scaling 110
scatter plot 369–70, 382, 385
schema 232–4
    defining length 233
    instance 232
Schema Theorem 14, 232–4
Schwefel, H.-P. 14, 20, 242, 255
scree plot 383–4
seed set 414–5
selection 303
self-organising map 13, 205–6, 337–43
    sample hit plot 338, 341
    U-matrix 338, 341
self-organising neural network 200–1, 205
semantic network 11
Sendai subway system 17, 20
sensitivity analysis 331–2
SEQUEL 389
set 89
    crisp 89–91
    fuzzy 89–94
S-expression, *see* LISP, S-expression
Shannon, C. 5, 19
Shapiro, E. 142
shell, *see* expert system shell
Shortliffe, E. 10, 19, 83
sigmoid activation function 169–70, 177
sign activation function 169, 189
Simon, H. 6, 7, 19, 30
Simpson, R. 56
Single Proton Emission Computed Tomography 348
singleton, *see* fuzzy singleton
slot 131, 133
slot value 133
    Boolean 133
    default 133
    numeric 133
    symbolic 133
Smalltalk 253
soft computing 259–60

soma 166
SPECT, *see* Single Proton Emission Computed Tomography
split 402, 403–5
Sputnik 8
SQL, *see* Structured Query Language
SQL query 389–91, 399
stacking a rule 38–40
starnet model 394–5
Statgraphics 369
statistics 369
Statistical Analysis System 369
step activation function 169
Sterling, L. 142
strength of belief 75
strength of disbelief 75
Structured Query Language 388–91
subspace decomposition 379
Sugeno, M. 20, 112
Sugeno fuzzy inference 112–13, 114
Sugeno fuzzy model 112–14, 277
  first-order 277
  zero-order 114, 277
Sugeno fuzzy rule 112, 114, 277
sum of squared errors 182–3
summation neuron 279
summary statistics 369
sum-product composition 273
supervised learning 171–2, 179–80
survival of the fittest 220
Sutton, R. 13
symbolic object 27
symbolic reasoning 34
synapse 166
synaptic weight, *see* weight

T

terminal node, *see* decision tree, leaf
test set 326, 335
theory of evolution 220
theory of natural selection 220
thinking 1
threshold 169–70, 181
threshold value, *see* threshold
time series 354
topographic map formation 205
toy problem 8
tracing facilities 33
training set 173, 327, 329
transfer function, *see* activation function

transitivity 102
travelling salesman problem 344
troubleshooting 308–12
truth value 107
Tryon, R. 336
TSP, *see* travelling salesman problem
tuple 387
Turing, A. 2, 17, 19, 219, 449
Turing Imitation Game 2–4
Turing test 2–4

U

U-matrix 338, 341
uncertainty 55–6
union 100, 107
universal machine 2
universe of discourse 90–1
unsupervised learning 200–3, 209–12
user 30
user interface 32, 263

V

vagueness 88
validation error 382
validation set 381
visualisation, *see* data visualisation
von Neumann, J. 5, 19

W

Waterman, D. 11, 19
Watrous, R. 185
weak method 7
weight 167–8
  distance matrix, *see* U-matrix
Weismann, A. 220
WHEN CHANGED method 133, 142
WHEN NEEDED method 133, 142, 146
Widrow's rule 329
winner-takes-all neuron 205–6

X

XOR, *see* logical operation, exclusive-OR

Y

Yager, R. 20

Z

Zadeh, L. 7, 15, 16, 20, 88–9, 92, 103, 125, 259, 260, 435
zero-order Sugeno fuzzy model 113, 277

华章经典原版书库

书　名	书号 7-111-	定价	出版年	作　者
系统分析与设计导论（英文版）	35278	79	2011	（美）Jeffrey L. Whitten 等
软件工程（英文版.第9版）	34825	99	2011	（美）Ian Sommerville
软件工程：面向对象和传统的方法（英文版.第8版）	34196	79	2011	（美）Stephen R. Schach 著
现代信息检索（英文精编版.第2版）	33174	78	2011	（美）Ricardo Baeza-Yates等
电子商务（英文精编版.第9版）	32673	66	2011	（美）Gary P. Schneider
编译原理（英文版.第2版）	32674	78	2011	（美）Alfred V. Aho
实用IT项目管理（英文版.第3版）	32594	59	2011	（美）Joseph Phillips
软件工程：实践者的研究方法（英文版.第7版）	31871	75	2010	（美）Roger S. Pressman
数字通信（英文版.第3版）	31669	98	2010	（英）Ian A. Glover
离散数学及其应用（英文版精编版.第6版）	31329	55	2010	（美）Kenneth H. Rosen
数据结构与算法分析——C语言描述（英文版.第2版）	31280	45	2010	（美）Mark Allen Weiss 著
Intel微处理器（英文版.第8版）	30485	89	2010	（美）Barry B. Brey
软件项目管理（英文版.第5版）	30537	39	2010	（英）Bob Hughes
计算机组成与设计：硬件/软件接口（英文版.第4版.ARM版）	30288	95	2010	（美）David A. Patterson
逻辑与计算机设计基础　英文版 第4版	30310	58	2010	（美）M. Morris Mano
计算机安全：原理与实践　英文版	29247	69	2010	（美）Willam Stallings
嵌入式微控制器与处理器设计（英文版）	29250	49	2010	（美）GregOsborn
数学建模（英文精编版 第4版）	28249	65	2009	（美）FrankR. Giordano
软件测试基础（英文版）	28246	42	2009	（美）Paul Ammann
C++程序设计原理与实践（英文版）	28248	89	2009	（美）Bjarne Stroustrup
搜索引擎信息检索实践（英文版）	28247	45	2009	（美）W. Bruce Croft
模式识别（英文版.第4版）	26896	89	2009	（希腊）Sergios Theodoridis
神经网络与机器学习　（英文版.第3版）	26528	69	2009	（加）Simon Haykin
现代操作系统（英文版.第3版）	26527	69	2009	（荷）Andrew S. Tanenbaum
面向对象软件工程　（英文版）	26526	49	2009	（美）Stephen R. Tanenbaum
组合数学　（英文版.第5版）	26525	49	2009	（美）Richard A. Brualdi
人工智能：复杂问题求解的结构和策略　（英文第6版）	25656	46	2009	（美）Geroge F. Luger
算法概论（注释版）	25361	55	2009	（美）Sanjoy Dasgupts 钱枫译
嵌入式计算系统设计原理　（英文版.第2版）	25360	75	2008	（美）Wayne Wolf
数学建模 方法与分析　（英文版.第3版）	25364	49	2008	（美）MarkM. Meerschaert
软件工程：实践者的研究方法（英文精编版.第6版）	24138	65	2008	（美）Roger S. Pressman
软件测试基础教程（英文版）	24732	49	2008	（美）Aditya P. Mathur
数据库系统基础教程　（英文版.第3版）	24733	45	2008	（美）Jeffrey D. Ullman
多处理器编程的艺术（英文版）	24735	69	2008	（美）Maurice Herlihy
数控加工导论（英文版.第4版）	24736	79	2008	（美）James V. Valentino
C++ 程序设计（英文版）	23996	45	2008	（美）Y. Daniel Liang
计算机图形学（英文版）	23916	36	2008	（美）Steve Cunningham
系统分析与设计（英文版.第4版）	23249	39	2008	（美）John W. Satzinger
计算机组成及汇编语言原理（英文版）	23917	42	2008	
自适应信号处理（英文版）	23918	56	2008	（美）威德罗，斯特恩斯
Java语言程序设计 进阶篇（英文版.第6版）	23368	69	2008	（美）Y. Daniel Liang
计算机科学概论（英文版.第3版）	23516	66	2008	（美）Nell Dale
自动网络管理系统（英文版）	23515	48	2008	（美）Douglas E. Comer
Java语言程序设计 基础篇（英文版.第6版）	23367	66	2008	（美）Y. Daniel Liang
微机电系统基础（英文版）	23167	59	2008	（美）Chang Liu
统一软件工程（英文版）	23164	69	2008	（美）Georges G. Merx
数据结构—从应用到实现（Java版）（英文版）	23165	55	2008	（美）Sesh Venugopal
自动机理论、语言和计算导论（英文版.第3版）	22392	59	2007	（美）Third Edition
计算机科学引论－基于C的结构化程序设计方法（英文版.第3版）	21402	59	2007	（美）Behrouz A. Forouzan
计算机网络－系统方法（英文版.第4版）	21401	85	2007	（美）Larry L. Peterson
线性代数（英文版.第7版）	21198	58	2007	（美）Steven J. Leon
算法设计与分析导论（英文版）	20821	69	2007	R. C. T. Lee、S. S. Tseng等
MIPS体系结构透视（英文版.第2版）	20681	65	2007	（英）Dominic Sweetman
计算机组成与结构量化研究方法（英文版.第4版）	20378	78	2006	（美）John L. Hennessy David A. Patterson
数据结构与算法分析：Java语言描述（英文版.第2版）	19876	55	2006	（美）Mark Allen Weiss
算法：C语言实现（第1～4部分）－基础知识、数据结构、排序及搜	19764	69	2006	（美）Robert Sedgewick
算法：C语言实现（第5部分）－图算法（英文版.第3版）	19769	49	2006	（美）Rpbert Sedgewick
C 程序设计语言　（英文版.第2版）	19626	35	2006	（美）Brian W. Kernighan
数据结构与算法（Java语言版）（英文版.第2版）	18826	79	2006	（美）Adam Drozdek
数据挖掘：概念与技术（英文版.第2版）	18828	79	2006	（美）Jiawei Han

教师服务登记表

尊敬的老师:

您好!感谢您购买我们出版的＿＿＿＿＿＿＿＿＿＿＿＿＿＿＿＿＿＿＿＿＿＿＿＿＿＿＿ 教材。

机械工业出版社华章公司为了进一步加强与高校教师的联系与沟通,更好地为高校教师服务,特制此表,请您填妥后发回给我们,我们将定期向您寄送华章公司最新的图书出版信息!感谢合作!

个人资料(请用正楷完整填写)

教师姓名		□先生 □女士	出生年月		职务		职称:□教授 □副教授 □讲师 □助教 □其他		
学校			学院				系别		
联系 电话	办公:			联系地址 及邮编					
	宅电:								
	移动:			E-mail					
学历		毕业院校		国外进修及讲学经历					
研究领域									

主讲课程	现用教材名	作者及 出版社	共同授 课教师	教材满意度
课程: □专 □本 □研 人数: 学期:□春□秋				□满意 □一般 □不满意 □希望更换
课程: □专 □本 □研 人数: 学期:□春□秋				□满意 □一般 □不满意 □希望更换

样书申请			
已出版著作		已出版译作	
是否愿意从事翻译/著作工作　□是　□否　方向			
意 见 和 建 议			

填妥后请选择以下任何一种方式将此表返回:(如方便请赐名片)

地 址: 北京市西城区百万庄南街1号 华章公司营销中心 邮编: 100037

电 话: (010) 68353079 88378995 传真: (010)68995260

E-mail:hzedu@hzbook.com markerting@hzbook.com 图书详情可登录http://www.hzbook.com网站查询